D0936106

Probability, Confirmation, and Simplicity

Readings in the Philosophy of Inductive Logic

Probability, Confirmation, and Simplicity

Readings in the Philosophy of Inductive Logic

Edited by
MARGUERITE H. FOSTER
MOORHEAD STATE COLLEGE
and
MICHAEL L. MARTIN
BOSTON UNIVERSITY

The Odyssey Press Inc.,
New York

PRINTED IN THE UNITED STATES

Library of Congress Catalog Card Number 65-17456

A 9 8 7 6 5 4 3 2 1

Preface

The purpose of this volume is to acquaint the reader with some of the major problems in the philosophy of inductive logic and to present some of the most important points of view philosophers have taken toward these problems. We wish that everyone who has made a genuine contribution to the philosophy of inductive logic could have been represented here, but for a number of reasons this was impossible. We have been obliged to omit the works of such major figures as Nelson Goodman, William Kneale, Karl Popper, and G. H. von Wright. Some of the views of Goodman and Popper, however, are expounded and discussed in papers which are included here.

The reader will note that we have attempted, wherever possible, to include critiques of the various viewpoints expressed here. It is hoped that this dialectical arrangement will exhibit the controversial nature of the philosophy of inductive logic and will stimulate further criticism as well as re-examination of its problems.

The guiding conception and organization of the book is explained in the General Introduction. This introduction is also intended to acquaint the student with the general character of the problems in the philosophy of inductive logic and to provide a brief historical sketch of some of the various concepts of inductive logic and non-demonstrative inference. The introductions to the four sections of the book are designed to place the problems with which these sections deal in perspective and to raise questions about the solutions which have been offered. The book contains a bibliography which we hope will help the student pursue further the topics considered here.

We are indebted to many persons for their encouragement and for their valuable criticisms. In particular, we wish to express our gratitude to Professors Carl G. Hempel of Princeton University and Israel Scheffler of Harvard University for their very useful comments on our proposed outline of the book and their many helpful suggestions; to Professor David Hawkins of the University of Colorado for his initial enthusiastic response to our plan for this book; and to Dr. Jane Martin of the University of Colorado for the enthusiasm, acumen, and patience with which she has taken part in every phase of the work. Finally, our warmest thanks are extended to Mrs. Ruth Martin for her careful and accurate typing of large portions of the manuscript.

Acknowledgments to publishers and individual authors for their kind permission to reproduce the selections included here are made in the body of the work. We wish also to thank those authors who supplied us with corrections and additions.

MARGUERITE H. FOSTER
MICHAEL L. MARTIN

Contents

II Problems of Confirmation Theory

III Simplicity

IV The Justification of Induction

General Introduction

The Philosophy of Inductive Logic

Scientists and non-scientists use many concepts and procedures in their work-a-day world without entering into an investigation of their meaning or justification, and this is as it should be. The practical demands of science and daily living make it impossible for scientists and ordinary men to undertake a theoretical investigation of this sort. The interest of the philosopher is fundamentally different, however. Unhampered by practical concerns, one of his tasks is to clarify and analyze critically the fundamental principles and concepts used by the scientist and ordinary man.

For example, an essential part of scientific procedure, and of rational procedure generally, consists of non-demonstrative inference: the kind of inference in which empirical premises provide support for, but do not logically entail, empirical hypotheses. The scientist and ordinary man use a cluster of important concepts in connection with such inferences but leave them unanalyzed, unclarified, and uncriticized. Thus a physicist may say that Einstein's theory is better confirmed today than it was fifty years ago without bothering to analyze the concept of confirmation; a farmer may speak of the probability of rain on the basis of a darkening sky without understanding precisely what is meant by "probable"; an astronomer may argue that the Copernican theory is to be preferred to the Ptolemaic theory for reasons of simplicity without examining the notion of simplicity; a housewife may assume that many past successes with a certain recipe give her good grounds for her belief in future successes without pondering the justification of her assumption. It is left to the philosopher to clarify and analyze critically such concepts as confirmation, likelihood, and simplicity and to provide theoretical justification for empirical beliefs about the future which are based upon past evidence. In short, the task of analyzing non-demonstrative inference is the philosopher's. In this book we will call one who engages in this task a "philosopher of inductive logic" and we will refer to the study of non-demonstrative inference and its related problems as the "philosophy of inductive logic."

Induction and Deduction

Since the scope of inductive logic and the difference between deductive and inductive logic have often been conceived differently from the way we conceive of them here, it is well to make this clear at the start. Most dictionary definitions contrast deduction and induction in this way: deductive arguments proceed from the general to the particular while inductive arguments proceed from the particular to the general. Thus an argument from the premises "All men are mortal" and "Socrates is a man" to the conclusion "Socrates is mortal" is said to typify deductive arguments while an argument from the premises "Jones is mortal" and "Smith is mortal" and "Brown is mortal" and so on to the conclusion "All men are mortal" is said to typify inductive arguments.

Now it takes but a moment's reflection to see that *this* difference is not the crucial difference between deductive and inductive arguments. Consider the argument from the premise "Socrates is a man" to the conclusion "Either Socrates is a man or all men are mortal." It is deductive, yet the inference is from a particular premise to a conclusion containing both particular and general elements. Consider the argument from the premise "Socrates is a man" to the conclusion "There is at least one thing which is a man." It is deductive, yet the inference is from a particular premise to an existential conclusion. Clearly, deductive arguments do not always proceed from the general to the particular.

Nor do inductive arguments always proceed from the particular to the general. For example, the premises "Smith is mortal," "Jones is mortal," "Brown is mortal," and so on, lend support to the conclusion "Gish is mortal." This argument is inductive, yet rather than moving from premises about some particular members of a class to a conclusion about the whole class, it moves from premises about examined members of a class to a hypothesis about an unexamined member of the same class. Again, the premises "Most men die before they are one hundred years of age" and "Jones is a man picked at random" lend support to the conclusion "Jones will die before he is one hundred." This argument is also inductive, yet it moves from premises about a particular member of a class and the statistical make-up of the class to a hypothesis about the future of this particular member.

The crucial difference between deductive and inductive arguments, then, lies in the relationship between premises and conclusion. Deductive arguments are characterized by their logical necessity; that is to say, the conclusion is entailed by the premises. Inductive arguments are not logically necessary; the premises lend support to the conclusion but do not logically entail it. Thus we find inductive arguments which do not move from the particular to the general and deductive arguments which do not move from the general to the particular. It is the logical necessity, or lack thereof, of the argument and not the degree of generality of the premises which determines[1] whether an argument is deductive or inductive.

Types of Inductive Inferences

The examples of inductive inferences we have just listed do not exhaust the possible kinds of inductive inferences. Although it is still an open question just how many kinds of inductive inferences there are, there does seem to be some agreement on the main types.[2] It may be useful, therefore, to classify and label some of these.

In view of the fact that inductive arguments are not logically necessary, it is not surprising that inductive inferences differ greatly from deductive inferences. Deductive inferences are literally transitions from one set of statements to a new set of statements: given certain true statements as premises, the rules of deductive inference enable one to acquire new true statements. In the case of inductive inferences, however, there is no transition from one statement to another. The rules of inductive logic merely indicate that a certain set of statements taken as true provides support or makes probable another set of statements: given true premises, there is no acquisition of new true statements.[3]

(1) Inferences from a sample to the whole population:

(a) Inductive generalization. This is an inference from a sample to a hypothesis which is universal in form. The following is an example of an inductive generalization: "All men thus far examined in a wide variety of circumstances are mortal" lends support to or makes probable the hypothesis "All men are mortal." Traditionally the word "induction" has been used only to refer to this type of inference.

(b) Statistical generalization. This is also an inference from a sample to the whole population, but now the hypothesis is statistical, not universal, in form. For example, "2/3 of the people in New York City so far examined in a wide variety of circumstances have not been west of the Mississippi River" lends support to or makes probable the hypothesis "2/3 of the people in New York City have not been west of the Mississippi River."

(2) Inferences from the whole population to some sample of the population:

(a) Direct statistical inference. The inference here is "downward" from the whole population to some sample of it taken at random. For example, "70% of the population of Boston are of Irish descent" and "This is a random

[1] This is not to say that lack of logical necessity is a *sufficient* condition for an argument's being inductive. Lack of logical necessity is, however, a necessary condition. On this point see Israel Scheffler's paper "Inductive Inference: A New Approach" reprinted here in Section IV.

[2] For an extended discussion of the various types of induction inferences see John P. Day, *Inductive Probability* (New York: The Humanities Press, 1961), pp. 15–25; Arthur Pap, *An Introduction to the Philosophy of Science* (New York: The Free Press of Glencoe, 1962), pp. 141–147; Rudolf Carnap, *The Logical Foundations of Probability* (Chicago: University of Chicago Press, 1962), pp. 205–208.

[3] See Carnap, *loc. cit.*

sample of people living in Boston" lends support to or makes probable the hypothesis "70% of this sample will be of Irish descent."

(b) Direct singular inference. Here also the inference is downward from the population, but now it is to some specific individual taken at random from the population. For example, "Most philosophers are not millionaires" and "Jones is a philosopher picked at random" lends support to or makes probable the hypothesis "Jones is not a millionaire."

It should be noted that the general premises used in these inferences, namely "70% of the population of Boston are of Irish descent" and "Most philosophers are not millionaires," are usually established by inductive inferences from a sample to the whole population. Hence, it can be maintained with some plausibility that inferences from the whole population to some sample of it are derivative, while inferences from a sample to the whole population are primary.

(3) Inferences from a sample of a population to some other sample of the same population:

(a) Standard predictive inference. This is an inference from the examined members of a population to some random sample taken from this population. For example, "All the ravens examined thus far in a wide variety of circumstances are black" and "This is a randomly selected sample of ravens" lends support to or makes probable the hypothesis "This sample of ravens is black."

(b) Statistical predictive inference. This inference is like the standard predictive inference except that the hypothesis which is supported or made probable states the statistical make-up of the sample. For example, "30% of bachelors examined so far in a wide variety of circumstances cook their own meals" and "This is a random sample of bachelors" lends support to or makes probable the hypothesis "30% of these bachelors cook their own meals."

(c) Singular predictive inference. Here the inference is from the examined members of a population to some specific unexamined member of this population. For example, "Most of the young single girls examined so far in a wide variety of circumstances are looking for a husband" and "Mary is a young single girl chosen at random" lends support to or makes probable the hypothesis "Mary is looking for a husband."

It has been argued that predictive inferences are best construed as a combination of inferences of type (1) and (2). Thus, for example, it has been maintained that a statistical predictive inference is implicitly a statistical generalization combined with a direct statistical inference.

(4) Inferences from the verified consequences of a hypothesis to the hypothesis.

This inference is a familiar one in science: the greater the number and variety of verified consequences of a hypothesis, the greater the probability of the hypothesis. This "conversion of deduction," as it has been called, has the following form: the premises "If hypothesis *H*, then consequences $C_1 \& C_2 \& \cdots C_n$" and "$C_1 \& C_2 \& \cdots C_n$" lend support to or make probable "*H*."[4]

Strictly speaking, however, a hypothesis is never tested in isolation but only against a background of assumptions. We may, therefore, formulate this sort of inductive argument more precisely as follows: the premises "If hypothesis *H* and assumptions $A_1 \& A_2 \& \cdots A_n$, then consequences $C_1 \& C_2 \& \cdots C_n$" and "$C_1 \& C_2 \& \cdots C_n$" lend support to or make probable "*H* and $A_1 \& A_2 \& \cdots A_n$." Thus, for example, if a deduction from some psychological hypothesis is verified, it supports the hypothesis provided certain assumptions are made, e.g. that the measuring instruments, perhaps some psychological tests, are valid. A similar point can be made about the inference from the falsified consequences of a hypothesis to the disconfirmation of the hypothesis. Since a hypothesis is always tested against a background of assumptions, $A_1 \& A_2 \& \cdots A_n$, a hypothesis *H* is disconfirmed by a false consequence only if $A_1 \& A_2 \& \cdots A_n$ are held to be true.

This kind of inductive inference is radically different from types (1), (2), and (3) mentioned above. The main reason is this: All of the inductive arguments mentioned above, except converse deduction, are arguments from premises referring to members of one class to conclusions referring to members of the same class. These sorts of inductive arguments cannot proceed from members of one class to members of a different class; in particular, they cannot proceed from premises which refer only to observables to conclusions which refer to non-observables. Converse deduction, however, allows inferences from observables to unobservables.[5] This peculiarity of converse deduction is important to note because an essential aspect of theoretical science consists in its reliance on hypotheses which refer to unobservable entities and processes, e.g. electrons, genes. Moreover, recent logical investigation makes it extremely implausible to maintain that such hypotheses are dispensible in scientific endeavors without great loss.[6] But if this is so, then we see that converse deduction plays a vital role in the procedure of science, for only it, of the kinds of inductive inferences mentioned above, can support such hypotheses.

Some Traditional Conceptions of Induction and Non-Demonstrative Inferences

It may be useful to review briefly several traditional conceptions of induction and non-demonstrative inference.

[4] This simple formulation, however, can easily lead to paradoxes if it is combined with other reasonable principles. See the introduction to Section II of this anthology and Hempel's paper "Studies in the Logic of Confirmation" reprinted in Section II.

[5] Cf. William Kneale, *Probability and Induction* (Oxford: Oxford University Press, 1949), pp. 97–110.

[6] See Carl G. Hempel, "The Theoretician's Dilemma," *Minnesota Studies in the Philosophy of Science*, II, *Concepts, Theories, and The Mind-Body Problem*, (eds.) H. Feigl, M. Scriven and G. Maxwell (Minneapolis: University of Minnesota Press, 1959), pp. 37–98.

(1) The term "induction" was originally a translation of the technical term ἐπαγωγή of Aristotle. He used the term in at least three different ways:

(a) Intuitive induction: In the *Posterior Analytics* [7] he argued that syllogistic reasoning from necessary premises cannot be the only source of universal truth for unless there is to be an infinite regress of syllogistic arguments the necessary premises of these arguments must be established by some non-syllogistic means. He argued further that the premises of syllogistic arguments must ultimately be established by induction — a kind of intellectual intuition — which grasps the universal as it is manifested in the particular case.

Now whether or not this is a correct account of the establishment of necessary propositions we need not consider here. It will suffice to remark that since empirical propositions are not necessary they cannot be established in this way; thus the vast bulk of the propositions that constitute our knowledge cannot be established by induction in this sense.

(b) Complete induction: In the *Prior Analytics* [8] Aristotle gave a different account of induction. Here he argued that induction proceeds by the complete enumeration of all particular cases covered by a generalization. Aristotle apparently took inductive arguments of this sort to be deductive, i.e. ones in which the premises entailed the conclusion. Thus he illustrated induction in this second sense by the following example: Man, the horse, and the mule are long-lived; but man, the horse, and the mule are all the bileless animals; therefore all bileless animals are long-lived. [9] He did not tell us how the premise "Man, the horse, and the mule are all the bileless animals" is established.

It should be noted how rarely we are in a position to establish a general proposition by complete enumeration of all its instances. In the first place, if the generalization were to cover an infinite number of instances it could not conceivably be established. Secondly, even if one knew that the number of instances covered by the generalization was finite this would still not be sufficient; no matter how many instances were examined, the possibility would remain that some instances covered by the generalization were unexamined. For all practical purposes the problem can be solved by restricting the generalization in some way, e.g. by restricting the generalization to some easily surveyable spatio-temporal region. But even here the logical possibility that some instances of the generalization have escaped notice is not excluded. In any case, the most important empirical generalizations formulated in science and everyday life are not those in which we have completely enumerated all instances of the generalization; rather they are the ones in which we have examined some members of a sample and have inferred to whole populations.

(c) Incomplete induction: In the *Topics* [10] Aristotle defined induction as a "passage from individual to universal." [11] He gave as an example "the argu-

[7] *Posterior Analytics*, Bk. I, chap. 1; Bk. 2, chap. 19.
[8] *Prior Analytics*, Bk. 2, chap. 12.
[9] *Ibid.*, 68b 19–24.
[10] *Topics*, Bk. 1, chap. 7.
[11] *Ibid.*, 105a 12.

ment that supposing the skilled pilot is the most effective and likewise the skilled charioteer, then in general the skilled man is the best at his particular task."[12] This kind of induction was said to proceed "from the known to the unknown."[13]

Here we seem to have an example of induction in the sense being used here, namely non-demonstrative inference. In particular, the inference that Aristotle outlined is what we have called an inductive generalization. Aristotle did not, however, make explicit the probabilistic character of this sort of inference.

(d) Aristotle also recognized non-demonstrative inferences from a whole class to some part of it, but he did not call these inferences inductive. He did, however, explicitly connect the notion of probability with these inferences. Both in the *Prior Analytics*[14] and the *Rhetoric*[15] he discussed arguments in which the major premise is almost, but not entirely, universal and in which, therefore, the conclusion is probable. He seemed to have had in mind what we have called a "singular predictive inference."[16]

(e) Aristotle seemed also to recognize a mode of argument similar to converse deduction as a form of non-demonstrative inference.[17] Again, he did not call such inferences inductive. In the context in which he discussed the probabilistic arguments just mentioned, he discussed arguments from "signs." He gives as an example: "This woman is pale, therefore she is pregnant." There is a suppressed major premise "All pregnant women are pale."[18] He dismissed such arguments as formally invalid, but he did not connect the notion of probability with such arguments. Elsewhere, he dismissed the argument "If it has been raining, the ground is wet, the ground is wet, so it has been raining" as formally invalid. He said, however, that such arguments ("proof from signs") are used in rhetoric.[19]

(2) Aristotle's views on "incomplete induction" suggested to those who followed him that the establishment of inductive generalizations should proceed by "simple enumeration," i.e., the more positive instances of a generalization discovered, the more established the generalization becomes. This view was challenged by Francis Bacon. He argued,

> For the induction of which the logicians speak, which proceeds by simple enumeration, is a puerile thing; concludes at hazard; is always liable to be upset by a contradictory instance; takes into account only what is known and ordinary; and leads to no result.[20]

[12] *Ibid.*, 105a 13–15.
[13] *Ibid.*, 156a 5.
[14] *Prior Analytics*, 70a, 4.
[15] *Rhetoric*, 1359a, 7.
[16] Cf. Day, *op. cit.*, pp. 122–124.
[17] See Edward H. Madden, "Aristotle's Treatment of Probability and Signs," *Philosophy of Science*, 24, 1957, pp. 167–172.
[18] *Prior Analytics*, 70a, 20–35.
[19] *Sophistici Elenchi*, 167b, 5–10.
[20] Francis Bacon, *The Works of Francis Bacon*, (eds.) James Spedding, Robert Leslie Ellis, and Douglas Denon Heath (London: 1883), Vol. IV, p. 25.

Bacon maintained that instead of proceeding by simple enumeration induction should proceed by "rejection and exclusion." Bacon's "induction by elimination," as it has been called,[21] turns on the simple logical point that a generalization cannot be conclusively established by favorable instances but can be conclusively refuted by one negative instance; thus by finding negative instances to possible laws of nature we can arrive — by a process of elimination — at the true laws of nature. Indeed, Bacon believed that with this method, unlike the uncertain method of induction by simple enumeration, absolutely certain conclusions could be arrived at.

Bacon, however, was mistaken. Induction by elimination may be a useful method of scientific procedure, but unless certain assumptions about the world are made, it can no more arrive at certain conclusions than can induction by simple enumeration. For example, one must assume that the number of possible laws of nature which will explain a given phenomenon are finite; otherwise elimination by negative instances could not hope to dispose of all possible laws but one. But what is worse, one must also assume that there are a *definite* finite number of possible laws of nature which could explain a given phenomena; otherwise we could never *know* whether we have eliminated all possible laws but one.[22] These and another assumption which we will discuss in connection with the inductive logic of John Stuart Mill are needed in order to assure that induction by elimination will attain absolute certainty.

Now Bacon did assume that the number of possible laws of nature was finite. He maintained that there are a limited number of causes (what he called "forms") of phenomena and that all the complexity of the world results from these causes in various combinations.[23] But he did not seem to recognize that by itself this assumption was not enough to guarantee that induction by elimination would reach absolute certainty.

(3) Bacon's method of induction by elimination was taken over by John Stuart Mill and developed into his four well-known methods of experimental inquiry. But Mill, unlike Bacon, explicitly stated that these methods presuppose the Law of Universal Causation: "Every event, or the beginning of every phenomena, must have some cause, some antecedent, on the existence of which it is invariably and unconditionally consequent."[24]

Now it should be clear that any eliminative method of induction that aims for absolute certainty, as Mill's methods do, must presuppose some such principle (as well as the principles already mentioned). For if we have eliminated — by Mill's Method of Difference, for example — all factors save one as the cause of a phenomenon, it still does not follow that this remaining factor *is* the cause unless we assume that the phenomenon *has* a cause.

[21] See G. H. von Wright, *The Logical Problem of Induction* (New York: The Macmillan Co., 1957), chap. 4. [22] *Ibid.*

[23] See G. H. von Wright, *A Treatise on Induction and Probability* (Patterson, N. J.: Littlefield, Adams, and Co., 1960), pp. 151–167.

[24] John Stuart Mill, *A System of Logic* (London: Longmans, Green, and Co., 1891), p. 369.

A problem arises, however, in establishing this Law of Universal Causation. Mill believed that it could be established by induction by simple enumeration. It is generally recognized, however, that Mill's argument is circular. According to Mill, the establishment of the Law of Universal Causation could come about only through the establishment of particular causal laws. But particular causal laws, on Mill's view, are established by eliminative induction and eliminative induction presupposes the Law of Universal Causality.

In any case, Mill apparently recognized at least five of the different kinds of inductive inferences mentioned above although he did not refer to all of them as inductive inferences.

(a) Mill argued that "induction, then, is that operation of the mind by which we infer that what we know to be true in a particular case or cases, will be true in all cases which resemble the former in certain assignable respects."[25] Mill seems to have in mind here what we have called "inductive generalization."

(b) Mill recognized as an inductive inference what we have called "statistical generalization" ("approximate generalization" in Mill's terms). He thought that such generalizations have little use in science except as approximations of universal generalizations.[26]

(c) Mill mentioned briefly what we have called "direct singular inference," but it is not completely clear if he wished to refer to this type of probabilistic inference as inductive inference. In any case, Mill's remarks on the probability of such inferences are sketchy and undeveloped.[27]

(d) Mill also recognized what we have called "standard predictive inferences." He maintained "Not only *may* we reason from particulars to particulars without passing through generals, but we perpetually do so reason."[28] Indeed, Mill believed that inferences from particulars to particulars are the fundamental kind of inference and that general propositions are merely "registers" of past particular inferences plus guiding principles for making new particular inferences.

(e) Mill was keenly aware of the use of converse deduction in science but he did not call this mode of non-demonstrative reasoning "inductive." He believed that converse deduction could not conclusively establish causal laws unless certain conditions were met, whereas he mistakenly believed that induction in his sense could. If the causes postulated by the hypothesis are real phenomena existing in nature and known (presumably by induction) to exercise some effect on the phenomena to be explained, then according to Mill the hypothesis is proven true when the phenomena are deduced from it. Mill did not condemn the use of hypotheses for which this condition was not fulfilled, but he demanded that genuine scientific hypotheses must be such that they could be established conclusively by evidence. Mill argued,

[25] *Ibid.*, p. 188.
[26] *Ibid.*, pp. 386–395.
[27] *Ibid.*
[28] *Ibid.*, p. 123.

It appears, then, to be a condition of the most genuinely scientific hypothesis, that it be not destined always to remain a hypothesis, but be of such a nature as to be either proved or disproved by comparison with observed facts.[29]

Thus Mill considered the ether theory to be only a conjecture, i.e. a theory that *may* be true but which could never be proven conclusively. Since Mill was laboring under the mistaken nineteenth-century view that true science aims and arrives at certainty, he failed to realize that hypotheses of high probability are the best one can have and that no hypothesis can be conclusively established. In particular, he failed to realize that a hypothesis which postulates a cause known to be real and known to exercise some effect on a phenomenon cannot be conclusively established by verified deductions from this hypothesis.

It is sometimes supposed that Mill did not realize the importance of hypotheses in science. Mill, like Bacon before him, thought that the methods of eliminative induction were not only methods of proof but were also methods of discovery. He argued against his critics that if "no discoveries were ever made by . . . The Four Methods, . . . none were ever made by observation and experiment; for assuredly if any [discoveries] were, it was by processes reducible to one or other of these methods."[30] It is almost universally recognized today that Mill's views on this subject are incorrect; that his canons of induction cannot serve as means of discovery. After all, it has been pointed out[31] that the number of factors involved in each case in which a cause of a phenomenon is sought is so large that Mill's methods are unusable as methods of discovery. Moreover, the factors that are relevant do not come already labeled but must be analyzed according to our past knowledge.

Mill's remarks on the use of his methods of induction would seem to justify the criticism that he neglected the use of hypotheses that limit the possible relevant circumstances and delimit the factors to be investigated. It is not just a little surprising, therefore, to find Mill saying elsewhere in the same work:

This function, however, [of suggesting observations and experiments] of hypotheses is one which must be reckoned absolutely indispensable in science. . . . Even in purely experimental science, some inducement is necessary for trying one experiment rather than another. . . . The process of tracing regularity in any complicated, and, at first sight confused set of appearances, is necessarily tentative: we must begin by making any supposition, even a false one, to see what consequences will follow from it. . . . Let anyone watch the manner in which he himself unravels a complicated mass of evidence . . . he will find that he does not take all the items of evidence into his mind at once, and attempt to weave them together: he extemporises, from a few of the particulars, a first rude theory of the mode in which the facts took place, and then looks at the other statements one by one, to try whether they can be reconciled with that provisional theory, or what alterations or additions it requires to make it square with them.[32]

These more perceptive remarks of Mill are often forgotten while his mistaken and naive views on the subject of scientific discovery have come to be associated with him.

[29] *Ibid.*, p. 325. [30] *Ibid.*, p. 283.
[31] See, for example, Morris R. Cohen and Ernest Nagel, *Introduction to Logic and Scientific Method* (New York: Harcourt Brace and Co., 1934), chap. 13.
[32] Mill, *op. cit.*, pp. 326–327.

(4) William Whewell, one of the most famous of Mill's contemporaries, criticized Mill's more naive views on the nature of scientific discovery. Indeed, Whewell's philosophy of induction is mostly concerned with the discovery of hypotheses which bring together a manifold of facts into a coherent pattern.[33] He argued that this is not the mechanical process Mill seemed to suggest at times but rather a stroke of genius — a bold imaginative introduction of a unifying conception. Yet he recognized that deduction of consequences from a hypothesis and their subsequent verifications is needed to establish the hypothesis. Whewell argued:

> Deduction descends steadily and methodically, step by step: Induction mounts by a leap which is out of reach of method. She bounds to the top of the stairs at once; and then it is the business of Deduction, by trying each step, in order, to establish the solidity of her companion's footing. . . . Every step of Induction must be confirmed by rigorous deductive reasoning. . . .[34]

One might suppose that this concept of scientific inquiry would lead Whewell to adopt the view that hypotheses can be made more and more probable by subsequent verifications but can never be established once and for all. On the contrary, he argued that widespread verifications of deductions from physical hypotheses, for example the undulatory theory of light, conclusively establish the truth of a theory:

> No false supposition could, after being adjusted to one class of phenomena, exactly represent a different class, where the agreement was unforeseen and uncontemplated. That rules springing from remote and unconnected quarters should thus leap to the same point, can only arise from *that* being the point where truth resides.[35]

But a simple logical consideration shows this view to be mistaken. No matter how many unrelated facts are accounted for by a hypothesis, the truth of the hypothesis is not thereby assured. The converse of a deductive inference is never conclusive.

(5) Whewell's view of converse deduction was soon corrected by W. Stanley Jevons. Unlike Whewell, Jevons was primarily concerned with induction not as a process of discovery but as a process of testing. He believed that all induction is converse deduction. He maintained,

> All inductive reasoning is but the inverse application of deductive reasoning. Being in possession of certain particular facts or events expressed in propositions, we imagine some more general proposition expressing the existence of a law or cause; and, deducing the particular results of that supposed general proposition, we observe whether they agree with the facts in question.[36]

Jevons argued that such converse deduction can never establish a conclusion with certainty. Indeed, he was one of the first inductive logicians to stress the irreducibly probabilistic quality of inductive procedure.

[33] See William Whewell, *Philosophy of Discovery* (London: J. W. Parker and Son, 1860).
[34] William Whewell, *Novum Organon Renovatum* (London: J. W. Parker and Son, 1858), pp. 114–115.
[35] *Ibid.*, p. 88.
[36] W. Stanley Jevons, *The Principles of Science* (London: Macmillan and Co., 1905), p. 265.

It is doubtful, however, whether the establishment of all generalizations can be reduced to converse deduction as Jevons seemed to have supposed. The conjunctive statement "x_1 is *B* and x_2 is *B* . . . and x_n is *B*" where $x_1 \ldots x_n$ are observed members of the class *A* does make probable the generalization" All *A* is *B*." But this conjunction does not follow from "All *A* is *B*" unless "All *A* is *B*" is construed as an infinite conjunction. Today, however, this interpretation of generalizations is not accepted. Modern logicians interpret "All *A* is *B*" as a hypothetical proposition; namely: "For every *x* if *x* is *A*, then *x* is *B*." Clearly no conjunction of statements follows from a generalization when it is interpreted hypothetically. Hence in the modern view "x_1 is *A* and x_1 is *B*" is not a deduction from "All *A* is *B*" and cannot by converse deduction increase the probability of "All *A* is *B*."[37]

The Purpose of This Anthology

Jevons was one of the first to realize what later inductive logicians took for granted. Inductive logic and probability became closely connected; the problems of one became inseparable from the problems of the other. If inductive inferences were not certain but only probable, then problems could be raised about such inferences:

(1) To say that inductive inference is probable inference is one thing; to analyze the notion of probability is another. After all, what does "probable" mean? Until we are clear about this notion we cannot be clear about the notion of inductive inference.

(2) One of the most important senses of the term "probable" for science is the sense in which it is used when people speak of the probability of a hypothesis, i.e. the confirmation or support given a hypothesis by the evidence. But a number of questions arise: What does "the confirmation of a hypothesis" mean? Can the confirmation of several competing hypotheses be compared with respect to a given body of evidence? Can the confirmation of a hypothesis be compared with respect to different bodies of evidence? Can we speak of the *degree* of confirmation of a hypothesis? How can we measure this degree of confirmation?

(3) In recent years a problem has come to light: Is the confirmation of a hypothesis the whole story in choosing between competing hypotheses? Surely, it has been said, it is not everything. Given several competing hypotheses all equally supported by the evidence, one should choose the simplest hypothesis; simplicity as well as degree of confirmation is important in scientific investigation. But then one may well ask: What does "simplicity" mean? How important is simplicity in choosing a scientific hypothesis? What is the relationship between probability and simplicity?

[37] Cf. Pap, *op. cit.*, pp. 143–144.

(4) To say that a hypothesis or generalization is probable on the basis of certain evidence is surely to suggest that we have some right to believe the hypothesis. But, it may be asked, why do we have this right? Why does certain evidence entitle one to believe a conclusion that "goes beyond" the evidence? Naturally if the conclusion is entailed by true premises there is no problem, for the conclusion is guaranteed by the premises. But if the conclusion is not entailed by the premises a problem seems to arise.

To be sure, this problem was raised by Hume many years before there was any coherent and systematic linking of induction and probability. But with an explicitly acknowledged connection between induction and probability Hume's problem takes on new light and significance. The question "What is the justification of induction?" becomes the question "What is the justification of probabilistic inference?"

The purpose of this anthology is to present solutions given by some of the most important philosophers of inductive logic of modern times to these four main problems: (1) the meaning of "probability," (2) the analysis of confirmation, (3) the analysis of simplicity, (4) the justification of induction. It should be evident from what we have said that these problems are by no means as isolated as our categorizing suggests; indeed the overlapping in many cases is quite evident. Thus some selections in Section IV on the justification of induction will be relevant to Section I which is devoted to the meaning of "probability"; some selections on the meaning of "probability" will be relevant to Section II which deals with problems of confirmation theory and to Section III which is concerned with simplicity, and so on.

It is our hope that this anthology includes much of the best philosophical thinking on some of the main problems of inductive logic and that it will stimulate further investigation of these problems. Inductive logic has surely come a long way in the last forty years. John Maynard Keynes was correct to insist in 1921 that inductive logic had progressed up to his time very little beyond Mill's methods.[38] More important work has been done in inductive logic since Keynes' time than in any period of history, but there is still a great deal to be done. There is, however, some reason to believe that this generation will come to realize the hope expressed by C. D. Broad:

> May we venture to hope that.... Inductive Reasoning which has long been the glory of Science, will have ceased to be the scandal of Philosophy? [39]

[38] John Maynard Keynes, *Treatise on Probability* (London: Macmillan and Co., 1921), chap. 23.

[39] C. D. Broad, *Ethics and the History of Philosophy* (New York: Humanities Press, 1952), pp. 142–143.

I
The Meaning of Probability

I

The Meaning of Probability

Introduction

The Task of Analysis

The task of analyzing the meaning of probability is twofold: First, one must distinguish all the important meanings of "probability" and its cognates and explain their relations to one another. Of course, it may be the case that "probability" has only one meaning. But this cannot be determined until different probability expressions are examined. Secondly, one's analysis of these different senses of "probability" (if there be different senses) must be clear and free from problems. It should be noted that these are relatively independent tasks. One might distinguish between the different senses of "probability" and explain their relations to one another without giving a completely coherent account of each sense. Again, one might give a completely coherent account of one particular sense of "probability" without understanding that this sense is not the only sense or that it is related in certain ways to other senses. Thus, for example, it may be the case that Rudolf Carnap has pinpointed different senses of "probability" without giving a correct analysis of these senses or that Hans Reichenbach has given a correct analysis of one sense of "probability" but wrongly supposed that his analysis will cover other senses.

"Probability": One or More Senses?

Until recently, inductive logicians have tended to assume that "probability" has only one meaning. Even some modern inductive logicians, e.g. Reichenbach, have maintained that the meaning of "probability" is univocal, despite powerful arguments to the contrary. Recent linguistic investigation, however, has suggested that such a view may be too simple and it is now commonly argued that probability expressions have more than one meaning.

Descriptive Meaning

Recent logical investigations have revealed an ambiguity in the descriptive meaning of "probability"; indeed it is now clear that "probability" in its descriptive sense means two quite different things.

FACTUAL

To make a probability statement may be to make a factual or empirical statement, i.e. to describe something in the world. In the selection by Reichenbach included here all probability statements are analyzed in this way. To say, "The probability that heads will occur is 1/2" is to assert something about the world; namely, it is to assert that the limit of relative frequency of heads in an infinite series of coin tosses is 1/2. As John Lenz points out, however, in his critique of the "frequency theory," it is extremely doubtful whether Reichenbach's theory can account for another descriptive meaning of "probability" — namely the degree of confirmation of a hypothesis which has been interpreted as a logical relation between evidence and hypothesis.

It is usually thought that Frank Ramsey's view of probability is descriptive in a factual sense. Indeed, in the selection from Ramsey's work which appears on pages 108–119, Ramsey seems to be arguing that probability statements are factual statements not about the limit of relative frequency but rather about people's psychological states, in particular their degrees of belief. The only difference, it would seem, between Reichenbach and Ramsey, is a difference in what empirical phenomena they believe probability statements to be about.

Now if this is what Ramsey means by "probability," his view is mistaken. Degrees of belief are subjective and personal; they may vary with a person's whims and prejudices. And probability is surely an objective concept whatever else it might be. However, a purely subjectivist or psychological interpretation of Ramsey is not justified. It is clear from many of the things that Ramsey has said elsewhere that by "probable," he does not mean degree of actual belief but degree of *rational* belief.[1] On this interpretation, probability statements are not empirical statements about people's actual beliefs, and the pitfalls of subjectivity are avoided. This interpretation, however, is not entirely free from other problems. As we shall see in a moment, there is the danger that an analysis in terms of degree of rational belief is based on some other analysis of probability.

LOGICAL

To make a probability statement may be to make a logical statement. "Probability" in this sense is analogous to an entailment relation in formal logic. Statements of formal logic specify that a certain relation — the entailment relation — holds between a premise and a conclusion: given the truth of the premises, the truth of the conclusion is necessitated. Probability statements may specify that a certain relation — the probability relation — holds between evidential premises and a hypothesis: given the truth of the evidential statement, the hypothesis is supported or made probable.

Several philosophers have explicitly held this view, most notably John Maynard Keynes and Rudolf Carnap. We shall discuss their theories in a moment and shall also examine a type of theory which can plausibly be con-

[1] F. P. Ramsey, *The Foundations of Mathematics* (Paterson, N. J.: Littlefield, Adams and Co., 1960), pp. 190–203; cf. R. Carnap, *Logical Foundations of Probability* (Chicago: University of Chicago Press, 1962), pp. 45–46.

strued as being based on a logical theory although its proponents do not explicitly say it is so based.

Evaluative Meaning

In contrast to Reichenbach, Carnap, and others who have concentrated on the descriptive meaning of probability statements, it has recently been maintained that "probability" is an evaluative term.[2] Indeed, it has been argued that at least some probability expressions, in particular "It is probable that *p*," have a purely evaluative meaning. To say "It is probable that *p*" is to recommend, not describe; it is to utter a value judgment, not a statement of fact or a logical truth.

Now this view presupposes a particular analysis of value judgments, namely that they are not descriptive, and a particular theory of meaning, namely that the use of an expression is its meaning. Both of these assumptions can be challenged, however. In the first place, it is by no means obvious that a statement cannot have both evaluative force and descriptive meaning.[3] Indeed, it can be argued that the evaluative force of "It is probable that *p*" is due to its descriptive meaning, for insofar as it can seriously be applied to establish that some belief be adopted or some course of action be followed it is surely *because* it has some objective reference.[4] Secondly, it may well be asked if meaning should be assimilated to use. Surely, many expressions have a variety of uses or functions yet their meaning remains constant. It is not implausible to suppose that "It is probable that *p*" is of this sort; that it may be used to recommend, advise, threaten although its meaning remains the same throughout.

In short, it does not follow from the fact that "It is probable that *p*" has evaluative force that it lacks descriptive meaning. Nor does it follow from the fact that it has different functions in different contexts that its meaning varies from context to context. While it is important that the evaluative aspects of probability expressions be recognized and clearly analyzed, it could be a mistake to suppose that they constitute the whole story.

Logical Theories of Probability

Because of the importance of the logical meaning of "probability," it will be useful to examine in some detail theories of probability in which this sense is basic.

Carnap's Theory

Carnap was one of the first philosophers to point out the difference between probability statements that refer to relative frequencies (his probability_2) and

[2] John Patrick Day, *Inductive Probability* (New York: The Humanities Press, 1961), pp. 29–39.

[3] Cf. Richard Brandt, *Ethical Theory* (Englewood Cliffs, N. J.: Prentice-Hall, 1959), chap. 9.

[4] Cf. Wesley C. Salmon, Review of *Inductive Probability* by John Patrick Day, *Philosophical Review*, 1963, p. 393.

probability statements that are about the relation between evidential statements and a hypothesis (his $probability_1$).[5] The former statements are factual statements while the latter statements are logical statements. These latter statements are true *a priori;* i.e. they are true simply by virtue of the meaning of the terms involved. It is to their analysis that Carnap addresses himself in his article "On Inductive Logic."

Consider, for example, a statement:

"The probability that heads will occur is 1/2." Now a person who asserts such a statement may, of course, intend to assert a factual statement, i.e. he may intend to predict that in the long run in a series of tosses of a coin the limit of relative frequency is 1/2. In this case such a statement would be true or false depending on the make-up of the world. But the person who asserts such a statement may not intend to make a factual statement at all. He may be making an elliptical logical statement which when completed would be:

"The probability that heads will occur is 1/2 on the basis of evidence *e*." Evidence *e* would consist, say, of 1,000 tosses of a coin in which 500 were heads. In this case the person would be asserting a logically true statement; no factual consideration could refute it.

Two things should be noted about this logical conception of probability. In the first place, $probability_1$, or the degree of confirmation (the "c^*-function" in Carnap's terms), is relational; it is a relation between an evidential statement *e*, e.g. "500 tosses of this coin out of 1,000 were heads" and a hypothesis *h*, e.g. "Heads will occur." In Carnap's notation: $c^*(h, e)$. In the second place, statements intended in this logical sense which do not mention the evidence *e* are elliptical; when they are completed they must refer to certain evidence. This means that probability statements are relative to certain evidence; when the evidence changes, the probability changes.

Because of the relational character of $probability_1$, different probability statements concerning the same hypotheses *h* will be true as long as they are based on different evidence. Moreover, since probability is construed as a logical relation between statements these different probability statements will all be necessarily true. It is to this point that A. J. Ayer addresses himself in his critique of the logical conception of probability. Ayer argues that there is no way to choose among the different probability statements about *h* all of which are necessarily true. But if we cannot determine which of several probability statements concerning *h* is superior, then the logical conception of probability is inadequate.

Carnap maintains that one should choose the probability statement which encompasses the total amount of evidence available. But Ayer argues that no reason can be given "on Carnap's principles" for choosing *this* probability statement since it is no more or less necessarily true than probability statements which do not encompass the total evidence.

[5] R. Carnap, *op. cit.*, chap. 2; R. Carnap, "The Two Concepts of Probability," *Philosophy and Phenomenological Research,* 5, 1945, pp. 513–32.

It may be asked, however, if Ayer's criticism has not overlooked a crucial distinction; namely the distinction between inductive logic and the *methodology* of inductive logic. The principle of total evidence is not, on Carnap's view, a rule of inductive logic, as Ayer seems to suggest, but rather a requirement of the methodology of inductive logic.[6] This principle can be interpreted as stating a necessary, but not a sufficient, condition for the rationality of inductive beliefs and decisions.

Analogous principles can be formulated for deductive logic: for instance, "If a set of statements is accepted as true, then any logical consequence of that set must be accepted as true." This is not a rule of deductive logic; deductive logic does not tell us what statements to accept or not to accept. Rather, it is a requirement of the methodology of deductive logic. This principle can no more be defined in terms of deductive logic than the principle of total evidence can be defined in terms of inductive logic.[7]

Keynes' Theory

John Maynard Keynes was perhaps the first inductive logician to recognize explicitly that "probability" has a logical meaning. Keynes argues in the selection included here that probability is a logical relation holding between evidential premises *h* and a conclusion *a*. In Keynes' notation: a/h. Like Carnap, he holds that probability statements are elliptical unless the evidence is stated; hence the value of a probability statement is always relative to some evidence. As Ernest Nagel points out in his critique of Keynes' theory, Keynes emphasizes the logical meaning of probability to the neglect of its empirical meaning in terms of relative frequency; indeed, he provides no account of the connection between the two senses. Carnap is not guilty of this error. He explicitly distinguishes between these two kinds of probability; moreover, he emphasizes that probability_1, the logical conception, may under certain circumstances provide an estimate of probability_2, the conception in terms of relative frequency.[8]

Keynes, moreover, in contrast to Carnap believes that the logical relation holding between evidential premises *h* and a conclusion *a* is undefinable. Closely connected to this belief is his view that one can "see" by logical intuition the logical relation between *h* and *a*. Nagel attacks this intuitionism in his critique. It should be noted that Carnap's theory is free from criticism on this score also; he does not hold a logical intuitionism.

Qualified Psychologism

Carnap has called theories which define "probability" in terms of degrees of rational belief "qualified psychologism" in order to distinguish them from theories which define "probability" in terms of actual degrees of belief which

[6] Carnap, *The Logical Foundations of Probability*, pp. 211–213.

[7] C. G. Hempel, "Inductive Inconsistencies," *Logic and Language* (Dordrecht, Holland: D. Reidel Publishing Co., 1962), pp. 141–143.

[8] Carnap, *The Logical Foundations of Probability*, pp. 168–175.

he calls "pure psychologism."[9] Carnap argues that the notion of degree of rational belief is based on the logical sense of probability: i.e. the degree of rational belief for person P at time t in hypothesis h is identical with the degree of confirmation of h afforded by the total evidence available to person P at time t.[10]

Keynes' views on this point are rather close to Carnap's. Keynes recognizes a sense of "probability" in terms of degree of rational belief, but he emphasizes that this is a derivative sense. It is derivative because the degree of rational belief assigned is based on an intuition of the undefinable logical relation holding between a hypothesis and evidence; hence the fundamental meaning of "probability" is a logical relation between evidential premises and conclusion.

Ramsey, as we have already noted, defines "probability" in terms of rational belief. J. O. Wisdom argues in the selection that follows that, depending on how Ramsey's view is interpreted, it seems to be based on either a relative frequency theory like Reichenbach's or on a logical theory like Keynes'. Since Ramsey maintains that the degree of rational belief one has in a hypothesis should be based on the weight and relevance of the evidence for the hypothesis,[11] it seems plausible to interpret Ramsey's theory as resting on a logical concept of probability despite his sharp criticism of Keynes' and his apparent sympathy with the frequency theory. Like Keynes, but not like Carnap, Ramsey believes that an exact rule is not always available to calculate the appropriate degree of rational belief in a hypothesis on the basis of certain evidence.

According to Ernest Nagel, the classical theory of probability, which is represented in this anthology by Laplace, seems to be psychological in character. As in Ramsey's case, however, it is plausible to suppose that the classical theorists held a "qualified psychologism," i.e. that "probability" was defined in terms of degree of rational belief and not in terms of actual belief. Moreover, it is likely that Laplace's view is also based on a logical theory of the meaning of "probability." In his discussion here of the three urns A, B, C, Laplace states that there are different degrees of the probability of a hypothesis depending on the evidence. He does not seem to be talking here about any physical property of the balls or urns; rather he can be taken to mean that there is some logical relation holding between evidence and a conclusion — a relation something like Carnap's $c^*(h, e)$ or Keynes' a/h.

The Principle of Indifference

Central to the classical theory of probability as well as to the theories of Carnap and Keynes is the Principle of Indifference. It would be useful, therefore, to explain this principle and its application in some detail.

[9] Carnap, *The Logical Foundations of Probability*, pp. 37–51.

[10] Rudolf Carnap, "The Aim of Inductive Logic," *Logic, Methodology and the Philosophy of Science* (eds.) E. Nagel, P. Suppes, and A. Tarski (Stanford: Stanford University Press, 1962), pp. 303–318.

[11] Ramsey, *op. cit.*, pp. 199–203.

On the classical theory as expounded by Laplace, "probability" is construed as the ratio of the number of events to be realized to the number of possible events. Unless one has some reason to suppose that one event will occur more often than another, it is held that one should regard these events as equally probable. Keynes has called this the "Principle of Indifference." As Nagel points out in his critique of the classical conception of probability included here, such a principle easily leads to absurdity.

For example, one might argue in accordance with the Principle of Indifference that the probability of throwing two with a die is 1/2 on the grounds that there are two equally possible alternatives: a throw of two or a throw of not two. On the same grounds one can argue that the probability of throwing a three is 1/2. But then the probability of throwing either two or three is 1, or certain. This is obviously absurd since one could instead throw a one, a four, a five, or a six. Again, one might argue that the probability of throwing two heads in a toss of 2 coins is 1/3 on the grounds that there are three equally possible alternatives: two heads, two tails, or one of each. But one might also argue that the probability of throwing heads is 1/4 on the grounds that there are four equally possible alternatives: two heads, two tails, one head and one tail, or one tail and one head. Therefore, the probability of throwing heads twice is *both* 1/3 and 1/4!

The absurdities and contradictions that can be generated by means of an unrestricted use of the Principle of Indifference were well understood by Keynes and he made use of the Principle only under the restricted conditions that Nagel outlines in his critique of the classical theory. Since Keynes believed that only when these conditions were satisfied could probability be measured, he maintained that probability could not in general be measured.

Carnap, on the other hand, makes restricted use of the Principle of Indifference, yet argues that probability can always be measured, given a certain formalized language. As S. F. Barker points out in his discussion of Carnap's theory, this language is much less complex than the language of science or ordinary life. But since Keynes' theory presupposes the language of science and everyday life it can be maintained that Keynes and Carnap are argiung from entirely different premises, hence that their views on the measurability of probability may not really conflict as much as one might first suppose.

In any case, we can best understand Carnap's application of the Principle of Indifference which he elaborates in the selection included here by taking an extremely simple case. Consider a universe *U* consisting of only three particulars named *a*, *b*, and *c*. Imagine that each particular could have or not have a property *P*. Let us call each description of these particulars in respect to their having or not having *P* a "state-description of *U*." Each state-description of *U* can be thought of as a possible way things could happen in this simple universe and all possible state-descriptions of *U* as all possible ways things could occur in *U*. All state-descriptions of this simple universe would be:

$$Pa \mathbin{\&} Pb \mathbin{\&} Pc$$
$$-Pa \mathbin{\&} Pb \mathbin{\&} Pc$$

$$Pa \ \& \ -Pb \ \& \ \ Pc$$
$$Pa \ \& \ \ Pb \ \& \ -Pc$$
$$-Pa \ \& \ -Pb \ \& \ \ Pc$$
$$-Pa \ \& \ \ Pb \ \& \ -Pc$$
$$Pa \ \& \ -Pb \ \& \ -Pc$$
$$-Pa \ \& \ -Pb \ \& \ -Pc$$

Consider now an evidential premise *e*. We wish to know the probability of a hypothesis *h* given *e*; that is, we wish to know $c(h, e)$. Let us call all state-descriptions where *e* occurs *the range of e* and all state-descriptions where *h* and *e* occur *the range of h and e*. Intuitively, on Carnap's interpretation of probability$_1$ (usually called *the range interpretation*) the degree of probability is the degree of overlap between the ranges of *e* and *h*. If *e* and *h* are contradictories there is no overlap between ranges; hence, the probability of *h* given *e* is 0. If *e* entails *h*, the range of *h* is completely included in the range of *e*; hence, the probability of *h* given *e* is 1 or certainty. Naturally there will be a degree of overlap, hence different degrees of probability relative to different *h*'s and *e*'s.

More precisely, then, the degree of probability of *h* given *e*, or $c(h, e)$, is the measure of the range of *h* and *e* divided by the measure of *e*:

$$c(h, e) = \frac{m(h \cdot e)}{m(e)}$$

The question now arises how these ranges are to be measured. A natural procedure would be to assign each state-description an equal probability in accordance with the Principle of Indifference. Thus, in our little universe *U* each state-description would be assigned the probability of 1/8. Carnap has shown, however, that this would have startling consequences: No matter how often a property recurred, the probability of the hypothesis that it would occur again would not be increased. One might suspect that in our little universe the evidence *Pa* and *Pb* would make the hypothesis *Pc* more probable than would the evidence *Pa* make probable the hypothesis *Pb*. This is not so, however, as the reader can easily check. Carnap has shown that this consequence holds in general so long as state-descriptions are assigned equal probability.

Carnap argues that such a use of the Principle of Indifference conflicts with our presystematic concept of probability. He has, however, suggested a way of overcoming this unacceptable consequence. Instead of assigning equal probability to each state-description in accordance with the Principle of Indifference, he suggests that equal probability be assigned to state-descriptions having the same *structure*. The structure of a state-description is determined by the number of individuals having the property in question regardless of which individuals have it. Once equal probabilities are assigned to state-descriptions having the same structure, *then* the probability assigned to a structure is equally divided among the state-descriptions having that structure.

Let us call this particular way of measuring the range of *h* and *e* the m^*-function and the particular confirmation relation generated by this method the c^*-function. Then

$$c^*(h, e) = \frac{m^*(h \cdot e)}{m^*(e)}$$

Considered in this way our little universe U would be divided up as follows:

$$\begin{array}{l} Pa \ \& \ \ Pb \ \& \ \ Pc \} 1/4 \\[1em] \left.\begin{array}{lr} Pa \ \& \ \ Pb \ \& -Pc & 1/12 \\ Pa \ \& -Pb \ \& \ \ Pc & 1/12 \\ -Pa \ \& \ \ Pb \ \& \ \ Pc & 1/12 \end{array}\right\} 1/4 \\[1em] \left.\begin{array}{lr} Pa \ \& -Pb \ \& -Pc & 1/12 \\ -Pa \ \& -Pb \ \& \ \ Pc & 1/12 \\ -Pa \ \& \ \ Pb \ \& -Pc & 1/12 \end{array}\right\} 1/4 \\[1em] -Pa \ \& -Pb \ \& -Pc \} 1/4 \end{array}$$

Measured in this way the probability of hypothesis Pc given evidence Pa and Pb is:

$$c^*(h, e) = \frac{1/4}{1/4 + 1/12}$$
$$= 3/4$$

The probability of hypothesis Pb given evidence Pa is:

$$c^*(h, e) = \frac{1/4 + 1/12}{1/4 + 1/12 + 1/12 + 1/12}$$
$$= 2/3$$

When probability is calculated in this way, an increase in evidence for a hypothesis about some particular event increases the degree of confirmation of a hypothesis. And this surely is in keeping with our presystematic notion of confirmation. This method of calculating probability for universe U has been generalized by Carnap; his theory allows for the calculation of probability for any universe with an infinite number of individuals and any finite number of non-relational properties. Thus it allows for the calculation of probability for any language with an infinite number of proper names and any finite number of monadic predicates.

Barker points out in his criticism of Carnap, however, that Carnap's scheme suffers from several drawbacks: (1) On his view, the degree of confirmation of a universal hypothesis is always 0 no matter what the evidence. This is surely not in accord with our presystematic notion of degree of confirmation. (2) Carnap's theory cannot handle hypotheses with non-monadic predicates. But since many hypotheses of this sort are used in the advanced sciences, Carnap's scheme is inadequate.

Moreover, there is a further problem with Carnap's scheme and this is brought out by Lenz in the paper included here called "Carnap On Defining 'Degree of Confirmation.' " Lenz argues that Carnap's c^*-function is not the only possible c-function. Indeed, as Carnap himself has shown in *The Continuum* *of Inductive Methods*,[12] there are an infinite number of different *c*-functions ranging all the way from a *c*-function (considered above) that does not allow an increase in evidence to increase the degree of confirmation to a *c*-function which is dependent only on past empirical evidence. The problem then, according to Lenz, is for Carnap to justify his choice of *c**-function over all the other *c*-functions. Lenz maintains that Carnap has by no means given an adequate justification for his choice.

It should be noted in conclusion that the problem pointed out by Lenz of justifying the choice of a *c*-function is a special case of the more general problem of justifying inductive reasoning. The last section of this anthology is devoted to this latter problem.

1 *Probability and Its Principles*

PIERRE SIMON, MARQUIS DE LAPLACE

Concerning Probability

All events, even those which on account of their insignificance do not seem to follow the great laws of nature, are a result of it just as necessarily as the revolutions of the sun. In ignorance of the ties which unite such events to the entire system of the universe, they have been made to depend upon final causes or upon hazard, according as they occur and are repeated with regularity, or appear without regard to order; but these imaginary causes have gradually receded with the widening bounds of knowledge and disappear entirely before sound philosophy, which sees in them only the expression of our ignorance of the true causes.

Present events are connected with preceding ones by a tie based upon the evident principle that a thing cannot occur without a cause which produces it. This axiom, known by the name of *the principle of sufficient reason*, extends even to actions which are considered indifferent; the freest will is unable without a determinative motive to give them birth; if we assume two positions with exactly similar circumstances and find that the will is active in the one and inactive in the other, we say that its choice is an effect without a cause. It is then, says Leibnitz, the blind chance of the Epicureans. The contrary opinion is an illusion of the mind, which, losing sight of the evasive reasons of the choice

[12] Rudolf Carnap, *The Continuum of Inductive Methods* (Chicago: University of Chicago Press, 1952).

From *A Philosophical Essay on Probabilities*, by P. S. de Laplace. Trans. by F. W. Truscott and F. L. Emory, from the 6th French edition; chapters 2 and 3, Dover Publications, Inc., N.Y. 14, N. Y., 1951.

of the will in indifferent things, believes that choice is determined of itself and without motives.

We ought then to regard the present state of the universe as the effect of its anterior state and as the cause of the one which is to follow. Given for one instant an intelligence which could comprehend all the forces by which nature is animated and the respective situation of the beings who compose it — an intelligence sufficiently vast to submit these data to analysis — it would embrace in the same formula the movements of the greatest bodies of the universe and those of the lightest atom; for it, nothing would be uncertain and the future, as the past, would be present to its eyes. The human mind offers, in the perfection which it has been able to give to astronomy, a feeble idea of this intelligence. Its discoveries in mechanics and geometry, added to that of universal gravity, have enabled it to comprehend in the same analytical expressions the past and future states of the system of the world. Applying the same method to some other objects of its knowledge, it has succeeded in referring to general laws observed phenomena and in foreseeing those which given circumstances ought to produce. All these efforts in the search for truth tend to lead it back continually to the vast intelligence which we have just mentioned, but from which it will always remain infinitely removed. This tendency, peculiar to the human race, is that which renders it superior to animals; and their progress in this respect distinguishes nations and ages and constitutes their true glory.

Let us recall that formerly, and at no remote epoch, an unusual rain or an extreme drought, a comet having in train a very long tail, the eclipses, the aurora borealis, and in general all the unusual phenomena were regarded as so many signs of celestial wrath. Heaven was invoked in order to avert their baneful influence. No one prayed to have the planets and the sun arrested in their courses: observation had soon made apparent the futility of such prayers. But as these phenomena, occurring and disappearing at long intervals, seemed to oppose the order of nature, it was supposed that Heaven, irritated by the crimes of the earth, had created them to announce its vengeance. Thus the long tail of the comet of 1456 spread terror through Europe, already thrown into consternation by the rapid successes of the Turks, who had just overthrown the Lower Empire. This star after four revolutions has excited among us a very different interest. The knowledge of the laws of the system of the world acquired in the interval had dissipated the fears begotten by the ignorance of the true relationship of man to the universe; and Halley, having recognized the identity of this comet with those of the years 1531, 1607, and 1682, announced its next return for the end of the year 1758 or the beginning of the year 1759. The learned world awaited with impatience this return which was to confirm one of the greatest discoveries that have been made in the sciences, and fulfil the prediction of Seneca when he said, in speaking of the revolutions of those stars which fall from an enormous height: "The day will come when, by study pursued through several ages, the things now concealed will appear with evidence; and posterity will be astonished that truths so clear had escaped us." Clairaut then undertook to submit to analysis the perturbations which the comet had experienced by the action of the two great planets, Jupiter and Saturn; after immense calculations he fixed its next passage at the perihelion toward the beginning of April, 1759, which was actually verified by observation. The regularity which astronomy shows us in the movements of the comets doubtless exists also in all phenomena.

The curve described by a simple molecule of air or vapor is regulated in a manner just as certain as the planetary orbits; the only difference between them is that which comes from our ignorance.

Probability is relative, in part to this ignorance, in part to our knowledge. We know that of three or a greater number of events a single one ought to occur; but nothing induces us to believe that one of them will occur rather than the others. In this state of indecision it is impossible for us to announce their occurrence with certainty. It is, however, probable that one of these events, chosen at will, will not occur because we see several cases equally possible which exclude its occurrence, while only a single one favors it.

The theory of chance consists in reducing all the events of the same kind to a certain number of cases equally possible, that is to say, to such as we may be equally undecided about in regard to their existence, and in determining the number of cases favorable to the event whose probability is sought. The ratio of this number to that of all the cases possible is the measure of this probability, which is thus simply a fraction whose numerator is the number of favorable cases and whose denominator is the number of all the cases possible.

The preceding notion of probability supposes that, in increasing in the same ratio the number of favorable cases and that of all the cases possible, the probability remains the same. In order to convince ourselves let us take two urns, *A* and *B*, the first containing four white and two black balls, and the second containing only two white balls and one black one. We may imagine the two black balls of the first urn attached by a thread which breaks at the moment when one of them is seized in order to be drawn out, and the four white balls thus forming two similar systems. All the chances which will favor the seizure of one of the balls of the black system will lead to a black ball. If we conceive now that the threads which unite the balls do not break at all, it is clear that the number of possible chances will not change any more than that of the chances favorable to the extraction of the black balls; but two balls will be drawn from the urn at the same time; the probability of drawing a black ball from the urn *A* will then be the same as at first. But then we have obviously the case of urn *B* with the single difference that the three balls of this last urn would be replaced by three systems of two balls invariably connected.

When all the cases are favorable to an event the probability changes to certainty and its expression becomes equal to unity. Upon this condition, certainty and probability are comparable, although there may be an essential difference between the two states of the mind when a truth is rigorously demonstrated to it, or when it still perceives a small source of error.

In things which are only probable the difference of the data, which each man has in regard to them, is one of the principal causes of the diversity of opinions which prevail in regard to the same objects. Let us suppose, for example, that we have three urns, *A*, *B*, *C*, one of which contains only black balls while the two others contain only white balls: a ball is to be drawn from the urn *C* and the probability is demanded that this ball will be black. If we do not know which of the three urns contains black balls only, so that there is no reason to believe that it is *C* rather than *B* or *A*, these three hypotheses will appear equally possible, and since a black ball can be drawn only in the first hypothesis, the probability of drawing it is equal to one third. If it is known that the urn *A* contains white balls only, the indecision then extends only to the urns *B* and *C*, and the probability that the ball drawn from the urn *C* will be black is one half. Finally this probability changes to certainty if we are assured that the urns *A* and *B* contain white balls only.

It is thus that an incident related to a numerous assembly finds various degrees of credence, according to the extent of knowledge of the auditors. If the man who reports it is fully convinced of it and if, by his position and character, he inspires great confidence, his statement, however extraordinary it may be, will have for the auditors who lack information the same degree of probability as an ordinary statement made by the same man, and they will have entire faith in it. But if some one of them knows that the same incident is rejected by other equally trustworthy men, he will be in doubt and the incident will be discredited by the enlightened auditors, who will reject it whether it be in regard to facts well averred or the immutable laws of nature.

It is to the influence of the opinion of those whom the multitude judges best informed and to whom it has been accustomed to give its confidence in regard to the most important matters of life that the propagation of those errors is due which in times of ignorance have covered the face of the earth. Magic and astrology offer us two great examples. These errors inculcated in infancy, adopted without examination, and having for a basis only universal credence, have maintained themselves during a very long time; but at last the progress of science has destroyed them in the minds of enlightened men, whose opinion consequently has caused them to disappear even among the common people, through the power of imitation and habit which had so generally spread them abroad. This power, the richest resource of the moral world, establishes and conserves in a whole nation ideas entirely contrary to those which it upholds elsewhere with the same authority. What indulgence ought we not then to have for opinions different from ours, when this difference often depends only upon the various points of view where circumstances have placed us! Let us enlighten those whom we judge insufficiently instructed; but first let us examine critically our own opinions and weigh with impartiality their respective probabilities.

The difference of opinions depends, however, upon the manner in which the influence of known data is determined. The theory of probabilities holds to considerations so delicate that it is not surprising that with the same data two persons arrive at different results, especially in very complicated questions. Let us examine now the general principles of this theory.

The General Principles of the Calculus of Probabilities

First Principle. — The first of these principles is the definition itself of probability, which, as has been seen, is the ratio of the number of favorable cases to that of all the cases possible.

Second Principle. — But that supposes the various cases equally possible. If they are not so, we will determine first their respective possibilities, whose exact appreciation is one of the most delicate points of the theory of chance. Then the probability will be the sum of the possibilities of each favorable case. Let us illustrate this principle by an example.

Let us suppose that we throw into the air a large and very thin coin whose two large opposite faces, which we will call heads and tails, are perfectly similar. Let us find the probability of throwing heads at least one time in two throws. It is clear that four equally possible cases may arise, namely, heads at the first and at the second throw; heads at the first throw and tails at the second; tails at the first throw and heads at the second; finally, tails at both throws. The first three cases are favorable to the event whose probability is sought; consequently this probability is equal to 3/4; so that it is a bet of three to one that heads will be thrown at least once in two throws.

We can count at this game only three different cases, namely, heads at the first throw, which dispenses with throwing a second time; tails at the first throw and heads at the second; finally, tails at the first and at the second throw. This would reduce the probability to 2/3 if we should consider with d'Alembert these three cases as equally possible. But it is apparent that the probability of throwing heads at the first throw is 1/2, while that of the two other cases is 1/4, the first case being a simple event which corresponds to two events combined: heads at the first and at the second throw, and heads at the first throw, tails at the second. If we then, conforming to the second principle, add the possibility 1/2 of heads at the first throw to the possibility 1/4 of tails at the first throw and heads at the second, we shall have 3/4 for the probability sought, which agrees with what is found in the supposition when we play the two throws. This supposition does not change at all the chance of that one who bets on this event; it simply serves to reduce the various cases to the cases equally possible.

Third Principle. — One of the most important points of the theory of probabilities and that which lends the most to illusions is the manner in which these probabilities increase or diminish by their mutual combination. If the events are independent of one another, the probability of their combined existence is the product of their respective probabilities. Thus the probability of throwing one ace with a single die is 1/6; that of throwing two aces in throwing two dice at the same time is 1/36. Each face of the one being able to combine with the six faces of the other, there are in fact thirty-six equally possible cases, among which one single case gives two aces. Generally the probability that a simple event in the same circumstances will occur consecutively a given number of times is equal to the probability of this simple event raised to the power indicated by this number. Having thus the successive powers of a fraction less than unity diminishing without ceasing, an event which depends upon a series of very great probabilities may become extremely improbable. Suppose then an incident be transmitted to us by twenty witnesses in such manner that the first has transmitted it to the second, the second to the third, and so on. Suppose again that the probability of each testimony be equal to the fraction 9/10; that of the incident resulting from the testimonies will be less than 1/8. We cannot better compare this diminution of the probability than with the extinction of the light of objects by the interposition of several pieces of glass. A relatively small number of pieces suffices to take away the view of an object that a single piece allows us to perceive in a distinct manner. The historians do not appear to have paid sufficient attention to this degradation of the probability of events when seen across a great number of successive generations; many historical events reputed as certain would be at least doubtful if they were submitted to this test.

In the purely mathematical sciences the most distant consequences participate in the certainty of the principle from which they are derived. In the applications of analysis to physics the results have all the certainty of facts or experiences. But in the moral sciences, where each inference is deduced from that which precedes it only in a probable manner, however probable these deductions may be, the chance of error increases with their number and ultimately surpasses the chance of truth in the consequences very remote from the principle.

Fourth Principle. — When two events depend upon each other, the probability of the compound event is the product of the probability of the first event and the probability that, this event having occurred, the second will occur. Thus in the preceding case of the three urns *A*, *B*, *C*, of which two contain only white balls and one contains only black balls, the probability of drawing a white ball from the urn *C* is 2/3, since of the three urns only two contain balls of that color. But when a white ball has been drawn from the urn *C*, the indecision relative to that one of the urns which contains only black balls extends only to the urns *A* and *B*; the probability of drawing a white ball from the urn *B* is 1/2; the product of 2/3 by 1/2, or 1/3, is then the probability of drawing two white balls at one time from the urns *B* and *C*.

We see by this example the influence of past events upon the probability of future events. For the probability of drawing a white ball from the urn *B*, which primarily is 2/3, becomes 1/2 when a white ball has been drawn from the urn *C*; it would change to certainty if a black ball had been drawn from the same urn. We will determine this influence by means of the following principle, which is a corollary of the preceding one.

Fifth Principle. — If we calculate *a priori* the probability of the occurred event and the probability of an event composed of that one and a second one which is expected, the second probability divided by the first will be the probability of the event expected, drawn from the observed event.

Here is presented the question raised by some philosophers touching the influence of the past upon the probability of the future. Let us suppose at the play of heads and tails that heads has occurred oftener than tails. By this alone we shall be led to believe that in the constitution of the coin there is a secret cause which favors it. Thus in the conduct of life constant happiness is a proof of competency which should induce us to employ preferably happy persons. But if by the unreliability of circumstances we are constantly brought back to a state of absolute indecision; if, for example, we change the coin at each throw at the play of heads and tails, the past can shed no light upon the future and it would be absurd to take account of it. . . .

2 The Classic Conception of Probability

ERNEST NAGEL

As already noted, the mathematical theory of probability was first developed in connection with games of chance, and the point of view from which it was cultivated received its classic formulation in the treatise of Laplace.* According to the Laplacian view, all our knowledge has a probable character, simply because we lack the requisite skill and information to forecast the future and know the past accurately. A degree of probability is therefore a measure of the amount of certainty associated with a belief: "I consider the word *probability*," De Morgan explained, "as meaning the state of the mind with respect to an assertion, a coming event, or any other matter on which absolute knowledge does not exist." What is required for a mathematical treatment of probability, however, is an exact statement of how this measure is defined; and the classical account is as follows.

Judgments of probability are a function of our partial ignorance and our partial knowledge. We may know that in a given situation the process studied will have an issue which will exhibit one out of a definite number of alternative properties; thus, in tossing a die any one of the six faces may turn up. (These alternative properties have been called the "possible events.") On the other hand, we may have no reason to suppose that one of these events will be realized rather than another, so that, as Laplace remarked, "in this state of indecision it is impossible for us to announce their occurrence with certainty." But a measure of the appropriate degree of belief in a specific outcome of the process can

Reprinted from *Principles of the Theory of Probability* (In *International Encyclopedia of Unified Science*, I, No. 6, 1939, pp. 44–48) by Ernest Nagel by permission of The University of Chicago Press and the author.

* [Ed. note: See the preceding selection from Laplace.]

be obtained. We need simply analyze the possible outcome into a set of "equi-possible alternatives," and then count the number of alternatives which are favorable to the event whose probability is sought. This measure, the probability of the event, is a fraction whose numerator is the number of favorable alternatives, and whose denominator is the total number of possible alternatives, provided that all the alternatives in question are equipossible. Thus, the probability of obtaining six points with a pair of dice is 5/36, because the dice can fall in any one of thirty-six equally possible ways, five of which are favorable to the occurrence of six points in all. On the basis of this definition, the probability calculus was developed as an application of the theory of permutations and combinations.

Almost all writers on probability in the nineteenth century (e.g., Poisson, Quetelet, De Morgan, Boole, Stumpf), and many contemporary mathematicians (e.g., Borel, De Finetti, Cantelli, Castelnuovo), follow Laplace with only relatively minor variations. Because of its historical role, as well as because of its contemporary influence, we shall briefly examine this view.

a) According to the Laplacian definition, a probability statement can be made only in such cases as are analyzable into a set of equipossible alternatives. But, while in some cases it seems possible to do this, in most cases where probability statements are made this is not possible. Thus suppose that a biased coin is assigned the probability of .63 that it presents a head when tossed; there is no clear way in which this number can be interpreted as the ratio of equipossible alternatives. This is perhaps even more evident for statements like 'The probability that a thirty-year-old man will live at least another year is .945.' It is absurd to interpret such a statement as meaning that there are a thousand possible eventuations to a man's career, 945 of which are favorable to his surviving at least another year. Moreover, the Laplacian definition requires a probability coefficient to be a rational number. But irrational numbers frequently occur as values for such coefficients, and there is no way of interpreting them as ratios of a number of alternatives. Thus, on the basis of certain assumptions, it can be calculated that the probability that two integers picked at random are relatively prime is $6/\pi^2$. This number cannot be made to mean that there are π^2 equally possible ways in which pairs of integers can be picked, six of which are favorable to getting relative primes.

b) Writers on the subject have not always been clear as to whether they regarded a probability as the measure of a (psychological) belief, or whether they regarded it as a measure of the degree of belief one *ought* to entertain as reasonable. If a probability coefficient is the measure of a degree of actual certainty or the strength of a belief, the addition and multiplication of probabilities require that we determine procedures for combining certainties or beliefs in some corresponding manner. There are, however, no known methods for adding beliefs to one another, and indeed it is difficult to know what could be meant by saying that beliefs are additive. The proposals of Ramsey* and De Finetti, to measure strength of beliefs by the relative size of the bets a man is willing

* [Ed. note: See the selection from Ramsey in this Section.]

to place, are based on a dubious psychological theory; and at least Ramsey's proposal leads directly to a definition of probability in terms of relative frequencies of actions. On the other hand, if probability is a measure of the amount of confidence one ought to have in a given situation, the Laplacian view offers no explanation of the source of the imperative. It is possible, finally, that a probability coefficient is simply a conventional measure of a degree of belief; in that case, however, probability statements turn out to be bare tautologies.

c) According to the Laplacian definition, the alternatives counted must be equally possible. But if 'equipossible' is synonymous with 'equiprobable,' the definition is circular, unless 'equiprobable' can be defined independently of 'probable.' To meet this difficulty, a rule known as the Principle of Indifference (also as the Principle of Insufficient Reason and as the Principle of the Equal Distribution of Ignorance) has been invoked for deciding when alternatives are to be regarded as equiprobable. According to one standard formulation of the rule, two events are equiprobable if there is no known reason for supposing that one of them will occur rather than the other.

It can be shown, however, that, when this form of the rule is applied, incompatible numerical values can be strictly deduced for the probability of an event. An emended form of the rule has been therefore proposed, according to which our *relevant* evidence must be *symmetrical* with respect to the alternatives, which must not, moreover, be divisible into further alternatives on the given evidence. This formulation seriously restricts the application of the Principle of Indifference. Apart from this, however, two points should be noted: A coin which is known to be symmetrically constructed (so that according to the principle its two faces are to be judged as equiprobable) may nevertheless present the head more frequently than the tail on being tossed; for the relative frequency of heads is a function not only of the physical construction of the coin, but also of the conditions under which it is tossed. Second, no evidence is perfectly symmetrical with respect to a set of alternatives. Thus, the two faces of a coin are differently marked, they do not lie symmetrically with respect to the earth's center at the instant before the coin rises into the air, etc. The emended rule therefore provides that it is only the relevant evidence which is to be considered. But if 'relevance' is defined in terms of 'probable,' the circle in the Laplacian definition is once more patent; while, if judgments of relevance are based on definite empirical knowledge, the ground is cut from under the basic assumption of the Laplacian point of view.

d) It is usually assumed that the ratio of the number of favorable alternatives to the number of possible ones (all being equipossible) is also a clue to the relative frequency with which an event occurs. There is, however, no obvious connection between the 'probability of obtaining a head on tossing a coin' as defined on the classical view, and 'the relative frequency with which heads turn up.' For there is in fact no *logical* relation between *the number of alternative ways* in which a coin can fall and *the frequency* with which these alternatives in fact occur. It has, however, often been supposed that Bernoulli's theorem demonstrates such a connection. For as already explained,* according to that theorem if the probability of heads is 1/2, then the probability approaches 1 that in *n* tosses there are approximately *n*/2 heads as *n* increases. But the supposition that Bernoulli's theorem establishes a relation between a priori (i.e., determined in accordance with the classical definition) and a posteriori probabilities (i.e., determined on the basis of relative frequencies of occurrence) is a serious error. It commits those who make it to a form of a priori rationalism. For within the framework of the classical interpretation of the calculus, Bernoulli's theorem simply specifies the relative number of certain types of equiprobable alternatives, each consisting of *n* tosses; it is no more than a theorem in arithmetic and does *not* permit us to conclude that these alternatives will *occur equally often*. That is to say, only if the expression 'The probability of heads is 1/2' designates a relative frequency of occurrence, can the phrase 'The probability approaches 1' be legitimately interpreted as designating relative frequencies of occurrences.

* [Ed. note: Nagel's explanation is not included here.]

3 *On Inductive Logic*

RUDOLF CARNAP

§1. Inductive Logic

Among the various meanings in which the word 'probability' is used in everyday language, in the discussion of scientists, and in the theories of probability, there are especially two which must be clearly distinguished. We shall use for them the terms 'probability$_1$' and 'probability$_2$'. Probability$_1$ is a logical concept, a certain logical relation between two sentences (or, alternatively, between two propositions); it is the same as the concept of degree of confirmation. I shall write briefly "$\mathfrak{c}$" for "degree of confirmation," and "$\mathfrak{c}(h, e)$" for "the degree of confirmation of the hypothesis *h* on the evidence *e*"; the evidence is usually a report on the results of our observations. On the other hand, probability$_2$ is an empirical concept; it is the relative frequency in the long run of one property with respect to another. The controversy between the so-called logical conception of probability, as represented e.g. by Keynes,[1] and Jeffreys,[2] and others,

From *Philosophy of Science*, Vol. 12, No. 2, pp. 72–97, Copyright © 1945. The Williams & Wilkins Co., Baltimore, Md. Reprinted by permission of the Williams & Wilkins Co. and the author.

[1] J. M. Keynes, *A Treatise on Probability*, 1921. [Ed. note: See selection from Keynes in this Section.] [2] H. Jeffreys, *Theory of Probability*, 1939.

and the frequency conception, maintained e.g. by v. Mises[3] and Reichenbach,[4] seems to me futile. These two theories deal with two different probability concepts which are both of great importance for science. Therefore, the theories are not incompatible, but rather supplement each other.[5]

In a certain sense we might regard deductive logic as the theory of L-implication (logical implication, entailment). And inductive logic may be construed as the theory of degree of confirmation, which is, so to speak, partial L-implication. "*e* L-implies *h*" says that *h* is implicitly given with *e*, in other words, that the whole logical content of *h* is contained in *e*. On the other hand, "$c(h, e) = 3/4$" says that *h* is not entirely given with *e* but that the assumption of *h* is supported to the degree 3/4 by the observational evidence expressed in *e*.

In the course of the last years, I have constructed a new system of inductive logic by laying down a definition for degree of confirmation and developing a theory based on this definition. A book containing this theory is in preparation.* The purpose of the present paper is to indicate briefly and informally the definition and a few of the results found; for lack of space, the reasons for the choice of this definition and the proofs for the results cannot be given here. The book will, of course, provide a better basis than the present informal summary for a critical evaluation of the theory and of the fundamental conception on which it is based.[6]

§2. Some Semantical Concepts

Inductive logic is, like deductive logic, in my conception a branch of semantics. However, I shall try to formulate the present outline in such a way that it does not presuppose knowledge of semantics.

Let us begin with explanations of some semantical concepts which are important both for deductive logic and for inductive logic.[7]

The system of inductive logic to be outlined applies to an infinite sequence of finite language systems L_N ($N = 1, 2, 3$, etc.) and an infinite language system L_∞. L_∞ refers to an infinite universe of individuals, designated by the individual constants 'a_1', 'a_2', etc. (or 'a', 'b', etc.), while L_N refers to a finite universe containing only N individuals designated by 'a_1', 'a_2', $\cdots$ 'a_N'. Individual

*[The reader is referred to the later works of Carnap, especially *Logical Foundations of Probability*, University of Chicago Press, 1950, 2nd edition 1962, and "The Aim of Inductive Logic" in *Logic, Methodology and Philosophy of Science*, eds. E. Nagel, P. Suppes, and A. Tarski, Stanford University Press, 1962.]

[3] R. v. Mises, *Probability, Statistics, and Truth* (orig. 1928), 1939.

[4] H. Reichenbach, *Wahrscheinlichkeitslehre*, 1935.

[5] The distinction briefly indicated here, is discussed more in detail in my paper "The Two Concepts of Probability," which appears in *Philos. and Phenom. Research*, Vol. V, No. 4, 1945.

[6] In an article by C. G. Hempel and Paul Oppenheim in the present issue of this journal, a new concept of degree of confirmation is proposed, which was developed by the two authors and Olaf Helmer in research independent of my own. [Ed. note: The Hempel and Oppenheim article is included in Section II of this volume.]

[7] For more detailed explanations of some of these concepts see my *Introduction to Semantics*, 1942.

variables 'x_1', 'x_2', etc. (or '*x*', '*y*', etc.) are the only variables occurring in these languages. The languages contain a finite number of predicates of any degree (number of arguments), designating properties of the individuals or relations between them. There are, furthermore, the customary connectives of negation ('$\sim$', corresponding to "not"), disjunction ('V', "or"), conjunction ('.', "and"); universal and existential quantifiers ("for every *x*," "there is an *x*"); the sign of identity between individuals '=', and '*t*' as an abbreviation for an arbitrarily chosen tautological sentence. (Thus the languages are certain forms of what is technically known as the lower functional logic with identity.) (The connectives will be used in this paper in three ways, as is customary: (1) between sentences, (2) between predicates (§ 8), (3) between names (or variables) of sentences (so that, if '*i*' and '*j*' refer to two sentences, '*i* V *j*' is meant to refer to their disjunction).)

A sentence consisting of a predicate of degree *n* with *n* individual constants is called an *atomic sentence* (e.g. 'Pa_1', i.e. 'a_1 has the property *P*', or 'Ra_3a_5', i.e. 'the relation *R* holds between a_3 and a_5'). The conjunction of all atomic sentences in a finite language L_N describes one of the possible states of the domain of the *N* individuals with respect to the properties and relations expressible in the language L_N. If we replace in this conjunction some of the atomic sentences by their negations, we obtain the description of another possible state. All the conjunctions which we can form in this way, including the original one, are called *state-descriptions* in L_N. Analogously, a state-description in L_∞ is a class containing some atomic sentences and the negations of the remaining atomic sentences; since this class is infinite, it cannot be transformed into a conjunction.

In the actual construction of the language systems, which cannot be given here, semantical rules are laid down determining for any given sentence *j* and any state-description *i* whether *j* holds in *i*, that is to say whether *j* would be true if *i* described the actual state among all possible states. The class of those state-descriptions in a language system *L* (either one of the systems L_N or L_∞) in which *j* holds is called the *range* of *j* in *L*.

The concept of range is fundamental both for deductive and for inductive logic; this has already been pointed out by Wittgenstein. If the range of a sentence *j* in the language system *L* is universal, i.e. if *j* holds in every state-description (in *L*), *j* must necessarily be true independently of the facts; therefore we call *j* (in *L*) in this case *L-true* (logically true, analytic). (The prefix 'L-' stands for "logical"; it is not meant to refer to the system *L*.) Analogously, if the range of *j* is null, we call *j* *L-false* (logically false, self-contradictory). If *j* is neither L-true nor L-false, we call it *factual* (synthetic, contingent). Suppose that the range of *e* is included in that of *h*. Then in every possible case in which *e* would be true, *h* would likewise be true. Therefore we say in this case that *e* *L-implies* (logically implies, entails) *h*. If two sentences have the same range, we call them *L-equivalent;* in this case, they are merely different formulations for the same content.

The L-concepts just explained are fundamental for deductive logic and therefore also for inductive logic. Inductive logic is constructed out of deductive logic by the introduction of the concept of degree of confirmation. This introduction will here be carried out in three steps: (1) the definition of regular $\mathfrak{c}$-functions (§ 3), (2) the definition of symmetrical $\mathfrak{c}$-functions (§ 5), (3) the definition of the degree of confirmation $\mathfrak{c}^*$ (§ 6).

§ 3. Regular $\mathfrak{c}$-Functions

A numerical function $\mathfrak{m}$ ascribing real numbers of the interval 0 to 1 to the sentences of a finite language L_N is called a regular $\mathfrak{m}$-function if it is constructed according to the following rules:

(1) We assign to the state-descriptions in L_N as values of $\mathfrak{m}$ any positive real numbers whose sum is 1.

(2) For every other sentence j in L_N, the value $\mathfrak{m}(j)$ is determined as follows:
  (a) If j is not L-false, $\mathfrak{m}(j)$ is the sum of the $\mathfrak{m}$-values of those state-descriptions which belong to the range of j.
  (b) If j is L-false and hence its range is null, $\mathfrak{m}(j) = 0$.

(The choice of the rule (2)(a) is motivated by the fact that j is L-equivalent to the disjunction of those state-descriptions which belong to the range of j and that these state-descriptions logically exclude each other.)

If any regular $\mathfrak{m}$-function $\mathfrak{m}$ is given, we define a corresponding function $\mathfrak{c}$ as follows:

(3) For any pair of sentences e, h in L_N, where e is not L-false, $\mathfrak{c}(h, e) = \frac{\mathfrak{m}(e \cdot h)}{\mathfrak{m}(e)}$.

$\mathfrak{m}(j)$ may be regarded as a measure ascribed to the range of j; thus the function $\mathfrak{m}$ constitutes a metric for the ranges. Since the range of the conjunction $e \cdot h$ is the common part of the ranges of e and of h, the quotient in (3) indicates, so to speak, how large a part of the range of e is included in the range of h. The numerical value of this ratio, however, depends on what particular $\mathfrak{m}$-function has been chosen. We saw earlier that a statement in deductive logic of the form "e L-implies h" says that the range of e is entirely included in that of h. Now we see that a statement in inductive logic of the form "$\mathfrak{c}(h, e) = 3/4$" says that a certain part — in the example, three fourths — of the range of e is included in the range of h.[8] Here, in order to express the partial inclusion numerically, it is necessary to choose a regular $\mathfrak{m}$-function for measuring the ranges. Any $\mathfrak{m}$ chosen leads to a particular $\mathfrak{c}$ as defined above. All functions $\mathfrak{c}$ obtained in this way are called *regular* $\mathfrak{c}$-*functions*.

One might perhaps have the feeling that the metric $\mathfrak{m}$ should not be chosen once for all but should rather be changed according to the accumulating experiences.[9] This feeling is correct in a certain sense. However, it is to be satisfied not by the function $\mathfrak{m}$ used in the definition (3) but by another function $\mathfrak{m}_e$ dependent upon e and leading to an alternative definition (5) for the corre-

[8] See F. Waismann, "Logische Analyse des Wahrscheinlichkeitsbegriffs," *Erkenntnis*, vol. 1, 1930, pp. 228–248.

[9] See Waismann, op. cit., p. 242.

sponding $\mathfrak{c}$. If a regular $\mathfrak{m}$ is chosen according to (1) and (2), then a corresponding function $\mathfrak{m}_e$ is defined for the state-descriptions in L_N as follows:

(4) Let i be a state-description in L_N, and e a non-L-false sentence in L_N.
(a) If e does not hold in i, $\mathfrak{m}_e(i) = 0$.
(b) If e holds in i, $\mathfrak{m}_e(i) = \dfrac{\mathfrak{m}(i)}{\mathfrak{m}(e)}$.

Thus $\mathfrak{m}_e$ represents a metric for the state-descriptions which changes with the changing evidence e. Now $\mathfrak{m}_e(j)$ for any other sentence j in L_N is defined in analogy to (2)(a) and (b). Then we define the function $\mathfrak{c}$ corresponding to $\mathfrak{m}$ as follows:

(5) For any pair of sentences e, h in L_N, where e is not L-false, $\mathfrak{c}(h, e) = \mathfrak{m}_e(h)$.

It can easily be shown that this alternative definition (5) yields the same values as the original definition (3).

Suppose that a sequence of regular $\mathfrak{m}$-functions is given, one for each of the finite languages L_N ($N = 1, 2$, etc.). Then we define a corresponding $\mathfrak{m}$-function for the infinite language as follows:

(6) $\mathfrak{m}(j)$ in L_∞ is the limit of the values $\mathfrak{m}(j)$ in L_N for $N \rightarrow \infty$.

$\mathfrak{c}$-functions for the finite languages are based on the given $\mathfrak{m}$-functions according to (3). We define a corresponding $\mathfrak{c}$-function for the infinite language as follows:

(7) $\mathfrak{c}(h, e)$ in L_∞ is the limit of the values $\mathfrak{c}(h, e)$ in L_N for $N \rightarrow \infty$.

The definitions (6) and (7) are applicable only in those cases where the specified limits exist.

We shall later see how to select a particular sub-class of regular $\mathfrak{c}$-functions (§ 5) and finally one particular $\mathfrak{c}$-function $\mathfrak{c}^*$ as the basis of a complete system of inductive logic (§ 6). For the moment, let us pause at our first step, the definition of regular $\mathfrak{c}$-functions just given, in order to see what results this definition alone can yield, before we add further definitions. The theory of regular $\mathfrak{c}$-functions, i.e. the totality of those theorems which are founded on the definition stated, is the first and fundamental part of inductive logic. It turns out that we find here many of the fundamental theorems of the classical theory of probability, e.g. those known as the theorem (or principle) of multiplication, the general and the special theorems of addition, the theorem of division and, based upon it, Bayes' theorem.

One of the cornerstones of the classical theory of probability is the principle of indifference (or principle of insufficient reason). It says that, if our evidence e does not give us any sufficient reason for regarding one of two hypotheses h and h' as more probable than the other, then we must take their probabilities$_1$ as equal: $\mathfrak{c}(h, e) = \mathfrak{c}(h', e)$. Modern authors, especially Keynes, have correctly pointed out that this principle has often been used beyond the limits of its original meaning and has then led to quite absurd results. Moreover, it can easily be shown that, even in its original meaning, the principle is by far too general and leads to contradictions. Therefore the principle must be abandoned If it is and we consider only those theorems of the classical theory which are provable without the help of this principle, then we find that these theorems hold for all regular $\mathfrak{c}$-functions. The same is true for those modern theories of probability$_1$ (e.g. that by Jeffreys, *op. cit.*) which make use of the principle of indifference. Most authors of modern axiom systems of probability$_1$ (e.g. Keynes, *op. cit.*, Waismann, *op. cit.*, Mazurkiewicz [10], Hosiasson [11], v. Wright [12]) are cautious enough not to accept that principle. An examination of these systems shows that their axioms and hence their theorems hold for all regular $\mathfrak{c}$-functions. Thus these systems restrict themselves to the first part of inductive logic, which, although fundamental and important, constitutes only a very small and weak section of the whole of inductive logic. The weakness of this part shows itself in the fact that it does not determine the value of $\mathfrak{c}$ for any pair *h*, *e* except in some special cases where the value is 0 or 1. The theorems of this part tell us merely how to calculate further values of $\mathfrak{c}$ if some values are given. Thus it is clear that this part alone is quite useless for application and must be supplemented by additional rules. (It may be remarked incidentally, that this point marks a fundamental difference between the theories of probability$_1$ and of probability$_2$ which otherwise are analogous in many respects. The theorems concerning probability$_2$ which are analogous to the theorems concerning regular $\mathfrak{c}$-functions constitute not only the first part but the whole of the logico-mathematical theory of probability$_2$. The task of determining the value of probability$_2$ for a given case is — in contradistinction to the corresponding task for probability$_1$ — an empirical one and hence lies outside the scope of the logical theory of probability$_2$.)

§ 4. The Comparative Concept of Confirmation

Some authors believe that a metrical (or quantitative) concept of degree of confirmation, that is, one with numerical values, can be applied, if at all, only in certain cases of a special kind and that in general we can make only a comparison in terms of higher or lower confirmation without ascribing numerical values. Whether these authors are right or not, the introduction of a merely comparative (or topological) concept of confirmation not presupposing a metrical concept is, in any case, of interest. We shall now discuss a way of defining a concept of this kind.

For technical reasons, we do not take the concept "more confirmed" but "more or equally confirmed." The following discussion refers to the sentences of any finite language L_N. We write, for brevity, "$MC(h, e, h', e')$" for "*h* is confirmed on the evidence *e* more highly or just as highly as *h'* on the evidence *e'*."

[10] St. Mazurkiewicz, "Zur Axiomatik der Wahrscheinlichkeitsrechnung," *C. R. Soc. Science Varsovie*, Cl. III, vol. 25, 1932, pp. 1–4.

[11] Janina Hosiasson-Lindenbaum, "On Confirmation," *Journal of Symbolic Logic*, vol. 5, 1940, pp. 133–148.

[12] G. H. von Wright, *The Logical Problem of Induction* (Acta Phil. Fennica, 1941, Fasc. III). See also C. D. Broad, *Mind*, vol. 53, 1944.

Although the definition of the comparative concept *MC* at which we aim will not make use of any metrical concept of degree of confirmation, let us now consider, for heuristic purposes, the relation between *MC* and the metrical concepts, i.e. the regular $\mathfrak{c}$-functions. Suppose we have chosen some concept of degree of confirmation, in other words, a regular $\mathfrak{c}$-function $\mathfrak{c}$, and further a comparative relation *MC*; then we shall say that *MC* is in accord with $\mathfrak{c}$ if the following holds:

(1) For any sentences h, e, h', e', if $MC(h, e, h', e')$ then $\mathfrak{c}(h, e) \geqq \mathfrak{c}(h', e')$.

However, we shall not proceed by selecting one $\mathfrak{c}$-function and then choosing a relation *MC* which is in accord with it. This would not fulfill our intention. Our aim is to find a comparative relation *MC* which grasps those logical relations between sentences which are, so to speak, prior to the introduction of any particular $\mathfrak{m}$-metric for the ranges and of any particular $\mathfrak{c}$-function; in other words, those logical relations with respect to which all the various regular $\mathfrak{c}$-functions agree. Therefore we lay down the following requirement:

(2) The relation *MC* is to be defined in such a way that it is in accord with *all* regular $\mathfrak{c}$-functions; in other words, if $MC(h, e, h', e')$, then for every regular $\mathfrak{c}$, $\mathfrak{c}(h, e) \geqq \mathfrak{c}(h', e')$.

It is not difficult to find relations which fulfill this requirement (2). First let us see whether we can find quadruples of sentences h, e, h', e' which satisfy the following condition occurring in (2):

(3) For every regular $\mathfrak{c}$, $\mathfrak{c}(h, e) \geqq \mathfrak{c}(h', e')$.

It is easy to find various kinds of such quadruples. (For instance, if e and e' are any non-L-false sentences, then the condition (3) is satisfied in all cases where e L-implies h, because here $\mathfrak{c}(h, e) = 1$; further in all cases where e' L-implies $\sim h'$, because here $\mathfrak{c}(h', e') = 0$; and in many other cases.) We could, of course, define a relation *MC* by taking some cases where we know that the condition (3) is satisfied and restricting the relation to these cases. Then the relation would fulfill the requirement (2); however, as long as there are cases which satisfy the condition (3) but which we have not included in the relation, the relation is unnecessarily restricted. Therefore we lay down the following as a second requirement for *MC*:

(4) *MC* is to be defined in such a way that it holds in all cases which satisfy the condition (3); in such a way, in other words, that it is the most comprehensive relation which fulfills the first requirement (2).

These two requirements (2) and (4) together stipulate that $MC(h, e, h', e')$ is to hold if and only if the condition (3) is satisfied; thus the requirements determine uniquely one relation *MC*. However, because they refer to the $\mathfrak{c}$-functions, we do not take these requirements as a definition for *MC*, for we intend to give a purely comparative definition for *MC*, a definition which does not make use of any metrical concepts but which leads nevertheless to a relation

MC which fulfills the requirements (2) and (4) referring to c-functions. This aim is reached by the following definition (where '$=_{Df}$' is used as sign of definition).

(5) $MC(h, e, h', e') =_{Df}$ the sentences h, e, h', e' (in L_N) are such that e and e' are not L-false and at least one of the following three conditions is fulfilled:

(a) e L-implies h,

(b) e' L-implies $\sim h'$,

(c) $e' \cdot h'$ L-implies $e \cdot h$ and simultaneously e L-implies $h \vee e'$.

((a) and (b) are the two kinds of rather trivial cases earlier mentioned; (c) comprehends the interesting cases; an explanation and discussion of them cannot be given here.)

The following theorem can then be proved concerning the relation *MC* defined by (5). It shows that this relation fulfills the two requirements (2) and (4).

(6) For any sentences h, e, h', e' in L_N the following holds:

(a) If $MC(h, e, h', e')$, then, for every regular c, $c(h, e) \geqq c(h', e')$.

(b) If, for every regular c, $c(h, e) \geqq c(h', e')$, then $MC(h, e, h', e')$.

(With respect to L_∞, the analogue of (6)(a) holds for all sentences, and that of (6)(b) for all sentences without variables.)

§ 5. Symmetrical c-Functions

The next step in the construction of our system of inductive logic consists in selecting a narrow sub-class of the comprehensive class of all regular c-functions. The guiding idea for this step will be the principle that inductive logic should treat all individuals on a par. The same principle holds for deductive logic; for instance, if '$\cdot\cdot a \cdot\cdot b \cdot\cdot$' L-implies '$--b--c--$' (where the first expression in quotation marks is meant to indicate some sentence containing 'a' and 'b', and the second another sentence containing 'b' and 'c'), then L-implication holds likewise between corresponding sentences with other individual constants, e.g. between '$\cdot\cdot d \cdot\cdot c \cdot\cdot$' and '$--c--a--$'. Now we require that this should hold also for inductive logic, e.g. that c('$--b--c--$', '$\cdot\cdot a \cdot\cdot b \cdot\cdot$') = c('$--c--a--$', '$\cdot\cdot d \cdot\cdot c \cdot\cdot$'). It seems that all authors on probability$_1$ have assumed this principle — although it has seldom, if ever, been stated explicitly — by formulating theorems in the following or similar terms: "On the basis of observations of s things of which s_1 were found to have the property M and s_2 not to have this property, the probability that another thing has this property is such and such." The fact that these theorems refer only to the number of things observed and do not mention particular things shows implicitly that it does not matter which things are involved; thus it is assumed, e.g., that c('Pd', '$Pa \cdot Pb \cdot \sim Pc$') = c('$Pc$', '$Pa \cdot Pd \cdot \sim Pb$').

The principle could also be formulated as follows. Inductive logic should, like deductive logic, make no discrimination among individuals. In other words, the value of c should be influenced only by those differences between individuals which are expressed in the two sentences involved; no differences between particular individuals should be stipulated by the rules of either deductive or inductive logic.

It can be shown that this principle of non-discrimination is fulfilled if $\mathfrak{c}$ belongs to the class of symmetrical $\mathfrak{c}$-functions which will now be defined. Two state-descriptions in a language L_N are said to be *isomorphic* or to have the same structure if one is formed from the other by replacements of the following kind: we take any one-one relation R such that both its domain and its converse domain is the class of all individual constants in L_N, and then replace every individual constant in the given state-description by the one correlated with it by R. If a regular $\mathfrak{m}$-function (for L_N) assigns to any two isomorphic state-descriptions (in L_N) equal values, it is called a symmetrical $\mathfrak{m}$-function; and a $\mathfrak{c}$-function based upon such an $\mathfrak{m}$-function in the way explained earlier (see (3) in § 3) is then called a *symmetrical* $\mathfrak{c}$*-function*.

§ 6. The Degree of Confirmation $\mathfrak{c}^*$

Let i be a state-description in L_N. Suppose there are n_i state-descriptions in L_N isomorphic to i (including i itself), say i, i', i'', etc. These n_i state-descriptions exhibit one and the same structure of the universe of L_N with respect to all the properties and relations designated by the primitive predicates in L_N. This concept of structure is an extension of the concept of structure or relation-number (Russell) usually applied to one dyadic relation. The common structure of the isomorphic state-descriptions i, i', i'', etc. can be described by their disjunction $i \vee i' \vee i'' \vee \cdots$. Therefore we call this disjunction, say j, a *structure-description* in L_N. It can be shown that the range of j contains only the isomorphic state-descriptions i, i', i'', etc. Therefore (see (2)(a) in § 3) $\mathfrak{m}(j)$ is the sum of the $\mathfrak{m}$-values for these state-descriptions. If $\mathfrak{m}$ is symmetrical, then these values are equal, and hence

(1) $$\mathfrak{m}(j) = n_i \times \mathfrak{m}(i).$$

And, conversely, if $\mathfrak{m}(j)$ is known to be q, then

(2) $$\mathfrak{m}(i) = \mathfrak{m}(i') = \mathfrak{m}(i'') = \cdots = q/n_i.$$

This shows that what remains to be decided, is merely the distribution of $\mathfrak{m}$-values among the structure-descriptions in L_N. We decide to give them equal $\mathfrak{m}$-values. This decision constitutes the third step in the construction of our inductive logic. This step leads to one particular $\mathfrak{m}$-function $\mathfrak{m}^*$ and to the $\mathfrak{c}$-function $\mathfrak{c}^*$ based upon $\mathfrak{m}^*$. According to the preceding discussion, $\mathfrak{m}^*$ is characterized by the following two stipulations:

(3) (a) $\mathfrak{m}^*$ is a symmetrical $\mathfrak{m}$-function;
(b) $\mathfrak{m}^*$ has the same value for all structure-descriptions (in L_N).

We shall see that these two stipulations characterize just one function. Every state-description (in L_N) belongs to the range of just one structure-description.

Therefore, the sum of the $\mathfrak{m}^*$-values for all structure-descriptions in L_N must be the same as for all state-descriptions, hence 1 (according to (1) in § 3). Thus, if the number of structure-descriptions in L_N is m, then, according to (3)(b),

(4) for every structure-description j in L_N, $\mathfrak{m}^*(j) = \frac{1}{m}$.

Therefore, if i is any state-description in L_N and n_i is the number of state-descriptions isomorphic to i, then, according to (3)(a) and (2),

$$\mathfrak{m}^*(i) = \frac{1}{mn_i}. \tag{5}$$

(5) constitutes a definition of $\mathfrak{m}^*$ as applied to the state-descriptions in L_N. On this basis, further definitions are laid down as explained above (see (2) and (3) in § 3): first a definition of $\mathfrak{m}^*$ as applied to all sentences in L_N, and then a definition of $\mathfrak{c}^*$ on the basis of $\mathfrak{m}^*$. Our inductive logic is the theory of this particular function $\mathfrak{c}^*$ as our concept of degree of confirmation.

It seems to me that there are good and even compelling reasons for the stipulation (3)(a), i.e. the choice of a symmetrical function. The proposal of any non-symmetrical $\mathfrak{c}$-function as degree of confirmation could hardly be regarded as acceptable. The same can not be said, however, for the stipulation (3)(b). No doubt, to the way of thinking which was customary in the classical period of the theory of probability, (3)(b) would appear as validated, like (3)(a), by the principle of indifference. However, to modern, more critical thought, this mode of reasoning appears as invalid because the structure-descriptions (in contradistinction to the individual constants) are by no means alike in their logical features but show very conspicuous differences. The definition of $\mathfrak{c}^*$ shows a great simplicity in comparison with other concepts which may be taken into consideration. Although this fact may influence our decision to choose $\mathfrak{c}^*$, it cannot, of course, be regarded as a sufficient reason for this choice. It seems to me that the choice of $\mathfrak{c}^*$ cannot be justified by any features of the definition which are immediately recognizable, but only by the consequences to which the definition leads.

There is another $\mathfrak{c}$-function $\mathfrak{c}_W$ which at the first glance appears not less plausible than $\mathfrak{c}^*$. The choice of this function may be suggested by the following consideration. Prior to experience, there seems to be no reason to regard one state-description as less probable than another. Accordingly, it might seem natural to assign equal $\mathfrak{m}$-values to all state-descriptions. Hence, if the number of the state-descriptions in L_N is n, we define for any state-description i

$$\mathfrak{m}_W(i) = 1/n. \tag{6}$$

This definition (6) for $\mathfrak{m}_W$ is even simpler than the definition (5) for $\mathfrak{m}^*$. The measure ascribed to the ranges is here simply taken as proportional to the cardinal numbers of the ranges. On the basis of the $\mathfrak{m}_W$-values for the state-descriptions defined by (6), the values for the sentences are determined as before (see (2) in § 3), and then $\mathfrak{c}_W$ is defined on the basis of $\mathfrak{m}_W$ (see (3) in § 3).[13]

In spite of its apparent plausibility, the function $\mathfrak{c}_W$ can easily be seen to be entirely inadequate as a concept of degree of confirmation. As an example, consider the language L_{101} with 'P' as the only primitive predicate. Let the number of state-descriptions in this language be n (it is 2^{101}). Then for any state-description, $\mathfrak{m}_W = 1/n$. Let e be the conjunction $Pa_1 \cdot Pa_2 \cdot Pa_3 \cdots Pa_{100}$ and let h be 'Pa_{101}'. Then $e \cdot h$ is a state-description and hence $\mathfrak{m}_W(e \cdot h) = 1/n$. e holds only in the two state-descriptions $e \cdot h$ and $e \cdot \sim h$; hence $\mathfrak{m}_W(e) = 2/n$. Therefore $\mathfrak{c}_W(h, e) = 1/2$. If e' is formed from e by replacing some or even all of the atomic sentences with their negations, we obtain likewise $\mathfrak{c}_W(h, e') = 1/2$. Thus the $\mathfrak{c}_W$-value for the prediction that a_{101} is P is always the same, no matter whether among the hundred observed individuals the number of those which we have found to be P is 100 or 50 or 0 or any other number. Thus the choice of $\mathfrak{c}_W$ as the degree of confirmation would be tantamount to the principle never to let our past experiences influence our expectations for the future. This would obviously be in striking contradiction to the basic principle of all inductive reasoning.

§ 7. Languages With One-Place Predicates Only

The discussions in the rest of this paper concern only those language systems whose primitive predicates are one-place predicates and hence designate properties, not relations. It seems that all theories of probability constructed so far have restricted themselves, or at least all of their important theorems, to properties. Although the definition of $\mathfrak{c}^*$ in the preceding section has been stated in a general way so as to apply also to languages with relations, the greater part of our inductive logic will be restricted to properties. An extension of this part of inductive logic to relations would require certain results in the deductive logic of relations, results which this discipline, although widely developed in other respects, has not yet reached (e.g. an answer to the apparently simple question as to the number of structures in a given finite language system).

Let $L_N{}^p$ be a language containing N individual constants 'a_1', $\cdots$ 'a_N', and p one-place primitive predicates 'P_1', $\cdots$ 'P_p'. Let us consider the following expressions (sentential matrices). We start with '$P_1x \cdot P_2x \cdots P_px$'; from this expres-

[13] It seems that Wittgenstein meant this function $\mathfrak{c}_W$ in his definition of probability, which he indicates briefly without examining its consequences. In his *Tractatus Logico-Philosophicus*, he says: "A proposition is the expression of agreement and disagreement with the truth-possibilities of the elementary [i.e. atomic] propositions" (*4.4); "The world is completely described by the specification of all elementary propositions plus the specification, which of them are true and which false" (*4.26). The truth-possibilities specified in this way correspond to our state-descriptions. Those truth-possibilities which verify a given proposition (in our terminology, those state-descriptions in which a given sentence holds) are called the truth-grounds of that proposition (*5.101). "If T_r is the number of the truth-grounds of the proposition "r", T_{rs} the number of those truth-grounds of the proposition "s" which are at the same time truth-grounds of "r", then we call the ratio $T_{rs}:T_r$ the measure of the *probability* which the proposition "r" gives to the proposition "s" " (*5.15). It seems that the concept of probability thus defined coincides with the function $\mathfrak{c}_W$.

sion we form others by negating some of the conjunctive components, until we come to '$\sim P_1x \cdot \sim P_2x \cdots \sim P_px$', where all components are negated. The number of these expressions is $k = 2^p$; we abbreviate them by 'Q_1x', $\cdots$ 'Q_kx'. We call the k properties expressed by those k expressions in conjunctive form and now designated by the k new Q-predicates the *Q-properties* with respect to the given language $L_N{}^p$. We see easily that these Q-properties are the strongest properties expressible in this language (except for the L-empty, i.e., logically self-contradictory, property); and further, that they constitute an exhaustive and non-overlapping classification, that is to say, every individual has one and only one of the Q-properties. Thus, if we state for each individual which of the Q-properties it has, then we have described the individuals completely. Every state-description can be brought into the form of such a statement, i.e. a conjunction of N Q-sentences, one for each of the N individuals. Suppose that in a given state-description i the number of individuals having the property Q_1 is N_1, the number for Q_2 is N_2, $\cdots$ that for Q_k is N_k. Then we call the numbers N_1, N_2, $\cdots$ N_k the *Q-numbers* of the state-description i; their sum is N. Two state-descriptions are isomorphic if and only if they have the same Q-numbers. Thus here a structure-description is a statistical description giving the Q-numbers N_1, N_2, etc., without specifying which individuals have the properties Q_1, Q_2, etc.

Here — in contradistinction to languages with relations — it is easy to find an explicit function for the number m of structure-descriptions and, for any given state-description i with the Q-numbers N_1, $\cdots$ N_k, an explicit function for the number n_i of state-descriptions isomorphic to i, and hence also a function for $\mathfrak{m}^*(i)$. [14]

Let j be a non-general sentence (i.e. one without variables) in $L_N{}^p$. Since there are effective procedures (that is, sets of fixed rules furnishing results in a finite number of steps) for constructing all state-descriptions in which j holds and for computing $\mathfrak{m}^*$ for any given state-description, these procedures together yield an effective procedure for computing $\mathfrak{m}^*(j)$ (according to (2) in § 3). However, the number of state-descriptions becomes very large even for small language systems (it is k^N, hence, e.g., in $L_7{}^3$ it is more than two million.) Therefore, while the procedure indicated for the computation of $\mathfrak{m}^*(j)$ is effective, nevertheless in most ordinary cases it is impracticable; that is to say, the number of steps to be taken, although finite, is so large that nobody will have the time to carry them out to the end. I have developed another procedure for

[14] The results are as follows.

(1) $$m = \frac{(N + k - 1)!}{N!(k - 1)!}$$

(2) $$n_i = \frac{N!}{N_1!N_2!\cdots N_k!}$$

Therefore (according to (5) in § 6):

(3) $$\mathfrak{m}^*(i) = \frac{N_1!N_2!\cdots N_k!(k - 1)!}{(N + k - 1)!}$$

the computation of $\mathfrak{m}^*(j)$ which is not only effective but also practicable if the number of individual constants occurring in j is not too large.

The value of $\mathfrak{m}^*$ for a sentence j in the infinite language has been defined (see (6) in § 3) as the limit of its values for the same sentence j in the finite languages. The question arises whether and under what conditions this limit exists. Here we have to distinguish two cases. (i) Suppose that j contains no variable. Here the situation is simple; it can be shown that in this case $\mathfrak{m}^*(j)$ is the same in all finite languages in which j occurs; hence it has the same value also in the infinite language. (ii) Let j be general, i.e., contain variables. Here the situation is quite different. For a given finite language with N individuals, j can of course easily be transformed into an L-equivalent sentence j'_N without variables, because in this language a universal sentence is L-equivalent to a conjunction of N components. The values of $\mathfrak{m}^*(j'_N)$ are in general different for each N; and although the simplified procedure mentioned above is available for the computation of these values, this procedure becomes impracticable even for moderate N. Thus for general sentences the problem of the existence and the practical computability of the limit becomes serious. It can be shown that for every general sentence the limit exists; hence $\mathfrak{m}^*$ has a value for all sentences in the infinite language. Moreover, an effective procedure for the computation of $\mathfrak{m}^*(j)$ for any sentence j in the infinite language has been constructed. This is based on a procedure for transforming any given general sentence j into a non-general sentence j' such that j and j', although not necessarily L-equivalent, have the same $\mathfrak{m}^*$-value in the infinite language and j' does not contain more individual constants than j; this procedure is not only effective but also practicable for sentences of customary length. Thus, the computation of $\mathfrak{m}^*(j)$ for a general sentence j is in fact much simpler for the infinite language than for a finite language with a large N.

With the help of the procedure mentioned, the following theorem is obtained:

If j is a purely general sentence (i.e. one without individual constants) in the infinite language, then $\mathfrak{m}^*(j)$ is either 0 or 1.

§ 8. Inductive Inferences

One of the chief tasks of inductive logic is to furnish general theorems concerning inductive inferences. We keep the traditional term "inference"; however, we do not mean by it merely a transition from one sentence to another (viz. from the evidence or premiss e to the hypothesis or conclusion h) but the determination of the degree of confirmation $\mathfrak{c}(h, e)$. In deductive logic it is sufficient to state that h follows with necessity from e; in inductive logic, on the other hand, it would not be sufficient to state that h follows — not with necessity but to some degree or other — from e. It must be specified to what degree h follows from e; in other words, the value of $\mathfrak{c}(h, e)$ must be given. We shall now indicate some results with respect to the most important kinds of inductive inference. These inferences are of special importance when the evidence or the hypothesis or both give statistical information, e.g. concerning the absolute or relative frequencies of given properties.

If a property can be expressed by primitive predicates together with the ordinary connectives of negation, disjunction, and conjunction (without the use of individual constants, quantifiers, or the identity sign), it is called an *elementary property*. We shall use 'M', 'M'', 'M_1', 'M_2', etc. for elementary properties. If a property is empty by logical necessity (e.g. the property designated by '$P \cdot \sim P$') we call it L-empty; if it is universal by logical necessity (e.g. '$P \vee \sim P$'), we call it L-universal. If it is neither L-empty nor L-universal (e.g. 'P_1', '$P_1 \cdot \sim P_2$'), we call it a *factual property*; in this case it may still happen to be universal or empty, but if so, then contingently, not necessarily. It can be shown that every elementary property which is not L-empty is uniquely analyzable into a disjunction (i.e. or-connection) of Q-properties. If M is a disjunction of n Q-properties ($n \geqq 1$), we say that the (logical) *width* of M is n; to an L-empty property we ascribe the width 0. If the width of M is w ($\geqq 0$), we call w/k its *relative width* (k is the number of Q-properties).

The concepts of width and relative width are very important for inductive logic. Their neglect seems to me one of the decisive defects in the classical theory of probability which formulates its theorems "for any property" without qualification. For instance, Laplace takes the probability a priori that a given thing has a given property, no matter of what kind, to be 1/2. However, it seems clear that this probability cannot be the same for a very strong property (e.g. '$P_1 \cdot P_2 \cdot P_3$') and for a very weak property (e.g. '$P_1 \vee P_2 \vee P_3$'). According to our definition, the first of the two properties just mentioned has the relative width 1/8, and the second 7/8. In this and in many other cases the probability or degree of confirmation must depend upon the widths of the properties involved. This will be seen in some of the theorems to be mentioned later.

§ 9. The Direct Inference

Inductive inferences often concern a situation where we investigate a whole population (of persons, things, atoms, or whatever else) and one or several samples picked out of the population. An inductive inference from the whole population to a sample is called a direct inductive inference. For the sake of simplicity, we shall discuss here and in most of the subsequent sections only the case of one property M, hence a classification of all individuals into M and $\sim M$. The theorems for classifications with more properties are analogous but more complicated. In the present case, the evidence e says that in a whole population of n individuals there are n_1 with the property M and $n_2 = n - n_1$ with $\sim M$; hence the relative frequency of M is $r = n_1/n$. The hypothesis h says that a sample of s individuals taken from the whole population will contain s_1 individuals with the property M and $s_2 = s - s_1$ with $\sim M$. Our theory yields in this case the same values as the classical theory. [15]

[15] The general theorem is as follows: $\mathfrak{c}^*(h, e) = \dfrac{\binom{n_1}{s_1}\binom{n_2}{s_1}}{\binom{n}{s}}$.

If we vary s_1, then $\mathfrak{c}^*$ has its maximum in the case where the relative frequency s_1/s in the sample is equal or close to that in the whole population.

If the sample consists of only one individual c, and h says that c is M, then $\mathfrak{c}^*(h, e) = r$.

As an approximation in the case that n is very large in relation to s, Newton's theorem holds.[16] If furthermore the sample is sufficiently large, we obtain as an approximation Bernoulli's theorem in its various forms.

It is worthwhile to note two characteristics which distinguish the direct inductive inference from the other inductive inferences and make it, in a sense, more closely related to deductive inferences:

(i) The results just mentioned hold not only for $\mathfrak{c}^*$ but likewise for all symmetrical $\mathfrak{c}$-functions; in other words, the results are independent of the particular $\mathfrak{m}$-metric chosen provided only that it takes all individuals on a par.

(ii) The results are independent of the width of M. This is the reason for the agreement between our theory and the classical theory at this point.

§ 10. The Predictive Inference

We call the inference from one sample to another the predictive inference. In this case, the evidence e says that in a first sample of s individuals, there are s_1 with the property M, and $s_2 = s - s_1$ with $\sim M$. The hypothesis h says that in a second sample of s' other individuals, there will be s'_1 with M, and $s'_2 = s' - s'_1$ with $\sim M$. Let the width of M be w_1; hence the width of $\sim M$ is $w_2 = k - w_1$.[17]

The most important special case is that where h refers to one individual c only and says that c is M. In this case,

$$\mathfrak{c}^*(h, e) = \frac{s_1 + w_1}{s + k}. \tag{1}$$

Laplace's much debated rule of succession gives in this case simply the value $\frac{s_1 + 1}{s + 2}$ for any property whatever; this, however, if applied to different properties, leads to contradictions. Other authors state the value s_1/s, that is, they take simply the observed relative frequency as the probability for the prediction that an unobserved individual has the property in question. This rule, however,

[16] $\mathfrak{c}^*(h, e) = \binom{s}{s_1} r^{s_1}(1 - r)^{s_2}$.

[17] The general theorem is as follows:

$$\mathfrak{c}^*(h, e) = \frac{\binom{s_1 + s'_1 + w_1 - 1}{s'_1}\binom{s_2 + s'_2 + w_2 - 1}{s'_2}}{\binom{s + s' + k - 1}{s'}}.$$

leads to quite implausible results. If $s_1 = s$, e.g., if three individuals have been observed and all of them have been found to be M, the last-mentioned rule gives the probability for the next individual being M as 1, which seems hardly acceptable. According to (1), $\mathfrak{c}^*$ is influenced by the following two factors (though not uniquely determined by them):

(i) w_1/k, the relative width of M;
(ii) s_1/s, the relative frequency of M in the observed sample.

The factor (i) is purely logical; it is determined by the semantical rules. (ii) is empirical; it is determined by observing and counting the individuals in the sample. The value of $\mathfrak{c}^*$ always lies between those of (i) and (ii). Before any individual has been observed, $\mathfrak{c}^*$ is equal to the logical factor (i). As we first begin to observe a sample, $\mathfrak{c}^*$ is influenced more by this factor than by (ii). As the sample is increased by observing more and more individuals (but not including the one mentioned in h), the empirical factor (ii) gains more and more influence upon $\mathfrak{c}^*$ which approaches closer and closer to (ii); and when the sample is sufficiently large, $\mathfrak{c}^*$ is practically equal to the relative frequency (ii). These results seem quite plausible.[18]

The predictive inference is the most important inductive inference. The kinds of inference discussed in the subsequent sections may be construed as special cases of the predictive inference.

§ 11. The Inference by Analogy

The inference by analogy applies to the following situation. The evidence known to us is the fact that individuals b and c agree in certain properties and, in addition, that b has a further property; thereupon we consider the hypothesis that c too has this property. Logicians have always felt that a peculiar difficulty is here involved. It seems plausible to assume that the probability of the hypothesis is the higher the more properties b and c are known to have in common; on the other hand, it is felt that these common properties should not simply be counted but weighed in some way. This becomes possible with the help of the concept of width. Let M_1 be the conjunction of all properties which b and c are known to have in common. The known similarity between b and c is the greater the stronger the property M_1, hence the smaller its width. Let M_2 be

[18] Another theorem may be mentioned which deals with the case where, in distinction to the case just discussed, the evidence already gives some information about the individual c mentioned in h. Let M_1 be a factual elementary property with the width w_1 ($w_1 \geqq 2$); thus M_1 is a disjunction of w_1 Q-properties. Let M_2 be the disjunction of w_2 among those w_1 Q-properties ($1 \leqq w_2 < w_1$); hence M_2 L-implies M_1 and has the width w_2. e specifies first how the s individuals of an observed sample are distributed among certain properties, and, in particular, it says that s_1 of them have the property M_1 and s_2 of these s_1 individuals have also the property M_2; in addition, e says that c is M_1; and h says that c is also M_2. Then,

$$\mathfrak{c}^*(h, e) = \frac{s_2 + w_2}{s_1 + w_1}.$$

This is analogous to (1); but in the place of the whole sample we have here that part of it which shows the property M_1.

the conjunction of all properties which *b* is known to have. Let the width of M_1 be w_1, and that of M_2, w_2. According to the above description of the situation, we presuppose that M_2 L-implies M_1 but is not L-equivalent to M_1; hence $w_1 > w_2$. Now we take as evidence the conjunction $e \cdot j$; *e* says that *b* is M_2, and *j* says that *c* is M_1. The hypothesis *h* says that *c* has not only the properties ascribed to it in the evidence but also the one (or several) ascribed in the evidence to *b* only, in other words, that *c* has all known properties of *b*, or briefly that *c* is M_2. Then

$$\text{(1)} \qquad \mathfrak{c}^*(h, e \cdot j) = \frac{w_2 + 1}{w_1 + 1}.$$

j and *h* speak only about *c*; *e* introduces the other individual *b* which serves to connect the known properties of *c* expressed by *j* with its unknown properties expressed by *h*. The chief question is whether the degree of confirmation of *h* is increased by the analogy between *c* and *b*, in other words, by the addition of *e* to our knowledge. A theorem [19] is found which gives an affirmative answer to this question. However, the increase of $\mathfrak{c}^*$ is under ordinary conditions rather small; this is in agreement with the general conception according to which reasoning by analogy, although admissible, can usually yield only rather weak results.

Hosiasson [20] has raised the question mentioned above and discussed it in detail. She says that an affirmative answer, a proof for the increase of the degree of confirmation in the situation described, would justify the universally accepted reasoning by analogy. However, she finally admits that she does not find such a proof on the basis of her axioms. I think it is not astonishing that neither the classical theory nor modern theories of probability have been able to give a satisfactory account of and justification for the inference by analogy. For, as the theorems mentioned show, the degree of confirmation and its increase depend here not on relative frequencies but entirely on the logical widths of the properties involved, thus on magnitudes neglected by both classical and modern theories.

The case discussed above is that of simple analogy. For the case of multiple analogy, based on the similarity of *c* not only with one other individual but with a number *n* of them, similar theorems hold. They show that $\mathfrak{c}^*$ increases with increasing *n* and approaches 1 asymptotically. Thus, multiple analogy is shown to be much more effective than simple analogy, as seems plausible.

§ 12. The Inverse Inference

The inference from a sample to the whole population is called the inverse inductive inference. This inference can be regarded as a special case of the

[19]
$$\frac{\mathfrak{c}^*(h, e \cdot j)}{\mathfrak{c}^*(h, j)} = 1 + \frac{w_1 - w_2}{w_2(w_1 + 1)}.$$

This theorem shows that the ratio of the increase of $\mathfrak{c}^*$ is greater than 1, since $w_1 > w_2$.

[20] Janina Lindenbaum-Hosiasson, "Induction et analogie: Comparaison de leur fondement," *Mind*, vol. 50, 1941, pp. 351–365; see especially pp. 361–365.

predictive inference with the second sample covering the whole remainder of the population. This inference is of much greater importance for practical statistical work than the direct inference, because we usually have statistical information only for some samples and not for the whole population.

Let the evidence e say that in an observed sample of s individuals there are s_1 individuals with the property M and $s_2 = s - s_1$ with $\sim M$. The hypothesis h says that in the whole population of n individuals, of which the sample is a part, there are n_1 individuals with M and n_2 with $\sim M$ ($n_1 \geqq s_1$, $n_2 \geqq s_2$). Let the width of M be w_1, and that of $\sim M$ be $w_2 = k - w_1$. Here, in distinction to the direct inference, $\mathfrak{c}^*(h, e)$ is dependent not only upon the frequencies but also upon the widths of the two properties.[21]

§ 13. The Universal Inference

The universal inductive inference is the inference from a report on an observed sample to a hypothesis of universal form. Sometimes the term 'induction' has been applied to this kind of inference alone, while we use it in a much wider sense for all non-deductive kinds of inference. The universal inference is not even the most important one; it seems to me now that the role of universal sentences in the inductive procedures of science has generally been overestimated. This will be explained in the next section.

Let us consider a simple law l, i.e. a factual universal sentence of the form "all M are M'" or, more exactly, "for every x, if x is M, then x is M'", where M and M' are elementary properties. As an example, take "all swans are white". Let us abbreviate '$M \cdot \sim M'$' ("non-white swan") by 'M_1' and let the width of M_1 be w_1. Then l can be formulated thus: "M_1 is empty", i.e. "there is no individual (in the domain of individuals of the language in question) with the property M_1" ("there are no non-white swans"). Since l is a factual sentence, M_1 is a factual property; hence $w_1 > 0$. To take an example, let w_1 be 3; hence M_1 is a disjunction of three Q-properties, say $Q \vee Q' \vee Q''$. Therefore, l can be transformed into: "Q is empty, and Q' is empty, and Q'' is empty". The weakest factual laws in a language are those which say that a certain Q-property is empty; we call them Q-laws. Thus we see that l can be transformed into a conjunction of w_1 Q-laws. Obviously l asserts more if w_1 is larger; therefore we say that the law l has the strength w_1.

Let the evidence e be a report about an observed sample of s individuals such that we see from e that none of these s individuals violates the law l; that is to

[21] The general theorem is as follows:

$$\mathfrak{c}^*(h, e) = \frac{\binom{n_1 + w_1 - 1}{s_1 + w_1 - 1}\binom{n_2 + w_2 - 1}{s_2 + w_2 - 1}}{\binom{n + k - 1}{n - s}}.$$

Other theorems, which cannot be stated here, concern the case where more than two properties are involved, or give approximations for the frequent case where the whole population is very large in relation to the sample.

say, e ascribes to each of the s individuals either simply the property $\sim M_1$ or some other property L-implying $\sim M_1$. Let l, as above, be a simple law which says that M_1 is empty, and w_1 be the width of M_1; hence the width of $\sim M_1$ is $w_2 = k - w_1$. For finite languages with N individuals, $c^*(l, e)$ is found to decrease with increasing N, as seems plausible.[22] If N is very large, c^* becomes very small; and for an infinite universe it becomes 0. The latter result may seem astonishing at first sight; it seems not in accordance with the fact that scientists often speak of "well-confirmed" laws. The problem involved here will be discussed later.

So far we have considered the case in which only positive instances of the law l have been observed. Inductive logic must, however, deal also with the case of negative instances. Therefore let us now examine another evidence e' which says that in the observed sample of s individuals there are s_1 which have the property M_1 (non-white swans) and hence violate the law l, and that $s_2 = s - s_1$ have $\sim M_1$ and hence satisfy the law l. Obviously, in this case there is no point in taking as hypothesis the law l in its original forms, because l is logically incompatible with the present evidence e', and hence $c^*(l, e') = 0$. That all individuals satisfy l is excluded by e'; the question remains whether at least all unobserved individuals satisfy l. Therefore we take here as hypothesis the restricted law l' corresponding to the original unrestricted law l; l' says that all individuals not belonging to the sample of s individuals described in e' have the property $\sim M_1$. w_1 and w_2 are, as previously, the widths of M_1 and $\sim M_1$ respectively. It is found that $c^*(l', e')$ decreases with an increase of N and even more with an increase in the number s_1 of violating cases.[23] It can be shown

[22] The general theorem is as follows:

$$c^*(l, e) = \frac{\binom{s+k-1}{w_1}}{\binom{N+k-1}{w_1}}. \tag{1}$$

In the special case of a language containing 'M_1' as the only primitive predicate, we have $w_1 = 1$ and $k = 2$, and hence $c^*(l, e) = \dfrac{s+1}{N+1}$. The latter value is given by some authors as holding generally (see Jeffreys, op. cit., p. 106 (16)). However, it seems plausible that the degree of confirmation must be smaller for a stronger law and hence depend upon w_1.

If s, and hence N, too, is very large in relation to k, the following holds as an approximation:

$$c^*(l, e) = \left(\frac{s}{N}\right)^{w_1/k}. \tag{2}$$

For the infinite language L_∞ we obtain, according to definition (7) in §3:

$$c^*(l, e) = 0. \tag{3}$$

[23] The theorem is as follows:

$$c^*(l', e') = \frac{\binom{s+k-1}{s_1+w_1}}{\binom{N+k-1}{s_1+w_1}}.$$

that, under ordinary circumstances with large N, $\mathfrak{c}^*$ increases moderately when a new individual is observed which satisfies the original law l. On the other hand, if the new individual violates l, $\mathfrak{c}^*$ decreases very much, its value becoming a small fraction of its previous value. This seems in good agreement with the general conception.

For the infinite universe, $\mathfrak{c}^*$ is again 0, as in the previous case. This result will be discussed in the next section.

§ 14. The Instance Confirmation of a Law

Suppose we ask an engineer who is building a bridge why he has chosen the building materials he is using, the arrangement and dimensions of the supports, etc. He will refer to certain physical laws, among them some general laws of mechanics and some specific laws concerning the strength of the materials. On further inquiry as to his confidence in these laws he may apply to them phrases like "very reliable", "well founded", "amply confirmed by numerous experiences". What do these phrases mean? It is clear that they are intended to say something about probability$_1$ or degree of confirmation. Hence, what is meant could be formulated more explicitly in a statement of the form "$\mathfrak{c}(h, e)$ is high" or the like. Here the evidence e is obviously the relevant observational knowledge of the engineer or of all physicists together at the present time. But what is to serve as the hypothesis h? One might perhaps think at first that h is the law in question, hence a universal sentence l of the form: "For every space-time point x, if such and such conditions are fulfilled at x, then such and such is the case at x". I think, however, that the engineer is chiefly interested not in this sentence l, which speaks about an immense number, perhaps an infinite number, of instances dispersed through all time and space, but rather in one instance of l or a relatively small number of instances. When he says that the law is very reliable, he does not mean to say that he is willing to bet that among the billion of billions, or an infinite number, of instances to which the law applies there is not one counter-instance, but merely that this bridge will not be a counter-instance, or that among all bridges which he will construct during his lifetime, or among those which all engineers will construct during the next one thousand years, there will be no counter-instance. Thus h is not the law l itself but only a prediction concerning one instance or a relatively small number of instances. Therefore, what is vaguely called the reliability of a law is measured not by the degree of confirmation of the law itself but by that of one or several instances. This suggests the subsequent definitions. They refer, for the sake of simplicity, to just one instance; the case of several, say one hundred, instances can then easily be judged likewise. Let e be any non-L-false sentence without variables. Let l be a simple law of the form earlier described (§ 13). Then we understand by the *instance confirmation* of l on the evidence e, in symbols "$\mathfrak{c}^*_i\ (l, e)$", the degree of confirmation, on the evidence e, of the hypothesis that a new individual not mentioned in e fulfills the law l.[24]

[24] In technical terms, the definition is as follows: $\mathfrak{c}^*_i(l, e) =_{Df} \mathfrak{c}^*(h, e)$, where h is an instance of l formed by the substitution of an individual constant not occurring in e.

The second concept, now to be defined, seems in many cases to represent still more accurately what is vaguely meant by the reliability of a law l. We suppose here that l has the frequently used conditional form mentioned earlier: "For every x, if x is M, then x is M'" (e.g. "all swans are white"). By the *qualified-instance confirmation* of the law that all swans are white we mean the degree of confirmation for the hypothesis h' that the next swan to be observed will likewise be white. The difference between the hypothesis h used previously for the instance confirmation and the hypothesis h' just described consists in the fact that the latter concerns an individual which is already qualified as fulfilling the condition M. That is the reason why we speak here of the qualified-instance confirmation, in symbols "$\mathfrak{c}^*_{qi}$".[25] The results obtained concerning instance confirmation and qualified-instance confirmation[26] show that the values of these two functions are independent of N and hence hold for all finite and infinite universes. It has been found that, if the number s_1 of observed counter-instances is a fixed small number, then, with the increase of the sample s, both $\mathfrak{c}^*_i$ and $\mathfrak{c}^*_{qi}$ grow close to 1, in contradistinction to $\mathfrak{c}^*$ for the law itself. This justifies the customary manner of speaking of "very reliable" or "well-founded" or "well confirmed" laws, provided we interpret these phrases as referring to a high value of either of our two concepts just introduced. Understood in this sense, the phrases are not in contradiction to our previous results that the degree of confirmation of a law is very small in a large domain of individuals and 0 in the infinite domain (§ 13).

These concepts will also be of help in situations of the following kind. Suppose a scientist has observed certain events, which are not sufficiently explained by the known physical laws. Therefore he looks for a new law as an explanation. Suppose he finds two incompatible laws l and l', each of which would explain the observed events satisfactorily. Which of them should he prefer? If the domain of individuals in question is finite, he may take the law with the higher degree of confirmation. In the infinite domain, however, this method of comparison fails, because the degree of confirmation is 0 for either law. Here the concept

[25] The technical definition will be given here. Let l be 'for every x, if x is M, then x is M''. Let l be non-L-false and without variables. Let 'c' be any individual constant not occurring in e; let j say that c is M, and h' that c is M'. Then the qualified-instance confirmation of l with respect to 'M' and 'M'' on the evidence e is defined as follows: $\mathfrak{c}^*_{qi}(\text{'}M\text{'}, \text{'}M'\text{'}, e) =_{\text{Df}} \mathfrak{c}^*(h', e \cdot j)$.

[26] Some of the theorems may here be given. Let the law l say, as above, that all M are M'. Let 'M_1' be defined, as earlier, by '$M \cdot {\sim} M'$' ("non-white swan") and 'M_2' by '$M \cdot M'$' ("white swan"). Let the widths of M_1 and M_2 be w_1 and w_2 respectively. Let e be a report about s observed individuals saying that s_1 of them are M_1 and s_2 are M_2, while the remaining ones are ${\sim}M$ and hence neither M_1 nor M_2. Then the following holds:

$$(1) \qquad \mathfrak{c}^*_i(l, e) = 1 - \frac{s_1 + w_1}{s + k}.$$

$$(2) \qquad \mathfrak{c}^*_{qi}(\text{'}M\text{'}, \text{'}M'\text{'}, e) = 1 - \frac{s_1 + w_1}{s_1 + w_1 + s_2 + w_2}.$$

The values of $\mathfrak{c}^*_i$ and $\mathfrak{c}^*_{qi}$ for the case that the observed sample does not contain any individuals violating the law l can easily be obtained from the values stated in (1) and (2) by taking $s_1 = 0$.

of instance confirmation (or that of qualified-instance confirmation) will help. If it has a higher value for one of the two laws, then this law will be preferable, if no reasons of another nature are against it.

It is clear that for any deliberate activity predictions are needed, and that these predictions must be "founded upon" or "(inductively) inferred from" past experiences, in some sense of those phrases. Let us examine the situation with the help of the following simplified schema. Suppose a man X wants to make a plan for his actions and, therefore, is interested in the prediction h that c is M'. Suppose further, X has observed (1) that many other things were M and that all of them were also M', let this be formulated in the sentence e; (2) that c is M, let this be j. Thus he knows e and j by observation. The problem is, how does he go from these premisses to the desired conclusion h? It is clear that this cannot be done by deduction; an inductive procedure must be applied. What is this inductive procedure? It is usually explained in the following way. From the evidence e, X infers inductively the law l which says that all M are M'; this inference is supposed to be inductively valid because e contains many positive and no negative instances of the law l; then he infers h ("c is white") from l ("all swans are white") and j ("c is a swan") deductively. Now let us see what the procedure looks like from the point of view of our inductive logic. One might perhaps be tempted to transcribe the usual description of the procedure just given into technical terms as follows. X infers l from e inductively because $\mathfrak{c}^*(l, e)$ is high; since $l \cdot j$ L-implies h, $\mathfrak{c}^*(h, e \cdot j)$ is likewise high; thus h may be inferred inductively from $e \cdot j$. However, this way of reasoning would not be correct, because, under ordinary conditions, $\mathfrak{c}^*(l, e)$ is not high but very low, and even 0 if the domain of individuals is infinite. The difficulty disappears when we realize on the basis of our previous discussions that X does not need a high $\mathfrak{c}^*$ for l in order to obtain the desired high $\mathfrak{c}^*$ for h; all he needs is a high $\mathfrak{c}^*_{qi}$ for l; and this he has by knowing e and j. To put it in another way, X need not take the roundabout way through the law l at all, as is usually believed; he can instead go from his observational knowledge $e \cdot j$ directly to the prediction h. That is to say, our inductive logic makes it possible to determine $\mathfrak{c}^*(h, e \cdot j)$ directly and to find that it has a high value, without making use of any law. Customary thinking in every-day life likewise often takes this short-cut, which is now justified by inductive logic. For instance, suppose somebody asks Mr. X what color he expects the next swan he will see to have. Then X may reason like this: he has seen many white swans and no non-white swans; therefore he presumes, admittedly not with certainty, that the next swan will likewise be white; and he is willing to bet on it. He does perhaps not even consider the question whether all swans in the universe without a single exception are white; and if he did, he would not be willing to bet on the affirmative answer.

We see that the use of laws is not indispensable for making predictions. Nevertheless it is expedient of course to state universal laws in books on physics, biology, psychology, etc. Although these laws stated by scientists do not have a high degree of confirmation, they have a high qualified-instance confirmation and thus serve us as efficient instruments for finding those highly confirmed singular predictions which we need for guiding our actions.

§ 15. The Variety of Instances

A generally accepted and applied rule of scientific method says that for testing a given law we should choose a variety of specimens as great as possible. For instance, in order to test the law that all metals expand by heat, we should examine not only specimens of iron, but of many different metals. It seems clear that a greater variety of instances allows a more effective examination of the law. Suppose three physicists examine the law mentioned; each of them makes one hundred experiments by heating one hundred metal pieces and observing their expansion; the first physicist neglects the rule of variety and takes only pieces of iron; the second follows the rule to a small extent by examining iron and copper pieces; the third satisfies the rule more thoroughly by taking his one hundred specimens from six different metals. Then we should say that the third physicist has confirmed the law by a more thoroughgoing examination than the two other physicists; therefore he has better reasons to declare the law well-founded and to expect that future instances will likewise be found to be in accordance with the law; and in the same way the second physicist has more reasons than the first. Accordingly, if there is at all an adequate concept of degree of confirmation with numerical values, then its value for the law, or for the prediction that a certain number of future instances will fulfill the law, should be higher on the evidence of the report of the third physicist about the positive results of his experiments than for the second physicist, and higher for the second than for the first. Generally speaking, the degree of confirmation of a law on the evidence of a number of confirming experiments should depend not only on the total number of (positive) instances found but also on their variety, i.e. on the way they are distributed among various kinds.

Ernest Nagel[27] has discussed this problem in detail. He explains the difficulties involved in finding a quantitative concept of degree of confirmation that would satisfy the requirement we have just discussed, and he therefore expresses his doubt whether such a concept can be found at all. He says (pp. 69f): "It follows, however, that the degree of confirmation for a theory seems to be a function not only of the absolute number of positive instances but also of the kinds of instances and of the relative number in each kind. It is not in general possible, therefore, to order degrees of confirmation in a linear order, because the evidence for theories may not be comparable in accordance with a simple linear schema; and a fortiori degrees of confirmation cannot, in general, be quantized."* He illustrates his point by a numerical example. A theory T is examined by a number E of experiments all of which yield positive instances; the specimens tested are taken from two non-overlapping kinds K_1 and K_2.

[27] E. Nagel, *Principles of the Theory of Probability.* Int. Encycl. of Unified Science, vol. I, No. 6, 1939; see pp. 68–71. [Ed. note: See pp. 188–190 in this volume.]

* [See page 190 in this volume.]

Nine possibilities P_1, ··· P_9 are discussed with different numbers of instances in K_1 and in K_2. The total number E increases from 50 in P_1 to 200 in P_9. In P_1, 50 instances are taken from K_1 and none from K_2; in P_9, 198 from K_1 and 2 from K_2. It does indeed seem difficult to find a concept of degree of confirmation that takes into account in an adequate way not only the absolute number E of instances but also their distribution among the two kinds in the different cases. And I agree with Nagel that this requirement is important. However, I do not think it impossible to satisfy the requirement; in fact, it is satisfied by our concept $\mathfrak{c}^*$.

This is shown by a theorem in our system of inductive logic, which states the ratio in which the $\mathfrak{c}^*$ of a law l is increased if s new positive instances of one or several different kinds are added by new observations to some former positive instances. The theorem, which is too complicated to be given here, shows that $\mathfrak{c}^*$ is greater under the following conditions: (1) if the total number s of the new instances is greater, *ceteris paribus;* (2) if, with equal numbers s, the number of different kinds from which the instances are taken is greater; (3) if the instances are distributed more evenly among the kinds. Suppose a physicist has made experiments for testing the law l with specimens of various kinds and he wishes to make one more experiment with a new specimen. Then it follows from (2), that the new specimen is best taken from one of those kinds from which so far no specimen has been examined; if there are no such kinds, then we see from (3) that the new specimen should best be taken from one of those kinds which contain the minimum number of instances tested so far. This seems in good agreement with scientific practice. [The above formulations of (2) and (3) hold in the case where all the kinds considered have equal width; in the general and more exact formulation, the increase of $\mathfrak{c}^*$ is shown to be dependent also upon the various widths of the kinds of instances.] The theorem shows further that $\mathfrak{c}^*$ is much more influenced by (2) and (3) than by (1); that is to say, it is much more important to improve the variety of instances than to increase merely their number.

The situation is best illustrated by a numerical example. The computation of the increase of $\mathfrak{c}^*$, for the nine possible cases discussed by Nagel, under certain plausible assumptions concerning the form of the law l and the widths of the properties involved, leads to the following results. If we arrange the nine possibilities in the order of ascending values of $\mathfrak{c}^*$, we obtain this: P_1, P_3, P_7, P_9; P_2, P_4, P_5, P_6, P_8. In this order we find first the four possibilities with a bad distribution among the two kinds, i.e. those where none or only very few (two) of the instances are taken from one of the two kinds, and these four possibilities occur in the order in which they are listed by Nagel; then the five possibilities with a good or fairly good distribution follow, again in the same order as Nagel's. Even for the smallest sample with a good distribution (viz., P_2, with 100 instances, 50 from each of the two kinds) $\mathfrak{c}^*$ is considerably higher — under the assumptions made, more than four times as high — than for the largest sample with a bad distribution (viz. P_9, with 200 instances, divided into 198 and 2). This shows that a good distribution of the instances is much more important than a mere increase in the total number of instances. This is in accordance with Nagel's remark (p. 69): "A large increase in the number of positive instances of one kind may therefore count for less, in the judgment of skilled experimenters, than a small increase in the number of positive instances of another kind." *

Thus we see that the concept $\mathfrak{c}^*$ is in satisfactory accordance with the principle of the variety of instances.

§ 16. The Problem of the Justification of Induction

Suppose that a theory is offered as a more exact formulation — sometimes called a "rational reconstruction" — of a body of generally accepted but more or less vague beliefs. Then the demand for a justification of this theory may be understood in two different ways. (1) The first, more modest task is to validate the claim that the new theory is a satisfactory reconstruction of the beliefs in question. It must be shown that the statements of the theory are in sufficient agreement with those beliefs; this comparison is possible only on those points where the beliefs are sufficiently precise. The question whether the given beliefs are true or false is here not even raised. (2) The second task is to show the validity of the new theory and thereby of the given beliefs. This is a much deeper going and often much more difficult problem.

For example, Euclid's axiom system of geometry was a rational reconstruction of the beliefs concerning spatial relations which were generally held, based on experience and intuition, and applied in the practices of measuring, surveying, building, etc. Euclid's axiom system was accepted because it was in sufficient agreement with those beliefs and gave a more exact and consistent formulation for them. A critical investigation of the validity, the factual truth, of the axioms and the beliefs was only made more than two thousand years later by Gauss.

Our system of inductive logic, that is, the theory of $\mathfrak{c}^*$ based on the definition of this concept, is intended as a rational reconstruction, restricted to a simple language form, of inductive thinking as customarily applied in everyday life and in science. Since the implicit rules of customary inductive thinking are rather vague, any rational reconstruction contains statements which are neither supported nor rejected by the ways of customary thinking. Therefore, a comparison is possible only on those points where the procedures of customary inductive thinking are precise enough. It seems to me, that on these points sufficient agreement is found to show that our theory is an adequate reconstruction; this agreement is seen in many theorems, of which a few have been mentioned in this paper.

An entirely different question is the problem of the validity of our or any other proposed system of inductive logic, and thereby of the customary methods of inductive thinking. This is the genuinely philosophical problem of induction. The construction of a systematic inductive logic is an important step towards the solution of the problem, but still only a preliminary step. It is important

* [See page 190 in this volume.]

because without an exact formulation of rules of induction, i.e. theorems on degree of confirmation, it is not clear what exactly is meant by "inductive procedures", and therefore the problem of the validity of these procedures cannot even be raised in precise terms. On the other hand, a construction of inductive logic, although it prepares the way towards a solution of the problem of induction, still does not by itself give a solution.

Older attempts at a justification of induction tried to transform it into a kind of deduction, by adding to the premisses a general assumption of universal form, e.g. the principle of the uniformity of nature. I think there is fairly general agreement today among scientists and philosophers that neither this nor any other way of reducing induction to deduction with the help of a general principle is possible. It is generally acknowledged that induction is fundamentally different from deduction, and that any prediction of a future event reached inductively on the basis of observed events can never have the certainty of a deductive conclusion; and, conversely, the fact that a prediction reached by certain inductive procedures turns out to be false does not show that those inductive procedures were incorrect.

The situation just described has sometimes been characterized by saying that a theoretical justification of induction is not possible, and hence, that there is no problem of induction. However, it would be better to say merely that a justification in the old sense is not possible. Reichenbach [28] was the first to raise the problem of the justification of induction in a new sense and to take the first step towards a positive solution. Although I do not agree with certain other features of Reichenbach's theory of induction, I think it has the merit of having first emphasized these important points with respect to the problem of justification: (1) the decisive justification of an inductive procedure does not consist in its plausibility, i.e., its accordance with customary ways of inductive reasoning, but must refer to its success in some sense; (2) the fact that the truth of the predictions reached by induction cannot be guaranteed does not preclude a justification in a weaker sense; (3) it can be proved (as a purely logical result) that induction leads in the long run to success in a certain sense, provided the world is "predictable" at all, i.e. such that success in that respect is possible. Reichenbach shows that his rule of induction R leads to success in the following sense: R yields in the long run an approximate estimate of the relative frequency in the whole of any given property. Thus suppose that we observe the relative frequencies of a property M in an increasing series of samples, and that we determine on the basis of each sample with the help of the rule R the probability q that an unobserved thing has the property M, then the values q thus found approach in the long run the relative frequency of M in the whole. (This is, of course merely a logical consequence of Reichenbach's definition or rule of induction, not a factual feature of the world.)

I think that the way in which Reichenbach examines and justifies his rule of induction is an important step in the right direction, but only a first step. What

[28] Hans Reichenbach, *Experience and Prediction*, 1938, §§ 38 ff., and earlier publications. [See: Reichenbach's selection in Section IV — Ed. note.]

remains to be done is to find a procedure for the examination of any given rule of induction in a more thoroughgoing way. To be more specific, Reichenbach is right in the assertion that any procedure which does not possess the characteristic described above (viz. approximation to the relative frequency in the whole) is inferior to his rule of induction. However, his rule, which he calls "the" rule of induction, is far from being the only one possessing that characteristic. The same holds for an infinite number of other rules of induction, e.g., for Laplace's rule of succession (see above, § 10; here restricted in a suitable way so as to avoid contradictions), and likewise for the corresponding rule of our theory of $\mathfrak{c}^*$ (as formulated in theorem (1), § 10). Thus our inductive logic is justified to the same extent as Reichenbach's rule of induction, as far as the only criterion of justification so far developed goes. (In other respects, our inductive logic covers a much more extensive field than Reichenbach's rule; this can be seen by the theorems on various kinds of inductive inference mentioned in this paper.) However, Reichenbach's rule and the other two rules mentioned yield different numerical values for the probability under discussion, although these values converge for an increasing sample towards the same limit. Therefore we need a more general and stronger method for examining and comparing any two given rules of induction in order to find out which of them has more chance of success. I think we have to measure the success of any given rule of induction by the total balance with respect to a comprehensive system of wagers made according to the given rule. For this task, here formulated in vague terms, there is so far not even an exact formulation; and much further investigation will be needed before a solution can be found.

4 *Enumerative Induction*

STEPHEN F. BARKER

I.

So far in our discussion of enumerative induction we have been considering rather informal theories; and we have observed that their somewhat loosely stated rules of induction tend to engender paradoxes and confusions. Perhaps, however, these difficulties could be avoided by a more rigorously formalized theory. This thought leads us to Carnap.[1] For Carnap's theory of induction does, in a certain sense, involve induction by simple enumeration; and it is the most elaborate and most fully formalized theory of the subject.

From *Induction and Hypotheses*, Cornell University Press, Ithaca, 1957, pp. 82–90.

[1] Rudolf Carnap, *Logical Foundations of Probability*, (Chicago, 1950).

Working out a detailed version of the "Spielraum" theory at which Wittgenstein had darkly hinted, Carnap asks us to imagine that the evidence and hypotheses with which we have to deal all are stated in a definite formalized language. This language will contain a suitably formulated deductive logic, and its extralogical vocabulary will consist of a finite number of predicates plus a supply of singular terms each of which is to designate exactly one individual thing. The strongest possible kind of noncontradictory statement which can be expressed in this language will be one which affirms or denies each predicate of each individual in turn: such statements are called state-descriptions, and each state-description depicts a different "possible world." Any empirical statement that can be formulated in this language will be implied by some state-descriptions and will be contradicted by the remaining state-descriptions of the language. In order to obtain the results that are desired it is necessary not to regard all state-descriptions as having the same antecedent probability, for if they were the same the scheme would not work out satisfactorily. Instead, their probabilities are weighted in such a way that any two state-descriptions having the samc structure are regarded as equally probable — two state-descriptions being said to have the same structure if and only if one can be obtained from the other simply by substituting some singular terms for others. Moreover, any two structures are regarded as equally probable: that is, the total probability assigned to the state-descriptions of one structure must equal the total probability assigned to the state-descriptions of any other structure. The a priori, or antecedent, probabilities of state-descriptions having been arranged in this way, we may then say that the a priori probability of any lesser statement is the sum of the a priori probabilities of all those state-descriptions that imply it (metaphorically speaking, the sum of the probabilities of all the "possible worlds" in which this statement comes out true). The a priori probability of a statement is its probability without empirical evidence; if empirical evidence becomes available, the probability of the statement is likely to be altered. Carnap defines the probability of a hypothesis H relative to evidence E as the ratio of the a priori probability of the conjunction of H with E to the a priori probability of E alone; that is, the probability of H on E is the total probability of all those possible worlds in which both H and E come out true divided by the total probability of all those possible worlds in which E with or without H comes out true.

Carnap's scheme enables him to treat inductive arguments within an explicit logical framework; and he is able to show that in terms of his definitions certain kinds of inductive evidence can increase the probabilities of certain kinds of hypotheses. The difficulties of the sort discussed in the preceding section* do not arise, for Carnap's scheme requires us always to consider the total evidence available; since we cannot leave out bits of evidence, and since his scheme shows us how in principle to manage total bodies of evidence, the puzzles arising from neglect of the principle of total evidence give no difficulty here. Instead of a casually formulated rule of induction which is ambiguous in its

* [Ed. note: This section not reprinted here.]

application, this more systematic scheme provides an unequivocal determination of the probability of any hypothesis with respect to any body of evidence in the language.

There are, however, several features of Carnap's theory which are less attractive. In the first place, Carnap follows Wittgenstein in assuming the availability of a language which contains one and only one proper name for every individual in the universe. From a philosophical point of view, this is a requirement which cannot be countenanced. Such a language at best could be available only to the Deity, and He presumably would have no need of empirical knowledge. We, unfortunately, do not know the exact number of individuals in the universe: nor could we possibly hope to form an opinion about how many there are — without restorting to inductive investigations.

Also, Carnap's theory requires that the primitive predicates employed in the language must all be logically independent of each other (if the statement 'All *F* are *G*' is necessarily true, then '*F*' and '*G*' are said not to be independent). Moreover, each place of a predicate must be independent of each other place (if '*Rxy*' implies '*Ryx*,' then the first and second places of '*R*' are not independent, for instance).[2] These are tiresome restrictions, and they prevent the application of Carnap's theory to some languages that we should like to employ.

These difficulties are significant, but they are not irremediable. Kemeny has indicated in a striking way how these troublesome requirements may be circumvented.[3] He undertakes to do this by dropping Carnap's syntactical notion of a state-description and using instead the semantical notion of a model. What Kemeny means by a model for statements of a language is parallel to what some other writers have meant by an interpretation of statement schemata.[4] What is involved is an assignment of the individuals of an *n*-membered universe to the various extralogical primitives of the language. To each singular term of the language (if it contains any) is assigned exactly one individual; to each one-placed predicate is assigned some set of individuals chosen from the universe; to each two-placed predicate is assigned some set of pairs of individuals; and so on. To each one-placed predicate of next higher logical type is assigned a set of sets of these individuals; to each two-placed such predicate, a set of pairs of sets of individuals; and so on, until every predicate in the language has been provided with an extension. Since the number of predicates in a language (at least in any language with which we should care to deal) must be finite (and each of finite type), no universe containing only a finite number of individuals will yield more than a finite number of different models for a given language. A model is said to be a model for a statement of the language if in it all these assignments are made in such a way that the statement comes out true.

Using this notion of model, Kemeny is able to define a measure function. Where M_n is the total number of models which a universe of n individuals will yield for the given language (or the total number of these consistent with the

[2] Y. Bar-Hillel, "A Note on State-Descriptions", *Philosophical Studies*, II (1951), 72–75.

[3] John Kemeny, "A Logical Measure Function," *Journal of Symbolic Logic*, XVIII (1953), 289–308.

[4] W. V. Quine, *Methods of Logic* (New York, 1950), sec. 24.

available empirical evidence) and where M_n^W is the total number of these models under which the statement W comes out true, we may write:

$$m(W) = \frac{M_n^W}{M_n}\,.$$

That is, the measure, with respect to universes of size n, of statement W in the language is the ratio of favorable models to the total number of models. Of course if we wish exactly to parallel Carnap's scheme, we may assign weights to the various models, equal weights to models having the same structure and the same total weight to every structure; then the measure of a statement will be the ratio of the total weight of the models in which the statement comes out true to the total weight of all the models.

It is now possible to go on to compare the measures of various statements. To say that $m(W_1)$ is greater than $m(W_2)$ will be to say that there is an integer j, such that for any integer k not less than j the value with respect to k-membered universes of $m(W_1)$ is greater than that of $m(W_2)$. Thus we are provided with a general technique for comparing the logical measures of statements in any given language. And obviously if we wish to do so we can employ logical measures in order to compare the degrees of confirmation of statements. For if one statement has a greater measure than another, then we could choose to regard it as the more probable — since the statement with the greater measure is the one which comes out true in more "possible worlds" (or in possible worlds of greater weight).

The difficulties mentioned, which afflicted Carnap's doctrine, are avoided by this approach of Kemeny's. There need be no restriction here to the effect that the primitive predicates of the language be independent. If some predicates are not independent, then all that happens is that some models will automatically be precluded which otherwise would have been available. Nor is there any need for the language to contain a proper name corresponding to each individual (as was necessary if we were to construct state-descriptions); indeed, the language does not have to contain any singular terms at all. And, as a further advantage, this technique deals in an obvious way with predicates of higher logical type, as Carnap's theory does not. Moreover, some of Carnap's somewhat counterintuitive results are avoided; specifically, a universal statement counts as more probable than a logically false statement. It appears that any desirable results and theorems obtainable in Carnap's theory could be obtained also using Kemeny's approach.

II.

One troublesome feature of Carnap's scheme, even as modified by Kemeny, concerns universal generalizations. Generalizations will not admit of being confirmed by inductive evidence, according to this scheme. The reason is that we have in general no grounds for being entitled to assume that the size of the universe with which we have to do is less than some given finite number; we may suppose the universe to be finite, but we have no certainty about its maximum possible size. This being the case, a universal generalization will have to receive an a priori probability which is vanishingly small (on Carnap's view, zero; on Kemeny's view, greater than zero but less than any specific number greater than zero). And worse, no matter how many favorable instances be examined, the probability of the generalization still remains vanishingly small.

Carnap's way of meeting this is to abandon hope of confirming generalizations (such as 'All swans are white') and to concern himself instead with "instance confirmations," that is, with the probability of the prediction that the next swan will be white (or that any particular unobserved swan will be white). One is reminded of Mill's "reasoning from particulars to particulars." Carnap is able, on this principle, to establish a version of the Laplacean rule of succession;[5] thus, as the number of favorable instances observed increases without bound, the probability that a given individual, if it is a swan, is white increases towards one as a limit.

Carnap argues that we ought to rest content with this, that for practical purposes instance confirmations are all we need and that we ought to be satisfied to give up hope of confirming generalizations (and other universal hypotheses). No doubt half a loaf is better than none; and a good deal of empirical knowledge could perhaps be construed as consisting of nothing stronger than instance confirmations — for instance, an engineer wants to know whether this particular bridge will stand, and he does not much care whether all bridges of its type do so. But it would seem that in theoretical science universal hypotheses may have a more indispensable role to play; at any rate, it does seem somewhat paradoxical to maintain that no universal hypothesis ever can be confirmed. Surely it would be more desirable to obtain a scheme which could permit the confirming of generalizations and other interesting universal hypotheses, if such a scheme could at all plausibly be worked out.

Furthermore, if we adhere to the prejudice against singular terms which the second chapter urged,* then instance confirmations would not be possible at all: for Carnap's instance confirmation requires that singular terms appear both in the hypothesis being confirmed and in the evidence adduced in its support. It would appear that arguments involving instance confirmation must covertly employ assumptions about the existence and uniqueness of the individuals named, assumptions which according to this scheme cannot possibly be confirmed.

Another question arises in connection with hypotheses involving predicates of two or more places. Carnap's scheme does of course envisage hypotheses (and evidence) in which predicates having any number of places may occur. But the number of possible structures increases very rapidly when languages involving predicates with two or more places are employed, and the problem of how in general to calculate the number of structures compatible with any

[5] Carnap, *op. cit.*, pp. 572 ff.

* **[Ed. note: This chapter not included here.]**

given statement becomes quite difficult.[6] Because of this complexity, Carnap has not yet dealt with such languages, but has considered only languages containing none but one-placed predicates. However, when one does come to consider more complex languages, it seems as though trouble may arise. For what can it mean to speak of the instance confirmation of a hypothesis which contains a two-placed predicate together with mixed universal and existential quantifications? For a generalization containing only one-placed predicates, the notion of instance confirmation makes clear sense: the generalization 'All dogs bark' has as an instance the statement 'Fido barks' (if we assume Fido to be a dog), and Carnap's scheme allows for confirmation of such instances as a practical substitute for confirmation of the generalization itself. But let us turn to a language containing some two-placed predicates and let us consider the hypothesis 'Every dog has a father,' whose logical form we assume to be '$(x)\ (Dx \supset (\exists y)Fyx)$.' We might at first suppose that statements such as 'Fido has a father' would serve as practical substitutes for this hypothesis: but Carnap's scheme does not provide any way whatever of confirming the statement 'Fido has a father' except by direct observation of something that is Fido's father — no finite amount of evidence about other dogs could enable us to predict that Fido probably has a father, according to Carnap's scheme. Therefore, this sort of instance will not do. We might try instead to take as our instances statements such as 'Rover is father of Fido' (assuming both to be dogs); statements like this can be thought of as containing no quantifiers, and evidence about other dogs might, at least under certain very special circumstances, increase the probability of 'Rover is father of Fido.' However, the statement 'Rover is father of Fido' is so unrelated to the original hypothesis 'Every dog has a father' as hardly to be a practical substitute for it; moreover, it would seem that the kind of evidence which we should need in order to increase the probability of 'Rover is father of Fido' would be evidence that most observed dogs are observed to be fathers of one another — scarcely the sort of evidence which we should expect to obtain. It would seem that there is no kind of specific statement about a finite number of particular individuals which can serve as a usable substitute for a hypothesis like 'Every dog has a father.' Thus there may be an inherent difficulty in extending to richer languages the idea that our reasoning proceeds "from particulars to particulars." If this be so, then it may be impossible for Carnap's scheme to offer any sort of confirmation at all in connection with hypotheses containing two-placed predicates together with mixed quantifications. Since such hypotheses sometimes are important, this would be a definite shortcoming in Carnap's scheme.

Carnap's elaborate theory is an impressive and sophisticated one. Yet perhaps we are entitled still to hope for some other theory which might prove free from these troubles.

[6] See R. L. Davis, "The Number of Structures of Finite Relations," *Proceedings of the American Mathematical Society*, IV (1953), 486–495.

5 The Conception of Probability as a Logical Relation

ALFRED J. AYER

There is a fairly widespread view that, at least in one important sense of the term, probability is most properly attributed to statements: and that what is being asserted when it is said that a statement is probable, in this sense, is that it bears a certain relation to another statement, or set of statements, which may also be described as confirming, or supporting, or providing evidence for it. There are some, indeed, who maintain that this is the only sense in which it is correct to speak of probability; that what we 'really mean' when we assert anything to be probable is always that some statement bears the requisite relation to such and such a piece of evidence. Thus Keynes [1] assumes that every significant probability statement can be fitted into his formula '$a/h = p$,' where a is the proposition which is said to be probable, h is the evidence on which it is probable, and p is the degree of probability that h confers on a, a quantity which may or may not be numerically measurable. And Kneale [2] takes it for granted that probability is relative to evidence: if this is often overlooked, it is because in talking about probability we seldom bother to specify the evidence on which we are relying: 'our probability statements are commonly elliptical.' [3] Other writers, like Carnap,[4] distinguish this sense of probability from one in which to speak of the probability of an event is to attribute a numerical frequency to the distribution of some property among events of a given class. Carnap himself allows that we have a use for this conception of probability in terms of observed frequencies, or of the limits towards which they are supposed to tend. He calls it probability$_2$ to differentiate it from the other, logical, conception of probability, what he calls probability$_1$. It is, however, on the basis of probability$_1$ that he develops his inductive logic.[5]

From S. Körner (Ed.), *Observation and Interpretation*, Butterworths Scientific Publications, London, 1957, pp. 12–17. Reprinted by permission of Butterworths Scientific Publishers and the Colston Research Society, The Macmillan and Co., Ltd., St. Martin's Press Inc., and the author.

[1] J. M. Keynes, *A Treatise on Probability*. [Ed. note: See selection from Keynes in this Section.]

[2] W. Kneale, *Probability and Induction*.

[3] *Op. cit.*, p. 10.

[4] R. Carnap, "The Two Concepts of Probability," *Philosophy and Phenomenological Research*, Vol. V, No. 4.

[5] Vide, *The Logical Foundations of Probability*.

Not all the advocates of this conception of probability agree with Keynes in regarding probability as an unanalysable logical relation. Certainly Carnap does not suppose his probability_1 to be unanalysable. But he does recognize that, on this interpretation of them, probability statements come to resemble statements of formal logic in the sense that if they are true they are analytic. This might, indeed, be disputed by philosophers like Kneale who wish to hold on to the synthetic *a priori*, and so to confine analyticity within more narrow limits: but they would at least allow that statements of probability, in this sense, are not empirical. They are necessarily true, if they are true at all. For it is characteristic of any view of this type that the existence of a probability relation between statements is made to depend, not on any contingent matter of fact, but solely on the meaning of the statements concerned. And this is my ground for saying that the advocates of such views treat probability as a logical relation, whether they assent to this form of words or not.

Now it seems to me that there is a very simple objection to theories of this type, which has strangely escaped the notice of their supporters [6] and even of their critics. Let us suppose that a disciple of Keynes has decided to bet upon a horse-race and that he is considering the chances of a horse named 'Eclipse.' He is determined to be rational and so to bring his degree of belief in the horse's victory into exact accordance with the objective probabilities. He assembles the evidence: h_1 that Eclipse will be ridden by the champion jockey; h_2 that the going will be hard; h_3 that Eclipse is suited by the distance; h_4 that it went lame after its last race; h_5 that it has previously beaten the more fancied of its competitors; h_6 that it has recently dropped in the betting, and so forth. Assume that he evaluates all the relevant evidence that he can acquire, or, in other words, that, so far as his knowledge goes, he has not omitted any true proposition which, if it were conjoined with his other data, would make any difference to the resultant probability. So, taking a to be the proposition that Eclipse will win, he decides that the probability of a on $h_1 = p_1$, $a/h_2 = p_2$, $a/h_3 = p_3$, $a/h_1h_2 = p_x$, $a/h_{1-4} = p_y$, . . . ; and finally that a/h_{1-n}, where h_{1-n} represents the totality of the relevant evidence at his command, $= p_z$. How is he to place his bet?

To common sense the answer is obvious. If his degree of belief in the proposition that Eclipse will win is to be rational, it must correspond to the probability p_z. He must find a means of comparing this with the odds that he is offered and bet accordingly. But what reason can he have, on his principles, for accepting the common-sense answer? In what way is the probability p_z better than the other probabilities, p_1, p_2n, . . . , p_x, p_y, which he has also estimated? If his estimates are correct, all these statements of probability are necessary truths. And in that case how can any one of them be superior to the others? What one wants to say is that the probability p_z, since it is the only one that is esti-

[6] Professor Braithwaite reminds me that Keynes does notice the point which I am about to raise when he discusses the Weight of Arguments in Chapter VI of his Treatise. But, since he concludes that probabilities are unaffected by the weight of evidence, he misses the force of the objection.

mated on the basis of all the relevant evidence, provides the best appraisal of what is actually likely to happen. But what can this mean to Keynes? An event will happen, or it will not. To say that it is likely to happen is, on his theory, only a misleading way of saying that the statement that it will happen is probable on the basis of certain other statements. But this leaves us free to choose these other statements in any way we like, provided only that we have sufficient warrant for accepting them. It may seem, indeed, that even this proviso sets a problem; for to say that we have sufficient warrant for accepting a given statement must mean, for Keynes, that it follows from, or is made probable by, another statement, or set of statements, which we have sufficient warrant for accepting: and then one appears to be threatened with an infinite regress. Keynes meets this difficulty, however, by assuming that there are certain statements which we can know directly to be true: and it is on statements of this sort that all rational judgments of probability must finally depend. This assumption may be questioned; but even if it be admitted, our original objection still holds. Once we have assembled some trustworthy data by these means, there can be no reason, on Keynes's system, why we should trouble to carry our investigations any further. The addition of more evidence may, indeed, yield a higher or lower probability for the statement in which we are interested. But unless we have made some logical mistake, this probability cannot be said to be more, or less, correct than the one that was yielded by the evidence with which we started. Neither can any sense be given to the claim that it is a better estimate of what is likely to happen.

Carnap has seen that there is a difficulty here, and he has tried to meet it by introducing what he calls 'the principle of total evidence.' 'Let $c(h, e)$,' he says, 'be the degree of confirmation of the hypothesis h with respect to the evidence e. Let us suppose that we have a definition of the function c and, based upon this definition, a theorem "$c(h, e) = q$," which states the value q of c for given h and e. A principle which seems generally recognized, although not always obeyed, says that if we wish to apply such a theorem of the theory of probability to a given knowledge situation, then we have to take as evidence e the *total evidence* available to the person in question at the time in question, that is to say, his total knowledge of the results of his observations.'[7]

But why *have* we to take as evidence the total evidence available to us, whatever that may mean? What sort of principle is this? It can hardly be a *moral* principle. So far as morality goes, we might equally well choose to rely on the evidence which yielded the highest degree of confirmation for the hypothesis in which we were interested, or on that which yielded the lowest, or on whatever evidence we found most pleasing. Unless we miscalculate, the result at which we arrive will in each case be a necessary truth; and there can surely be no moral reason for preferring any one of these necessary truths to any other. It might, however, be thought that there was a practical reason: and indeed one may suppose that Carnap intended his principle of total evidence to be

[7] R. Carnap, "On the Application of Inductive Logic," *Philosophy and Phenomenological Research*, Vol. VIII, No. 1.

pragmatic. The suggestion would seem to be that we should trust hypotheses to the degree to which they are confirmed; and that by taking all the available evidence into account, we diminish the risk of falling foul of the facts, that is, of over- or under-estimating the likelihood of the actual occurrence of the event to which our hypothesis refers. Once again, this is in accordance with common sense: but how can it possibly be justified on Carnap's principles? The event will occur or it will not. To say that there is a probability, of a given degree, that it will occur is to say only that the hypothesis that it will occur is confirmed to that degree by such and such evidence. If this proposition is true, it is necessarily true: but so are all the other true propositions which, on the basis of greater, or less, or partly, or wholly different evidence, assign to the hypothesis a different degree of confirmation. There is no sense, therefore, in which the proposition which brings in all the available evidence can be superior to any of the others as a measure of probability. And this being so, there can be no practical reason why we should take it as a guide.

So far as I can see, the only way in which Carnap might hope to meet this objection would be to make his principle of total evidence a part of the definition of probability$_1$. He might claim that what we must be understood to mean by saying that a hypothesis is probable, in this sense, to a certain degree is just that it is confirmed, to this degree, by the totality of the evidence which is available to us. But what is this totality? If it be only 'the total knowledge of the results of our observations,' then the difficulty will not be met. For, to revert to my example of the horse race, it may well be that the only information I have bothered to acquire, which is in any way relevant to the hypothesis that Eclipse will win, is that it is to be ridden by the champion jockey; and in that case I shall be justified in regarding the hypothesis as probable to the extent that this single piece of evidence confirms it, and betting accordingly. No doubt if I were to investigate further, as any sensible punter would, I should find evidence which would lead me to revise my estimate of Eclipse's chances. But why should I take the trouble? If what I mean by saying that it is probable to such and such a degree that Eclipse will win is that the hypothesis that it will win is confirmed to this degree by the totality of the relevant observations that I have actually made, then the fact that the probability might be different if I had extended my observations need not concern me. For, on this view, if I do not miscalculate, there is no sense in which this second estimate of probability could be any better than the first.

The answer to this might seem to be that the probability is to be defined by reference not to the results of all the relevant observations that one happens to have made, but to those of all the relevant observations that one could make if one chose. The totality of evidence that is available to me will not as a rule be limited to the evidence that I actually have. But then what are its limits? What means is there of deciding which are the observations that it is possible for me to make? Presumably, in the case of the horse race, the condition of the horse's lungs is relevant. Is this within the range of evidence that is available to me? Well, I could use X-rays to find it out. But what if I have not the skill?

Then, I can employ a radiologist to do it for me. But what if I cannot discover a radiologist who is willing? What if he asks more money than I can afford to pay? Then, perhaps, I can find some way of forcing him to do it: perhaps I can steal the money. But will this always be possible? I do not see how there can be a general answer to such questions; nor, therefore, how there can be a rule for determining what is the totality of the available evidence. But in default of such a rule, this definition of probability would seem to be both vague in principle, and of little practical use.

Furthermore, it makes judgements of probability at least partly subjective. If the stable guards its secrets well, the totality of the evidence that is available to me will fall short of the totality of the evidence that is available to the horse's trainer. Let us make the implausible assumption that both he and I are in fact possessed of all the relevant evidence that is respectively available to us, and that we correctly calculate the degree of confirmation of the hypothesis that Eclipse will win, arriving naturally at different results. Both results will be valid, but the one that is valid for him will not be valid for me. If I take over his estimate I shall fall into error, for I shall then be asserting that the hypothesis is confirmed to the degree he says by the totality of the evidence that is available to *me*, when it is not in fact confirmed to that degree by the totality of the evidence that is available to me but only by the different totality of the evidence that is available to *him*. It follows also, on this view, that there is no such thing as *the* probability of a hypothesis: there are as many different probabilities as there are persons who have access to different quantities of evidence. This conclusion may or may not be objectionable in itself; but I think it would be regarded as disturbing at least by some of those who wish us to look upon probability as a logical relation.

It may be suggested that they can avoid this conclusion by assuming that everyone has access, in principle, to all the evidence that there is. Then to say that a statement is probable to such and such a degree will be to say that it is confirmed to that degree by the totality of true statements. There is no need to put in the proviso that these statements must all be relevant, since the inclusion of irrelevant truths will make no difference to the result. This does indeed yield an objective definition of probability, but it has the fatal disadvantage that the probability of every hypothesis becomes either 0 or 1. For the totality of true statements must include either the negation of the hypothesis in question, or the hypothesis itself.

To escape from this predicament, one would have to restrict the range of the available evidence in such a way that it excluded any statement, or set of statements, which entailed either the hypothesis or its negation. And then one might equate the probability of the hypothesis with the degree to which it was confirmed by the totality of true statements that satisfied this condition. One objection to this would be that in assessing probabilities we could never draw on any universal statement of law. For if the event, to which our hypothesis referred, were subject to causal laws, the relevant statements of law, when combined with the statements affirming the appropriate initial conditions, would always entail the hypothesis or its negation. We could indeed keep the statements of law if we excluded the singular statements which joined with them in producing the entailments; but this would be an absurd proceeding, since it is only through establishing singular statements that we ever acquire any evidence at all. And just for this reason, it may be said, we can afford to forgo the universal statements of law; for they draw all their support from the singular statements which are derivable from them; and these we shall have. Moreover, statistical laws, with frequencies of less than a hundred per cent, will not be excluded, though it may well be argued that they too will be superfluous, if all true singular statements are to be comprised in the available evidence.

A more serious objection to this definition of probability is that it allows us to have very little confidence in any of the judgements of probability that we actually make. For it can very seldom be the case that we in fact know every true singular statement that is relevant to the hypothesis in which we are interested. But in so far as the evidence at our disposal falls short of the total evidence, we cannot infer that the hypotheses which it is supposed to confirm are at all likely to be true. For all that is meant by their being likely to be true is that they are confirmed, to whatever degree, by the total evidence; and this is not in our possession. What we want to say is that, even if we can never be sure of having all the requisite evidence, nevertheless by acquiring more evidence, and incorporating it into our calculations, we bring our estimates of probability nearer to the truth. And clearly this is the view that Carnap holds. But I am not at all sure that he, or anyone else who conceives of probability as a logical relation, is entitled to hold it. For, as we have already remarked, each necessary truth to the effect that a given hypothesis is confirmed by some collection of evidence to such and such a degree is in itself as good as every other: we can pick out a special set of these propositions and say that they alone are to be regarded, by definition, as statements of probability; but then it will follow that the others, which fall outside this privileged set, are not statements of probability at all; there will be no justification for treating them even as approximations to the measures of objective probability for which we are in search.

Perhaps this difficulty could be met by introducing the concept of second-order probabilities. They might then be defined in such a way that one could assign a probability to the hypothesis that a given statement of confirmation was a statement of probability: and this probability would be made to increase, as one added to the evidence on which the statement of confirmation was based.

It seems to me, however, that such devices do not, in the end, remove the fundamental weakness of the logical theory. It has been well remarked by Kneale that 'no analysis of the probability relation can be accepted as adequate, i.e. as explaining the ordinary usage of the word "probability," unless it enables us to understand why it is rational to take as a basis for action a proposition which stands in that relation to the evidence at our disposal.'[8]

[8] *Probability and Induction*, p. 20.

And, even if the other objections to it can be met, I maintain that the view which we have been considering fails this test. For, if we are presented only with a stock of necessary facts to the effect that certain statements, or groups of statements, bear logical relations to each other in virtue solely of their meaning, I do not see what reason there could be for differentiating between the items of this stock as bases for action. I am not clear even what could be meant within the terms of this theory, by saying that one of them was a better basis for action than another. It is true that one may select a subclass of these necessary propositions and decide to *call* its members statements of probability; but in so doing one will beg the question. For the use of the word 'probability,' in this connexion, itself implies that it is most rational to act on the basis of the propositions which have thus been selected: and this has not been proved.

In conclusion, I do not wish to say that probability, in the sense which here concerns us, is in no way relative to evidence. It seems clear that an appeal to evidence is needed to justify the belief that such and such an event is more or less likely to happen; and also that it is rational in such cases to take all the evidence at our disposal into account, the ground for this being, I suppose, that experience has shown us that our forecasts are more often right when this is done than when it is not. It does not follow, however, that statements of probability, in this sense, are statements *about* the relations of hypotheses to their evidence; and I do not think that they are. Nor, in the sense in which probability is the guide of life, do I think that statements of probability can be logically true.

6 Carnap on Defining "Degree of Confirmation"

JOHN W. LENZ

The logical theory of probability interprets probability as a logical relation between sentences, namely, as the degree to which stated evidence confirms a proposed hypothesis. It holds, that is, that the probability of a hypothesis on the basis of evidence can be determined purely logically once a definition of "degree of confirmation" is given. The central problem of the logical theory is, therefore, to find such a definition. Since this definition must uniquely deter-

From *Philosophy of Science*, Vol. 23, No. 3, July, 1956, pp. 230–236.

mine the probability, c, of any hypothesis, h, on the basis of given evidence, e, the problem may also be put as one of finding a suitable c-function, $c(h, e)$.

That this problem is an insurmountable one was the chief objection to the logical theory by the late Hans Reichenbach, one of the leading exponents of the frequency conception of probability. He charged that it is impossible to find a non-arbitrary definition of "degree of confirmation" without either presupposing the frequency view or else committing oneself to the *a priori*.[1] In his recent book, *The Continuum of Inductive Methods*,[2] Prof. Carnap, one of the main proponents of the logical theory, has himself pointed out this problem in a very forceful way. There Carnap shows that an infinite number of c-functions can be formulated, so that the problem is not that we can not find one c-function but rather that we have too many from which to choose.

However, Carnap has in this book outlined his choice of a c-function and given his reasons for it. He has, even more significantly, for the first time discussed the general procedure of choosing a c-function.[3] It is this procedure that I want to examine critically in this paper. We shall find, I believe, that it raises a serious difficulty.

I must mention one thing before stating what I conceive this difficulty to be. Carnap's discussion of how to choose a c-function is extremely brief, and in order to bring out the difficulty in it I have had to expand it considerably. I can not, accordingly, be certain that Carnap would accept this expansion. I do mean my discussion to be a consistent development of his, and I am quite sure that it is. But should Carnap disagree, I should still claim that I have, in fact, stated how indeed one would and should choose a c-function.

1. *The Problem.* — Let us see in more detail what the problem of choosing a c-function is by seeing how it arises in a single problem.[4] Suppose that we have an urn filled with balls that are either white or black, that we have drawn 100 of the balls, returning each one to the urn after having recorded its color, and that of the 100 balls drawn 80 have been black and 20 white. The problem which we wish to solve is this: how well confirmed is the hypothesis that the next ball drawn will be black? What Carnap shows in his *Continuum of Inductive Methods* is that the degree to which this hypothesis is confirmed will vary with the particular c-function that is chosen. He shows furthermore that an infinite number of such c-functions are available. One c-function, the straight rule, gives .80 as the degree to which the above hypothesis is confirmed, while another, proposed by Keynes and Wittgenstein, gives .50. There are, moreover, an infinite number of c-functions which yield values between .50 and .80. So the question is: which of these c-functions shall we choose as the most adequate?

[1] *Theory of Probability*, University of California Press. Berkeley, 1949, Chap. 9, esp. 352–359; and *Experience and Prediction*, University of Chicago Press, Chicago, 1938, 297–312.

[2] *The Continuum of Inductive Methods*, University of Chicago Press, Chicago, 1950. (Hereafter referred to as C.I.M.)

[3] C.I.M., 53–55, esp. 55.

[4] The simple problem I have chosen involves, as Carnap shows, the basic type of inductive inference in the logical theory. Thus, we can restrict our discussion to just this type of inference without any loss of generality.

It is apparent from the above example that the straight rule and the Keynes-Wittgenstein *c*-function can be regarded as "extreme" *c*-functions. The straight rule, in the above problem, confirms the hypothesis to the degree .80, a value which coincides with the observed frequency of black balls, 80/100. If we call this observed relative frequency the "empirical factor" involved in the value yielded by the *c*-function, we can regard the straight rule as giving all the weight, in its determination of probability values, to this empirical factor. The Keynes-Wittgenstein *c*-function, on the other hand, disregards this empirical factor completely. It gives as the degree of confirmation .50, a probability which is based upon the logical truth that the ball concerned in the hypothesis must be either white or black. We can say, therefore, that whereas the straight rule gives all the weight to the empirical factor, the Keynes-Wittgenstein *c*-function gives all the weight to what can be called the "logical factor". All those *c*-functions giving values between .80 and .50, as for example Carnap's own choice c^*, can be regarded as non-extreme methods which divide up the weight given the logical and empirical factors in varying ways. Thus the problem of choosing a *c*-function comes down to this: how much weight shall be given the logical and empirical factors?

2. *The Criterion of Performance.* — According to Carnap the choice of a specific *c*-function is not an assertion that is true or false. It is rather of the nature of a practical decision. Yet Carnap does believe, as surely anyone must, that the choice of a *c*-function is not arbitrary. Carnap insists that certain choices will be more *adequate* than others. Basically he gives us three criteria of adequacy: performance, economy, and esthetic satisfaction.[5]

Of these three criteria the first is by far the primary consideration, as Carnap's own choice shows. It is true that Carnap's choice, c^*, makes probability calculations comparatively simple and that it does have a certain logical elegance about it. But the same is true (perhaps to an even higher degree) of other *c*-functions that Carnap explicitly rejects. It is necessary, accordingly, that we give the closest examination to the criterion of performance.

Perhaps the best way to begin our discussion of this criterion is by noting a seemingly paradoxical characteristic of the logical theory. The probability statements it supplies are not in themselves predictive but are, nonetheless, meant to be a "guide" for decisions.[6]

In the logical theory probability statements express a purely logical relation between stated evidence and a given hypothesis. Logical probability statements are, if true, logically true, and thus can not be verified or disconfirmed by later empirical results. But like all logically true statements they do not have any factual content. Therefore, they can not possibly be regarded as predictions of fact.

[5] C.I.M., 55. "Relevant points of view for his preference might be: performance, economy, and aesthetic satisfaction, and others."

[6] Rudolf Carnap, *Logical Foundations of Probability*, University of Chicago Press, Chicago, 1950, 264–254. (Hereafter I shall refer to this book as L.F.P.)

Yet logical probability statements are meant to aid one in making actual decisions. They can be regarded as a guide to decisions in the sense that they tell us how "reasonable" certain decisions are. Other things being equal, the "reasonable" man will act in accordance with hypotheses which, on the evidence, are highly confirmed rather than in accordance with those which are only slightly confirmed.

This point can be illustrated if we return to the simple problem we discussed previously. Suppose, that is, we have an urn filled with balls that are either white or black, that we have drawn 100 of the balls, replacing each one after having recorded its color, and that 80 of the balls drawn have been black. We have to make a choice between acting either on the hypothesis that the next ball is black or on the hypothesis that it is white. Suppose that with a given *c*-function the hypothesis that the next ball is black has been confirmed to the degree .75, while the hypothesis that the next ball is white is confirmed to the degree .25. Then, other things being equal, it would be more reasonable to make our decision on the basis of the more highly confirmed hypothesis that the next ball is black. In no sense, though, can the probability value itself be regarded as predicting anything, say, that the next ball will be black, or even that, were we to keep drawing, the long run relative frequency of black balls is .75. If the more highly confirmed hypothesis turned out to be false, in no sense would the probability value be regarded as disconfirmed.

But suppose that we have dealt with a great many problems whose conditions are exactly like the above problem. Suppose, that is, we have many urns each filled with white or black balls, and that from each urn we have drawn 100 balls, 80 of which were black. Suppose then we have many hypotheses, each of which states concerning one of the urns that the next ball drawn from it will be black. Let us suppose further that on the basis of a given *c*-function each of the hypotheses is confirmed to the degree .75. And, finally, let us suppose that we have observed only half of the hypotheses are true. What shall we conclude? We surely can not literally say that the probability values have been disconfirmed. After all they were not predictive, and they were, as a matter of fact, logically true on the basis of the *c*-function employed. We might say that had we acted on the basis of the highly confirmed hypotheses we had acted reasonably. We might say that we had acted reasonably and complain that the world itself was unreasonable.

I am certain, however, that there is something else we can say, indeed, would and should say, and this brings us to the criterion of performance. We should say, I am sure, that the *c*-function we had employed was not a good one. The probability values it yielded were not an adequate guide for decisions. To put this more exactly, the degree to which each of the hypotheses was confirmed did not coincide with the actual relative truth frequency of the hypotheses. Since each of the hypotheses was confirmed to the degree of .75, we should not have expected all of them to be true, but we should have expected 75 per cent of them to be true. We should, accordingly, not complain that the world itself was unreasonable but insist rather that our *c*-function was inadequate. And remembering that the chosen *c*-function was only one of many possible *c*-functions, only one way of defining what was reasonable, we should indeed question whether we had really done the "reasonable" thing.

Of course, I have given only one way in which we might find a *c*-function inadequate. It could happen that a given *c*-function did not lead to probability values that were too high but to ones that were too low. Suppose, keeping all the conditions the same as indicated previously, the actual relative truth frequency of the hypotheses in question was .80. Then since each was confirmed to the degree .75, our probability values were a bit too low. We thought 75 per cent of the hypotheses were true whereas actually 80 per cent of them were true.

In general then, an adequate *c*-function is one which confirms hypotheses to a degree that corresponds with the actual truth frequency of those hypotheses. The more closely these two values, one a logically ascertained value, the other an empirically ascertained value, correspond, the more successful as a guide for decisions will the *c*-function be. The more closely these two values correspond the better will be the performance of the *c*-function.[7]

3. *The Difficulty of Choosing a c-Function.* — We have now examined what an adequate *c*-function would be. The next question we must consider is this: how shall we find such a *c*-function?

This would be an easy matter, undoubtedly, could we know ahead of time the actual truth frequency of the hypotheses we wished to evaluate. For we could always find a *c*-function which, when we are given any evidence whatsoever, yielded probability values which exactly corresponded to the actual truth frequency of the hypotheses evaluated. All we would need to do is to adjust the weight given the empirical and logical factors so this would result.

But the trouble is, of course, that we do not know the actual truth frequency of hypotheses ahead of time. So the above method is obviously of no avail. What we have to go on simply is our past experience of the success of various *c*-functions. Suppose that we had used all of the possible *c*-functions to evaluate certain hypotheses. Suppose further that we had later observed the truth frequency of those same hypotheses. Then the *c*-function which *had* been most adequate could easily be found. The one which had been most adequate was the one which confirmed each of the hypotheses to a degree equal to the actual truth frequency of the hypotheses so confirmed. We would choose as the *c*-function to use in the future the one which had been most adequate in the past.

The difficulty in all this should now be apparent. The decision to pick for future use the *c*-function which had been most adequate in the past is based upon the hypothesis that that *c*-function will continue to be successful in the future. This hypothesis is a synthetic one which, however, is not known to be true. Thus, this hypothesis itself demands justification.

[7] C.I.M., 55. "Similarly, after working with a particular inductive method for a time, he may not be quite satisfied and therefore look around for another method. He will take into consideration the performance of a method, that is, the values it supplies and their relation to later empirical results, e.g., the truth frequency of predictions and the error of estimates. . . ."

One thing needs to be emphasized here. Carnap is right when he calls the adoption of a certain *c*-function a practical decision which is not true or false. The objection is that the decision is based upon a synthetic hypothesis which is true or false but whose truth value is not known. Calling the choice of a *c*-function a practical decision in no way avoids the above difficulty.

4. *A Questionable Solution.* — A possible escape from this difficulty might seem to be to regard the hypothesis that a certain *c*-function will continue to be a successful guide to predictions as one which can not be asserted with assurance but as one whose probability is high. That is, it is possible to regard this hypothesis as one whose degree of confirmation can be determined. In this way one would justify it without assuming that the hypothesis is true.

However, there are two telling objections to this proposed way out. In the first place, this only postpones the difficulty. In the second place, this procedure would almost certainly be circular. Let us consider these objections in turn.

Suppose one were to determine the probability of the hypothesis that a certain *c*-function will be adequate in the future. Suppose further that the probability of this hypothesis was extremely high. The trouble is that before one could determine this probability one would already have to have chosen a *c*-function, and thus the question of justifying this choice would recur. In practice, one could not get himself into an infinite regress. Finally some *c*-function would in fact have to be the unassessed basis for assessing other hypotheses.[8]

The second objection is that the above way of assessing the future success of a *c*-function would very likely be circular. It is very likely that one would assess the hypothesis that a certain *c*-function is adequate in terms of that very *c*-function. Of course, one could choose some other *c*-function for this assessment, but it would be hard to defend doing so. In the first place, it is difficult to find positive reasons, beside the aim of avoiding circularity, for doing so. In the second place, it would be a strange procedure, as Carnap himself says,[9] not to employ one *c*-function consistently for all the assessments one makes.

5. *Another Questionable Solution.* — Because of the above objections, it is impossible to justify by showing that the degree of its confirmation is high, the hypothesis that a *c*-function is adequate. However, one thing may be said in favor of this method of justification. It at least remains consistent with Carnap's own explicitly formulated views on inductive logic. The same, as we shall now see, can not be said about a second, and, perhaps, more plausible way out that might be proposed.

[8] Carnap, I believe, would very likely accept this criticism and thus not choose the first way out. He says, for example, "Questions concerning the success of a given inductive method in the actual world would be of a factual, nonlogical nature. And if they concerned not merely that part of the world which is known to us by past observations but also a part or whole of the future, then the answer could be given with certainty only after all observation reports were in, if that were ever possible. And if our question concerned not the actual success but the probability of success or an estimate of success, then it would make sense only on the basis of a chosen inductive method." C.I.M., 59–60.

[9] [Once a man adopts a method] "he will be able to apply it to all inductive problems, problems of confirmation for all kinds of hypotheses." C.I.M., 54.

This second way out would be for Carnap to assume some synthetic principle of induction. He could assume, for example, that the degree of uniformity of the world is high. Then, given this principle of induction, one could infer on the basis of the past success of a *c*-function that it will continue to be so in the future.

It is admittedly dangerous to charge someone with tacitly or implicitly assuming something. Yet I think a good case can be made for saying that Carnap's decision to choose c^* rather than the straight rule or the Keynes-Wittgenstein *c*-function does rest largely upon tacitly assuming a synthetic principle of induction. Surely there is nothing self-evident about his choice. Surely without any experience to go on all *c*-functions are equally plausible. What makes c^* seem to be more adequate (and I agree that it is more adequate) is that we have seen the past inadequacy of the other two functions and the past adequacy of c^*. But to infer that c^* will continue to be more adequate in the future is to make an induction from past experience on the basis of a synthetic principle of induction.

I do not want to discuss the defensibility of assuming a synthetic principle of induction. Nor do I want to discuss the several proposed ways of justifying or vindicating such a principle. I do, however, want to make, in conclusion, three points.

The first is that Carnap does not believe it possible to justify the principle of induction.[10] Thus, if he were to accept this second way out, he would be doing something which he himself admits is indefensible. The second point is that in having to assume the principle of induction the logical theory would ironically be doing just what it was supposed not to have to do, indeed, something that it was designed not to have to do. For it is thought by Carnap that since logical probability statements are not predictive they do not rest upon any principle of induction.[11] It remains true, of course, that since they are not predictive, the principle of induction does not directly have to be assumed to justify them. However, the principle of induction, as we have seen, must be assumed in choosing an adequate *c*-function. And *where* the principle needs to be assumed seems to me less important than that it has to be assumed.

The third point is that certain of the applications of the logical theory would be circular. Carnap, as we have noted, regards an inductive principle such as "the degree of uniformity of the world is high" as a hypothesis whose truth can not be known. Yet he has suggested that it is a hypothesis whose degree of confirmation can perhaps be seen to be high.[12] Such a procedure would be circular, however, for before we could determine the degree of its confirmation, we should have to assume the very same principle in choosing the *c*-function in terms of which it is assessed.

[10] L.F.P., 180–181.
[11] L.F.P., 177–182.
[12] L.F.P., 177–182.

7 The Frequency Interpretation

HANS REICHENBACH

§ 16. . . . The laws of the calculus of probability are difficult to understand, however, if one does not envisage a definite interpretation. Thus, for didactic reasons, an interpretation of the probability concept must be added, at this point, to the axiomatic construction. But this method will not prejudice later investigations of the problem. The interpretation is employed merely as a means of illustrating the system of formal laws of the probability concept, and it will always be possible to separate the conceptual system from the interpretation, because, for the derivation of theorems, the axioms will be used in the sense of merely formal statements, without reference to the interpretation.

This presentation follows a method applied in the teaching of geometry, where the conceptual formulation of geometrical axioms is always accompanied by spatial imagery. Although logical precision requires that the premises of the inferences be restricted to the meaning given in the conceptual formulation, the interpretation is used as a parallel meaning in order to make the conceptual part easier to understand. The method of teaching thus follows the historical path of the development of geometry, since, historically speaking, the separation of the conceptual system of geometry from its interpretation is a later discovery. The history of the calculus of probability has followed a similar path. The mathematicians who developed the laws of this calculus in the seventeenth and eighteenth centuries always had in mind an interpretation of probability, usually the frequency interpretation, though it was sometimes accompanied by other interpretations.

In order to develop the frequency interpretation, we define probability as the *limit of a frequency* within an infinite sequence. The definition follows a path that was pointed out by S. D. Poisson [1] in 1837. In 1854 it was used by George Boole,[2] and in recent times it was brought to the fore by Richard von Mises,[3] who defended it successfully against critical objections.

The following notation will be used for the formulation of the frequency interpretation. In order to secure sufficient generality for the definition, we

From *Theory of Probability*, University of California Press, Berkeley, 1949, pp. 68–69, 372–383, 434–442. Reprinted by permission of the University of California Press, Berkeley, California.

[1] *Recherches sur la probabilité des jugements en matière criminelle et en matière civile* . . . (Paris, 1837).

[2] *The Laws of Thought* (London, 1854), p. 295.

[3] "Grundlagen der Wahrscheinlichkeitsrechnung," in *Math. Zs.*, Vol. V (1919), p. 52, and later publications.

shall not yet assume that all elements x_i of the sequence belong to the class A. We assume, therefore, that the sequence is *interspersed* with elements x_i of a different kind. For instance, the sequence of throws of a coin may be interspersed with throws of a second coin. In this case only certain elements x_i will belong to the class A, if the class is defined as representing the throws of one of the coins only. Similarly, only some among the elements y_i will belong to the class B, which may signify the occurrence of tails lying up. It may happen that y_i represents a case of tails up, whereas the corresponding x_i does not belong to the class A, that is, the event of tails lying up is produced by the second coin. When the frequency is counted out in such a sequence pair, the result is expressed by the symbol

$$\overset{n}{\underset{i=1}{N}} (x_i \epsilon A) \tag{1a}$$

which means the number of such x_i between 1 and n that satisfy $x_i \epsilon A$. The symbol is extended correspondingly to apply to different variables and to different classes and also to a pair, a triplet, and so on, of variables. For instance, the expression

$$\overset{n}{\underset{i=1}{N}} (x_i \epsilon A) \cdot (y_i \epsilon B) \tag{1b}$$

represents the number of pairs x_i, y_i such that x_i belongs to A and simultaneously y_i belongs to B; it signifies the number of pairs x_i, y_i that are elements of the common class A and B. To abbreviate the notation, the following symbol is introduced:

$$N^n(A) =_{Df} \overset{n}{\underset{i=1}{N}} (x_i \epsilon A) \qquad N^n(A \cdot B) =_{Df} \overset{n}{\underset{i=1}{N}} (x_i \epsilon A) \cdot (y_i \epsilon B) \tag{2}$$

Furthermore, the *relative frequency* $F^n(A,B)$ is defined by

$$F^n(A,B) = \frac{N^n(A \cdot B)}{N^n(A)} \tag{3}$$

In the special case in which all elements x_i belong to the class A, that is, when the sequence x_i is *compact*, the denominator of the fraction is equal to n, whereas in the numerator the expression A may be dropped; then (3) assumes the simpler form

$$F^n(A,B) = \frac{1}{n} \cdot N^n(B) \tag{4}$$

With the help of the concept of relative frequency, the frequency interpretation of the concept of probability may be formulated:

If for a sequence pair $x_i y_i$ the relative frequency $F^n(A,B)$ goes toward a limit p for $n \to \infty$, the limit p is called the probability from A to B within the sequence pair. In other words, the following coördinative definition is introduced:

$$P(A,B) = \lim_{n \to \infty} F^n(A,B) \tag{5}$$

No further statement is required concerning the properties of probability sequences. In particular, randomness (see § 30) need not be postulated. . . .

§ 72. The Frequency Interpretation of the Probability of the Single Case

The analysis of meaning has suffered from too close an attachment to psychological considerations. The meaning of a sentence has been identified with the mental images associated with the utterance of the sentence. Such conception leads to meanings varying from person to person; and it will not help to find the meaning that a man would adopt if he had a clear insight into the implications of his words. Logic is interested not in what a man means but in what he *should* mean, that is, in the meaning that, if assumed for his words, would make his words compatible with his actions.

When the meaning of probability statements about single events is analyzed according to this objective criterion, it is found that the frequency interpretation can be applied to this case too. True, we must renounce a reconstruction of subjective psychological intentions; but, since we found that it is not possible to translate the expectation associated with the anticipation of a future event into a logical category, we shall welcome the construction of a logical substitute that can take over the function of a probability of the single case without being such a thing in the verbal sense.

Assume that the frequency of an event B in a sequence is $= 5/6$. Confronted by the question whether an individual event B will happen, we prefer to answer in the affirmative because, if we do so repeatedly, we shall be right in 5/6 of the cases. Obviously, we cannot maintain that the assertion about the individual event is true. In what sense, then, can the assertion be made? The answer is given by regarding the statement not as an assertion but as a *posit*. We do not say that B will occur, but we posit B. We do so if $P(B) > 1/2$; otherwise we posit $\bar{B}$. The word "posit" is used here in the same sense as the word "wager" or "bet" in games of chance. When we bet on a horse we do not want to say by such a wager that it is true that the horse will win; but we behave as though it were true by staking money on it. *A posit is a statement with which we deal as true, although the truth value is unknown.* We would not do so, of course, without some reason; we decide for a posit, or a wager, when it seems to be the best we can make. The term "best" occurring here has a meaning that can be numerically interpreted; it refers to the posit that will be the most successful when applied repeatedly.

If we wish to improve a posit, we must make a selection S such that $P(A \cdot S, B) > P(A, B)$.[4] If we now posit B only in the case $A \cdot S$ and omit a posit in the case $A \cdot \bar{S}$, we obtain a relatively greater number of successes than by the origi-

[4] If we have $P(A.S, B) < P(A, B)$, the selection $\overline{S}$ will have the desired property because it then follows from the rule of elimination that $P(A.\overline{S}, B) > P(A, B)$. See the discussion following (11*b*, § 19).

nal posit. It is even more favorable to construct the selection so that at the same time $P(A \cdot \bar{S}, B)$ is $< 1/2$. We then always posit $\bar{B}$ in the case $A \cdot \bar{S}$. We can thus make a posit for each element of the original sequence and obtain a greater number of successes. The procedure may be called the *method of the double posit.*

It should be noticed that we cannot improve a posit without knowing a selection S that leads to a greater probability. If we were to posit arbitrarily sometimes B, sometimes $\bar{B}$, we would in general construct a selection S for which $P(A \cdot S, B) = P(A, B) = P(A \cdot \bar{S}, B)$, that is, a selection of the domain of invariance. Positing B in the case $A \cdot S$ would then lead to the same relative number of successes as in the main sequence, whereas positing $\bar{B}$ in the case $A \cdot \bar{S}$ would lead to a smaller ratio of successes.

In dealing with exclusive disjunctions $B_1 \vee \cdots \vee B_r$ of more than two terms, if we are compelled to posit only one of the terms (if a posit $B_2 \vee \cdots \vee B_r$ is impossible because of practical reasons), the B_k that carries the greatest probability will be the best posit. In this case, therefore, the probability 1/2 no longer represents a critical value.

The method of positing serves to utilize probability statements for decisions in regard to single cases. It plays an important role in all practical applications. The merchant who stores a great amount of merchandise for the season, the farmer who wants to get in his crop, the physician who prescribes a cure — all must make decisions, though they know only probability statements about the factors determining success: the merchant about the prospective demand, the farmer about the prospective weather, the physician about the illness that presumably confronts him. They make posits by assuming the occurrence of the events that they consider to be the most probable, according to their experience. Each endeavors to improve his posit by increasing the probability through a more precise analysis of the actual conditions, that is, by making a selection S such that a greater probability will hold for the subsequence determined by S, and such that, if possible, even the method of the double posit becomes applicable. The merchant will explore the market situation more thoroughly, the farmer will study the official weather forecast, the physician may try to analyze the condition of his patient more exactly by taking X-rays. There is no instance in which certainty is reached; only a very high probability is attainable.

It is not necessary for the construction of a sequence that similar cases repeat themselves. If we must make a decision today about the prospective weather, tomorrow about the state of an illness, the day after tomorrow about some financial transaction, and if we always posit the most probable case, our decisions represent a sequence in which the probability changes from element to element, that is, a sequence that belongs to the type of the Poisson sequence (§ 56). Here only one horizontal sequence of the Poisson lattice is realized. But this sequence suffices to obtain a statistical success. Since probabilities usually have values around 1 or 0, we shall be able to apply the method of the double posit. The sequence of the numerous actions of a single day — when we turn on the faucet, hoping that the water will run; when we call the telephone number of a friend, hoping to obtain a connection; and so on — represents a rather long Poisson sequence. The statistical justification of the posit, therefore, is applicable to the actions of a single person.

If we are asked to find the probability holding for an individual future event, we must first incorporate the case in a suitable reference class. An individual thing or event may be incorporated in many reference classes, from which different probabilities will result. This ambiguity has been called the *problem of the reference class.* Assume that a case of illness can be characterized by its inclusion in the class of cases of tuberculosis. If additional information is obtained from an X-ray, the same case may be incorporated in the class of serious cases of tuberculosis. Depending on the classification, different probabilities will result for the prospective issue of the illness.

We then proceed by considering *the narrowest class for which reliable statistics can be compiled.* If we are confronted by two overlapping classes, we shall choose their common class. Thus, if a man is 21 years old and has tuberculosis, we shall regard the class of persons of 21 who have tuberculosis. Classes that are known to be irrelevant for the statistical result may be disregarded. A class C is irrelevant with respect to the reference class A and the attribute class B if the transition to the common class $A \cdot C$ does not change the probability, that is, if $P(A \cdot C,B) = P(A,B)$. For instance, the class of persons having the same initials is irrelevant for the life expectation of a person.

We do not affirm that this method is perfectly unambiguous. Sometimes it may be questioned whether a transition to a narrower class is advisable, because, perhaps, the statistical knowledge regarding the class is incomplete. We are dealing here with a method of technical statistics; the decision for a certain reference class will depend on balancing the importance of the prediction against the reliability available. It is no objection to this interpretation that it makes the probability constructed for the single case dependent on the state of our knowledge. This knowledge may even be of such a kind that it does not determine one class as the best. For instance, we may have reliable statistics concerning a reference class A, and likewise reliable statistics for a reference class C, whereas we have insufficient statistics for the reference class $A \cdot C$. The calculus of probability cannot help in such a case because the probabilities $P(A,B)$ and $P(C,B)$ do not determine the probability $P(A \cdot C,B)$. The logician can only indicate a method by which our knowledge may be improved. This is achieved by the rule: look for a larger number of cases in the narrowest common class at your disposal.

Whereas the probability of a single case is thus made dependent on our state of knowledge, this consequence does not hold for a probability referred to classes. If the reference class is stated, the probability of an attribute is objectively determined, though we may be mistaken in the numerical value we assume for it on the basis of inductions. The probability of death for men 21 years old concerns a frequency that holds for events of nature and has nothing to do with our knowledge about them, nor is it changed by the fact that the death probability is higher in the narrower class of tuberculous men of the same age. The dependence of a single-case probability on our state of knowledge originates from the impossibility of giving this concept an independent interpretation; there exist only substitutes for it, given by class probabilities, and the choice of the substitute depends on our state of knowledge. My thesis that there exists only one concept of probability, which applies both to classes and to single cases, must therefore be given the more precise formulation: there exists only one legitimate concept of probability, which refers to classes, and the pseudo-concept of a probability of a single case must be replaced by a substitute constructed in terms of class probabilities.

The substitute is constructed by regarding the individual case as the limit of classes becoming gradually narrower and narrower. The method is justified in the theory of probability by the fact that, as explained above, we obtain a greater number of successes if we employ the probability of the subsequence $P(A \cdot S, B)$ and not the probability $P(A, B)$ as the basis of our posits. A repeated division of the main sequence into subsequences will lead to progressively better results as long as the probability is increased at each step. According to general experience, the probability will approach a limit when the single case is enclosed in narrower and narrower classes, to the effect that, from a certain step on, further narrowing will no longer result in noticeable improvement. It is not necessary for the justification of this method that the limit of the probability, respectively, is $= 1$ or $= 0$, as the hypothesis of causality assumes. Neither is this necessary *a priori;* modern quantum mechanics asserts the contrary.[5] It is obvious that for the limit 1 or 0 the probability still refers to a class, not to an individual event, and that the probability 1 cannot exclude the possibility that in the particular case considered the prediction is false. Even in the limit the substitute for the probability of a single case will thus be a class probability, and we shall always depend on the method of positing.

Besides choosing a suitable reference class, we must also choose a sequence into which the individual case considered is to be incorporated. This choice is usually less difficult than that of the reference class because the frequency will be the same for most sequences that can be reasonably chosen. We often follow the time order of the events observed or of the observations made. One of the rules to be required is that a knowledge of the attribute of the individual case should not be used for the construction of the order of the sequence. (See the remarks on random sequences in § 30.)

There are, however, instances in which the choice of the sequence is connected with ambiguities, as in lattice arrangements where the horizontal and the vertical sequences converge to different limits. If a particular element y_{ki} of the lattice is considered, the probability assumed for it depends on whether further observations concern the horizontal or the vertical sequence to which it belongs. An illustration is offered by the rule of succession (22, § 62), the probability value $\frac{n+1}{n+2}$ of which refers to a column and is applicable only

[5] See H. Reichenbach, "Das Kausalprinzip in der Physik," in *Naturwissenschaften*, Vol. 19 (1931), p. 716; and *Philosophic Foundations of Quantum Mechanics* (Berkeley, 1944), § 1.

if a sequence in the vertical direction, supplied by a set of horizontal initial sections of a certain kind, represents the experiences to be envisaged. If, on the contrary, the horizontal sequence to which y_{ki} belongs is continued, the probability value characterized by the maximum inverse probability v_n is $p = 1$, a value which is then preferable to the value $\frac{n+1}{n+2}$. This result means that if many horizontal sequences of this kind are considered, most of them will have a limit of the frequency close to 1, which is thus the most appropriate value to be transferred to the element y_{ki}. The illustration makes it obvious that the probability assumed for the single case depends on the mode of procedure by which the single case is incorporated in a sequence.

The solution offered here for the probability of the single case is essentially different from the interpretations discussed in § 71. I regard the statement about the probability of the single case, not as having a meaning of its own, but as representing an elliptic mode of speech. In order to acquire meaning, the statement must be translated into a statement about a frequency in a sequence of repeated occurrences. The statement concerning the probability of the single case thus is given a *fictitious meaning*, constructed by a *transfer of meaning from the general to the particular case*. The adoption of the fictitious meaning is justifiable, not for cognitive reasons, but because it serves the purpose of action to deal with such statements as meaningful.

For a better understanding of the solution, consider the analogous solution of a problem of deductive logic. When we speak of a necessary synthetic or physical implication in an individual case, we mean that the case is an instance of a general law. The statement, "If you press this button, the bell will ring", expresses a physical necessity and thus a reasonable implication. And yet by this classification of the statement we mean only that the same adjunctive implication holds in all similar cases. Physical necessity is interpretable in terms of "always". It was explained in the discussion of the general implication (3, § 6) that this interpretation involves a transfer of meaning from the general to the particular case. A similar transfer is characteristic for probability statements. The statement, "If you press this button, the bomb will hit the target with the probability 2/3", derives its meaning from a reference to generality, just as does the statement about the bell. The only difference is that the probability statement indicates a frequency relation that does not hold for all cases, but is restricted to a certain fraction of cases.

This interpretation of probability statements is complicated by the following peculiarity. If we have an implication $(A \supset B)$, we can add an arbitrary term in the implicans, that is, we can derive the implication $(A \cdot C \supset B)$. If we have a probability implication $(A \underset{p}{\ni} B)$, however, the addition of a term in the implicans will, in general, lead to a different degree of probability, that is, to a probability implication $(A \cdot C \underset{q}{\ni} B)$ where q is different from p. This is why the choice of the reference class is easily made for a general implication, whereas it is difficult to make it for a probability implication. Once a class A is found such that $(A \supset B)$ holds, we know that if $x_i \epsilon A$ we shall have $y_i \epsilon B$; it does not matter to what other classes the event x_i belongs. For a probability implication there is no such simple relation. We must be aware of the possibility that, if x_i belongs to both A and C, the reference to the common class $A \cdot C$ may lead to a value of the probability different from the one resulting for the reference class A.

Therefore, we can ask only for the best reference class available, the reference class that, on the basis of our present knowledge, will lead to the greatest number of successful predictions, whether they concern hits of bombs, cases of disease, or political events. If no statistics are available for the common class $A \cdot C$, we shall base our probability calculations on the reference class A, and must renounce the improvement in the success ratio that might result from the use of the reference class $A \cdot C$ in combination with the method of the double posit. Such a procedure seems reasonable if we realize that narrowing the reference class means nothing but increasing the success ratio, and that there is no reference class that permits the prediction of a single case. This goal, which could be reached if we had a knowledge of synthetic logical implications combining past and future events, is unattainable if probability implications are all that we have to connect the past with the future.

We must renounce all remnants of absolutism in order to understand the significance of the frequency interpretation of a probability statement about a single case. But there is no place for absolutism in the theory of probability statements concerning physical reality. Such statements are used as rules of behavior, as rules that determine the most successful behavior attainable in a given state of knowledge. Whoever wants to find more in these statements will eventually discover that he has been pursuing a chimera.

§ 73. The Logical Interpretation of Probability*

In order to construct a logical form for probability statements concerning single cases, it is advisable to introduce a change in the logical classification of probabilities. In the frequency interpretation, a probability is regarded as a property of a sequence of events. Correspondingly, the statement about the probability of a single case is regarded as stating a property, though fictitious, of an individual event. It is possible, however, to go from events to sentences about events, and to regard a probability, not as a property of the event, but as a property of the sentence about the event. Instead of saying, for instance, that the probability of obtaining face 6 with a die is $= 1/6$, we can say that the probability of the sentence, "Face 6 will turn up", is $= 1/6$. By this transition, probability is made a rating of propositions; and probability statements belong not in the object language but in the metalanguage.

* [Ed. note: Reichenbach's "Logical Interpretation of Probability" should not be confused with the logical meaning of probability of Keynes and Carnap. Reichenbach's logical interpretation is better called "the truth-frequency interpretation."]

The dual possibility of conceiving probability was first seen by George Boole,[6] who wrote, "There is another form under which all questions in the theory of probabilities may be viewed; and this form consists in substituting for *events* the propositions which assert that those events have occurred, or will occur". I shall introduce the term *logical interpretation of probability* for this conception; the conception previously used will be called *object interpretation.* The logical interpretation offers the advantage that the probability attached to the single case assumes the form of a truth value of a proposition or, rather, since the proposition can be maintained only in the sense of a posit, of the truth value of a posit. We shall use the term *weight* for the truth value of the posit; the probability of the single case, therefore, is regarded, in the logical interpretation, as the weight of a posit. A posit the weight of which is known is called an *appraised posit.*

When we say that probability assumes the form of a truth value, we use the latter term in a wider sense than usual. Classical logic is two-valued; it knows only the two truth values *true* and *false.* In regarding probability as a truth value we construct a multivalued logic, differing from other such logics in that it is a logic with a continuous scale of truth values ranging from 0 to 1. The formal construction of this *probability logic* will be carried through in chapter 10.

An analysis of language reveals that many of its elements can be understood only from the viewpoint of probability logic. We often use sentences referring to individual events that are not asserted to be certainly true; and we indicate our truth evaluation by words like "probably", "likely", or "presumably". The Turkish language possesses a particular mood of the verb expressing that a statement about a past event is not maintained as certain, but only probable.[7] Such forms of language are expressions of the predicate "weight".

That the weight referred to in such sentences is reducible to a frequency meaning is demonstrable, not only for sentences for which the reference class is obvious — as, for example, "It will probably rain tomorrow" — but also for statements that do not easily lend themselves to statistical interpretation. For instance, the statement that Julius Caesar was in Britain must be regarded as a posit having a certain weight that is translatable into a frequency statement. When we look for the methods by which the weight is ascertained, we usually discover the statistical origin of the weight. Thus, in order to ascertain the reliability of the statement about Caesar's stay in Britain, we investigate the number of chroniclers who report such a fact; and we measure the reliability of the individual chronicler by the number of his reports that are corroborated by reports of other writers.[8]

True, we often prefer an intuitive appraisal of the weight to a statistical enumeration. For instance, we judge intuitively from his presentation whether a writer is a reliable authority. But though an intuitive appraisal may sometimes make a rationalized inference unnecessary, it does not invalidate the

[6] *The Laws of Thought* (London, 1854), p. 247.

[7] See *Elements of Symbolic Logic*, p. 338.

[8] In a more precise analysis the inference must be interpreted through explanatory induction (see § 84); my presentation applies a simplification.

inference. Thus the inferences of the meteorologist in regard to the weather of the next day are not made false by the fact that the intuitive appraisal of a sailor may arrive at the same result by simpler methods. We prefer an intuitive appraisal to a statistical determination only if statistics are incomplete. The human mind is fortunate in being endowed with the ability of intuitive appraisal; in many cases the use of this talent leads to a better determination of probability values than the compilation of incomplete statistics.

The analysis of mental processes during an intuitive action must be left to the psychologist — the logician can ask only for the rational reconstruction of an action. Such a reconstruction is given in the statistical interpretation. For instance, we must regard the scientific inference of the meteorologist as a rational reconstruction of what the sailor does intuitively. In the same sense, the statistical interpretation of the weight of sentences about individual events, like Caesar's stay in Britain, must be regarded as the rational reconstruction of an intuitive estimate of the weight. That, on the other hand, statistics are necessary not only in ascertaining the weight but also in establishing the meaning of the probability statement is apparent from the fact that we use statistics for further verification of the statement, in the form of a verification of the statistical predictions included in the statement.

It has been argued [9] that probability statements of the kind considered are not quantifiable, that they are intended to state only a relation of order expressible by the terms "more probable" or "less probable". It is true that we often restrict ourselves to the statement of order relations. The verification, obviously, will be easier than that of quantitative relations because the statement of order states less than that of quantity. It would be a serious mistake, however, to believe that the employment of relations of order is a proof that quantitative relations cannot be established. When relations of order are asserted, we are often able to supplement them, at least, by rough estimates of numerical probabilities. This ability is demonstrated in the habit of betting. We bet on the outcome of a boxing match, a scientific experiment, a political election, or a war, expressing the numerical value of the appraised degree of probability by the height of our stakes. The rational reconstruction of such bets would lead to statistical evaluations.

The logical interpretation, which was defined for the probability of a single case, can be extended to the case where a sequence is used as the object of interpretation; it then leads to the consideration of sequences of propositions, or *propositional sequences*. Both interpretations thus have correlates in logical interpretations. The logical interpretation of sequence probabilities, however, has only a theoretical interest, and will be discussed later from that point of view. The practical importance of the logical interpretation springs from its application to the single case, because, in this application, probability assumes the function of a substitute for a truth value.

Because of its analogy with the concept of a statement of known truth value, the concept of appraised posit is indispensable for the understanding of language.

[9] By J. M. Keynes, *A Treatise on Probability* (London, 1921), p. 34.

It defines the logical category under which probability statements concerning individual cases are to be subsumed, and allots to such statements a legitimate place within the body of knowledge. A two-valued logic has no place for unknown truth values; so long as the truth value of a statement is not known, as for statements about future events, classical logic does not allow us to judge the truth of the statement. All it offers is a "wait and see". Our actual behavior, however, does not follow this maxim of passivity. We form judgments about the likelihood of the event and use them as a guide for action. We must do so, because action presupposes judgments about future events; if we had to wait until direct observation informed us about the occurrence or nonoccurrence of an event, it would be too late to plan actions influencing the event.

Probability logic supplies the logical form of a truth evaluation by degrees that is applicable before the occurrence of an event. It allows us to coördinate to the sentence about the individual event a fictitious truth value, derived from the frequency within an appropriate sequence, in such a way that, so far as actions are concerned, the fictitious truth value, or weight, satisfies to a certain extent the requirements that can be asked with respect to a truth value. The logical interpretation repeats the procedure followed in the object-language interpretation of the probability statement about the single case: the metalinguistic conception of the probability of the single case as a weight of a statement, too, is constructed by a transfer of meaning from the general to the particular case. The numerical value of the frequency in the sequence is transferred to the individual statement in the sense of a rating, although the individual statement taken alone exhibits no features that could be measured by the rating.

In spite of the fictitious nature of the rating so constructed, the system of posits endowed with weights can be substituted for a system of statements known as true or false. The essential difference between the two systems consists in the fact that in the substitute system our action is determined, not by a knowledge of the truth value of the statement about the individual event, but by a knowledge of a truth frequency in a sequence. The substitution of this statistical knowledge for unavailable specific knowledge is justified because it offers success in the greatest number of cases. This is why we can act when the truth of the sentence about the individual event remains unknown: the frequency interpretation of probability replaces the unattainable ascertainment of truth by a procedure that accords the best success attainable in the totality of cases.

It has been objected that the frequency interpretation of the probability of the single case does not correspond to what a person actually means when he regards an individual event as probable. My answer may be found in the discussion of meanings at the beginning of § 72: the objection seems irrelevant because logical analysis is not concerned with the description of subjective images and intentions associated with words. The use of the word "probable" with reference to individual events, or as denoting a truth value of sentences about individual events, can be given a meaning in terms of frequencies; if this meaning is assumed, our words will be made compatible with our actions. This result seems to be established beyond doubt. Since there is no other way of determining meanings than by defining interpretations that make language correspond to behavior, I do not see on what grounds the universal applicability of the frequency interpretation of probability can be questioned.

§ 74. Probability Meaning

The interpretation of probability as a truth value permits the introduction of a new category of meaning. The verifiability theory of meaning, in its strict form, makes meaning dependent on verifiability as true or false. The theory can be extended, however, so that a sentence is regarded as meaningful when it is possible to determine a weight for the sentence.[10] By "possible" we understand here "physically possible", that is, "compatible with physical laws". The meaning so defined is called *probability meaning*.

The advantage of the new category of meaning derives from the fact that a determination of weight may be physically possible, whereas a corresponding absolute verification is not physically, but only logically, possible. With respect to simple sentences, for example, sentences concerning the weather of the next day, the distinction is irrelevant; here it is physically possible both to determine a weight in advance and to verify after the occurrence of an event. But this cannot be done with more complicated sentences. Thus, a statement about the temperature of the sun cannot be strictly verified in the sense of a physical possibility of verification, but it is physically possible to determine a weight for it. *Probability meaning*, therefore, represents a wider category than *physical truth meaning*, that is, a meaning defined by the physical possibility of strict verification. But it is a narrower category than *logical meaning*, a meaning defined by the logical possibility of strict verification (see § 66). When the term "verification" is used in a wider sense, to include the determination of a weight, probability meaning represents a *physical* meaning, since it is based on the physical possibility of verification. It can be shown that probability meaning constitutes the very category of meaning that underlies conversational and scientific language, for which physical truth meaning is too narrow and logical meaning too wide.

The meaning of limit statements, analyzed in § 66, may now be reconsidered in the light of the category of probability meaning. It is only logically, not physically, meaningful to speak about the limit of the frequency of an infinite sequence that is extensionally given; therefore a *finitization* of limit statements is required for applications to physical reality. This classification is based on the postulate of absolute verification. If verification in the wider sense is admitted, it is sometimes physically possible to verify the limit statement for an infinite extensional sequence, namely, when it is physically possible to determine a weight for it.

[10] See *Experience and Prediction*, § 7.

These conditions are realized in a probability lattice. Here the individual horizontal sequence may be regarded as a single case the weight of which is determined by a frequency of sequences counted in the vertical direction. In an arrangement of this kind the limit statement concerning the infinite extensional sequence has probability meaning.

These considerations correspond to actual situations. We make statements about the probability of a limit of the frequency at a certain value p, and we can also compute the probability that for a given degree of convergence ϵ the n-th element of the sequence is a place of convergence. Such results concerning probabilities of a higher level can be derived within the frame of Bernoulli's theorem. If we admit probability meaning, therefore, we can dispense with the requirement of finitization.

This analysis, however, has a restricted value. A computation of probabilities of the higher level is possible only when limits of the higher level are known. Whereas statements about limits of the first level are thus given a probability meaning, those concerning limits of the second level do not have this sort of meaning. True, a probability meaning for statements of the second level can be constructed by computing probabilities of the third level, but then new statements are introduced that do not have a probability meaning. In other words, a probability meaning can be constructed for *every* limit statement, but not for *all*.

The use of probability meaning for the discussion of limit statements is therefore restricted to an *advanced state of knowledge*, a state in which a sufficient number of probabilities is known (see § 70). However, within a *primitive state of knowledge* — a state preceding the determination of probability values and therefore the kind of state on which the determination of the first probability values must be based — probability meaning cannot be used. Since no weight is known for limit statements of the highest level, they cannot be incorporated in the frame of probability meaning and must be subject to the method of finitization explained above (§ 66). The general theory of induction, in particular, must be given with respect to primitive knowledge and, therefore, without the use of probability considerations.

The Probability of Hypotheses

§ 85. The thesis that explanatory induction can be construed in terms of the theorems of the calculus of probability and is therefore reducible to induction by enumeration is attacked by the argument that the probability of hypotheses is not interpretable as a frequency. Although the general discussion of nonfrequency probabilities (§ 71) covers this case also, and shows that the probability of a hypothesis, like that of any other single case, must be interpreted as a relative frequency, I should like to add some remarks on how the interpretation can be carried through — how, in particular, the reference class of a hypothesis is to be determined.

Scientific hypotheses are all-statements: they assert that for all things of a certain kind, at all times and places, a certain relation holds. So we begin this inquiry by studying the probability of all-statements.

When a scientific law is stated in the form of a general implication, symbolized as

$$(x)[f(x) \supset g(x)] \tag{1}$$

the formulation must be regarded as a schematization, introduced because the logical treatment of all-statements in a two-valued logic is much simpler than the use of probability implications within the framework of probability logic. What can be proved by inductive methods is only that a probability implication of a high degree exists; the transition to the general implication is bound to certain conditions the neglect of which leads to paradoxes.

Such paradoxes appeared in the theory of confirmation when it was applied to the establishment of implications like (1), as was shown by C. G. Hempel.[11] The theory employs, as confirming cases, observations of the kind $f(x) \cdot g(x)$; the larger the number of such cases, it is argued, the better is the general implication confirmed. But since, according to the rule of contraposition (6*c*, § 4), (1) is tautologically equivalent to the form

$$(x)[\overline{g(x)} \supset \overline{f(x)}] \tag{2}$$

we must regard as confirming cases observations of the form $\overline{g(x)} \cdot \overline{f(x)}$ also. This consequence seems absurd. Returning to the example of the swans, we would have to regard as confirming cases of the statement, "All swans are white", not only observations of white swans, but also of anything that is not white and not a swan, for instance, of red flowers.

The paradox seems to be unsolvable within the theory of confirmation. It disappears, however, as soon as probabilities are introduced. For a probability implication, even of the degree 1, contraposition does not hold, and thus the two forms corresponding to (1) and (2)

$$(x_i)(f(x_i) \underset{1}{\ni} g(x_i)] \tag{3}$$

$$(x_i)[\overline{g(x_i)} \underset{1}{\ni} \overline{f(x_i)}] \tag{4}$$

are not equivalent. This fact can also be made clear as follows. If (3) were manifestly false and we had only a probability implication of a low degree, (4) might remain virtually true. The reason is that only a small number of things that are not white will be swans. Consequently, if the truth of (4) is established to a high degree of probability, (3) need not be true, and we cannot use an establishment of (4) as a proof for the validity of (3). From the standpoint of probability theory, a general implication represents a degenerate case. It can be substituted for a probability implication of a high degree only after both the relations (3) and (4) have been established independently. Conversely, the use of all-statements must be interpreted as indicating, not that the degree

[11] "A Purely Syntactical Definition of Confirmation," in *Jour. of Symbolic Logic*, Vol. VIII (1943), p. 128. [Ed. note: See selection from Hempel in Section II.]

of probability is assumed as strictly = 1 (all that empirical evidence can prove is a probability within a small interval 1 — δ), but that both the relations (3) and (4) have been verified practically within an interval δ of exactness. The analysis shows that the method of inductive verification must be attached to probability statements and not to the schematized form of knowledge in which such statements are replaced by two-valued statements.

Apart from contraposition, a further difference between general implications and probability implications of the degree 1, or of a high degree of probability, is given in the fact that from $(A \supset B)$ we can derive $(A \cdot C \supset B)$ for every C; whereas if $(A \underset{p}{\ni} B)$ holds, with p almost equal to 1, there exist always classes C such that $(A \cdot C \underset{q}{\ni} B)$, where q is a low probability.[12] When we use a general implication as a schematization for a probability implication of a high degree of probability, we usually require, therefore, that at least no class C *be known* such that $P(A \cdot C, B)$ is small. If such a class C *is* known, we can derive that $P(A \cdot \bar{C}, B) > P(A, B)$ [see the remarks following (11*b*, § 19)], and we then reformulate the all-statement by the use of $A \cdot \bar{C}$ as reference class, that is, by excluding the known exceptions from the implicans. In other words, we require that no rule be known by means of which exceptions to the all-statement could be predicted. This usage of language makes it evident that the use of all-statements in place of probability implications of high degrees depends on more conditions than are given by the existence of a high degree of probability.

In this connection, an objection by E. Nagel may be discussed. It concerns the question why scientific all-statements are usually conceived as so strictly valid that even one exception would be regarded as a sufficient reason to renounce the all-statement. If what is meant by an all-statement is only a high probability, occasional exceptions should not be regarded as evidence to the contrary.

This criticism can be answered in various ways. First, if the limits of exactness are narrowly drawn, there will always be exceptions to scientific all-statements; that such exceptions are called observational errors does not change the fact that the all-statement is not strictly satisfied. Second, it is true that for wide limits of exactness, or merely qualitative statements, a case of one exception is regarded as incompatible with the all-statement. For instance, in scientific language we would not say that all human beings have hearts, if one exception were known. This attitude can be explained in two ways. First, the degrees of probability for such all-statements are usually so high that one exception, in fact, must be regarded as a noticeable diminution of the degree of probability. Second, one exception proves that the strict all-statement is false, and we dislike using an all-statement as a schematization if it is known that the all-statement is false. If a statement is used as a schematization, it should at least be

[12] This is true even if $p = 1$, though in this case $q \neq 1$ is possible only if $P(A,C) = 0$; see (6, § 25). See also the discussion of this peculiarity of probability implication at the end of § 72. [Ed. note: See p. 86 of this Section.]

compatible with the existing observational evidence to assume that the schematization is verbally true.

We shall turn now to the question how to discuss schematized statements like (1), in the sense of approximations, within the frame of probability statements. Before the schematization, we have, instead of (1), a statement of the form [13]

$$P[f(x), g(x)] = p \tag{5}$$

We shall consider also the probability of the statement (5) and thus a statement of the form

$$P\{P[f(x), g(x)] = p \pm \delta\} = q\,dp \tag{6}$$

where $dp = 2\delta$ (for the notation $p \pm \delta$ see footnote, p. 462). The value q is a probability density; for $\delta = 0$, that is, a precise value p, the probability (6) would be $= 0$.

We begin with the discussion of (5). The statement can be transformed so that it informs us about the probability of individual implications of the form $f(x) \supset g(x)$. To demonstrate the procedure we use the tautological equivalence

$$(A \supset B \equiv A \cdot B \vee \bar{A}) \tag{7}$$

which is easily derivable from the truth table of implication, and have

$$\begin{aligned} P(A \supset B) &= P(A) \cdot P(A,B) + P(\bar{A}) \\ &= 1 - P(A) \cdot [1 - P(A,B)] \end{aligned} \tag{8}$$

If $P(A) = 1$, we have $P(A \supset B) = P(A,B)$. If $P(A) < 1$, the value of $P(A \supset B)$ must be closer to 1 than that of $P(A,B)$, since the brackets in (8) then are multiplied by a factor smaller than 1. Therefore we have the general inequality

$$P(A \supset B) \geq P(A,B) \tag{9}$$

The equality sign holds only when $P(A) = 1$ or $P(A,B) = 1$. If $P(A,B) = 1$, we have also $P(A \supset B) = 1$.

Because of (9) we can always replace a probability implication of the degree p by a logical implication, an individual adjunctive implication, with the qualification that the probability of the resulting statement is $\geqq p$. Thus, when we find that 95% of all swans are white, we can express the result in the form that the probability of the statement, "A swan is white", is $\geqq$ 95%. The degree of the probability implication, therefore, appears as a lower limit of the probability of the corresponding logical implication. This interpretation offers itself when p is close to 1; instead of a probability implication, we then apply a logical implication with the qualification that the probability of the statement does not quite attain certainty.

We now proceed to the discussion of (6). When p is practically $= 1$ and the conditions of a transition to an all-statement are satisfied, (6) assumes the form

$$P\{(x)[f(x) \supset g(x)]\} = q\,dp \tag{10}$$

[13] We omit the subscript i because in the P-notation the order of the elements x is not expressed.

From the form of (6) it is clear that we must employ a lattice for the interpretation of this probability, though the lattice superscripts are omitted in (6); the probability of all-statements, consequently, must be defined as a second-level probability in a probability lattice. The occurrence of the factor dp on the right of (10) shows that the probability of a strict all-statement would be $= 0$. Only if the all-statement is regarded as admitting of a small inexactness $dp = \delta$, such that $p \geqq 1 - \delta$, will its probability be > 0.

With respect to all-statements, therefore, we can distinguish two kinds of probabilities. Probabilities of the first level of the lattice, that is, probabilities of the form (5), represent probabilities of individual implications comprised by the all-statement, to be used when the all-statement is not strictly verified but serves only as an approximation. The probability of the second level supplies the probability of the all-statement itself.[14]

Newton's law of gravitation may be used an example. It states that for all bodies, at all times and in all places, the relation

$$f = k \cdot \frac{m_1 m_2}{r^2} \tag{11}$$

holds, where f is the force of attraction, m_1 and m_2 the respective masses of the bodies, r their distance, and k a constant. The abbreviation x may denote a set of individual conditions, including a specification of the bodies involved and the time and space coördinates. Then, if (11) holds for the individual conditions to a certain degree δ of exactness, we write $\varphi(x)$, otherwise $\overline{\varphi(x)}$. Assume that the relation (11) has been tested for various positions of the planet Mars; we can write the results in the form of a sequence of terms $\varphi(x)$ or $\overline{\varphi(x)}$. Doing the same for other planets, the moon, and other tests of Newton's law (for example, Cavendish's experiment with a torsion balance), we arrive at a lattice

$$\begin{array}{cccccc} \varphi(x_{11}) & \varphi(x_{12}) & \overline{\varphi(x_{13})} & \varphi(x_{14}) & \cdot & \cdot \\ \varphi(x_{21}) & \overline{\varphi(x_{22})} & \varphi(x_{23}) & \varphi(x_{24}) & \cdot & \cdot \\ \cdot & \cdot & \cdot & \cdot & \cdot & \cdot \end{array} \tag{12}$$

Each row belongs to one planet or other test object. The negative cases are usually said to result from errors of observation; for us they are indications that observation can never strictly establish a general implication, but only a probability implication of a high degree.

We now establish the degree of probability for each row by means of a posit based on the inductive rule. Assuming the posits to be true, we count in the vertical direction and thus construct the probability of the second level holding for the statement that the probability of a row is $= p$. This probability, again, is stated in the form of a posit. For the probability of the first level the reference class is rather easily constructed. It is the same class that is used in implications

[14] This treatment of the probability of hypotheses was first developed by H. Reichenbach in *Erkenntnis*, Vol. V (1935), pp. 274–278. The present treatment, however, includes some additions and clarifications.

of the all-statement if such a statement is introduced in the sense of a schematization. For the probability of the second level the definition of the reference class is not unambiguous and thus offers the usual complications combined with this definition. In principle, however, the definition of the reference class follows the same procedure as in all other such problems. In this example, the class is constructed by reference to other instances where the law applies. The second-level probability, then, expresses the probability of an all-statement restricted to one planet.

In the astronomical tests of Newton's law, the observation was made that the planet Mercury does not satisfy the law to the same degree of exactness as the other planets. This example illustrates an exception to an all-statement that was formerly regarded as true without exception. Since the exception is restricted to one planet, it is regarded as an example in which one negative case is sufficient to disprove a physical law. This interpretation is not entirely correct. The measurements of the orbit of Mercury cover a large number of individual observations, and in schema (12) the exception would be represented by one row that does not converge toward the same limit as the others. But it is at least true that one negative row is regarded as sufficient to disprove the all-statement extended in the vertical direction. The law has therefore been restricted to planets that are not too close to the sun, that is, to the center of attraction. This is an instance of a transition from a reference class A to a reference class $A.\bar{C}$, as explained above (see also the discussion of the independence of the single case at the end of § 89). That the reference class C in which we incorporate the exception is, in this case, assumed to be the class of planets near the sun is based on other inductions, including those validating Einstein's theory of general relativity.

Instead of constructing an individual sequence for each planet, we can include in the first horizontal row all observed instances of the law, regardless of the individual planet or test object to which they belong. Then the limit of the frequency posited for this row determines the probability of the first level for the general case, that is, for an individual implication not restricted to one planet. In order to define the probability of the second level and thus the probability of Newton's law in general, not restricted to one test object, we must construct a reference class by filling out the other rows with observations pertaining to other physical laws. For instance, for the second row we can use the law of the conservation of energy; for the third, the law of entropy; and so on. The reference class employed corresponds to the way in which a scientific theory is actually judged, since confidence in an individual law of physics is undoubtedly increased by the fact that other laws, too, have proved to be reliable. Conversely, negative experiences with some physical laws are regarded as a reason for restricting the validity of other laws that so far have not been invalidated. For instance, the fact that Maxwell's equations do not apply to Bohr's atom is regarded as a reason to question the applicability of Newton's or Einstein's law of gravitation to the quantum domain.

These considerations show that the probability of a hypothesis or a scientific theory can be defined in terms of frequencies. Applied to the individual hypothesis, the probability assumes the character of a weight; all that was said about the use of a weight for statements of single cases holds likewise for the weight of hypotheses. In fact, speaking of the probability of an individual hypothesis offers no more logical difficulties than speaking of the probability of an individual event, say, the death of a certain person.

It is sometimes argued that in cases of the latter kind the choice of the reference class is easily made — that, for example, the reference class "all persons in the same condition of health" offers itself quite naturally. But critics of the frequency interpretation of the probability of theories forget how much experience and inductive theory is invested in the choice of the reference class of the probability of death. Should we some day reach a stage in which we have as many statistics on theories as we have today on cases of disease and subsequent death, we could select a reference class that satisfies the condition of homogeneity (see § 86), and the choice of the reference class for the probability of theories would seem as natural as that of the reference class for the probability of death. In some domains we have actually been witnesses of such a development. For instance, we know how to find a reference class for the probability of good weather tomorrow; but before the evolution of a scientific meteorology this reference class seemed as ambiguous as that of a scientific theory may seem today. The selection of a suitable reference class is always a problem of advanced knowledge.

The method described for the statistical definition of the probability of a theory, though it is of a schematized form, is not very different from the procedure actually used. What is different, however, is that we do not directly observe instances of the form $\varphi(x)$, but use other observations from which we infer that the form $\varphi(x)$ holds. Thus we do not directly observe, for a certain position of a planet, the force of attraction; we observe, instead, successive positions from which we infer the acceleration, and identify it with the force of attraction. The distance between the planet and the sun, too, is computed by complicated inferences. Apart from this difference, however, the inductive inference is expressed by schema (12). Thus, when a certain position and acceleration of the planet confirm the law, we assume that for this instance the numerical values of the force of attraction, of the distance, and so on, satisfy the relation φ; but we do not regard a single instance as proof that φ will always be satisfied. There might exist a different law φ', which, however, is so constructed that, for the special case observed, the numerical values of φ and φ' coincide. That such an assumption is false, and that φ always holds, is a result based on the great number of instances in which φ is satisfied.

We can explain why we prefer, for the establishment of the general law, a variation of instances from planet to planet rather than a repetition of instances for the same planet. By previous inductions we have established a general rule that the various positions of one planet, or the various states of one body, are controlled by a simple law; therefore, when we have tested a law for the various states of one body, we assume it to hold for all states of the body, so that further observation virtually does not supply new information. Observations of other planets, on the contrary, must be regarded as independent observations.

The logical analysis of this inference is as follows: we have a probability of the second level telling us when the horizontal sequence is long enough to justify a posit of its persistence, whereas the posit in the vertical direction requires independent evidence and is not justifiable by an analogy with the posit in the horizontal direction. What is called the *weight of an evidence* is to be interpreted as the result of previous inductions, all of which are ultimately reducible to induction by enumeration. The analysis shows that the actual inferences by which the probability of a theory is established include the results of a great many previous inductions, and that any reconstruction of the method will remain a simplified schematization.

A further difference from induction by enumeration results when we ask for the probability, not that the law φ holds, but that it holds *when* verifying observations of a certain kind have been made. This question concerns a lattice inference applied to schema (12) and is answered by the probability density $v_n(f; p)$ of (5, § 62). The answer is constructed in terms of the rule of Bayes and presupposes a knowledge of the antecedent probability density $q(p)$. The latter function can be found, in principle, by counting sequences vertically in schema (12); a division of the range 0 to 1 for the possible values p of the horizontal probability by small but finite intervals dp leads to an approximate determination (the precise analysis of this method is given in § 89). The probability $v_n(f; p)dp$ thus ascertained, in which f measures the frequency of conforming instances of the law φ in the observed initial section, possesses Bernoulli properties and satisfies Laplace's convergence theorem (9, § 62). Whatever be the antecedent probabilities, if n is large enough, v_n is close to 1 for an interval $p \pm \delta$ that includes the value $p = f$.

In the theory of confirmation, which is intended to supply the probability $v_n(f; p)dp$, the inference is falsely construed as governed by laws that are not included in the calculus of probability. The analysis presented shows that the calculus possesses all the means to account for the inference, and that recourse to laws of an independent "inductive logic" is unnecessary. The use of a knowledge of antecedent probabilities for the inference is visible in the fact that the scientist usually knows when the frequency n of observed instances is large enough to warrant the conclusion of its persistence. His judgment about the number n may be construed as following computations as explained with respect to (12, § 62).

The considerations presented make it evident that the probability of hypotheses offers no difficulties of principle to a statistical interpretation. That, in most practical instances, the statistics cannot be carried through numerically because of insufficient data, and that, instead, crude estimates are used, do not constitute objections to a theory that claims to embody only the rational reconstruction of knowledge, not knowledge in its actual procedure.

8 The Frequency Theory of Probability

JOHN W. LENZ

The frequency interpretation of probability is far from new. It is already suggested by Aristotle's remarks that probable events are those which happen for the most part. Only in recent times, however, has a succession of writers (for example, Venn, v. Mises, and Reichenbach) developed this interpretation into a systematic theory.[1] Since Reichenbach has carried this development the furthest, I shall usually refer to his views in the critical discussion that follows.

1. The Frequency Interpretation

The essence of the frequency interpretation can be easily seen from a consideration of the following simple example. Suppose that a sympathetic nurse attempts to calm a prospective father by remarking, "The probability of twins is only 1/87." The frequentist interprets the nurse as asserting that one birth in 87 results in twins. More generally, the frequentist interprets the probability of A's being B's as the relative frequency with which things that are A are also B. The numerical value of such probabilities is m/n, where n is the number of A's and m is the number of A's that are B's.

A more precise indication of the frequency interpretation can be obtained from noting what would verify or refute one's claim that the probability of A's being B's is, say, 1/2. The observation of 10 A's, of which only three were B's, would certainly not refute this claim, for the claim is that "in the long run" the relative frequency with which A's are B's is 1/2. On the other hand, if in the long run, that is, as one observed more and more A's, the frequency with which A's are B's differs less and less from the value 1/2, one would regard the above claim as established. However, such phrases as "in the long run" are imprecise, and any definition employing them would not be subject to exact mathematical treatment. Accordingly frequentists such as Reichenbach "idealize" the definition as follows: the probability of A's being B's is defined as the limit of the fraction m/n (where n is the number of A's and m the number of A's that are B's) as m approaches infinity. The non-mathematical reader can be assured

From *The Structure of Scientific Thought, An Introduction to the Philosophy of Science*, E. H. Madden (Ed.), Houghton Mifflin Co., Boston, 1960, pp. 263–269. Reprinted by permission of the author.

[1] John Venn, *The Logic of Chance* (London, 1866). Richard von Mises, *Probability, Statistics, and Truth* (New York, 1939). Hans Reichenbach, *Theory of Probability* (Berkeley, 1949). *Experience and Prediction* (Chicago, 1938).

that nothing philosophically important hangs on the exact "mathematical" way of putting this definition.[2]

It is important, rather, that we note the essential features of probability statements when interpreted along frequentist lines. 1) Probability statements assert the relative frequency of the members of two *classes* of things. 2) Probability statements are, therefore, factual claims. 3) Probability statements are, moreover, predictive in their force, for a statement about "long run" relative frequencies must be based upon the "shorter run" relative frequencies that have been observed. In all three ways they differ from probability statements as interpreted by a logical theorist such as Carnap.[3]

Before turning our attention to the merits of the frequency interpretation I want to point out one more thing. Frequentists need not, as Venn did, limit themselves to speaking about the relative frequency of two classes of *events*. Very significantly they can talk about the frequency with which certain statements are true. They may, for example, speak about the relative frequency with which hypotheses based upon certain methodological rules are true, and thus be able to speak of the probable reliability of these methods. To take just one example, they may speak of the relative frequency with which statistical hypotheses made on the basis of small samples are true. Since statistical hypotheses are probability statements, the frequentist can in this way speak about the probability of probability statements being true. He can allow a whole "hierarchy" of probabilities of different levels. As we shall see, this is extremely important to remember when we consider some of the standard objections against the frequency interpretation.

2. Types of Criticism

The frequency interpretation has many virtues. It has enabled frequentists to give a complex and useful mathematical treatment of the subject of probability. Reichenbach is able to show that given the frequency interpretation, the commonly accepted axioms of the probability calculus are all logically true. Nonetheless, the frequentist faces many serious objections.[4]

These objections may be divided into two types. One type challenges the frequentist's claim to be explicating the concept of probability as actually employed in science and daily life. Another challenges what may be called the assertability of probability statements when given the frequency interpretation. These two kinds of objection are not unrelated, as we shall see, but I shall make

[2] A more complete but still simple explanation of the frequency interpretation can be found in Ernest Nagel, *Principles of the Theory of Probability* (Chicago, 1939), pp. 19–26.

[3] Cf. Rudolf Carnap, "The Two Concepts of Probability," contained in *Readings in Philosophical Analysis*, ed. H. Feigl and W. Sellars (New York, 1949).

[4] A good discussion of the frequency theory can be found in "A Symposium on Probability," *Philosophy and Phenomenological Research*, 1945 and 1946. This contains comments on the frequency interpretation by D. Williams, E. Nagel, H. Margenau, G. Bergmann, and F. Kaufman, among others. The articles by Nagel are especially important. Another good critical discussion of the frequency interpretation is Nagel's "Probability and the Theory of Knowledge," contained in *Sovereign Reason* (Glencoe, Illinois, 1954), pp. 225–265.

use of this convenient distinction in ordering the many objections we shall consider. I shall first discuss objections of type one.

It must be said immediately that Reichenbach, at least to some extent, does not claim to be analyzing "probability" in all its many uses. He claims, rather, to be saying how "probability" *should* be employed in any "rational reconstruction" of human knowledge. Thus, he is ready to challenge the force of objections of the first kind. My own view is that we need neither over-emphasize nor under-emphasize the importance of such objections. It is surely important to see to what extent the frequency interpretation does or does not fit the ordinary employment of "probability" in science and every day living. However, two additional points must also be made. First, we must be careful to see whether certain uses of "probability" which, prima facie, the frequency interpretation does not fit can in fact be assimilated to it. Secondly, we must ascertain if those uses it does not fit are themselves defensible.

3. Short Run Frequencies

There is an obvious objection to Reichenbach's definition of probability. I do not regard it as a crucial one, but since many critics have offered it, I shall consider it right off. The objection is that in many, if not most cases, one does not wish to talk about relative frequencies in the very long run. (In technical terms, one does not wish to speak of the limit of the relative frequency in an infinite series of events.) For example, suppose two insurance company executives wish, in order to set insurance rates, to determine the probability of healthy male Americans of the age 32 surviving to the age 60. Here it would be fanciful to suppose that the insurance executives are concerned with the limit of m/n as n approaches infinity (where n would be the number of healthy male Americans 32 years old and m would be the number of healthy male Americans 32 years old who survive to the age 60). The insurance executives are only concerned with the relative frequency m/n where n is fairly large, perhaps the number of healthy male Americans who reach the age 32 within the next 50 years or so.

Two points can be made in reply to this objection. First, it is not true that this objection is of unlimited applicability. It is plausible to suppose that physicists, in their formulation of statistical laws, use the term "probability" in a way that exactly fits Reichenbach's definition. Physicists, after all, are concerned to state laws "that hold for all time." Second, Reichenbach's definition can easily be amended to fit examples like that involving the insurance executives. One could define the probability of A's being B's as m/n (where n is the number of A's and m is the number of A's that are B's) where n is large enough for our purposes. However, it must be pointed out that, while this emendation is easily made, it is made at the price of destroying the mathematical simplicity and elegance of the frequency theory. This, however, does not seem to me to be too serious; one could regard Reichenbach's definition as simply an "idealization" of our more usual employment of the concept of probability. Accordingly, I conclude that this first objection to the frequency interpretation can be answered satisfactorily.

4. Probabilities Do Not Refer to Relative Frequencies

A second more serious objection to the frequency interpretation has also been made by many writers. I shall consider Toulmin's most recent version of it. Toulmin claims that "probability" (and its cognates "probably," "probable," etc.) [5] are never used to speak about relative frequencies. Toulmin claims that, on the contrary, "probability" and its cognates are used to *guard* predictions, as when the weather man says, "probably it will rain tomorrow."

The extreme claim of Toulmin's that "probability" never refers to relative frequencies must, as our previous discussion already shows, be rejected. It is perfectly respectable for a biologist to say, "The probability of twins is 1/87" and mean by this that in the long run approximately 1 out of 87 births results in twins.

However, rejecting Toulmin's extreme claim does not refute more modest objections to the frequency interpretation. It may be that this interpretation does not fit all justifiable uses of "probability." It is an interesting question, for example, whether the frequentist can in fact assimilate the use Toulmin emphasizes, that of guarding our predictions. It must be pointed out, however, that if it turns out, as we examine such questions, that the frequency interpretation does not fit all justifiable uses of "probability" it does not follow that it is a completely worthless interpretation. As we have already seen, it does fit at least one very important type of probability statement. Sophisticated logical theorists such as Carnap would be the first to point this out.

5. The Single Case

Another traditional objection to the frequency interpretation is its alleged inability to speak of probabilities of single events. An example will make this objection clear. When the frequentist speaks of the probability of American marriages ending in divorce as 1/7, he is speaking about the relative frequency of the members of two classes of events. He does not speak specifically about the probability of this or that particular marriage breaking up, as, it seems, we often do. The question in general is: can the frequency interpretation assimilate such statements?

The logical theory advocated by Carnap has no difficulty in speaking about "probabilities of single events." It allows one to say that the hypothesis, "This particular marriage will end in divorce" is, on the given evidence, confirmed to such and such a degree. The frequency theory must deny that it makes sense to speak of the probability of single events unless this is an elliptical way of speaking about the relative frequency of the members of two classes of events. Here, it would seem, the logical theorist has the nod over the frequentist.

[5] Stephen Toulmin, *The Uses of Argument* (Cambridge, 1958), p. 79.

However, the frequentist can attempt to show how in an indirect way one can in fact speak about the probability of a single event. This answer takes us into an extremely important aspect of Reichenbach's theory of probability, his concept of weight. Suppose that an insurance company must decide whether to insure a relatively healthy American man who is 32 years old. Suppose further that the insurance company believes that the probability of such men living to the age 60 is 9/10. It may then predict, says Reichenbach, that this man will survive to the age 60. It could add, Reichenbach says further, that the weight of this prediction, or wager, is 9/10, meaning by this that 9/10 of such predictions will be true. Thus weight here is interpreted essentially as the frequency with which predictions of a certain type are true, and thus the concept of weight is given a frequency interpretation. Reichenbach's reply to the single case objection is that, while we cannot directly speak of the probability of a single event, we can make predictions concerning single events and then speak of the weight of such predictions. Reichenbach claims that this answer is sufficient in view of our actual purposes.

This answer to the problem of the single case raises many issues, some of which I shall discuss in connection with another objection. At this point I shall discuss only one difficulty that is especially relevant here. This is the so-called problem of choosing the best "reference class" in which to place the single event in question. Let us go back to the insurance company that is trying to decide whether it ought to insure a particular man, say John Jones, who is a relatively healthy American male 32 years old. Now the probability of American males living to the age 60 no doubt differs from the probability of 32 year old American males living to the age 60, and both of these probabilities will in turn differ from the probability of relatively healthy American males aged 32 living to the age 60. The question is: which of these probabilities shall we make use of in making our wagers about John Jones' surviving till the age 60? The frequentist will answer that we should choose the last mentioned probability since it makes use of the most information we have about Jones. However, the frequentist cannot say that in general we should make use of the most information we have about Jones. Let us assume that John Jones has only 9 fingers. We cannot make use of this information because we have no reliable statistics about the relative frequency with which nine fingered men survive to the age 60. The general rule must be, therefore, to make use of the most information about a single event so long as we are able to make reliable probability statements. The general lines of this answer are undoubtedly correct; at least it is the best answer that the frequentist can give. But it is important to note that what will be the best predictions we can make concerning single events will vary with the state of our knowledge. [6]

[6] Reichenbach, *Theory of Probability*, pp. 366–378; *Experience and Prediction*, pp. 297–319. A good discussion of Reichenbach's concept of weight and its application to the problem of the single case can be found in Nagel's "Probability and the Theory of Knowledge," contained in *Sovereign Reason*, pp.228–248.

6. Guarding Predictions

Let us now examine Toulmin's claim that words such as "probably," "likely" are used to guard predictions. I think it is evident that from what was said concerning the objection of the single case that Reichenbach can, in all essential ways, assimilate this use to the frequency interpretation. Consider, for example, Toulmin's favorite case, the weather man's saying, "Probably it will rain tomorrow." The frequentist could say that the weather man was not only predicting rain but saying that this prediction had a relatively high weight. In saying the latter the weather man would not be telling us to expect that all such predictions are correct, but only a high percentage of them. Surely this is the direct way of guarding one's predictions.[7]

7. Probability as Degree of Evidential Support

We come now to what I consider to be the most crucial objection to Reichenbach's claim that all probability statements can be interpreted along frequentist lines. We often say such things as, "On the basis of the present evidence, the hypothesis that Shakespeare wrote Hamlet is highly probable," "Relative to the evidence then available, Newton's law of universal gravitation was highly probable," "In the light of new evidence, the theory of probability is more probable than before." Writers such as Carnap have suggested that such probability statements assert a certain relation between a hypothesis and given evidence, namely, the degree to which the evidence supports or confirms the hypothesis. Carnap has further claimed that the concept of probability employed here is essentially different from that given by the frequency interpretation. This objection, in my opinion, must be handled very carefully.[8]

In a sense this objection is but a generalized version of the objection that the frequency interpretation cannot handle probabilities about single events, and much of what was said concerning that objection is again relevant here. We saw, for example, that while the frequentist could not speak directly about probabilities of single events, he could speak about the weight of predictions concerning single events, where weight was interpreted as the truth frequency of such predictions. The frequentist's reply to this latest objection would be simply that "degree of evidential support" is to be equated with this notion of weight. His reply would be that to speak of certain evidence highly confirming a hypothesis about a single event is to speak about the frequency with which such hypotheses based upon such evidence are true.

The frequentist could generalize this claim to say that whenever we speak about the degree to which evidence confirms a hypothesis, we are saying that this hypothesis has a certain weight. Let us consider another example. Suppose that we are considering the general hypothesis that all smokers will contract

[7] Toulmin admits that we expect a weather man who repeatedly predicts "Probably it will rain tomorrow" to be right a high proportion of times.

[8] Cf. Carnap's "Two Concepts of Probability."

lung cancer. And suppose that our evidence is that we have observed three smokers from Los Angeles and have found that all three have contracted lung cancer. Relative to this evidence, surely, the general hypothesis is confirmed only to a small degree. The frequentist would take this to mean that the truth frequency of general hypotheses made on the basis of small "biased" samples was very low.

To what extent the frequentist can assimilate all such statements about evidential support is, in my opinion, a very complex question. I surely cannot settle the matter in this paper. It must be pointed out, however, that so far no frequentist has shown that this is possible in all cases. And it must be pointed out, too, that in principle it seems implausible to suppose that it is. Consider the statement, "Upon the latest evidence, the theory of relativity is highly confirmed." Does the frequentist really believe that this statement asserts that the truth frequency of such hypotheses based upon such evidence is very high? How shall we delineate the class of such hypotheses, and where shall we find reliable statistics upon which we could establish the truth frequency of such hypotheses? Here the frequentist's way of trying to assimilate statements asserting a degree of confirmation seems little more than an *ad hoc* suggestion with no ring of plausibility.

In any case Carnap can point out that there remains a radical difference between *his* concept of degree of confirmation and the concept of weight. On his interpretation statements asserting a degree of confirmation are logically true and, thus, do not predict anything at all, whereas statements asserting weights predict something, namely, the truth frequency of predictions or hypotheses. I myself think that so interpreted statements asserting a degree of confirmation cannot be assimilated to the frequency view. Let me say more cautiously, that *given* a good definition of "degree of confirmation" statements asserting degrees of evidential support can be obtained purely logically, whereas statements asserting that a prediction has a certain weight are themselves predictions and thus must be established inductively. However, two things more must be said. First, there is the difficult question as to how such a definition of degree of confirmation can be established.[9] Secondly, there is the further difficult question as to whether statements that are established purely logically can ever be good guides to life. But to discuss these questions would take us into a full discussion of the logical theory itself.

8. The Assertability of Probability Statements

All the objections so far have concerned the degree to which the frequency interpretation can assimilate "probability" as actually employed in science and

[9] Cf. Carnap's "Statistical and Inductive Probability," in E. H. Madden, *The Structure of Scientific Thought*, Houghton Mifflin Co., Boston, 1960; see p. 269. For a more thorough statement of the problem see Rudolf Carnap, *Continuum of Inductive Methods* (Chicago, 1952). For a critical examination of Carnap's solution and a further amplification of my point here see John Lenz, "Carnap on Defining 'Degree of Confirmation'," *Philosophy of Science*, July 1956, pp. 230–236. [Ed. note: This article is reprinted in this Section.]

daily life. We turn now to the question of the assertability of probability statements when given the frequency interpretation. On the frequentist's own admission, this is a very serious problem confronting him.

The problem as to whether we are ever justified in asserting probability statements when interpreted along frequentist lines arises in this way. Such probability statements are always factual statements, purporting to describe the world. They are, moreover, predictive in character; they assert that certain relative frequencies will obtain. While such predictions are based upon empirical evidence, namely, observed relative frequencies, they "go beyond" that evidence. The question is: what justification do we have for making such statements?

Frequentists have at times seemed to think that this problem can be solved by the use of second order probabilities. As we have seen, the frequentist can speak of the probability of a probability statement being true. Frequentists have at times seemed to say that, therefore, while we cannot give any assurance of the truth of probability statements, we can always assess the probability of their being true. This answer, however, does not solve the problem; it only postpones having to raise it. As we have seen, "second order" probability statements are themselves predictive; while based upon observed evidence, namely, the observed truth frequency of predictions, they go beyond it. Thus, the problem of the assertability of probability statements simply occurs at the higher level.

The logical theorist is ready to step in at this point to say that the frequentist needs to supplement his theory with the notion of degree of confirmation. In that case we could say that probability statements, while not known to be true, are at least confirmed to such and such a degree. This answer involves difficulties of its own, but in any case it cannot be given by the thoroughgoing frequentist who has denied the need or validity of the concept of degree of confirmation.

The frequentist has another way out, one which Reichenbach himself takes, but this solution only raises further difficulties. Reichenbach, unlike many other frequentists, agrees that the frequency theory of probability must postulate some inductive rule, by means of which one can make predictions about long run relative frequencies on the basis of the short run relative frequencies that are observed. Reichenbach admits, furthermore, that such a rule of induction stands in need of justification.[10] Thus, Reichenbach solves the problem of the assertability of frequency probability statements only at the cost of facing a more difficult one, the infamous problem of justifying induction.

[10] Reichenbach's own "pragmatic" justification of induction is contained in *Theory of Probability*, pp. 469–482. [Ed. note: See the selection from Reichenbach in Section IV.] For a critical examination of this justification see John Lenz, "The Pragmatic Justification of Induction," in E. H. Madden, *The Structure of Scientific Thought*, Houghton Mifflin Co., Boston, 1960, pp. 299–303. [Ed. note: See also "Reichenbach's Defense of Induction" by John Lenz in Section IV of this volume.]

9 Degrees of Belief

FRANK P. RAMSEY

The subject of our inquiry is the logic of partial belief, and I do not think we can carry it far unless we have at least an approximate notion of what partial belief is, and how, if at all, it can be measured. It will not be very enlightening to be told that in such circumstances it would be rational to believe a proposition to the extent of 2/3, unless we know what sort of a belief in it that means. We must therefore try to develop a purely psychological method of measuring belief. It is not enough to measure probability; in order to apportion correctly our belief to the probability we must also be able to measure our belief.

It is a common view that belief and other psychological variables are not measurable, and if this is true our inquiry will be vain; and so will the whole theory of probability conceived as a logic of partial belief; for if the phrase 'a belief two-thirds of certainty' is meaningless, a calculus whose sole object is to enjoin such beliefs will be meaningless also. Therefore unless we are prepared to give up the whole thing as a bad job we are bound to hold that beliefs can to some extent be measured. If we were to follow the analogy of Mr. Keynes' treatment of probabilities we should say that some beliefs were measurable and some not; but this does not seem to me likely to be a correct account of the matter: I do not see how we can sharply divide beliefs into those which have a position in the numerical scale and those which have not. But I think beliefs do differ in measurability in the following two ways. First, some beliefs can be measured more accurately than others; and, secondly, the measurement of beliefs is almost certainly an ambiguous process leading to a variable answer depending on how exactly the measurement is conducted. The degree of a belief is in this respect like the time interval between two events; before Einstein it was supposed that all the ordinary ways of measuring a time interval would lead to the same result if properly performed. Einstein showed that this was not the case; and time interval can no longer be regarded as an exact notion, but must be discarded in all precise investigations. Nevertheless, time interval and the Newtonian system are sufficiently accurate for many purposes and easier to apply.

I shall try to argue later that the degree of a belief is just like a time interval; it has no precise meaning unless we specify more exactly how it is to be measured.

From *The Foundations of Mathematics and Other Logical Essays*, Paterson, New Jersey, Littlefield, Adams and Co., 1960, pp. 166–184. Reprinted by permission of Humanities Press Inc., New York.

But for many purposes we can assume that the alternative ways of measuring it lead to the same result, although this is only approximately true. The resulting discrepancies are more glaring in connection with some beliefs than with others, and these therefore appear less measurable. Both these types of deficiency in measurability, due respectively to the difficulty in getting an exact enough measurement and to an important ambiguity in the definition of the measurement process, occur also in physics and so are not difficulties peculiar to our problem; what is peculiar is that it is difficult to form any idea of how the measurement is to be conducted, how a unit is to be obtained, and so on.

Let us then consider what is implied in the measurement of beliefs. A satisfactory system must in the first place assign to any belief a magnitude or degree having a definite position in an order of magnitudes; beliefs which are of the same degree as the same belief must be of the same degree as one another, and so on. Of course this cannot be accomplished without introducing a certain amount of hypothesis or fiction. Even in physics we cannot maintain that things that are equal to the same thing are equal to one another unless we take 'equal' not as meaning 'sensibly equal' but a fictitious or hypothetical realtion. I do not want to discuss the metaphysics or epistemology of this process, but merely to remark that if it is allowable in physics it is allowable in psychology also. The logical simplicity characteristic of the relations dealt with in a science is never attained by nature alone without any admixture of fiction.

But to construct such an ordered series of degrees is not the whole of our task; we have also to assign numbers to these degrees in some intelligible manner. We can of course easily explain that we denote full belief by 1, full belief in the contradictory by 0, and equal beliefs in the proposition and its contradictory by 1/2. But it is not so easy to say what is meant by a belief 2/3 of certainty, or a belief in the proposition being twice as strong as that in its contradictory. This is the harder part of the task, but it is absolutely necessary; for we do calculate numerical probabilities, and if they are to correspond to degrees of belief we must discover some definite way of attaching numbers to degrees of belief. In physics we often attach numbers by discovering a physical process of addition[1]: the measure-numbers of lengths are not assigned arbitrarily subject only to the proviso that the greater length shall have the greater measure; we determine them further by deciding on a physical meaning for addition; the length got by putting together two given lengths must have for its measure the sum of their measures. A system of measurement in which there is nothing corresponding to this is immediately recognized as arbitrary, for instance Mohs' scale of hardness[2] in which 10 is arbitrarily assigned to diamond, the hardest known material, 9 to the next hardest, and so on. We have therefore to find a process of addition for degrees of belief, or some substitute for this which will be equally adequate to determine a numerical scale.

Such is our problem; how are we to solve it? There are, I think, two ways in which we can begin. We can, in the first place, suppose that the degree of a

[1] See N. Campbell, *Physics: The Elements* (1920), p. 277.

[2] *Ibid.*, p. 271.

belief is something perceptible by its owner; for instance that beliefs differ in the intensity of a feeling by which they are accompanied, which might be called a belief-feeling or feeling of conviction, and that by the degree of belief we mean the intensity of this feeling. This view would be very inconvenient, for it is not easy to ascribe numbers to the intensities of feelings; but apart from this it seems to me observably false, for the beliefs which we hold most strongly are often accompanied by practically no feeling at all; no one feels strongly about things he takes for granted.

We are driven therefore to the second supposition that the degree of a belief is a causal property of it, which we can express vaguely as the extent to which we are prepared to act on it. This is a generalization of the well-known view, that the differentia of belief lies in its causal efficacy, which is discussed by Mr. Russell in his *Analysis of Mind*. He there dismisses it for two reasons, one of which seems entirely to miss the point. He argues that in the course of trains of thought we believe many things which do not lead to action. This objection is however beside the mark, because it is not asserted that a belief is an idea which does actually lead to action, but one which would lead to action in suitable circumstances; just as a lump of arsenic is called poisonous not because it actually has killed or will kill anyone, but because it would kill anyone if he ate it. Mr. Russell's second argument is, however, more formidable. He points out that it is not possible to suppose that beliefs differ from other ideas only in their effects, for if they were otherwise identical their effects would be identical also. This is perfectly true, but it may still remain the case that the nature of the difference between the causes is entirely unknown or very vaguely known, and that what we want to talk about is the difference between the effects, which is readily observable and important.

As soon as we regard belief quantitatively, this seems to me the only view we can take of it. It could well be held that the difference between believing and not believing lies in the presence or absence of introspectible feelings. But when we seek to know what is the difference between believing more firmly and believing less firmly, we can no longer regard it as consisting in having more or less of certain observable feelings; at least I personally cannot recognize any such feelings. The difference seems to me to lie in how far we should act on these beliefs: this may depend on the degree of some feeling or feelings, but I do not know exactly what feelings and I do not see that it is indispensable that we should know. Just the same thing is found in physics; men found that a wire connecting plates of zinc and copper standing in acid deflected a magnetic needle in its neighbourhood. Accordingly as the needle was more or less deflected the wire was said to carry a larger or a smaller current. The nature of this 'current' could only be conjectured: what were observed and measured were simply its effects.

It will no doubt be objected that we know how strongly we believe things, and that we can only know this if we can measure our belief by introspection. This does not seem to me necessarily true; in many cases, I think, our judgment about the strength of our belief is really about how we should act in hypothetical circumstances. It will be answered that we can only tell how we should act by observing the present belief-feeling which determines how we should act; but again I doubt the cogency of the argument. It is possible that what determines how we should act determines us also directly or indirectly to have a correct opinion as to how we should act, without its ever coming into consciousness.

Suppose, however, I am wrong about this and that we can decide by introspection the nature of belief, and measure its degree; still, I shall argue, the kind of measurement of belief with which probability is concerned is not this kind but is a measurement of belief *qua* basis of action. This can, I think, be shown in two ways. First, by considering the scale of probabilities between 0 and 1, and the sort of way we use it, we shall find that it is very appropriate to the measurement of belief as a basis of action, but in no way related to the measurement of an introspected feeling. For the units in terms of which such feelings or sensations are measured are always, I think, differences which are just perceptible: there is no other way of obtaining units. But I see no ground for supposing that the interval between a belief of degree 1/3 and one of degree 1/2 consists of as many just perceptible changes as does that between one of 2/3 and one of 5/6, or that a scale based on just perceptible differences would have any simple relation to the theory of probability. On the other hand the probability of 1/3 is clearly related to the kind of belief which would lead to a bet of 2 to 1, and it will be shown below how to generalize this relation so as to apply to action in general. Secondly, the quantitative aspects of beliefs as the basis of action are evidently more important than the intensities of belief-feelings. The latter are no doubt interesting, but may be very variable from individual to individual, and their practical interest is entirely due to their position as the hypothetical causes of beliefs *qua* bases of action.

It is possible that some one will say that the extent to which we should act on a belief in suitable circumstances is a hypothetical thing, and therefore not capable of measurement. But to say this is merely to reveal ignorance of the physical sciences which constantly deal with and measure hypothetical quantities; for instance, the electric intensity at a given point is the force which would act on a unit charge if it were placed at the point.

Let us now try to find a method of measuring beliefs as bases of possible actions. It is clear that we are concerned with dispositional rather than with actualized beliefs; that is to say, not with beliefs at the moment when we are thinking of them, but with beliefs like my belief that the earth is round, which I rarely think of, but which would guide my action in any case to which it was relevant.

The old-established way of measuring a person's belief is to propose a bet, and see what are the lowest odds which he will accept. This method I regard as fundamentally sound; but it suffers from being insufficiently general, and from being necessarily inexact. It is inexact partly because of the diminishing marginal utility of money, partly because the person may have a special eagerness or reluctance to bet, because he either enjoys or dislikes excitement or for any other reason, e.g. to make a book. The difficulty is like that of separating two different co-operating forces. Besides, the proposal of a bet may inevitably alter his state of opinion; just as we could not always measure electric intensity by actually introducing a charge and seeing what force it was subject to, because the introduction of the charge would change the distribution to be measured.

In order therefore to construct a theory of quantities of belief which shall be both general and more exact, I propose to take as a basis a general psychological theory, which is now universally discarded, but nevertheless comes, I think, fairly close to the truth in the sort of cases with which we are most concerned. I mean the theory that we act in the way we think most likely to realize the objects of our desires, so that a person's actions are completely determined by his desires and opinions. This theory cannot be made adequate to all the facts, but it seems to me a useful approximation to the truth particularly in the case of our self-conscious or professional life, and it is presupposed in a great deal of our thought. It is a simple theory and one which many psychologists would obviously like to preserve by introducing unconscious desires and unconscious opinions in order to bring it more into harmony with the facts. How far such fictions can achieve the required result I do not attempt to judge: I only claim for what follows approximate truth, or truth in relation to this artificial system of psychology, which like Newtonian mechanics can, I think, still be profitably used even though it is known to be false.

It must be observed that this theory is not to be identified with the psychology of the Utilitarians, in which pleasure had a dominating position. The theory I propose to adopt is that we seek things which we want, which may be our own or other people's pleasure, or anything else whatever, and our actions are such as we think most likely to realize these goods. But this is not a precise statement, for a precise statement of the theory can only be made after we have introduced the notion of quantity of belief.

Let us call the things a person ultimately desires 'goods', and let us at first assume that they are numerically measurable and additive. That is to say that if he prefers for its own sake an hour's swimming to an hour's reading, he will prefer two hours' swimming to one hour's swimming and one hour's reading. This is of course absurd in the given case but this may only be because swimming and reading are not ultimate goods, and because we cannot imagine a second hour's swimming precisely similar to the first, owing to fatigue, etc.

Let us begin by supposing that our subject has no doubts about anything, but certain opinions about all propositions. Then we can say that he will always choose the course of action which will lead in his opinion to the greatest sum of good.

It should be emphasized that in this essay good and bad are never to be understood in any ethical sense but simply as denoting that to which a given person feels desire and aversion.

The question then arises how we are to modify this simple system to take account of varying degrees of certainty in his beliefs. I suggest that we introduce as a law of psychology that his behaviour is governed by what is called the mathematical expectation; that is to say that, if p is a proposition about which he is doubtful, any goods or bads for whose realization p is in his view a necessary and sufficient condition enter into his calculations multiplied by the same fraction, which is called the 'degree of his belief in p'. We thus define degree of belief in a way which presupposes the use of the mathematical expectation.

We can put this in a different way. Suppose his degree of belief in p is $\frac{m}{n}$; then his action is such as he would choose it to be if he had to repeat it exactly n times, in m of which p was true, and in the others false. [Here it may be necessary to suppose that in each of the n times he had no memory of the previous ones.]

This can also be taken as a definition of the degree of belief, and can easily be seen to be equivalent to the previous definition. Let us give an instance of the sort of case which might occur. I am at a cross-roads and do not know the way; but I rather think one of the two ways is right. I propose therefore to go that way but keep my eyes open for someone to ask; if now I see someone half a mile away over the fields, whether I turn aside to ask him will depend on the relative inconvenience of going out of my way to cross the fields or of continuing on the wrong road if it is the wrong road. But it will also depend on how confident I am that I am right; and clearly the more confident I am of this the less distance I should be willing to go from the road to check my opinion. I propose therefore to use the distance I would be prepared to go to ask, as a measure of the confidence of my opinion; and what I have said above explains how this is to be done. We can set it out as follows: suppose the disadvantage of going x yards to ask is $f(x)$, the advantage of arriving at the right destination is r, that of arriving at the wrong one w. Then if I should just be willing to go a distance d to ask, the degree of my belief that I am on the right road is given by $p = 1 - \frac{f(d)}{r - w}$.

For such an action is one it would just pay me to take, if I had to act in the same way n times, in np of which I was on the right way but in the others not.

For the total good resulting from not asking each time

$$= npr + n(1 - p)w$$

$$= nw + np(r - w),$$

that resulting from asking at distance x each time

$$= nr - nf(x). \qquad \text{[I now always go right.]}$$

This is greater than the preceding expression, provided

$$f(x) < (r - w)(1 - p),$$

∴ the critical distance d is connected with p, the degree of belief, by the relation $f(d) = (r - w)(1 - p)$

$$\text{or} \quad p = 1 - \frac{f(d)}{r - w} \qquad \text{as asserted above.}$$

It is easy to see that this way of measuring beliefs gives results agreeing with ordinary ideas; at any rate to the extent that full belief is denoted by 1, full belief in the contradictory by 0, and equal belief in the two by 1/2. Further, it allows validity to betting as means of measuring beliefs. By proposing a bet on p we give the subject a possible course of action from which so much extra good will result to him if p is true and so much extra bad if p is false. Supposing the bet to be in goods and bads instead of in money, he will take a bet at any better odds than those corresponding to his state of belief; in fact his state of belief is measured by the odds he will just take; but this is vitiated, as already explained, by love or hatred of excitement, and by the fact that the bet is in money and not in goods and bads. Since it is universally agreed that money has a diminishing marginal utility, if money bets are to be used, it is evident that they should be for as small stakes as possible. But then again the measurement is spoiled by introducing the new factor of reluctance to bother about trifles.

Let us now discard the assumption that goods are additive and immediately measurable, and try to work out a system with as few assumptions as possible. To begin with we shall suppose, as before, that our subject has certain beliefs about everything; then he will act so that what he believes to be the total consequences of his action will be the best possible. If then we had the power of the Almighty, and could persuade our subject of our power, we could, by offering him options, discover how he placed in order of merit all possible courses of the world. In this way all possible worlds would be put in an order of value, but we should have no definite way of representing them by numbers. There would be no meaning in the assertion that the difference in value between α and β was equal to that between γ and δ. [Here and elsewhere we use Greek letters to represent the different possible totalities of events between which our subject chooses — the ultimate organic unities.]

Suppose next that the subject is capable of doubt; then we could test his degree of belief in different propositions by making him offers of the following kind. Would you rather have world α in any event; or world β if p is true, and world γ if p is false? If, then, he were certain that p was true, he would simply compare α and β and choose between them as if no conditions were attached; but if he were doubtful his choice would not be decided so simply. I propose to lay down axioms and definitions concerning the principles governing choices of this kind. This is, of course, a very schematic version of the situation in real life, but it is, I think, easier to consider it in this form.

There is first a difficulty which must be dealt with; the propositions like p in the above case which are used as conditions in the options offered may be such that their truth or falsity is an object of desire to the subject. This will be found to complicate the problem, and we have to assume that there are propositions for which this is not the case, which we shall call ethically neutral. More precisely an atomic proposition p is called ethically neutral if two possible worlds differing only in regard to the truth of p are always of equal value; and a non-atomic proposition p is called ethically neutral if all its atomic truth-arguments [3] are ethically neutral.

We begin by defining belief of degree 1/2 in an ethically neutral proposition. The subject is said to have belief of degree 1/2 in such a proposition p if he has no preference between the options (1) α if p is true, β if p is false, and (2) α if p is false, β if p is true, but has a preference between α and β simply. We suppose by an axiom that if this is true of any one pair α, β it is true of all such pairs.[4] This comes roughly to defining belief of degree 1/2 as such a degree of belief as leads to indifference between betting one way and betting the other for the same stakes.

Belief of degree 1/2 as thus defined can be used to measure values numerically in the following way. We have to explain what is meant by the difference in value between α and β being equal to that between γ and δ; and we define this to mean that, if p is an ethically neutral proposition believed to degree 1/2, the subject has no preference between the options (1) α if p is true, δ if p is false, and (2) β if p is true, γ if p is false.

This definition can form the basis of a system of measuring values in the following way: —

Let us call any set of all worlds equally preferable to a given world a value: we suppose that if world α is preferable to β any world with the same value as α is preferable to any world with the same value as β and shall say that the value of α is greater than that of β. This relation 'greater than' orders values in a series. We shall use α henceforth both for the world and its value.

Axioms.

(1) There is an ethically neutral proposition p believed to degree 1/2.

(2) If p, q are such propositions and the option

α if p, δ if not-p is equivalent to β if p, γ if not-p
then α if q, δ if not-q is equivalent to β if q, γ if not-q.

Def. In the above case we say $\alpha\beta = \gamma\delta$.

Theorems. If $\alpha\beta = \gamma\delta$,

then $\beta\alpha = \delta\gamma$, $\alpha\gamma = \beta\delta$, $\gamma\alpha = \delta\beta$.

(2*a*) If $\alpha\beta = \gamma\delta$, then $\alpha > \beta$ is equivalent to $\gamma > \delta$

and $\alpha = \beta$ is equivalent to $\gamma = \delta$.

(3) If option A is equivalent to option B and B to C then A to C.

[3] I assume here Wittgenstein's theory of propositions; it would probably be possible to give an equivalent definition in terms of any other theory.

[4] α and β must be supposed so far undefined as to be compatible with both p and not-p.

Theorem. If $\alpha\beta = \gamma\delta$ and $\beta\eta = \zeta\gamma$,

then $\alpha\eta = \zeta\delta$.

(4) If $\alpha\beta = \gamma\delta$, $\gamma\delta = \eta\zeta$, then $\alpha\beta = \eta\zeta$.

(5) $(\alpha, \beta, \gamma) . \text{E!} (\imath x) (\alpha x = \beta\gamma)$.

(6) $(\alpha, \beta) . \text{E!} (\imath x) (\alpha x = x\beta)$.

(7) Axiom of continuity: — Any progression has a limit (ordinal).

(8) Axiom of Archimedes

These axioms enable the values to be correlated one-one with real numbers so that if α^1 corresponds to α, etc.

$$\alpha\beta = \gamma\delta . \equiv . \alpha^1 - \beta^1 = \gamma^1 - \delta^1.$$

Henceforth we use α for the correlated real number α^1 also.

Having thus defined a way of measuring value we can now derive a way of measuring belief in general. If the option of α for certain is indifferent with that of β if p is true and γ if p is false,[5] we can define the subject's degree of belief in p as the ratio of the difference between α and γ to that between β and γ; which we must suppose the same for all α's, β's and γ's that satisfy the conditions. This amounts roughly to defining the degree of belief in p by the odds at which the subject would bet on p, the bet being conducted in terms of differences of value as defined. The definition only applies to partial belief and does not include certain beliefs; for belief of degree 1 in p, α for certain is indifferent with α if p and any β if not-p.

We are also able to define a very useful new idea — 'the degree of belief in p given q'. This does not mean the degree of belief in 'If p then q', or that in 'p entails q', or that which the subject would have in p if he knew q, or that which he ought to have. It roughly expresses the odds at which he would now bet on p, the bet only to be valid if q is true. Such conditional bets were often made in the eighteenth century.

The degree of belief in p given q is measured thus. Suppose the subject indifferent between the options (1) α if q true, β if q false, (2) γ if p true and q true, δ if p false and q true, β if q false. Then the degree of his belief in p given q is the ratio of the difference between α and δ to that between γ and δ, which we must suppose the same for any α, β, γ, δ which satisfy the given conditions. This is not the same as the degree to which he would believe p, if he believed q for certain; for knowledge of q might for psychological reasons profoundly alter his whole system of beliefs.

Each of our definitions has been accompanied by an axiom of consistency, and in so far as this is false, the notion of the corresponding degree of belief becomes invalid. This bears some analogy to the situation in regard to simultaneity discussed above.

[5] Here β must include the truth of p, γ its falsity; p need no longer be ethically neutral. But we have to assume that there is a world with any assigned value in which p is true, and one in which p is false.

I have not worked out the mathematical logic of this in detail, because this would, I think, be rather like working out to seven places of decimals a result only valid to two. My logic cannot be regarded as giving more than the sort of way it might work.

From these definitions and axioms it is possible to prove the fundamental laws of probable belief (degrees of belief lie between 0 and 1):

(1) Degree of belief in p + degree of belief in $\bar{p}$ = 1.

(2) Degree of belief in p given q + degree of belief in $\bar{p}$ given q = 1.

(3) Degree of belief in (p and q) = degree of belief in p × degree of belief in q given p.

(4) Degree of belief in (p and q) + degree of belief in (p and $\bar{q}$) = degree of belief in p.

The first two are immediate. (3) is proved as follows.

Let degree of belief in $p = x$, that in q given $p = y$.

Then ξ for certain $\equiv \xi + (1 - x)t$ if p true, $\xi - xt$ if p false, for any t.

$\xi + (1 - x)t$ if p true $\equiv$

$$\begin{cases} \xi + (1-x)t + (1-y)u & \text{if `}p\text{ and }q\text{' true,} \\ \xi + (1-x)t - yu & \text{if } p \text{ true } q \text{ false;} \end{cases} \qquad \text{for any } u.$$

Choose u so that $\xi + (1 - x)t - yu = \xi - xt$,

i.e. let $u = t/y (y \neq 0)$

Then ξ for certain $\equiv$

$$\begin{cases} \xi + (1-x)t + (1-y)t/y & \text{if } p \text{ and } q \text{ true} \\ \xi - xt & \text{otherwise,} \end{cases}$$

$$\therefore \text{degree of belief in `}p\text{ and }q\text{'} = \frac{xt}{t + (1-y)\,t/y} = xy \cdot (t \neq 0)$$

If $y = 0$, take $t = 0$.

Then ξ for certain $\equiv \xi$ if p true, ξ if p false

$\equiv \xi + u$ if p true, q true; ξ if p false, q false; ξ if p false

$\equiv \xi + u$, pq true; ξ, pq false

$\therefore$ degree of belief in $pq = 0$.

(4) follows from (2), (3) as follows: —

Degree of belief in pq = that in p × that in q given p, by (3). Similarly degree of belief in $p\bar{q}$ = that in p × that in $\bar{q}$ given p

$\therefore$ sum = degree of belief in p, by (2).

These are the laws of probability, which we have proved to be necessarily true of any consistent set of degrees of belief. Any definite set of degrees of belief which broke them would be inconsistent in the sense that it violated the laws of preference between options, such as that preferability is a transitive asymmetrical relation, and that if α is preferable to β, β for certain cannot be preferable to α if p, β if not-p. If anyone's mental condition violated these laws, his choice would depend on the precise form in which the options were offered him, which would be absurd. He could have a book made against him by a cunning bettor and would then stand to lose in any event.

We find, therefore, that a precise account of the nature of partial belief reveals that the laws of probability are laws of consistency, an extension to partial beliefs of formal logic, the logic of consistency. They do not depend for their meaning on any degree of belief in a proposition being uniquely determined as the rational one; they merely distinguish those sets of beliefs which obey them as consistent ones.

Having any definite degree of belief implies a certain measure of consistency, namely willingness to bet on a given proposition at the same odds for any stake, the stakes being measured in terms of ultimate values. Having degrees of belief obeying the laws of probability implies a further measure of consistency, namely such a consistency between the odds acceptable on different propositions as shall prevent a book being made against you.

Some concluding remarks on this section may not be out of place. First, it is based fundamentally on betting, but this will not seem unreasonable when it is seen that all our lives we are in a sense betting. Whenever we go to the station we are betting that a train will really run, and if we had not a sufficient degree of belief in this we should decline the bet and stay at home. The options God gives us are always conditional on our guessing whether a certain proposition is true. Secondly, it is based throughout on the idea of mathematical expectation; the dissatisfaction often felt with this idea is due mainly to the inaccurate measurement of goods. Clearly mathematical expectations in terms of money are not proper guides to conduct. It should be remembered, in judging my system, that in it value is actually defined by means of mathematical expectation in the case of beliefs of degree 1/2, and so may be expected to be scaled suitably for the valid application of the mathematical expectation in the case of other degrees of belief also.

Thirdly, nothing has been said about degrees of belief when the number of alternatives is infinite. About this I have nothing useful to say, except that I doubt if the mind is capable of contemplating more than a finite number of alternatives. It can consider questions to which an infinite number of answers are possible, but in order to consider the answers it must lump them into a finite number of groups. The difficulty becomes practically relevant when discussing induction, but even then there seems to me no need to introduce it. We can discuss whether past experience gives a high probability to the sun's rising to-morrow without bothering about what probability it gives to the sun's rising each morning for evermore. For this reason I cannot but feel that

Mr. Ritchie's discussion of the problem[6] is unsatisfactory; it is true that we can agree that inductive generalizations need have no finite probability, but particular expectations entertained on inductive grounds undoubtedly do have a high numerical probability in the minds of all of us. We all are more certain that the sun will rise to-morrow than that I shall not throw 12 with two dice the first time, i.e. we have a belief of higher degree than 35/36 in it. If induction ever needs a logical justification it is in connection with the probability of an event like this.

[6] A. D. Ritchie, "Induction and Probability," *Mind*, 1926, p. 318. The conclusion of the foregoing discussion may be simply put. If the problem of induction be stated to be "How can inductive generalizations acquire a large numerical probability?" then this is a pseudo-problem, because the answer is "They cannot." This answer is not, however, a denial of the validity of induction but is a direct consequence of the nature of probability. It still leaves untouched the real problem of induction which is "How can the probability of induction be increased?" and it leaves standing the whole of Keynes' discussion on this point.

10 *The Meaning of Probability*

JOHN O. WISDOM

"Probability" has been defined by Ramsey[1] as degree of rational belief. Keynes also held that his view made probability identical with degree of rational belief; but Ramsey takes this concept to be definable. He does not hold that the degree is to be found by introspection; he defines it by the behaviour of the believer. Thus a man believes that the probability of an ace is 1/6, i.e. he believes to the degree 1/6 that an ace will fall, if he would accept odds of 5 to 1 against it. Since beliefs are often not tested, Ramsey modifies this way of putting the matter by his suggestion that the degree of belief is measured by the behaviour of the believer in hypothetical circumstances — his degree of belief in an ace being measured by the odds he would accept.

Against Ramsey's view, there is the obvious objection that action is not always determined solely by the degree of belief, and this for two entirely different reasons.

Suppose you find some mushrooms that may be poisonous though this is not very likely — you assess the probability of their being poisonous at 1/100. On the other hand there are also gooseberries to be had, but they often disagree with you — you assess the probability of their giving you indigestion at 1/2. Which will you eat if you are very hungry? Your action is determined not by

From *Foundations of Inference in the Natural Sciences*, Methuen and Co., London, 1952, pp. 187–188. Reprinted by permission of the author.

[1] F. P. Ramsey, *The Foundations of Mathematics and Other Logical Essays*, London, 1931, VII, VIII.

the probabilities but by the values of the alternatives. The mushrooms are very unlikely to do you any harm, but if they do the result is disastrous; whereas the gooseberries are quite likely to give you a slight pain but this will pass. It seems to me that your possible actions can be compared numerically only by multiplying the probability of each alternative by what I would call a "coefficient of valuation". You would multiply the probability of death by poisoning by 0 and the probability of pain from gooseberries by 1. Then $1 \times 1/2$ is greater than $0 \times 1/100$ and hence act on the gooseberry alternative. This seems to me to answer to rational behaviour. Ramsey, it is true, discusses a similar point.[2] But it would seem that, if anything like this describes rational behaviour, then the notion of probability or of degrees of belief is *presupposed;* in short one bases rational behaviour upon rational belief — one does not identify them.

The other difficulty with Ramsey's view concerns the meaning of "rational belief". Now the only meaning I can find for "rational" in this connection is that the belief should correlate closely with the realities of the world. If a man has a belief to the degree 3/4 that some disaster will overtake him if he walks under a ladder, the degree of his belief does not correspond to the proportion of disasters that actually happen when people walk under ladders. Moreover, some people do in fact act on 'hunches', i.e. they act without relevant information. Their belief amounts to certainty, but there is no reason to suppose that there is a good correlation between such beliefs and realities. Irrational beliefs would seem to be those that ignore the demands of reality for some psychological reason. Certainly people do act in accordance with irrational belief, and I would concede that Ramsey's view of degrees of belief is correct, subject to two qualifications; action is the outcome of belief weighted with coefficients of valuation; and belief must not be restricted to being rational. What, then, is to be the criterion of rational belief or believing in accordance with reality? It must be belief in the light of *past experience* (of what is objective), which would seem to lead to the frequency theory — unless we take rational belief as being due to some faculty of the rational mind that gives probabilities *a priori*, and thus return to something like Keynes's view.*

[2] *Ibid.*, p. 175.

* It is worth referring to a formula devised by Ramsey to give the degree of belief in terms of the valuation of alternatives. The interesting feature of his result is that it involves such valuations and nothing else. In his proof he introduces the number of times a specific positive alternative would occur. But this number is irrelevant to his proof, because he does not contrast it with the number of negative alternatives. He should have noticed this, for the number divides out and does not appear in his final equation. In short, his formula makes no reference to the probabilities of the alternatives. And, just as I have maintained that probabilities should be weighted by coefficients of valuation, so I would hold here that a formula of valuation should be weighted by probabilities.

11 *The Meaning of Probability*

JOHN MAYNARD KEYNES

J'ai dit plus d'une fois qu'il faudrait une nouvelle espèce de logique, qui traiteroit des degrés de Probabilité. — LEIBNIZ

1. Part of our knowledge we obtain direct; and part by argument. The Theory of Probability is concerned with that part which we obtain by argument, and it treats of the different degrees in which the results so obtained are conclusive or inconclusive.

In most branches of academic logic, such as the theory of the syllogism or the geometry of ideal space, all the arguments aim at demonstrative certainty. They claim to be *conclusive*. But many other arguments are rational and claim some weight without pretending to be certain. In Metaphysics, in Science, and in Conduct, most of the arguments, upon which we habitually base our rational beliefs, are admitted to be inconclusive in a greater or less degree. Thus for a philosophical treatment of these branches of knowledge, the study of probability is required.

The course which the history of thought has led Logic to follow has encouraged the view that doubtful arguments are not within its scope. But in the actual exercise of reason we do not wait on certainty, or deem it irrational to depend on a doubtful argument. If logic investigates the general principles of valid thought, the study of arguments, to which it is rational to attach *some* weight, is as much a part of it as the study of those which are demonstrative.

2. The terms *certain* and *probable* describe the various degrees of rational belief about a proposition which different amounts of knowledge authorise us to entertain. All propositions are true or false, but the knowledge we have of them depends on our circumstances; and while it is often convenient to speak of propositions as certain or probable, this expresses strictly a relationship in which they stand to a *corpus* of knowledge, actual or hypothetical, and not a characteristic of the propositions in themselves. A proposition is capable at the same time of varying degrees of this relationship, depending upon the knowledge to which it is related, so that it is without significance to call a proposition probable unless we specify the knowledge to which we are relating it.

To this extent, therefore, probability may be called subjective. But in the sense important to logic, probability is not subjective. It is not, that is to say,

From *A Treatise on Probability*, Harper and Row, New York, 1962, pp. 3–8. Reprinted by permission of Macmillan & Company, Ltd.

subject to human caprice. A proposition is not probable because we think it so. When once the facts are given which determine our knowledge, what is probable or improbable in these circumstances has been fixed objectively, and is independent of our opinion. The Theory of Probability is logical, therefore, because it is concerned with the degree of belief which it is *rational* to entertain in given conditions, and not merely with the actual beliefs of particular individuals, which may or may not be rational.

Given the body of direct knowledge which constitutes our ultimate premisses, this theory tells us what further rational beliefs, certain or probable, can be derived by valid argument from our direct knowledge. This involves purely logical relations between the propositions which embody our direct knowledge and the propositions about which we seek indirect knowledge. What particular propositions we select as the premisses of *our* argument naturally depends on subjective factors peculiar to ourselves; but the relations, in which other propositions stand to these, and which entitle us to probable beliefs, are objective and logical.

3. Let our premisses consist of any set of propositions h, and our conclusion consist of any set of propositions a, then, if a knowledge of h justifies a rational belief in a of degree α, we say that there is a *probability-relation* of degree α between a and h.[1]

In ordinary speech we often describe the *conclusion* as being doubtful, uncertain, or only probable. But, strictly, these terms ought to be applied, either to the degree of our *rational belief* in the conclusion, or to the relation or argument between two sets of propositions, knowledge of which would afford grounds for a corresponding degree of rational belief.[2]

4. With the term "event," which has taken hitherto so important a place in the phraseology of the subject, I shall dispense altogether.[3] Writers on Probability have generally dealt with what they term the "happening" of "events." In the problems which they first studied this did not involve much departure from common usage. But these expressions are now used in a way which is vague and ambiguous; and it will be more than a verbal improvement to discuss the truth and the probability of *propositions* instead of the occurrence and the probability of *events*.[4]

5. These general ideas are not likely to provoke much criticism. In the ordinary course of thought and argument, we are constantly assuming that knowledge of one statement, while not *proving* the truth of a second, yields nevertheless *some ground* for believing it. We assert that we *ought* on the evidence to prefer such and such a belief. We claim rational grounds for assertions which are not

[1] This will be written $a/h = \alpha$.

[2] See also Chapter II. § 5.

[3] Except in those chapters (Chap. XVII., for example) where I am dealing chiefly with the work of others.

[4] The first writer I know of to notice this was Ancillon in *Doutes sur les bases du calcul des probabilités* (1794): "Dire qu'un fait passé, présent ou à venir est probable, c'est dire qu'une proposition est probable." The point was emphasized by Boole, *Laws of Thought*, pp. 7 and 167. See also Czuber, *Wahrscheinlichkeitsrechnung*, vol. i. p. 5, and Stumpf, *Über den Begriff der mathematischen Wahrscheinlichkeit*.

conclusively demonstrated. We allow, in fact, that statements may be unproved, without, for that reason, being unfounded. And it does not seem on reflection that the information we convey by these expressions is wholly subjective. When we argue that Darwin gives valid grounds for our accepting his theory of natural selection, we do not simply mean that we are psychologically inclined to agree with him; it is certain that we also intend to convey our belief that we are acting rationally in regarding his theory as probable. We believe that there is some real objective relation between Darwin's evidence and his conclusions, which is independent of the mere fact of our belief, and which is just as real and objective, though of a different degree, as that which would exist if the argument were as demonstrative as a syllogism. We are claiming, in fact, to cognise correctly a logical connection between one set of propositions which we call our evidence and which we suppose ourselves to know, and another set which we call our conclusions, and to which we attach more or less weight according to the grounds supplied by the first. It is this type of objective relation between sets of propositions — the type which we claim to be correctly perceiving when we make such assertions as these — to which the reader's attention must be directed.

6. It is not straining the use of words to speak of this as the relation of probability. It is true that mathematicians have employed the term in a narrower sense; for they have often confined it to the limited class of instances in which the relation is adapted to an algebraical treatment. But in common usage the word has never received this limitation.

Students of probability in the sense which is meant by the authors of typical treatises on *Wahrscheinlichkeitsrechnung* or *Calcul des probabilités*, will find that I do eventually reach topics with which they are familiar. But in making a serious attempt to deal with the fundamental difficulties with which all students of mathematical probabilities have met and which are notoriously unsolved, we must begin at the beginning (or almost at the beginning) and treat our subject widely. As soon as mathematical probability ceases to be the merest algebra or pretends to guide our decisions, it immediately meets with problems against which its own weapons are quite powerless. And even if we wish later on to use probability in a narrow sense, it will be well to know first what it means in the widest.

7. Between two sets of propositions, therefore, there exists a relation, in virtue of which, if we know the first, we can attach to the latter some degree of rational belief. This relation is the subject-matter of the logic of probability.

A great deal of confusion and error has arisen out of a failure to take due account of this *relational* aspect of probability. From the premisses "*a* implies *b*" and "*a* is true," we can conclude something about *b* — namely that *b* is true — which does not involve *a*. But, if *a* is so related to *b*, that a knowledge of it renders a probable belief in *b* rational, we cannot conclude anything whatever about *b* which has not reference to *a*; and it is not true that every set of self-consistent premisses which includes *a* has this same relation to *b*. It is as useless, therefore, to say "*b* is probable" as it would be to say "*b* is equal," or "*b* is greater than," and as unwarranted to conclude that, because *a* makes *b* probable, therefore *a* and *c* together make *b* probable, as to argue that because *a* is less than *b*, therefore *a* and *c* together are less than *b*.

Thus, when in ordinary speech we name some opinion as probable without further qualification, the phrase is generally elliptical. We mean that it is probable when certain considerations, implicitly or explicitly present to our minds at the moment, are taken into account. We use the word for the sake of shortness, just as we speak of a place as being three miles distant, when we mean three miles distant from where we are then situated, or from some starting-point to which we tacitly refer. No proposition is in itself either probable or improbable, just as no place can be intrinsically distant; and the probability of the same statement varies with the evidence presented, which is, as it were, its origin of reference. We may fix our attention on our own knowledge and, treating this as our origin, consider the probabilities of all other suppositions, — according to the usual practice which leads to the elliptical form of common speech; or we may, equally well, fix it on a proposed conclusion and consider what degree of probability this would derive from various sets of assumptions, which might constitute the *corpus* of knowledge of ourselves or others, or which are merely hypotheses.

Reflection will show that this account harmonises with familiar experience. There is nothing novel in the supposition that the probability of a theory turns upon the evidence by which it is supported; and it is common to assert that an opinion was probable on the evidence at first to hand, but on further information was untenable. As our knowledge or our hypothesis changes, our conclusions have new probabilities, not in themselves, but relatively to these new premisses. New logical relations have now become important, namely those between the conclusions which we are investigating and our new assumptions; but the old relations between the conclusions and the former assumptions still exist and are just as real as these new ones. It would be as absurd to deny that an opinion *was* probable, when at a later stage certain objections have come to light, as to deny, when we have reached our destination, that it was ever three miles distant; and the opinion still *is* probable in relation to the old hypotheses, just as the destination is still three miles distant from our starting-point.

8. A *definition* of probability is not possible, unless it contents us to define degrees of the probability-relation by reference to degrees of rational belief. We cannot analyse the probability-relation in terms of simpler ideas. As soon as we have passed from the logic of implication and the categories of truth and falsehood to the logic of probability and the categories of knowledge, ignorance, and rational belief, we are paying attention to a new logical relation in which, although it is logical, we were not previously interested, and which cannot be explained or defined in terms of our previous notions.

This opinion is, from the nature of the case, incapable of positive proof. The presumption in its favour must arise partly out of our failure to find a definition, and partly because the notion presents itself to the mind as something new and independent. If the statement that an opinion was probable on the evidence at first to hand, but became untenable on further information, is not solely concerned with psychological belief, I do not know how the element of logical doubt is to be defined, or how its substance is to be stated, in terms of the other indefinables of formal logic. The attempts at definition, which have been made hitherto, will be criticised in later chapters. I do not believe that any of them accurately represent that particular logical relation which we have in our minds when we speak of the probability of an argument.

In the great majority of cases the term "probable" seems to be used consistently by different persons to describe the same concept. Differences of opinion have not been due, I think, to a radical ambiguity of language. In any case a desire to reduce the indefinables of logic can easily be carried too far. Even if a definition is discoverable in the end, there is no harm in postponing it until our enquiry into the object of definition is far advanced. In the case of "probability" the object before the mind is so familiar that the danger of misdescribing its qualities through lack of a definition is less than if it were a highly abstract entity far removed from the normal channels of thought.

12 *Probability as a Unique Logical Relation*

ERNEST NAGEL

A number of modern writers, conscious of the difficulties in the classical view of probability as a measure of strength of belief, have advanced the view that probability is an objective logical relation between propositions analogous to the relation of deducibility or entailment. According to this version, a degree of probability measures what is often called "the logical distance" between a conclusion and its premisses. The evaluation of a degree of probability therefore depends upon recognizing the inclusion, exclusion, or overlapping of logical ranges of possible facts. Though varying considerably among themselves, something like this view (which has had its forerunners in Leibniz and Bolzano) is central to von Kries, Keynes,* J. Nicod, F. Waismann, and several other writers. Only the standpoint of Keynes will be examined here.

Reprinted from *Principles of the Theory of Probability* (In *International Encyclopedia of Unified Science*, I, No. 6, 1939, pp. 48–50) by Ernest Nagel by permission of The University of Chicago Press and the author.

* [Ed. note: See the selection from Keynes in this Section.]

For Keynes, probability is a unique, unanalyzable relation between two propositions. No proposition as such is probable; it has a degree of probability only with respect to specified evidence. This relation of probability is not a degree of subjective expectation; on the contrary, it is only when we have perceived this relation between evidence and conclusion that we can attach some degree of "rational belief" to the latter. (As already noted, Keynes's formulation of his view is not unambiguous. His occasional language to the contrary notwithstanding, it does not seem likely that he regards his probability relation as a syntactical one. The present writer is inclined to the opinion that it is a semantical relation.) It is characteristic of Keynes's standpoint that the *secondary* proposition, which asserts that a proposition p has the probability relation of degree α to the proposition h, can and must be known to be true "with the highest degree of rational certainty." Such a highest degree of rational certainty is obtainable, according to Keynes, when we see that the conclusion of a syllogism follows from its premisses, as well as when we see that a conclusion "nearly follows" from its premisses with degree α of probability. However, degrees of probability are not quantitative and are not in general capable of measurement; indeed, according to Keynes, probabilities cannot in general be even ordered serially, although in some cases they are comparable. The comparison of probabilities, whenever this is possible, is effected with the help of the modified Principle of Indifference* mentioned above; and the judgments of relevance which the principle presupposes are themselves direct judgments of degrees of probability. In terms of such an apparatus of concepts, Keynes develops a calculus which formulates the relations between comparable probabilities, and finally explains how and under what limited circumstances numerical values may be assigned to degrees of probability.

Although Keynes avoids some of the difficulties of the classical view of probability, his general standpoint has difficulties of its own. Omitting all discussion of the technical difficulties in his calculus, we shall confine ourselves to a brief mention of three central issues.

a) On Keynes's view we must have a "logical intuition" of the probable relations between propositions. However, few if any students can be found who claim for themselves such an intuitive power; and no way has been proposed to check and control the alleged deliverances of such direct perceptions in cases where students claim it. Moreover, the possession or lack of this power is wholly irrelevant in the actual estimation of probabilities by the various sciences. No physicist will seriously propose to decide whether two quantum transitions are equiprobable by appealing to a direct perception of probability relations; and, as N. R. Campbell remarked, "anyone who proposed to attribute to the chances of a given deflection of an α-ray in passing through a given film any sense other than that determined by frequency could convince us of nothing but his ignorance of physics."

b) Since on Keynes's view numerical probabilities can be introduced only

* [Ed. note: See the Nagel selection entitled "The Classical Conception of Probability" in this Section.]

when equiprobable alternatives are present, he cannot account for the use of numerical probabilities when such an analysis is not possible. Moreover, like the classic interpretation, Keynes cannot establish any connection between numerical probabilities and relative frequencies of occurrences. His theory, when strictly interpreted, is incapable of application to the problems discussed in physics and statistics, and at least from this point of view remains a vestal virgin.

c) On Keynes's view it is significant to assign a probability, with respect to given evidence, to a proposition dealing with a single occasion. For example, it is permissible to declare that on given evidence the probability of a given coin falling head uppermost *on the next toss* is 1/2. However, the coin, after it is thrown and comes to rest, will show a head or it will show a tail; and no matter what the issue of the given throw is, the probability of obtaining a head on the initial evidence is and remains 1/2. No empirical evidence is therefore relevant either for the confirmation or for the disconfirmation of that probability judgment, unless we invoke indirectly a relative frequency in a group of statements — which would be contrary to Keynes's intent. But this is to fly in the face of every rule of sound scientific procedure. A conception of probability according to which we cannot in principle control by experiment and observation the probability statements we make is not a conception which recommends itself as germane to scientific inquiry.

II
Problems of Confirmation Theory

II

Problems of Confirmation Theory

Introduction

The Analysis of Confirmation

Carnap, in his article entitled "Truth and Confirmation" reprinted here, emphasizes the importance of distinguishing between the notions of truth and confirmation and points out that many confusions are generated by the failure to do so. He adopts the definition of "truth" provided by the Polish semanticist and logician Alfred Tarski, a definition which is considered by many students of the subject to be free from the vagueness and ambiguity of other proposed definitions and to be logically adequate. It is important to emphasize that Tarski has given an analysis of the *meaning* of "truth" and that his definition must in no sense be taken as an account of how we *know* what is true. Thus, even if Tarski's analysis of the concept of truth is adequate, an adequate analysis of the concept of confirmation remains to be given. It will be evident to the reader that Carnap does not attempt to provide such an analysis in this article.

An adequate analysis of the concept of confirmation must deal with three problems. First of all, it must give an account of qualitative confirmation. In other words, it must provide an analysis of the following expression where e is an evidential statement and h is a hypothesis:

(1) e confirms h

Secondly, an analysis of the comparative uses of "confirm" is required. Consider the following expressions:

(2) (a) e confirms h_1 more than e confirms h_2

(2) (b) e_1 confirms h more than e_2 confirms h

Expressions of this sort are certainly used in scientific inquiry. For example, it might be said that Einstein's theory is more confirmed in the light of present evidence than it was 50 years ago in the light of the evidence available at that time. But although such expressions are used in science, it is by no means clear what they mean. An adequate analysis of the concept of confirmation must make clear what it means to say that an evidential statement confirms one hypothesis more than another hypothesis or that one evidential statement confirms a hypothesis more than other evidential statements do. It should be pointed out that if an adequate analysis of (1) is provided, this in no way means that an adequate analysis of (2) (a) or (2) (b) has been provided.

Finally, an analysis of the concept of confirmation must include an analysis of the quantitative sense of "confirmation," i.e. an analysis of expressions of this sort:

(3) *e* confirms *h* to degree *x*

Again it should be emphasized that an adequate analysis of (2)(a) and (2)(b) does not necessarily provide an adequate analysis of (3).

Qualitative Confirmation

The problem of saying exactly what constitutes confirmatory evidence for a hypothesis is much more difficult than it first appears to be. Consider the following two requirements:

(1) Whatever confirms a hypothesis confirms the logical consequences of the hypothesis.

(2) Whatever confirms the logical consequences of a hypothesis confirms the hypothesis.

Now these requirements seem to be very reasonable. Consider the first requirement. We certainly suppose that if a statement is confirmed, then any logically weaker statement is confirmed. And the second requirement seems just as reasonable. Certainly an essential part of the confirmation of hypotheses in science is the testing of their logical consequences. Indeed, this method of confirmation is the method expounded by standard textbooks on the logic of science.[1] But these two requirements taken together have paradoxical consequences.

Let

P = The Universe is in a steady state.

Q = The lights are on in this room.

Now on the basis of (2) "*P* and *Q*" is confirmed by "*Q*" if "*Q*" is confirmed, and on the basis of (1) "*P*" is then confirmed since "*P*" is a consequence of "*P* and *Q*." Hence, if it is confirmed that the lights are on in this room, the hypothesis that the Universe is in a steady state is confirmed. But it seems paradoxical in the extreme that we should be able to confirm a speculative theory of cosmology by turning on a light.

It might be supposed that this problem could be avoided if the second requirement were modified. The trouble with the example, it might be argued, is that "*P*" has nothing to do with the deduction of "*Q*": "*P*," in other words, plays no role in the establishment of "*Q*"; hence the confirmation of "*Q*" endows the compound statement "*P* and *Q*" with no credibility; hence credibility cannot

[1] See M. R. Cohen and E. Nagel, *An Introduction to Logic and Scientific Method* (New York: Harcourt, Brace and Co., 1934), pp. 202–206.

be transmitted to the other component of the statement, namely "*P*." One might argue, therefore, that the requirement should be tightened up in order to make every component of the hypothesis essential for the deduction. Thus (2) might be replaced by (2′):

(2′) Whatever confirms the logical sequences of a hypothesis confirms the hypothesis only if every component of the hypothesis is essential for the deduction.

Unfortunately, however, although this requirement rules out the kind of result mentioned above, other unacceptable results are easily generated. Let

P = The Universe is in a steady state.

Q = The lights are on in this room.

R = Some roses are red.

Once again, if "*Q*" is confirmed, then "*P*" is confirmed; i.e. if it is confirmed that the lights are on in this room, then the hypothesis that the Universe is in a steady state is confirmed. This can be seen clearly if we consider that on the basis of (2′) the hypothesis "*R* and (if *R*, then *P*) and (if *P*, then *Q*)" is confirmed by "*Q*" if "*Q*" is confirmed, and that on the basis of (1) "*P*" is then confirmed. In this case every component of the hypothesis is essential for the deduction of "*Q*" yet nevertheless a paradoxical result is generated.

Perhaps it might be said that (2) has not been tightened up sufficiently; that the permissible confirmatory deductions should be limited even more. It has been suggested by Goodman, for example, that the paradox can be removed by requiring that a hypothesis is confirmed only by statements that are derivable from it by instantiation.[2] Thus a hypothesis that says something about all things is confirmed by an evidence statement that says *that* about one thing. For example, "All copper conducts electricity" is confirmed by a piece of copper that conducts electricity. Thus Goodman's suggestion amounts to the replacement of (2) by (2″).

(2″) Whatever confirms the logical consequences of a hypothesis confirms the hypothesis only if the consequences follow from it by instantiation.

This requirement would surely eliminate the paradox of the steady state, but it would do so at a great price. It would seem to rule out the possibility of confirming theoretical hypotheses in science, i.e. hypotheses couched in theoretical, in contrast to observational, terms. For obviously the instantiations of theoretical hypotheses would not be in terms of observables and hence could not be confirmed by empirical observation. But since hypotheses of this sort are fundamental to theoretical science, the use of (2″) would have far reaching and undesirable consequences. What is needed, surely, is some formulation of (2)

[2] Nelson Goodman, *Fact, Fiction and Forecast* (Cambridge: Harvard University Press, 1955), p. 71.

that does not rule out all of theoretical science as unconfirmable and yet excludes the steady state paradox. Up till now such a formulation has not been produced.

Even though few of us would want to embrace (2″), we surely would want to say that verified instantiated consequences do confirm a hypothesis. In other words, it does seem quite plausible to suppose that verified instantiated consequences are a sufficient, but not a necessary, condition for the confirmation of a hypothesis. We might formulate our belief by means of the following requirement:

(3) A hypothesis of the form "All *A* is *B*" is confirmed by an object that is both *A* and *B*.

But this innocent and eminently reasonable requirement, when combined with another seemingly equally reasonable requirement, leads to another paradox of confirmation. Consider the following requirement:

(4) Whatever confirms a hypothesis confirms a logically equivalent hypothesis and conversely.

This requirement seems quite acceptable. Surely, hypotheses which are logically equivalent in form have the same logical content. Differences in form should make no difference in what confirms the seemingly invariant content of logically equivalent hypotheses.

But now consider the hypothesis "All ravens are black" which on the basis of (3) would be confirmed by an object that is a raven and black. This hypothesis is equivalent to "All non-black things are non-ravens." This, by (3), would be confirmed by an object that is non-black and not a raven. Then by (4) "All ravens are black" would be confirmed by an object that is not black and not a raven, e.g. a white piece of chalk, a red rose, a blue sky, etc.

The solution of this paradox, the so-called "raven paradox," can be approached in different ways. One obvious way is to eliminate one or the other of the requirements which generated the paradox. For example, one might eliminate requirement (4). This would surely prevent the paradox, but to give up this requirement is almost as unacceptable or counter-intuitive as is the paradox itself. This holds true for the elimination of requirement (3) also. A seemingly more promising approach would be to keep the two requirements intact and to explain away the paradoxical results. One might, for example, endeavor to show either that the paradoxical results have a perfectly reasonable explanation, i.e. the apparently paradoxical results are just what one should expect, or that the paradoxical results are based on incorrect assumptions and that once these assumptions are exposed the paradox disappears.

The former approach has been used by Janina Hosiasson-Lindenbaum and and her proposed solution is expounded and critically examined by Carl Hempel in this section. Hempel himself, however, takes the latter approach. He argues that the paradox is a "psychological illusion" based on certain untenable logical assumptions. Hempel goes on to give a rigorous formulation of the requirements for qualitative confirmation and argues that these requirements avoid the difficulty of other formulations. There is, however, a serious limitation to Hempel's formulation (which he is the first to admit) even if it is free from these other problems. Hempel's formulation of the requirement for qualitative confirmation is restricted to languages with a simple logical structure. Thus it would not be applicable to most of the hypotheses of theoretical science, e.g. hypotheses couched in terms of theoretical predicates or mathematical notation.

Comparative Confirmation

That comparative judgments of confirmation are legitimately made in everyday life and science is obvious. Whether they can *always* be legitimately made is not obvious, however, and whether the notion of comparative confirmation can be given a precise meaning is problematic.

Certain situations do not seem to permit of comparative judgments of confirmation. Consider, for example, the following cases:

(1) One investigator is interested in testing the hypothesis "All Irishmen are red-headed." He examines one thousand Irishmen with positive results.

(2) Another investigator is interested in testing the same hypothesis. He, however, systematically varies the conditions of the test. He examines 10 old Irishmen, 10 young Irishmen, 10 brown-eyed Irishmen, 10 blue-eyed Irishmen, 10 light-complexioned Irishmen, and 10 dark-complexioned Irishmen. His results are also positive.

Notice that in these two cases there are two different ways of increasing the probability of a hypothesis: first, by increasing the *number* of positive instances; and second, by varying the *kind* of positive instances. Now, although these both seem to be legitimate ways of increasing the degree of confirmation of a hypothesis, there is doubt whether it is possible to say which way increases the degree of confirmation more; e.g. whether "All Irishmen are red-headed" is more confirmed by the one hundred non-varied positive instances or by the sixty varied positive instances.

Ernest Nagel, in the selection that follows (pp. 184–194), argues against the possibility of placing in serial order the amount of confirmation afforded a hypothesis such as Newton's theory by different sets of evidence where these sets differ with respect to the variety and amount of positive instances. Carnap's answer to Nagel's argument can be found in Section I of this book.[3] Carnap argues that his system of inductive logic is able to take into account the variety of instances and that it is possible to rank the confirmation afforded a hypothesis by evidence that differs in amount and variety.

It has already been noted, however, that Carnap's system presupposes a precisely formalized language which is much simpler than the language of science. This simple language, it should be recalled, does not contain relational predicates let alone metric terms. It has also been noted that Carnap's scheme does not allow for the confirmation of universal hypotheses. It seems unlikely, therefore, that laws governing the complex physical phenomena of which

[3] See section 15 of Carnap's paper, "On Inductive Logic."

Nagel speaks—namely, planetary motion and capillarity phenomena—could be formulated in this language. Moreover, it is certain that no general laws about these phenomena could be confirmed in Carnap's scheme. But general laws about these phenomena are surely what Nagel has in mind. It seems, therefore, that Carnap cannot meet Nagel's argument.

The problem of trying to give a precise meaning to the comparative sense of "confirmation" is closely connected with the difficulty of ranking the confirmation afforded a hypothesis by different sets of positive evidence which vary with respect to amount, variety, and other factors. Thus, it seems possible to specify with some precision what it means to say that e_1 confirms h more than e_2 if the only relevant difference between e_1 and e_2 is that e_1 contains more positive instances of h than does e_2. Similarly, it seems possible to specify with some precision what it means to say that e_1 confirms h more than e_2 if the only relevant difference between e_1 and e_2 is that e_1 contains a greater variety of instances of h than does e_2. But when, for example, e_1 and e_2 differ with respect to both amount and variety of instances it is difficult to say what "e_1 confirms h more than e_2" does mean.

The usual attempts to give a precise account of the comparative sense of "confirmation" either operate with a formalized language which is much simpler than the language of science or they ignore all factors except the amount of evidence. These attempts, therefore, have serious theoretical and practical limitations even if they are free from other problems.

Quantitative Confirmation

A necessary condition for an adequate account of the quantitative sense of "confirmation" is an adequate account of the comparative sense (although an adequate account of the quantitative sense of "confirmation" is not a necessary condition for an adequate account of the comparative sense). We can predict with some certainty, therefore, that the limitations which plague accounts of the comparative sense of "confirmation" will affect accounts of the quantitative sense of "confirmation."

We have already seen the limitations of Carnap's account. Hempel and Paul Oppenheim in the selection that follows (pp. 194–211) give an explication of the concept of the degree of confirmation that has similar limitations. Hempel and Oppenheim define "degree of confirmation" in terms of the empirical frequency of events rather than in terms of *a priori* assignments of probabilities to "state-descriptions" as does Carnap. But their explication, like Carnap's, presupposes a simple formalized language which contains neither relational predicates nor metric terms. And unlike Carnap, they make no attempt to deal with confirmation-increasing factors such as the variety of instances. It should also be noted that their account, like Carnap's, has a counter-intuitive result for universal hypotheses: If the evidence for a universal hypothesis is all positive, the degree of confirmation is 1 no matter how much or how little evidence is involved.

John Kemeny and Oppenheim (pp. 212–230) avoid some of the problems which beset both Hempel and Oppenheim, and Carnap. Their formulation of the quantitative sense of "confirmation" does not presuppose a language with restrictions on the logical complexity of the predicates involved. Moreover, they avoid the paradoxical results of both Hempel and Oppenheim's, and Carnap's systems for universal hypotheses. Nevertheless, although the language of their system is richer than the simple languages of either Carnap, or Hempel and Oppenheim, it is still far less rich than is the language of science. Their system, for example, does not allow for the metric terms that are so essential for theoretical physics and other advanced science. Furthermore, Kemeny and Oppenheim do not purport to give a complete explication of the concept of degree of confirmation. Rather they purport to explicate the concept of degree of factual support which, as they themselves emphasize, is only *one* aspect of the concept of degree of confirmation. Thus Kemeny and Oppenheim take into account only the amount of evidence for a hypothesis; as in the case of Hempel and Oppenheim they do not concern themselves with either the variety of the evidence or with other factors which increase the degree of confirmation.

To point out the shortcomings of attempts to analyze the notion of confirmation is not, however, to detract from the results already achieved. The pioneering efforts of Carnap, Hempel, Kemeny and Oppenheim have served, and will continue to serve, as a stimulus and a taking-off point for future investigation. Inductive logic is in this respect not unlike empirical science: present investigators build, expand, and improve upon earlier work; their progress would not be possible without the earlier work despite all of its limitations.

13 *Truth and Confirmation*

RUDOLF CARNAP

The difference between the two concepts 'true' and 'confirmed' ('verified', 'scientifically accepted') is important and yet frequently not sufficiently recognized. 'True' in its customary meaning is a time-independent term; i.e., it is employed without a temporal specification. For example, one cannot say "such and such a statement is true today (was true yesterday; will be true tomorrow)" but only "the statement is true." 'Confirmed', however, is time-dependendent. When we say "such and such a statement is confirmed to a high degree by observations" then we must add: "at such and such a time." This is the pragmatical concept of degree of confirmation. The semantical concept of the degree of confirmation of a statement *with respect to other statements* which formulate the evidence is again independent of the temporal aspect; in using this concept we are merely asserting an analytic or logical truth which is a sheer consequence of the definition of 'degree of confirmation' (weight, strength of evidence) presupposed.

As is well known, the concept of truth, when used without restrictions (as in conversational language), leads to contradictions (the so-called antinomies). For this reason some logicians in recent times have been rather diffident in regard to this concept and have tried to avoid it. At times it was considered altogether impossible to establish an exact and consistent definition of truth (in its customary meaning); this has brought it about that the term 'true' was used in the sense of the entirely different concept 'confirmed'. But this leads to considerable deviations from the common usage of language. Thus one would find it necessary to abandon, e.g., the principle of the excluded middle. This principle maintains for every statement that either it or its negation is true. But as to the vast majority of statements, neither they nor their negations are confirmed or scientifically accepted. Tarski,[1] however, succeeded in establishing an unobjectionable definition of truth which explicates adequately the meaning of this word in common language (but of course is also bound to restrict its employment, as compared with common usage, in order to eliminate the contradictions). Hence the term 'true' should properly no longer be used in the sense of 'confirmed'. We must not expect the definition of truth to furnish a criterion of confirmation such as is sought in epistemological analyses. On the basis of this definition the question regarding the criterion of truth can be given only a trivial answer, which consists in the statement itself. Thus, from the definition of truth we can conclude only, e.g.: The statement "Snow is white" is true if and only if snow is white. This conclusion is surely correct; which shows that the definition was adequately established. But the question of the criterion of confirmation is thereby left unanswered.

The neglect of the distinction between truth and knowledge of truth (verification, confirmation) is widespread and has led to serious confusions. Perhaps the following analysis will help towards a clarification.

Let us consider the following four sentences:

1. "The substance in this vessel is alcohol."
2. "The sentence 'the substance in this vessel is alcohol' is true."
3. "*X* knows (at the present moment) that the substance in this vessel is alcohol."
4. "*X* knows that the sentence 'the substance in this vessel is alcohol' is true."

[1] Cf. Tarski's "The Semantic Concept of Truth and the Foundations of Semantics," in *Readings in Philosophical Analysis*, H. Feigl and W. Sellers, eds., Appleton-Century-Crofts.

First a remark concerning the interpretation of the term 'to know' as it occurs in (3) and (4), and generally as it is applied with respect to synthetic propositions concerning physical things. In which of the following two senses (*a*) and (*b*) should it be understood?

a. It is meant in the sense of *perfect knowledge*, that is, knowledge which cannot possibly be refuted or even weakened by any future experience.
b. It is meant in the sense of *imperfect knowledge*, that is, knowledge which has only a certain degree of assurance, not absolute certainty, and which therefore may possibly be refuted or weakened by future experience. (This is meant as a theoretical possibility; if the degree of assurance is sufficiently high we may, for all practical purposes, disregard the possibility of a future refutation.)

I am in agreement with practically everybody that sentences of the kind (3) should always be understood in the sense (*b*), not (*a*). For the following discussion I presuppose this interpretation of the sentences (3) and (4).

Now the decisive point for our whole problem is this: *the sentences* (*1*) *and* (*2*) *are logically equivalent;* in other words, they entail each other; they are merely different formulations for the same factual content; nobody may accept the one and reject the other; if used as communications, both sentences convey the same information though in different form. The difference in form is indeed important; the two sentences belong to two quite different parts of the language. (In my terminology, (1) belongs to the object part of the language, (2) to its meta-part, and, more specifically, to its semantical part.) This difference in form, however, does not prevent their logical equivalence. The fact that this equivalence has been overlooked by many authors (e.g., C. S. Peirce and John Dewey,[2] Reichenbach,[3] and Neurath[4]) seems to be the source of many misunderstandings in current discussions on the concept of truth. It must be admitted that any statement of the logical equivalence of two sentences in English can only be made with certain qualifications, because of the ambiguity of ordinary words, here the word 'true'. The equivalence holds certainly if 'true' is understood in the sense of the semantical concept of truth.[5] I believe with Tarski that this is also the sense in which the word 'true' is mostly used both in everyday life and in science.[6] However, this is a psychological or historical ques-

[2] See John Dewey, *Logic: The Theory of Inquiry*, 1938, p. 345, footnote 6, with quotations from Peirce.

[3] Hans Reichenbach, *Experience and Prediction*, 1938; see §§ 22, 35.

[4] Otto Neurath, "Universal Jargon and Terminology," *Proceedings Aristotelian Society*, 1940–41, pp. 127–148; see especially pp. 138 f.

[5] For this point and the subsequent discussion compare Alfred Tarski, "The Semantic Conception of Truth and the Foundations of Semantics" in *Readings in Philosophical Analysis*, H. Feigl and W. Sellers, eds., Appleton-Century-Crofts, where a number of common misunderstandings are cleared up. Compare also my *Introduction to Semantics*, 1942; see p. 26: "We use the term ['true'] here in such a sense that *to assert that a sentence is true means the same as to assert the sentence itself*."

[6] Arne Ness has expressed doubts in this respect; but he has admitted that in 90% of the cases examined by him the persons questioned reacted in the sense of equivalence. See Tarski, with reference to Ness.

tion, which we need not here examine further. In this discussion, at any rate, I use the word 'true' in the semantical sense.

The sentences (1) and (3) obviously do not say the same. This leads to the important result, which is rather obvious but often overlooked, that *the sentences (2) and (3) have different contents.* (3) and (4) are logically equivalent since (1) and (2) are. It follows that (2) and (4) have different contents. It is now clear that a certain terminological possibility cannot be accepted. "If we constantly bear in mind that the acceptance of any proposition may be reversed," in other words, that we have always to use interpretation (*b*), not (*a*), "then we might instead call an accepted proposition a true proposition." This usage, however, would be quite misleading because it would blur the fundamental distinction between (2) and (3).

Felix Kaufmann [7] comes to the conclusion that my conception, although in agreement with "the traditional view", "is incompatible with the principle of inquiry which rules out the invariable truth of synthetic propositions. It is impossible for an empirical procedure to confirm to any degree something which is excluded by a general (constitutive) principle of empirical procedure. *Knowledge of invariable truth of synthetic propositions (whether perfect or imperfect) is unobtainable, not because of limitations of human knowledge, but because the conception of such knowledge involves a contradiction in terms.*" This reasoning seems to me based on the wrong identification of truth with perfect knowledge, hence, in the example, the identification of (2) with (3) in interpretation (*a*). The principles of scientific procedure do indeed rule out perfect knowledge but not truth. They cannot rule out (2), because this says nothing else than sentence (1), which, I suppose, will be acknowledged by all of us as empirically meaningful. When Kaufmann declares that even imperfect knowledge of truth is unobtainable, then this means that even imperfect knowledge of (2) is unobtainable and hence that an event as described in (4) even in interpretation (*b*), cannot occur. However, as soon as the event (3) occurs (now always assuming interpretation (*b*)), which nobody regards as impossible, the event (4) thereby occurs too; for the sentences (3) and (4) describe merely in different words one and the same event, a certain state of knowledge of the person *X*.

Let us represent in a slightly different way the objection raised against the concept of truth, in order to examine the presupposition underlying its chief argument. The objection concerns the concept of truth in its semantical sense; Kaufmann uses here the term "invariable truth" because truth in this sense is independent of person and state of knowledge, and hence of time. (Incidentally, the word "invariable" is not quite appropriate; it would be more correct to say instead that truth is a "time-independent" or "non-temporal" concept. The volume of a body *b* may or may not change in the course of time; hence we may say that it is variable or that it is invariable. The sentence "the volume of *b* at the time *t* is *v*" is meaningful but without the phrase "at the time *t*" it would be incomplete. On the other hand, the formulation "the sentence *S* is

[7] *Philosophy and Phenomenological Research*, Vol. II (1942), pp. 457–471; and, especially Vol. IV (1944), pp. 267–284.

true at the time *t*" is meaningless; when the phrase "at the time *t*" is omitted we obtain a complete statement. Therefore, to speak of change or non-change, of variability or invariability of truth, is not quite correct.) Now Kaufmann, Reichenbach,[8] Neurath,[9] and other authors are of the opinion that the semantical concept of truth, at least in its application to synthetic sentences concerning physical things, ought to be abandoned because it can never be decided with absolute certainty for any given sentence whether it is true or not. I agree that this can never be decided. But is the inference valid which leads from this result to the conclusion that the concept of truth is inadmissible? It seems that this inference presupposes the following major premise *P*: "A term (predicate) must be rejected if it is such that we can never decide with absolute certainty for any given instance whether or not the term applies." The argumentation by the authors would be valid if this principle *P* were presupposed, and I do not see how they reach the conclusion without this presupposition. However, I think that the authors do not actually believe in the principle *P*. In any case, it can easily be seen that the acceptance of *P* would lead to absurd consequences. For instance, we can never decide with absolute certainty whether a given substance is alcohol or not; thus, according to the principle *P*, the term "alcohol" would have to be rejected. And the same holds obviously for *every* term of the physical language. Thus I suppose that we all agree that instead of *P* the following weaker principle *P** must be used; this is indeed one of the principles of empiricism or of scientific inquiry: "A term (predicate) is a legitimate scientific term (has cognitive content, is empirically meaningful) if and only if a sentence applying the term to a given instance can possibly be confirmed to at least some degree." "Possibly" means here "if certain specifiable observations occur"; "to some degree" is not meant as necessarily implying a numerical evaluation. *P** is a simplified formulation of the "requirement of confirmability"[10] which, I think, is essentially in agreement with Reichenbach's "first principle of the probability theory of meaning,"[11] both being liberalized versions of the older requirement of verifiability as stated by C. S. Peirce, Wittgenstein, and others.[12] Now, according to *P**, 'al-

[8] Reichenbach, *op. cit.*, footnote 20, p. 188: "Thus there are left no propositions at all which can be absolutely verified. The predicate of truth-value of a proposition, therefore [!], is a mere fictive quality, its place is in an ideal world of science only, whereas actual science cannot make use of it. Actual science instead employs throughout the predicate of weight."

[9] I agree with Neurath when he rejects the possibility of absolutely certain knowledge, for example, in his criticism of Schlick, who believed that the knowledge of certain basic sentences ("Konstatierungen") was absolutely certain. See Neurath, "Radikaler Physikalismus und 'Wirkliche Welt,'" *Erkenntnis*, Vol. IV (1934), pp. 346–362. But I cannot agree with him when he proceeds from this view to the rejection of the concept of truth. In the paper mentioned earlier (in footnote 21) he says (pp. 138 f.): "In accordance with our traditional language we may say that some statements are accepted at a certain time by a certain person and not accepted by the same person at another time, but we cannot say that some statements are true today but not tomorrow; 'true' and 'false' are 'absolute' terms, which we avoid."

[10] Compare my "Testability and Meaning," *Philosophy of Science*, Vol. III (1936), pp. 419–471, and Vol. IV (1937), pp. 1–40; see Vol. IV, p. 34.

[11] See Reichenbach, *op. cit.*, footnote 20, § 7; he formulated this principle first in 1936.

[12] See the references in Reichenbach, *op. cit.*, footnote 20, p. 49.

cohol' is a legitimate scientific term, because the sentence (1) can be confirmed to some degree if certain observations are made. But the same observations would confirm (2) to the same degree because it is logically equivalent to (1). Therefore, according to P^*, 'true' is likewise a legitimate scientific term.

We shall now examine more closely the concept of confirmation. This will require that we describe the procedure of scientific testing and that we specify the conditions under which a statement, as a result of such testing, is considered as more or less confirmed, i.e., scientifically accepted or rejected. The description of that procedure is not a matter of logic but is itself empirically-scientific (psychological and sociological). One might call it 'methodological', especially if it is presented in the form of proposals and precepts. Only the essential features of the scientific procedure will here be schematically outlined; what matters here are not so much the details but rather a clear emphasis upon the distinction between the two most important operations of the procedure.

The statements of (empirical) science are such that they can never be definitively accepted or rejected. They can only be confirmed or disconfirmed to a certain degree. For the sake of simplicity we may distinguish two types of statements which are, however, not sharply separable (i.e., differing only by degree): the directly testable and the (only) indirectly testable statements. We shall speak of 'directly testable statement' when circumstances are conceivable in which we confidently consider the statement so strongly confirmed or else disconfirmed on the basis of one or very few observations that we would either accept or reject it outright. Examples: "There is a key on my desk". Conditions for the test: I stand near my desk, sufficient illumination is provided, etc. Condition of acceptance: I see a key on my desk; condition of rejection: I don't see a key there. Indirect testing of a statement consists in directly testing other statements which stand in specifiable logical relations to the statement in question. These other statements may be called 'test-sentences' for the given statement. Occasionally an indirectly testable statement may be confirmed by confirming statements from which it is deducible; this is the case, e.g., with existential statements. Scientific laws, however, have the form of universal statements. A universal statement (of simplest form) can be confirmed to ever higher degrees by confirming more and more statements derivable from the law and thereby accepting them (while none are rejected). There are important questions as to the logical relations between such statements which are to be tested and their respective test-sentences. We shall however not examine these any further but rather attend to the analysis of the confirmation of directly testable statements. Here we must distinguish mainly the following two operations:

1. *Confrontation of a statement with observation.* Observations are performed and a statement is formulated such that it may be recognized as confirmed on the basis of these observations. If, e.g., I see a key on my desk and I make the statement: "There is a key on my desk", I accept this statement because I acknowledge it as highly confirmed on the basis of my visual and, possibly, tactual observations. (The concept of observation is here understood in its widest

sense; "I am hungry" or "I am angry" in this context are also taken as observation statements.[13] Ordinarily no definite rules are expressly stipulated as to how a statement may or must be formulated when certain observations have been made. Children learn the use of common language, and thereby the correct performance of the operation described, through practice, imitation, and usually without the benefit of rules. These rules, however, could be specified. But if no foreign language or the introduction of new terms is involved, the rules are trivial. For example: "If one is hungry, the statement 'I am hungry' may be accepted"; or: "If one sees a key one may accept the statement 'there lies a key'". In this context the definition of the concept of truth enters into the question of confirmation; the rules we mentioned originate from this definition.

2. *Confrontation of a statement with previously accepted statements.* A statement established on the basis of the first operation is held as (sufficiently strongly) confirmed as long as in the second operation no statements are found which were previously established by confirmation but are incompatible with the statement under consideration. In the event of such an incompatibility either the new statement or at least one of the previously accepted statements must be revoked. Certain methodological rules have to be stipulated; they tell us which of the two decisions is to be made in a given case (see Popper, *loc. cit.*). This sheds light upon the relation of the two operations to one another. The first one is more important. Without it there could be nothing like confirmation. The second one is an auxiliary operation. Its function is mostly negative or regulative: it serves in the elimination of incongruous elements from the system of statements in science.

Closer attention to these two operations and their mutual relations will help to clarify a number of recently much discussed questions. There has been a good deal of dispute as to whether in the procedure of scientific testing *statements must be compared with facts* or as to whether such comparison be unnecessary, if not impossible. If 'comparison of statement with fact' means the procedure which we called the first operation then it must be admitted that this procedure is not only possible, but even indispensable for scientific testing. Yet it must be remarked that the formulation 'comparison of statement and fact' is not unobjectionable. First, the concept 'comparison' is not quite appropriate here. Two objects can be compared in regard to a property which may characterize them in various ways (e.g., in regard to color, size, or number of parts, and so on). We therefore prefer to speak of 'confrontation' rather than 'comparison'. Confrontation is understood to consist in finding out as to whether one object (the statement in this case) properly fits the other (the fact); i.e., as to whether the fact is such as it is described in the statement, or, to express it differently, as to whether the statement is true to fact. Furthermore, the formulation in terms of

[13] It is a matter of convention as to whether these directly established statements (protocol statements) are to be taken as referring to observed things and processes ("there is on the table . . .") or to the act of perception ("I see . . ."). Cf. Carnap, "Ueber Protokollsaetze," *Erkenntnis*, 3, 1933; also K. Popper, *Logik der Forschung*.

'comparison', in speaking of 'facts' or 'realities', easily tempts one into the absolutistic view according to which we are said to search for an absolute reality whose nature is assumed as fixed independently of the language chosen for its description. The answer to a question concerning reality however depends not only upon that 'reality', or upon the facts but also upon the structure (and the set of concepts) of the language used for the description. In translating one language into another the factual content of an empirical statement cannot always be preserved unchanged. Such changes are inevitable if the structures of the two languages differ in essential points. For example: while many statements of modern physics are completely translatable into statements of classical physics, this is not so or only incompletely so with other statements. The latter situation arises when the statement in question contains concepts (like, e.g., 'wave-function' or 'quantization') which simply do not occur in classical physics; the essential point being that these concepts cannot be subsequently included since they presuppose a different form of language. This becomes still more obvious if we contemplate the possibility of a language with a discontinuous spatio-temporal order which might be adopted in a future physics. Then, obviously, some statements of classical physics could not be translated into the new language, and others only incompletely. (This means not only that previously accepted statements would have to be rejected; but also that to certain statements—regardless of whether they were held true or false — there is no corresponding statement at all in the new language.)

The scruples here advanced regarding the assertion that statements are to be compared with facts (or reality) were directed not so much against its content but rather against its form. The assertion is not false — if only it is interpreted in the manner indicated — but formulated in a potentially misleading fashion. Hence, one must not, in repudiating the assertion, replace it by its denial: "Statements cannot be compared with facts (or with reality)"; for this negative formulation is as much open to objection as the original affirmative one. In repudiating the formulation one must take care not to reject the procedure which was presumably intended, viz., the confrontation with observation. Nor must the significance and indispensability of such confrontation be overshadowed by exclusive attention to the second operation. (Besides, the phrase 'Comparison of statements with each other', instead of 'confrontation', seems open to the same objections.) He who really repudiates the first operation —I do not think that anyone in scientifically oriented circles does — could not be considered an empiricist.

The result of these considerations may now be briefly summarized:

1. The question of the definition of *truth* must be clearly distinguished from the question of a criterion of *confirmation*.

2. In connection with confirmation two different operations have to be performed: the formulation of an observation and the confrontation of statements with each other; especially, we must not lose sight of the first operation.

14 *Studies in the Logic of Confirmation*

To the memory of my wife, Eva Ahrends Hempel

CARL G. HEMPEL

1. *Objective of the Study.*[1]—The defining characteristic of an empirical statement is its capability of being tested by a confrontation with experimental finding, i.e. with the results of suitable experiments or "focussed" observations. This feature distinguishes statements which have empirical content both from the statements of the formal sciences, logic and mathematics, which require no experimental test for their validation, and from the formulations of transempirical metaphysics, which do not admit of any.

The testability here referred to has to be understood in the comprehensive sense of "testability in principle"; there are many empirical statements which, for practical reasons, cannot be actually tested at present. To call a statement of this kind testable in principle means that it is possible to state just what experiential findings, if they were actually obtained, would constitute favourable evidence for it, and what findings or "data", as we shall say for brevity, would constitute unfavourable evidence; in other words, a statement is called testable in principle, if it is possible to describe the kind of data which would confirm or disconfirm it.

From *Mind*, Vol. LIV, 1945, pp. 1–26, 97–120. Reprinted by permission of the editor of *Mind* and the author.

[1] The present analysis of confirmation was to a large extent suggested and stimulated by a co-operative study of certain more general problems which were raised by Dr. Paul Oppenheim, and which I have been investigating with him for several years. These problems concern the form and the function of scientific laws and the comparative methodology of the different branches of empirical science. The discussion with Mr. Oppenheim of these issues suggested to me the central problem of the present essay. The more comprehensive problems just referred to will be dealt with by Mr. Oppenheim in a publication which he is now preparing.

In my occupation with the logical aspects of confirmation, I have benefited greatly by discussions with several students of logic, including Professor R. Carnap, Professor A. Tarski, and particularly Dr. Nelson Goodman, to whom I am indebted for several valuable suggestions which will be indicated subsequently.

A detailed exposition of the more technical aspects of the analysis of confirmation presented in this article is included in my article "A Purely Syntactical Definition of Confirmation", *The Journal of Symbolic Logic*, vol. 8 (1943).

The concepts of confirmation and of disconfirmation as here understood are clearly more comprehensive than those of conclusive verification and falsification. Thus, e.g. no finite amount of experiential evidence can conclusively verify a hypothesis expressing a general law such as the law of gravitation, which covers an infinity of potential instances, many of which belong either to the as yet inaccessible future, or to the irretrievable past; but a finite set of relevant data may well be "in accord with" the hypothesis and thus constitute confirming evidence for it. Similarly, an existential hypothesis, asserting, say, the existence of an as yet unknown chemical element with certain specified characteristics, cannot be conclusively proved false by a finite amount of evidence which fails to "bear out" the hypothesis; but such unfavourable data may, under certain conditions, be considered as weakening the hypothesis in question, or as constituting disconfirming evidence for it.[2]

While, in the practice of scientific research, judgments as to the confirming or disconfirming character of experiential data obtained in the test of a hypothesis are often made without hesitation and with a wide consensus of opinion, it can hardly be said that these judgments are based on an explicit theory providing general criteria of confirmation and of disconfirmation. In this respect, the situation is comparable to the manner in which deductive inferences are carried out in the practice of scientific research: This, too, is often done without reference to an explicitly stated system of rules of logical inference. But while criteria of valid deduction can be and have been supplied by formal logic, no satisfactory theory providing general criteria of confirmation and disconfirmation appears to be available so far.

In the present essay, an attempt will be made to provide the elements of a theory of this kind. After a brief survey of the significance and the present status of the problem, I propose to present a detailed critical analysis of some common conceptions of confirmation and disconfirmation and then to construct explicit definitions for these concepts and to formulate some basic principles of what might be called the logic of confirmation.

2. *Significance and Present Status of the Problem.*—The establishment of a general theory of confirmation may well be regarded as one of the most urgent desiderata of the present methodology of empirical science.[3] Indeed, it seems that a precise analysis of the concept of confirmation is a necessary condition for an adequate solution of various fundamental problems concerning the logical structure of scientific procedure. Let us briefly survey the most outstanding of these problems.

(*a*) In the discussion of scientific method, the concept of relevant evidence plays an important part. And while certain "inductivist" accounts of scientific procedure seem to assume that relevant evidence, or relevant data, can be collected in the context of an inquiry prior to the formulation of any hypothesis,

[2] This point as well as the possibility of conclusive verification and conclusive falsification will be discussed in some detail in section 10 of the present paper.

[3] Or of the "logic of science," as understood by R. Carnap; cf. *The Logical Syntax of Language* (New York and London, 1937), sect. 72, and the supplementary remarks in *Introduction to Semantics* (Cambridge, Mass., 1942), p. 250.

it should be clear upon brief reflection that relevance is a relative concept; experiential data can be said to be relevant or irrelevant only with respect to a given hypothesis; and it is the hypothesis which determines what kind of data or evidence are relevant for it. Indeed, an empirical finding is relevant for a hypothesis if and only if it constitutes either favourable or unfavourable evidence for it; in other words, if it either confirms or disconfirms the hypothesis. Thus, a precise definition of relevance presupposes an analysis of confirmation and disconfirmation.

(*b*) A closely related concept is that of instance of a hypothesis. The so-called method of inductive inference is usually presented as proceeding from specific cases to a general hypothesis of which each of the special cases is an "instance" in the sense that it "conforms to" the general hypothesis in question, and thus constitutes confirming evidence for it.

Thus, any discussion of induction which refers to the establishment of general hypotheses on the strength of particular instances is fraught with all those logical difficulties — soon to be expounded — which beset the concept of confirmation. A precise analysis of this concept is, therefore, a necessary condition for a clear statement of the issues involved in the problem complex of induction and of the ideas suggested for their solution — no matter what their theoretical merits or demerits may be.

(*c*) Another issue customarily connected with the study of scientific method is the quest for "rules of induction". Generally speaking, such rules would enable us to "infer", from a given set of data, that hypothesis or generalization which accounts best for all the particular data in the given set. Recent logical analyses have made it increasingly clear that this way of conceiving the problem involves a misconception: While the process of invention by which scientific discoveries are made is as a rule *psychologically guided and stimulated* by antecedent knowledge of specific facts, its results are *not logically determined* by them; the way in which scientific hypotheses or theories are discovered cannot be mirrored in a set of general rules of inductive inference.[4] One of the crucial considerations which lead to this conclusion is the following: Take a scientific theory such as the atomic theory of matter. The evidence on which it rests may be described in terms referring to directly observable phenomena, namely to certain "macroscopic" aspects of the various experimental and observational data which are relevant to the theory. On the other hand, the theory itself contains a large number of highly abstract, non-observational terms such as "atom", "electron", "nucleus", "dissociation", "valence" and others, none of which figures in the description of the observational data. An adequate rule of induction would therefore have to provide, for this and for every conceivable other case, mechanically applicable criteria determining unambiguously, and without any reliance on the inventiveness or additional scientific knowledge

[4] See the lucid presentation of this point in Karl Popper's *Logik der Forschung* (Wien, 1935), esp. sect. 1, 2, 3, and 25, 26, 27; cf. also Albert Einstein's remarks in his lecture *On the Method of Theoretical Physics* (Oxford, 1933), pp. 11 and 12. Also of interest in this context is the critical discussion of induction by H. Feigl in "The Logical Character of the Principle of Induction," *Philosophy of Science*, vol. 1 (1934).

of its user, all those new abstract concepts which need to be created for the formulation of the theory that will account for the given evidence. Clearly, this requirement cannot be satisfied by any set of rules, however ingeniously devised; there can be no general rules of induction in the above sense; the demand for them rests on a confusion of logical and psychological issues. What determines the soundness of a hypothesis is not the way it is arrived at (it may even have been suggested by a dream or a hallucination), but the way it stands up when tested, i.e. when confronted with relevant observational data. Accordingly, the quest for rules of induction in the original sense of canons of scientific discovery has to be replaced, in the logic of science, by the quest for general objective criteria determining (A) whether, and — if possible — even (B) to what degree, a hypothesis *H* may be said to be corroborated by a given body of evidence *E*. This approach differs essentially from the inductivist conception of the problem in that it presupposes not only *E*, but also *H* as given and then seeks to determine a certain logical relationship between them. The two parts of this latter problem can be restated in somewhat more precise terms as follows:

(A) To give precise definitions of the two non-quantitative relational concepts of confirmation and of disconfirmation; i.e. to define the meaning of the phrases "*E* confirms *H*" and "*E* disconfirms *H*". (When *E* neither confirms nor disconfirms *H*, we shall say that *E* is neutral, or irrelevant, with respect to *H*.)

(B) (1) To lay down criteria defining a metrical concept "degree of confirmation of *H* with respect to *E*", whose values are real numbers; or, failing this,

(2) To lay down criteria defining two relational concepts, "more highly confirmed than" and "equally well confirmed with", which make possible a non-metrical comparison of hypotheses (each with a body of evidence assigned to it) with respect to the extent of their confirmation.

Interestingly, problem B has received much more attention in methodological research than problem A; in particular, the various theories of the "probability of hypotheses" may be regarded as concerning this problem complex; we have here adopted[5] the more neutral term "degree of confirmation" instead of "probability" because the latter is used in science in a definite technical sense involving reference to the relative frequency of the occurrence of a given event in a sequence, and it is at least an open question whether the degree of confirmation of a hypothesis can generally be defined as a probability in this statistical sense.

The theories dealing with the probability of hypotheses fall into two main groups: the "logical" theories construe probability as a logical relation between sentences (or propositions; it is not always clear which is meant)[6]; the "statistical" theories interpret the probability of a hypothesis in substance as the

[5] Following R. Carnap's usage in "Testability and Meaning", *Philosophy of Science*, vols. 3 (1936) and 4 (1937); esp. sect. 3 (in vol. 3).

[6] This group includes the work of such writers as Janina Hosiasson-Lindenbaum (cf. for instance, her article "Induction et analogie: Comparaison de leur fondement", *Mind*, vol. L (1941); also see n. 24), H. Jeffreys, J. M. Keynes, B. O. Koopman, J. Nicod (see n. 15), St. Mazurkiewicz, F. Waismann. For a brief discussion of this conception of probability, see Ernest Nagel, *Principles of the Theory of Probability* (Internat. Encyclopedia of Unified Science, vol. 1, no. 6, Chicago, 1939), esp. sects. 6 and 8. [Ed. note: section 8 reprinted in this Section.]

limit of the relative frequency of its confirming instances among all relevant cases.[7] Now it is a remarkable fact that none of the theories of the first type which have been developed so far provides an explicit general definition of the probability (or degree of confirmation) of a hypothesis H with respect to a body of evidence E; they all limit themselves essentially to the construction of an uninterpreted postulational system of logical probability. For this reason, these theories fail to provide a complete solution of problem B. The statistical approach, on the other hand, would, if successful, provide an explicit numerical definition of the degree of confirmation of a hypothesis; this definition would be formulated in terms of the numbers of confirming and disconfirming instances for H which constitute the body of evidence E. Thus, a necessary condition for an adequate interpretation of degrees of confirmation as statistical probabilities is the establishment of precise criteria of confirmation and disconfirmation, in other words, the solution of problem A.

However, despite their great ingenuity and suggestiveness, the attempts which have been made so far to formulate a precise statistical definition of the degree of confirmation of a hypothesis seem open to certain objections,[8] and several authors[9] have expressed doubts as to the possibility of defining the degree of confirmation of a hypothesis as a metrical magnitude, though some of them consider it as possible, under certain conditions, to solve at least the less exacting problem B (2), i.e. to establish standards of non-metrical comparison between hypotheses with respect to the extent of their confirmation. An adequate comparison of this kind might have to take into account a variety of different factors[10]; but again the numbers of the confirming and of the disconfirming instances which the given evidence includes will be among the most important of those factors.

Thus, of the two problems, A and B, the former appears to be the more basic one, first, because it does not presuppose the possibility of defining numerical degrees of confirmation or of comparing different hypotheses as to the extent of their confirmation; and second because our considerations indicate that any attempt to solve problem B — unless it is to remain in the stage of an axiomatized system without interpretation — is likely to require a precise definition of the concepts of confirming and disconfirming instance of a hy-

[7] The chief proponent of this view is Hans Reichenbach; cf. especially "Ueber Induktion und Wahrscheinlichkeit", *Erkenntnis*, vol. v (1935), and *Experience and Prediction* (Chicago, 1938), Ch. V.

[8] Cf. Karl Popper, *Logik der Forschung* (Wien, 1935), sect. 80; Ernest Nagel, *l.c.*, sect. 8, and "Probability and the Theory of Knowledge", *Philosophy of Science*, vol. 6 (1939); C. G. Hempel, "Le problème de la vérité", *Theoria* (Göteborg), vol. 3 (1937), sect. 5, and "On the Logical Form of Probability Statements", *Erkenntnis*, vol. 7 (1937–38), esp. sect. 5. Cf. also Morton White, "Probability and Confirmation", *The Journal of Philosophy*, vol. 36 (1939).

[9] See, for example, J. M. Keynes, *A Treatise on Probability* (London, 1929), esp. Ch. III; Ernest Nagel, *Principles of the Theory of Probability* (cf. n. 6 above), esp. p. 70 [Ed. note: See p. 189 of this volume.]; compare also the somewhat less definitely sceptical statement by Carnap, *l.c.* (see n. 5), sect. 3, p. 427.

[10] See especially the survey of such factors given by Ernest Nagel in *Principles of the Theory of Probability* (cf. note 6), pp. 66–73. [Ed. note: See pp. 184–194 of this volume.]

pothesis before it can proceed to define numerical degrees of confirmation, or to lay down non-metrical standards of comparison.

(*d*) It is now clear that an analysis of confirmation is of fundamental importance also for the study of the central problem of what is customarily called epistemology; this problem may be characterized as the elaboration of "standards of rational belief" or of criteria of warranted assertibility. In the methodology of empirical science this problem is usually phrased as concerning the rules governing the test and the subsequent acceptance or rejection of empirical hypotheses on the basis of experimental or observational findings, while in its "epistemological" version the issue is oftern formulated as concerning the validation of beliefs by reference to perceptions, sense data, or the like. But no matter how the final empirical evidence is construed and in what terms it is accordingly expressed, the theoretical problem remains the same: to characterize, in precise and general terms, the conditions under which a body of evidence can be said to confirm, or to disconfirm, a hypothesis of empirical character; and that is again our problem A.

(*e*) The same problem arises when one attempts to give a precise statement of the empiricist and operationalist criteria for the empirical meaningfulness of a sentence; these criteria, as is well known, are formulated by reference to the theoretical testability of the sentence by means of experimental evidence [11]; and the concept of theoretical testability, as was pointed out earlier, is closely related to the concepts of confirmation and disconfirmation.[12]

Considering the great importance of the concept of confirmation, it is surprising that no systematic theory of the non-quantitative relation of confirmation seems to have been developed so far. Perhaps this fact reflects the tacit assumption that the concepts of confirmation and of disconfirmation have a sufficiently clear meaning to make explicit definitions unnecessary or at least comparatively trivial. And indeed, as will be shown below, there are certain features which are rather generally associated with the intuitive notion of confirming evidence, and which, at first, seem well-suited to serve as defining characteristics of confirmation. Closer examination will reveal the definitions thus obtainable to be seriously deficient and will make it clear that an adequate definition of confirmation involves considerable difficulties.

Now the very existence of such difficulties suggests the question whether the problem we are considering does not rest on a false assumption: Perhaps there are no objective criteria of confirmation; perhaps the decision as to whether a given hypothesis is acceptable in the light of a given body of evidence is no more subject to rational, objective rules than is the process of inventing a scientific

[11] Cf. for example, A. J. Ayer, *Language, Truth and Logic* (London and New York, 1936), Ch. I; R. Carnap, "Testability and Meaning" (cf. note 5), sects. 1, 2, 3; H. Feigl, *Logical Empiricism* (in *Twentieth Century Philosophy*, ed. by Dagobert D. Runes, New York, 1943); P. W. Bridgman, *The Logic of Modern Physics* (New York, 1928).

[12] It should be noted, however, that in his essay "Testability and Meaning" (cf. note 5), R. Carnap has constructed definitions of testability and confirmability which avoid reference to the concept of confirming and of disconfirming evidence; in fact, no proposal for the definition of these latter concepts is made in that study.

hypothesis or theory; perhaps, in the last analysis, it is a "sense of evidence", or a feeling of plausibility in view of the relevant data, which ultimately decides whether a hypothesis is scientifically acceptable.[13] This view is comparable to the opinion that the validity of a mathematical proof or of a logical argument has to be judged ultimately by reference to a feeling of soundness or convincingness; and both theses have to be rejected on analogous grounds: They involve a confusion of logical and psychological considerations. Clearly, the occurrence or non-occurrence of a feeling of conviction upon the presentation of grounds for an assertion is a subjective matter which varies from person to person, and with the same person in the course of time; it is often deceptive, and can certainly serve neither as a necessary nor as a sufficient condition for the soundness of the given assertion.[14] A rational reconstruction of the standards of scientific validation cannot, therefore, involve reference to a sense of evidence; it has to be based on objective criteria. In fact, it seems reasonable to require that the criteria of empirical confirmation, besides being objective in character, should contain no reference to the specific subject-matter of the hypothesis or of the evidence in question; it ought to be possible, one feels, to set up purely formal criteria of confirmation in a manner similar to that in which deductive logic provides purely for malcriteria for the validity of deductive inferences.

With this goal in mind, we now turn to a study of the non-quantitative concept of confirmation. We shall begin by examining some current conceptions of confirmation and exhibiting their logical and methodological inadequacies; in the course of this analysis, we shall develop a set of conditions for the adequacy of any proposed definition of confirmation; and finally, we shall construct a definition of confirmation which satisfies those general standards of adequacy.

3. *Nicod's Criterion of Confirmation and its Shortcomings.* — We consider first a conception of confirmation which underlies many recent studies of induction and of scientific method. A very explicit statement of this conception has been given by Jean Nicod in the following passage: "Consider the formula or the law: *A entails B*. How can a particular proposition, or more briefly, a fact, affect its probability? If this fact consists of the presence of B in a case of A, it is favourable to the law '*A entails B*'; on the contrary, if it consists of the absence of B in a case of A, it is unfavourable to this law. It is conceivable that we have here the only two direct modes in which a fact can influence the probability of a law. . . . Thus, the entire influence of particular truths or facts on the probability of universal propositions or laws would operate by means of these two elementary relations which we shall call *confirmation* and *invalidation*."[15] Note that the applicability of this criterion is restricted to hypotheses of the form "*A entails B*". Any hypothesis H of this kind may be expressed in the notation

[13] A view of this kind has been expressed, for example, by M. Mandelbaum in "Causal Analyses in History", *Journal of the History of Ideas*, vol. 3 (1942); cf. esp. pp. 46–47.

[14] See Karl Popper's pertinent statement, *l.c.*, sect. 8.

[15] Jean Nicod, *Foundations of Geometry and Induction* (transl. by P. P. Wiener) (London, 1930), p. 219; cf. also R. M. Eaton's discussion of "Confirmation and Infirmation," which is based on Nicod's views; it is included in Ch. III of his *General Logic* (New York, 1931).

of symbolic logic[16] by means of a universal conditional sentence, such as, in the simplest case,

$$(x)(P(x) \supset Q(x)),$$

i.e. "For any object x: if x is a P, then x is a Q", or also "Occurrences of the quality P entails occurrence of the quality Q". According to the above criterion this hypothesis is confirmed by an object a, if a is P and Q; and the hypothesis is disconfirmed by a if a is P, but not Q. In other words, an object confirms a universal conditional hypothesis if and only if it satisfies both the antecedent (here: '$P(x)$') and the consequent (here: '$Q(x)$') of the conditional; it disconfirms the hypothesis if and only if it satisfies the antecedent, but not the consequent of the conditional; and (we add to this Nicod's statement) it is neutral, or irrelevant, with respect to the hypothesis if it does not satisfy the antecedent.

This criterion can readily be extended so as to be applicable also to universal conditionals containing more than one quantifier, such as "Twins always resemble each other", or, in symbolic notation, '$(x)(y)(\mathrm{Twins}(x, y) \supset \mathrm{Rsbl}(x, y))$'. In these cases, a confirming instance consists of an ordered couple, or triple, etc., of objects satisfying the antecedent and the consequent of the conditional. (In the case of the last illustration, any two persons who are twins and who resemble each other would confirm the hypothesis; twins who do not resemble each other would disconfirm it; and any two persons not twins — no matter whether they resemble each other or not — would constitute irrelevant evidence.)

We shall refer to this criterion as Nicod's criterion.[17] It states explicitly what is perhaps the most common tacit interpretation of the concept of confirmation. While seemingly quite adequate, it suffers from serious shortcomings, as will now be shown.

(*a*) First, the applicability of this criterion is restricted to hypotheses of universal conditional form; it provides no standards for existential hypotheses (such as "There exists organic life on other stars", or "Poliomyelitis is caused by some virus") or for hypotheses whose explicit formulation calls for the use of both universal and existential quantifiers (such as "Every human being dies some finite number of years after his birth", or the psychological hypothesis, "You can fool all of the people some of the time and some of the people all of the time, but you cannot fool all of the people all of the time", which may be symbolized by '$(x)(Et)\mathrm{Fl}(x, t) \cdot (Ex)(t)\mathrm{Fl}(x, t) \cdot \sim (x)(t)\mathrm{Fl}(x, t)$', (where '$\mathrm{Fl}(x, t)$' stands for "You can fool (person) x at time t"). We note, therefore, the de-

[16] In this paper, only the most elementary devices of this notation are used; the symbolism is essentially that of *Principia Mathematica,* except that parentheses are used instead of dots, and that existential quantification is symbolized by '(E)' instead of by the inverted 'E'.

[17] This term is chosen for convenience, and in view of the above explicit formulation given by Nicod; it is not, of course, intended to imply that this conception of confirmation originated with Nicod.

sideratum of establishing a criterion of confirmation which is applicable to hypotheses of any form.[18]

(*b*) We now turn to a second shortcoming of Nicod's criterion. Consider the two sentences

$$S_1\text{: `}(x)(\text{Raven}(x) \supset \text{Black}(x))\text{';}$$
$$S_2\text{: `}(x)(\sim\text{Black}(x) \supset \sim\text{Raven}(x))\text{'}$$

(i.e. "All ravens are black" and "Whatever is not black is not a raven"), and let *a*, *b*, *c*, *d* be four objects such that *a* is a raven and black, *b* a raven but not black, *c* not a raven but black, and *d* neither a raven nor black. Then, according to Nicod's criterion, *a* would confirm S_1, but be neutral with respect to S_2; *b* would disconfirm both S_1 and S_2; *c* would be neutral with respect to both S_1 and S_2, and *d* would confirm S_2, but be neutral with respect to S_1.

But S_1 and S_2 are logically equivalent; they have the same content, they are different formulations of the same hypothesis. And yet, by Nicod's criterion, either of the objects *a* and *d* would be confirming for one of the two sentences, but neutral with respect to the other. This means that Nicod's criterion makes confirmation depend not only on the content of the hypothesis, but also on its formulation.[19]

One remarkable consequence of this situation is that every hypothesis to which the criterion is applicable — i.e. every universal conditional — can be stated in a form for which there cannot possibly exist any confirming instances. Thus, e.g. the sentence

$$(x)[(\text{Raven}(x) \cdot \sim \text{Black}(x)) \supset (\text{Raven}(x) \cdot \sim \text{Raven}(x)]$$

is readily recognized as equivalent to both S_1 and S_2 above; yet no object whatever can confirm this sentence, i.e. satisfy both its antecedent and its consequent; for the consequent is contradictory. An analogous transformation is, of course, applicable to any other sentence of universal conditional form.

4. *The Equivalence Condition.* — The results just obtained call attention to a condition which an adequately defined concept of confirmation should satisfy, and in the light of which Nicod's criterion has to be rejected as inadequate: *Equivalence condition:* Whatever confirms (disconfirms) one of two equivalent sentences, also confirms (disconfirms) the other.

Fulfilment of this condition makes the confirmation of a hypothesis independent of the way in which it is formulated; and no doubt it will be conceded that this is a necessary condition for the adequacy of any proposed criterion of tion will have to do justice to the way in which empirical hypotheses function

[18] For a rigorous formulation of the problem, it is necessary first to lay down assumptions as to the means of expression and the logical structure of the language in which the hypotheses are supposed to be formulated; the desideratum then calls for a definition of confirmation applicable to any hypotheses which can be expressed in the given language. Generally speaking, the problem becomes increasingly difficult with increasing richness and complexity of the assumed "language of science."

[19] This difficulty was pointed out, in substance, in my article "Le problème de la vérité", *Theoria* (Göteborg), vol. 3 (1937), esp. p. 222.

confirmation. Otherwise, the question as to whether certain data confirm a given hypothesis would have to be answered by saying: "That depends on which of the different equivalent formulations of the hypothesis is considered" — which appears absurd. Furthermore — and this is a more important point than an appeal to a feeling of absurdity — an adequate definition of confirma-in theoretical scientific contexts such as explanations and predictions; but when hypotheses are used for purposes of explanation or prediction,[20] they serve as premisses in a deductive argument whose conclusion is a description of the event to be explained or predicted. The deduction is governed by the principles of formal logic, and according to the latter, a deduction which is valid will remain so if some or all of the premisses are replaced by different, but equivalent statements; and indeed, a scientist will feel free, in any theoretical reasoning involving certain hypotheses, to use the latter in whichever of their equivalent formulations is most convenient for the development of his conclusions. But if we adopted a concept of confirmation which did not satisfy the equivalence condition, then it would be possible, and indeed necessary, to argue in certain cases that it was sound scientific procedure to base a prediction on a given hypothesis if formulated in a sentence S_1, because a good deal of confirming evidence had been found for S_1; but that it was altogether inadmissible to base the prediction (say, for convenience of deduction) on an equivalent formulation S_2, because no confirming evidence for S_2 was available. Thus, the equivalence condition has to be regarded as a necessary condition for the adequacy of any definition of confirmation.

5. *The "Paradoxes" of Confirmation.* — Perhaps we seem to have been labouring the obvious in stressing the necessity of satisfying the equivalence condition. This impression is likely to vanish upon consideration of certain consequences which derive from a combination of the equivalence condition with a most natural and plausible assumption concerning a sufficient condition of confirmation.

The essence of the criticism we have levelled so far against Nicod's criterion is that it certainly cannot serve as a necessary condition of confirmation; thus, in the illustration given in the beginning of section 3, the object *a* confirms S_1 and should therefore also be considered as confirming S_2, while according to Nicod's criterion it is not. Satisfaction of the latter is therefore not a necessary condition for confirming evidence.

On the other hand, Nicod's criterion might still be considered as stating a particularly obvious and important sufficient condition of confirmation. And indeed, if we restrict ourselves to universal conditional hypotheses in one variable [21] — such as S_1 and S_2 in the above illustration — then it seems perfectly

[20] For a more detailed account of the logical structure of scientific explanation and prediction, cf. C. G. Hempel, "The Function of General Laws in History", *The Journal of Philosophy*, vol. 39, (1942), esp. sects. 2, 3, 4. The characterization, given in that paper as well as in the above text, of explanations and predictions as arguments of a deductive logical structure, embodies an over-simplification: as will be shown in sect. 7 of the present essay, explanations and predictions often involve "quasi-inductive" steps besides deductive ones. This point, however, does not affect the validity of the above argument.

[21] This restriction is essential: In its general form, which applies to universal conditionals in any number of variables, Nicod's criterion cannot even be construed as expressing a sufficient

reasonable to qualify an object as confirming such a hypothesis if it satisfies both its antecedent and its consequent. The plausibility of this view will be further corroborated in the course of our subsequent analyses.

Thus, we shall agree that if a is both a raven and black, then a certainly confirms S_1: '$(x)(\text{Raven}(x) \supset \text{Black}(x))$', and if d is neither black nor a raven, d certainly confirms S_2:

$$\text{'}(x)(\sim\text{Black}(x) \supset \sim\text{Raven}(x))\text{'}.$$

Let us now combine this simple stipulation with the equivalence condition: Since S_1 and S_2 are equivalent, d is confirming also for S_1; and thus, we have to recognize as confirming for S_1 any object which is neither black nor a raven. Consequently, any red pencil, any green leaf, and yellow cow, etc., becomes confirming evidence for the hypothesis that all ravens are black. This surprising consequence of two very adequate assumptions (the equivalence condition and the above sufficient condition of confirmation) can be further expanded: The following sentence can readily be shown to be equivalent to S_1:S_3: '$(x)[(\text{Raven}(x) \vee \sim \text{Raven}(x)) \supset (\sim \text{Raven}(x) \vee \text{Black}(x))]$', i.e. "Anything which is or is not a raven is either no raven or black". According to the above sufficient condition, S_3 is certainly confirmed by any object, say e, such that (1) e is or is not a raven and, in addition, (2) e is not a raven or also black. Since (1) is analytic, these conditions reduce to (2). By virtue of the equivalence condition, we have therefore to consider as confirming for S_1 any object which is either no raven or also black (in other words: any object which is no raven at all, or a black raven).

Of the four objects characterized in section 3, a, c and d would therefore constitute confirming evidence for S_1, while b would be disconfirming for S_1. This implies that any non-raven represents confirming evidence for the hypothesis that all ravens are black.

We shall refer to these implications of the equivalence criterion and of the above sufficient condition of confirmation as the *paradoxes of confirmation*.

How are these paradoxes to be dealt with? Renouncing the equivalence

---

condition of confirmation. This is shown by the following rather surprising example: Consider the hypothesis S_1: $(x)(y)[\sim(R(x,y) \cdot R(y,x)) \supset (R(x,y) \cdot \sim R(y,x))]$.

Let a, b be two objects such that $R(a,b)$ and $\sim R(b,a)$. Then clearly, the couple (a,b) satisfies both the antecedent and the consequent of the universal conditional S_1; hence, if Nicod's criterion in its general form is accepted as stating a sufficient condition of confirmation, (a,b) constitutes confirming evidence for S_1. However, S_1 can be shown to be equivalent to

$$S_2\text{: } (x)(y)R(x,y)$$

Now, by hypothesis, we have $\sim R(b,a)$; and this flatly contradicts S_2 and thus S_1. Thus, the couple (a,b), although satisfying both the antecedent and the consequent of the universal conditional S_1 actually constitutes disconfirming evidence of the strongest kind (conclusively disconfirming evidence, as we shall say later) for that sentence. This illustration reveals a striking and — as far as I am aware — hitherto unnoticed weakness of that conception of confirmation which underlies Nicod's criterion. In order to realize the bearing of our illustration upon Nicod's original formulation, let A and B be $\sim(R(x,y) \cdot R(y,x))$ and $R(x,y) \cdot \sim R(y,x)$ respectively. Then S_1 asserts that A entails B, and the couple (a,b) is a case of the presence of B in the presence of A; this should, according to Nicod, be favourable to S_1.

condition would not represent an acceptable solution, as is shown by the consideration presented in section 4. Nor does it seem possible to dispense with the stipulation that an object satisfying two conditions, C_1 and C_2, should be considered as confirming a general hypothesis to the effect that any object which satisfies C_1, also satisfies C_2.

But the deduction of the above paradoxical results rests on one other assumption which is usually taken for granted, namely, that the meaning of general empirical hypotheses, such as that all ravens are black, or that all sodium salts burn yellow, can be adequately expressed by means of sentences of universal conditional form, such as '$(x)(\text{Raven}(x) \supset \text{Black}(x))$' and '$(x)(\text{Sod. Salt}(x) \supset \text{Burn Yellow}(x))$', etc. Perhaps this customary mode of presentation has to be modified; and perhaps such a modification would automatically remove the paradoxes of confirmation? If this is not so, there seems to be only one alternative left, namely to show that the impression of the paradoxical character of those consequences is due to misunderstanding and can be dispelled, so that no theoretical difficulty remains. We shall now consider these two possibilities in turn: The sub-sections 5.11 and 5.12 are devoted to a discussion of two different proposals for a modified representation of general hypotheses; in subsection 5.2, we shall discuss the second alternative, i.e. the possibility of tracing the impression of paradoxicality back to a misunderstanding.

5.11. It has often been pointed out that while Aristotelian logic, in agreement with prevalent every day usage, confers "existential import" upon sentences of the form "All *P*'s are *Q*'s", a universal conditional sentence, in the sense of modern logic, has no existential import; thus, the sentence

$$`(x)(\text{Mermaid}(x) \supset \text{Green}(x))'$$

does not imply the existence of mermaids; it merely asserts that any object either is not a mermaid at all, or a green mermaid; and it is true simply because of the fact that there are no mermaids. General laws and hypotheses in science, however — so it might be argued — are meant to have existential import; and one might attempt to express the latter by supplementing the customary universal conditional by an existential clause. Thus, the hypothesis that all ravens are black would be expressed by means of the sentence S_1: '$(x)(\text{Raven}(x) \supset \text{Black}(x)) \cdot (Ex)\text{Raven}(x)$; and the hypothesis that no non-black things are ravens by S_2: '$(x)(\sim \text{Black}(x) \supset \sim \text{Raven}(x)) \cdot (Ex) \sim \text{Black}(x)$. Clearly, these sentences are not equivalent, and of the four objects *a*, *b*, *c*, *d* characterized in section 3, part (*b*), only *a* might reasonably be said to confirm S_1, and only *d* to confirm S_2. Yet this method of avoiding the paradoxes of confirmation is open to serious objections:

(*a*) First of all, the representation of every general hypothesis by a conjunction of a universal conditional and an existential sentence would invalidate many logical inferences which are generally accepted as permissible in a theoretical argument. Thus, for example, the assertions that all sodium salts burn yellow, and that whatever does not burn yellow is no sodium salt are logically equivalent according to customary understanding and usage; and their representation by universal conditionals preserves this equivalence; but if existential clauses are added, the two assertions are no longer equivalent, as is illustrated above by the analogous case of S_1 and S_2.

(*b*) Second, the customary formulation of general hypotheses in empirical science clearly does not contain an existential clause, nor does it, as a rule, even indirectly determine such a clause unambiguously. Thus, consider the hypothesis that if a person after receiving an injection of a certain test substance has a positive skin reaction, he has diphtheria. Should we construe the existential clause here as referring to persons, to persons receiving the injection, or to persons who, upon receiving the injection, show a positive skin reaction? A more or less arbitrary decision has to be made; each of the possible decisions gives a different interpretation to the hypothesis, and none of them seems to be really implied by the latter.

(*c*) Finally, many universal hypotheses cannot be said to imply an existential clause at all. Thus, it may happen that from a certain astrophysical theory a universal hypothesis is deduced concerning the character of the phenomena which would take place under certain specified extreme conditions. A hypothesis of this kind need not (and, as a rule, does not) imply that such extreme conditions ever were or will be realized; it has no existential import. Or consider a biological hypothesis to the effect that whenever man and ape are crossed, the offspring will have such and such characteristics. This is a general hypothesis; it might be contemplated as a mere conjecture, or as a consequence of a broader genetic theory, other implications of which may already have been tested with positive results; but unquestionably the hypothesis does not imply an existential clause asserting that the contemplated kind of cross-breeding referred to will, at some time, actually take place.

While, therefore, the adjunction of an existential clause to the customary symbolization of a general hypothesis cannot be considered as an adequate *general* method of coping with the paradoxes of confirmation, there is a purpose which the use of an existential clause may serve very well, as was pointed out to me by Dr. Paul Oppenheim[22]: if somebody feels that objects of the types *c* and *d* mentioned above are irrelevant rather than confirming for the hypothesis in question, and that qualifying them as confirming evidence does violence to the meaning of the hypothesis, then this may indicate that he is consciously or unconsciously construing the latter as having existential import; and this kind of understanding of general hypotheses is in fact very common. In this case, the "paradox" may be removed by pointing out that an adequate symbolization of the intended meaning requires the adjunction of an existential clause. The formulation thus obtained is more restrictive than the universal conditional alone; and while we have as yet set up no criteria of confirmation applicable to hypotheses of this more complex form, it is clear that according to every acceptable definition of confirmation objects of the types *c* and *d* will fail to qualify as confirming cases. In this manner, the use of an existential clause may prove helpful in distinguishing and rendering explicit different possible

[22] This observation is related to Mr. Oppenheim's methodological studies referred to in n. 1.

interpretations of a given general hypothesis which is stated in non-symbolic terms

5.12. Perhaps the impression of the paradoxical character of the cases discussed in the beginning of section 5 may be said to grow out of the feeling that the hypothesis that all ravens are black is about ravens, and not about non-black things, nor about all things. The use of an existential clause was one attempt at expressing this presumed peculiarity of the hypothesis. The attempt has failed, and if we wish to reflect the point in question, we shall have to look for a stronger device. The idea suggests itself of representing a general hypothesis by the customary universal conditional, supplemented by the indication of the specific "field of application" of the hypothesis; thus, we might represent the hypothesis that all ravens are black by the sentence '$(x)(\text{Raven}(x) \supset \text{Black}(x))$' (or any one of its equivalents), plus the indication "Class of ravens" characterizing the field of application; and we might then require that every confirming instance should belong to the field of application. This procedure would exclude the objects *c* and *d* from those constituting confirming evidence and would thus avoid those undesirable consequences of the existential-clause device which were pointed out in 5.11 (*c*). But apart from this advantage, the second method is open to objections similar to those which apply to the first: (*a*) The way in which general hypotheses are used in science never involves the statement of a field of application; and the choice of the latter in a symbolic formulation of a given hypothesis thus introduces again a considerable measure of arbitrariness. In particular, for a scientific hypothesis to the effect that all *P*'s are *Q*'s, the field of application cannot simply be said to be the class of all *P*'s; for a hypothesis such as that all sodium salts burn yellow finds important applications in tests with negative results; i.e. it may be applied to a substance of which it is not known whether it contains sodium salts, nor whether it burns yellow; and if the flame does not turn yellow, the hypothesis serves to establish the absence of sodium salts. The same is true of all other hypotheses used for tests of this type. (*b*) Again, the consistent use of a domain of application in the formulation of general hypotheses would involve considerable logical complications, and yet would have no counterpart in the theoretical procedure of science, where hypotheses are subjected to various kinds of logical transformation and inference without any consideration that might be regarded as referring to changes in the fields of application. This method of meeting the paradoxes would therefore amount to dodging the problem by means of an *ad hoc* device which cannot be justified by reference to actual scientific procedure.

5.2. We have examined two alternatives to the customary method of representing general hypotheses by means of universal conditionals; neither of them proved an adequate means of precluding the paradoxes of confirmation. We shall now try to show that what is wrong does not lie in the customary way of construing and representing general hypotheses, but rather in our reliance on a misleading intuition in the matter: The impression of a paradoxical situation is not objectively founded; it is a psychological illusion.

(*a*) One source of misunderstanding is the view, referred to before, that a hypothesis of the simple form "Every *P* is a *Q*" such as "All sodium salts burn yellow", asserts something about a certain limited class of objects only, namely, the class of all *P*'s. This idea involves a confusion of logical and practical considerations: Our interest in the hypothesis may be focussed upon its applicability to that particular class of objects, but the hypothesis nevertheless asserts something about, and indeed imposes restrictions upon, *all* objects (within the logical type of the variable occurring in the hypothesis, which in the case of our last illustration might be the class of all physical objects). Indeed, a hypothesis of the form "Every *P* is a *Q*" forbids the occurrence of any objects having the property *P* but lacking the property *Q*; i.e. it restricts all objects whatsoever to the class of those which either lack the property *P* or also have the property *Q*. Now, every object either belongs to this class or falls outside it, and thus, every object — and not only the *P*'s — either conforms to the hypothesis or violates it; there is no object which is not implicitly "referred to" by a hypothesis of this type. In particular, every object which either is no sodium salt or burns yellow conforms to, and thus "bears out" the hypothesis that all sodium salts burn yellow; every other object violates that hypothesis.

The weakness of the idea under consideration is evidenced also by the observation that the class of objects about which a hypothesis is supposed to assert something is in no way clearly determined, and that it changes with the context, as was shown in 5.12 (*a*).

(*b*) A second important source of the appearance of paradoxicality in certain cases of confirmation is exhibited by the following consideration.

Suppose that in support of the assertion "All sodium salts burn yellow" somebody were to adduce an experiment in which a piece of pure ice was held into a colourless flame and did not turn the flame yellow. This result would confirm the assertion, "Whatever does not burn yellow is no sodium salt", and consequently, by virtue of the equivalence condition, it would confirm the original formulation. Why does this impress us as paradoxical? The reason becomes clear when we compare the previous situation with the case of an experiment where an object whose chemical constitution is as yet unknown to us is held into a flame and fails to turn it yellow, and where subsequent analysis reveals it to contain no sodium salt. This outcome, we should no doubt agree, is what was to be expected on the basis of the hypothesis that all sodium salts burn yellow — no matter in which of its various equivalent formulations it may be expressed; thus, the data here obtained constitute confirming evidence for the hypothesis. Now the only difference between the two situations here considered is that in the first case we are told beforehand the test substance is ice, and we happen to "know anyhow" that ice contains no sodium salt; this has the consequence that the outcome of the flame-colour test becomes entirely irrelevant for the confirmation of the hypothesis and thus can yield no new evidence for us. Indeed, if the flame should not turn yellow, the hypothesis requires that the substance contain no sodium salt — and we know beforehand that ice does not — and if the flame should turn yellow, the hypothesis would impose no further restrictions on the substance; hence, either of the possible outcomes of the experiment would be in accord with the hypothesis.

The analysis of this example illustrates a general point: In the seemingly paradoxical cases of confirmation, we are often not actually judging the relation of the given evidence, *E* alone to the hypothesis *H* (we fail to observe the "methodological fiction", characteristic of every case of confirmation, that we have no relevant evidence for *H* other than that included in *E*); instead, we tacitly introduce a comparison of *H* with a body of evidence which consists of *E* in conjunction with an additional amount of information which we happen to have at our disposal; in our illustration, this information includes the knowledge (1) that the substance used in the experiment is ice, and (2) that ice contains no sodium salt. If we assume this additional information as given, then, of course, the outcome of the experiment can add no strength to the hypothesis under consideration. But if we are careful to avoid this tacit reference to additional knowledge (which entirely changes the character of the problem), and if we formulate the question as to the confirming character of the evidence in a manner adequate to the concept of confirmation as used in this paper, we have to ask: Given some object *a* (it happens to be a piece of ice, but this fact is not included in the evidence), and given the fact that *a* does not turn the flame yellow and is no sodium salt — does *a* then constitute confirming evidence for the hypothesis? And now — no matter whether *a* is ice or some other substance — it is clear that the answer has to be in the affirmative; and the paradoxes vanish.

So far, in section (*b*), we have considered mainly that type of paradoxical case which is illustrated by the assertion that any non-black non-raven constitutes confirming evidence for the hypothesis, "All ravens are black". However, the general idea just outlined applies as well to the even more extreme cases exemplified by the assertion that any non-raven as well as any black object confirms the hypothesis in question. Let us illustrate this by reference to the latter case. If the given evidence *E* — i.e. in the sense of the required methodological fiction, all our data relevant for the hypothesis — consists only of one object which, in addition, is black, then *E* may reasonably be said to support even the hypothesis that all objects are black, and *a fortiori* *E* supports the weaker assertion that all ravens are black. In this case, again, our factual knowledge that not all objects are black tends to create an impression of paradoxicality which is not justified on logical grounds. Other "paradoxical" cases of confirmation may be dealt with analogously, and it thus turns out that the "paradoxes of confirmation", as formulated above, are due to a misguided intuition in the matter rather than to a logical flaw in the two stipulations from which the "paradoxes" were derived.[23, 24]

[23] The basic idea of sect. (b) in the above analysis of the "paradoxes of confirmation" is due to Dr. Nelson Goodman, to whom I wish to reiterate my thanks for the help he rendered me, through many discussions, in clarifying my ideas on this point.

[24] The considerations presented in section (*b*) above are also influenced by, though not identical in content with, the very illuminating discussion of the "paradoxes" by the Polish

6. *Confirmation Construed as a Relation between Sentences.* — Our analysis of Nicod's criterion has so far led to two main results: The rejection of that criterion in view of several deficiencies, and the emergence of the equivalence condition as a necessary condition of adequacy for any proposed definition of confirmation. Another aspect of Nicod's criterion requires consideration now. In our formulation of the criterion, confirmation was construed as a dyadic relation between an object or an ordered set of objects, representing the evidence, and a sentence, representing the hypothesis. This means that confirmation was conceived of as a semantical relation [25] obtaining between certain extra-linguistic objects [26] on one hand and certain sentences on the other. It is possible, however, to construe confirmation in an alternative fashion as a relation

methodologist and logician Janina Hosiasson-Lindenbaum; cf. her article "On Confirmation", *The Journal of Symbolic Logic*, vol. 5 (1940), especially sect. 4. Dr. Hosiasson's attention had been called to the paradoxes by the article referred to in n. 2, and by discussions with the author. To my knowledge, hers has so far been the only publication which presents an explicit attempt to solve the problem. Her solution is based on a theory of degrees of confirmation, which is developed in the form of an uninterpreted axiomatic system (cf. n. 6 and part (b) in sect. 1 of the present article), and most of her arguments presuppose that theoretical framework. I have profited, however, by some of Miss Hosiasson's more general observations which proved relevant for the analysis of the paradoxes of the non-gradated relation of confirmation which forms the object of the present study.

One point in those of Miss Hosiasson's comments which rest on her theory of degrees of confirmation is of particular interest, and I should like to discuss it briefly. Stated in reference to the raven-hypothesis, it consists in the suggestion that the finding of one non-black object which is no raven, while constituting confirming evidence for the hypothesis, would increase the degree of confirmation of the hypothesis by a smaller amount than the finding of one raven which is black. This is said to be so because the class of all ravens is much less numerous than that of all non-black objects, so that — to put the idea in suggestive though somewhat misleading terms — the finding of one black raven confirms a larger portion of the total content of the hypothesis than the finding of one non-black non-raven. In fact, from the basic assumptions of her theory, Miss Hosiasson is able to derive a theorem according to which the above statement about the relative increase in degree of confirmation will hold provided that actually the number of all ravens is small compared with the number of all non-black objects. But is this last numerical assumption actually warranted in the present case and analogously in all other "paradoxical" cases? The answer depends in part upon the logical structure of the language of science. If a "co-ordinate language" is used, in which, say, finite space-time regions figure as individuals, then the raven-hypothesis assumes some such form as "Every space-time region which contains a raven, contains something black"; and even if the total number of ravens ever to exist is finite, the class of space-time regions containing a raven has the power of the continuum, and so does the class of space-time regions containing something non-black; thus, for a co-ordinate language of the type under consideration, the above numerical assumption is not warranted. Now the use of a co-ordinate language may appear quite artificial in this particular illustration; but it will seem very appropriate in many other contexts, such as, e.g., that of physical field theories. On the other hand, Miss Hosiasson's numerical assumption may well be justified on the basis of a "thing language", in which physical objects of finite size function as individuals. Of course, even on this basis, it remains an empirical question, for every hypothesis of the form "All P's are Q's", whether actually the class of non-Q's is much more numerous than the class of P's; and in many cases this question will be very difficult to decide.

[25] For a detailed account of this concept, see C. W. Morris, *Foundations of the Theory of Signs* (Internat. Encyclopedia of Unified Science, vol. i, no. 2, Chicago, 1938), and R. Carnap, *Introduction to Semantics* (Cambridge, Mass., 1942), esp. sects. 4 and 37.

[26] Instead of making the first term of the relation an object or a sequence of objects, we might construe it as a "state of affairs" (or perhaps as a "fact", or a "proposition", as Nicod puts it), such as that state of affairs which consists in a being a black raven, etc.

between two sentences, one describing the given evidence, the other expressing the hypothesis. Thus, e.g. instead of saying that an object *a* which is both a raven and black (or the "fact" of *a* being both a raven and black) confirms the hypothesis, "All ravens are black", we may say that the evidence sentence, "*a* is a raven, and *a* is black", confirms the hypothesis-sentence (briefly, the hypothesis), "All ravens are black". We shall adopt this conception of confirmation as a relation between sentences here for the following reasons: First, the evidence adduced in support or criticism of a scientific hypothesis is always expressed in sentences, which frequently have the character of observation reports; and second, it will prove very fruitful to pursue the parallel, alluded to in section 2 above, between the concepts of confirmation and of logical consequence. And just as in the theory of the consequence relation, i.e. in deductive logic, the premisses of which a given conclusion is a consequence are construed as sentences rather than as "facts", so we propose to construe the data which confirm a given hypothesis as given in the form of sentences.

The preceding reference to observation reports suggests a certain restriction which might be imposed on evidence sentences. Indeed, the evidence adduced in support of a scientific hypothesis or theory consists, in the last analysis, in data accessible to what is loosely called "direct observation", and such data are expressible in the form of "observation reports". In view of this consideration, we shall restrict the evidence sentences which form the domain of the relation of confirmation, to sentences of the character of observation reports. In order to give a precise meaning to the concept of observation report, we shall assume that we are given a well-determined "language of science", in terms of which all sentences under consideration, hypotheses as well as evidence sentences, are formulated. We shall further assume that this language contains, among other terms, a clearly delimited "observational vocabulary" which consists of terms designating more or less directly observable attributes of things or events, such as, say, "black", "taller than", "burning with a yellow light", etc., but no theoretical constructs such as "aliphatic compound", "circularly polarized light", "heavy hydrogen", etc.

We shall now understand by a hypothesis any sentence which can be expressed in the assumed language of science, no matter whether it is a generalized sentence, containing quantifiers, or a particular sentence referring only to a finite number of particular objects. An observation report will be construed as a finite class (or a conjunction of a finite number) of observation sentences; and an observation sentence as a sentence which either asserts or denies that a given object has a certain observable property (such as "*a* is a raven", "*d* is not black"), or that a given sequence of objects stand in a certain observable relation (such as "*a* is between *b* and *c*").

Now the concept of observability itself obviously is relative to the techniques of observation used. What is unobservable to the unaided senses may well be observable by means of suitable devices such as telescopes, microscopes, polariscopes, lie-detectors, Gallup-polls, etc. If by direct observation we mean such observational procedures as do not make use of auxiliary devices, then such property terms as "black", "hard", "liquid", "cool", and such relation terms as "above", "between", "spatially coincident", etc., might be said to refer to directly observable attributes; if observability is construed in a broader sense, so as to allow for the use of certain specified instruments or other devices, the concept of observable attribute becomes more comprehensive. If, in our study of confirmation, we wanted to analyze the manner in which the hypotheses and theories of empirical science are ultimately supported by "evidence of the senses", then we should have to require that observation reports refer exclusively to directly observable attributes. This view was taken, for simplicity and concreteness, in the preceding parts of this section. Actually, however, the general logical characteristics of that relation which obtains between a hypothesis and a group of empirical statements which "support" it, can be studied in isolation from this restriction to direct observability. All we will assume here is that in the context of the scientific test of a given hypothesis or theory, certain specified techniques of observation have been agreed upon; these determine an observational vocabulary, namely a set of terms designating properties and relations observable by means of the accepted techniques. For our purposes it is entirely sufficient that these terms, constituting the "observational vocabulary", be given. An observation sentence is then defined simply as a sentence affirming or denying that a given object, or sequence of objects, possesses one of those observable attributes.[27]

Let it be noted that we do not require an observation sentence to be true, nor to be accepted on the basis of actual observations; rather, an observation sentence expresses something that is decidable by means of the accepted techniques of observation; in other words: An observation sentence describes a possible outcome of the accepted observational techniques; it asserts something that might conceivably be established by means of those techniques. Possibly, the term "observation-type sentence" would be more suggestive; but for con-

[27] The concept of observation sentence has, in the context of our study, a status and a logical function closely akin to that of the concepts of protocol statement or basic sentence, etc., as used in many recent studies of empiricism. However, the conception of observation sentence which is being proposed in the present study is more liberal in that it renders the discussion of the logical problems of testing and confirmation independent of various highly controversial epistemological issues; thus, e.g. we do not stipulate that observation reports must be about psychic acts, or about sense perceptions (i.e. that they have to be expressed in terms of a vocabulary of phenomenology, or of introspective psychology). According to the conception of observation sentence adopted in the present study, the "objects" referred to in an observation sentence may be construed in any one of the senses just referred to, or in various other ways; for example, they might be space-time regions, or again physical objects such as stones, trees, etc. (most of the illustrations given throughout this article represent observation sentences belonging to this kind of "thing-language"); all that we require is that the few very general conditions stated above be satisfied.

These conditions impose on observation sentences and on observation reports certain restrictions with respect to their form; in particular, neither kind of sentence may contain any quantifiers. This stipulation recommends itself for the purposes of the logical analysis here to be undertaken; but we do not wish to claim that this formal restriction is indispensable. On the contrary, it is quite possible and perhaps desirable also to allow for observation sentences containing quantifiers: our simplifying assumption is introduced mainly in order to avoid considerable logical complications in the definition of confirmation.

venience we give preference to the shorter term. An analogous comment applies, of course, to our definition of an observation report as a class or a conjunction of observation sentences. The need for this broad conception of observation sentences and observation reports is readily recognized: Confirmation as here conceived is a logical relationship between sentences, just as logical consequence is. Now whether a sentence S_2 is a consequence of a sentence S_1 does not depend on whether S_1 is true (or known to be true), or not; and analogously, the criteria of whether a given statement, expressed in terms of the observational vocabulary, confirms a certain hypothesis cannot depend on whether the statements in the report are true, or based on actual experience, or the like. Our definition of confirmation must enable us to indicate what kind of evidence *would* confirm a given hypothesis *if* it were available; and clearly the sentence characterizing such evidence can be required only to express something that might be observed, but not necessarily something that has actually been established by observation.

It may be helpful to carry the analogy between confirmation and consequence one step further. The truth or falsity of S_1 is irrelevant for the question of whether S_2 is a consequence of S_1 (whether S_2 can be validly inferred from S_1); but in a logical inference which justifies a sentence S_2 by showing that it is a logical consequence of a conjunction of premisses, S_1, we can be certain of the truth of S_2 only if we know S_1 to be true. Analogously, the question of whether an observation report stands in the relation of confirmation to a given hypothesis does not depend on whether the report states actual or fictitious observational findings; but for a decision as to the soundness or acceptability of a hypothesis which is confirmed by a certain report, it is of course necessary to know whether the report is based on actual experience or not. Just as a conclusion of a logical inference, in order to be reliably true must be (a1) validly inferred from (a2) a set of true premisses, so a hypothesis, in order to be scientifically acceptable, must be (b1) formally confirmed by (b2) reliable reports on observational findings.

The central problem of this essay is to establish general criteria for the formal relation of confirmation as referred to in (b1); the analysis of the concept of a reliable observation report, which belongs largely to the field of pragmatics,[28] falls outside the scope of the present study. One point, however, deserves mention here: A statement of the form of an observation report (for example, about the position of the pointer of a certain thermograph at 3 a.m.) may be accepted or rejected in science either on the basis of direct observation, or because it is indirectly confirmed or disconfirmed by other accepted observation sentences (in the example, these might be sentences describing the curve traced by the pointer during the night), and because of this possibility of indirect confirmation, our study has a bearing also on the question of the acceptance of hypotheses which have themselves the form of observation reports.

The conception of confirmation as a relation between sentences analogous to that of logical consequence suggests yet another specification for the attempted definition of confirmation: While logical consequence has to be conceived of as

[28] An account of the concept of pragmatics may be found in the publications listed in n. 25.

a basically semantical relation between sentences, it has been possible, for certain languages, to establish criteria of logical consequence in purely syntactical terms.[29] Analogously, confirmation may be conceived of as a semantical relation between an observation report and a hypothesis; but the parallel with the consequence relation suggests that it should be possible for certain languages, to establish purely syntactical criteria of confirmation. The subsequent considerations will indeed eventuate in a definition of confirmation based on the concept of logical consequence and other purely syntactical concepts.

The interpretation of confirmation as a logical relation between sentences involves no essential change in the central problem of the present study. In particular, all the points made in the preceding sections can readily be rephrased in accordance with this interpretation. Thus, for example, the assertion that an object *a* which is a swan and white confirms the hypothesis '$(x)(\text{Swan}(x) \supset \text{White}(x))$' can be expressed by saying that the observation report '$\text{Swan}(a) \cdot \text{White}(a)$' confirms that hypothesis. Similarly, the equivalence condition can be reformulated as follows: If an observation report confirms a certain sentence, then it also confirms every sentence which is logically equivalent with the latter. Nicod's criterion as well as our grounds for rejecting it can be re-formulated along the same lines. We presented Nicod's concept of confirmation as referring to a relation between non-linguistic objects on one hand and sentences on the other because this approach seemed to approximate most closely Nicod's own formulations, and because it enabled us to avoid certain technicalities which are actually unnecessary in that context.

7. *The Prediction-criterion of Confirmation and its Shortcomings.* — We are now in a position to analyze a second conception of confirmation which is reflected in many methodological discussions and which can claim a great deal of plausibility. Its basic idea is very simple: General hypotheses in science as well as in everyday usage are intended to enable us to anticipate future events; hence, it seems reasonable to count any prediction which is borne out by subsequent observation as confirming evidence for the hypothesis on which it is based, and any prediction that fails as disconfirming evidence. To illustrate: Let H_1 be the hypothesis that all metals, when heated, expand; symbolically: '$(x)((\text{Metal}(x) \cdot \text{Heated}(x)) \supset \text{Exp}(x))$'. If we are given an observation report to the effect that a certain object *a* is a metal and is heated, then by means of H_1 we can derive the prediction that *a* expands. Suppose that this is borne out by observation and described in an additional observation statement. We should then have the total observation report. $\{\text{Metal}(a), \text{Heated}(a), \text{Exp.}(a)\}$.[30] This report would be qualified as confirming evidence for H_1 because its last sentence bears out what could be predicted, or derived, from the first two by means of H_1; more explicitly: because the last sentence can be derived from the first two in conjunction with H_1. — Now let H_2 be the hypothesis that all swans are white;

[29] Cf. especially the two publications by R. Carnap listed in n. 3.

[30] An (observation) report, it will be recalled, may be represented by a conjunction or by a class of observation sentences; in the latter case, we characterize it by writing the sentences between braces; the quotation marks which normally would be used are, for convenience, assumed to be absorbed by the braces.

symbolically: '$(x)(\text{Swan}(x) \supset \text{White}(x))$'; and consider the observation report $\{\text{Swan}(a), \sim \text{White}(a)\}$. This report would constitute disconfirming evidence for H_2 because the second of its sentences contradicts (and thus fails to bear out) the prediction 'White(a)' which can be deduced from the first sentence in conjunction with H_2; or, symmetrically, because the first sentence contradicts the consequence '$\sim$Swan(a)' which can be derived from the second in conjunction with H_2. Obviously, either of these formulations implies that H_2 is incompatible with the given observation report.

These illustrations suggest the following general definition of confirmation as successful prediction:

Prediction-criterion of Confirmation: Let H be a hypothesis, B an observation report, i.e. a class of observation sentences. Then

(*a*) B is said to confirm H if B can be divided into two mutually exclusive subclasses B_1 and B_2 such that B_2 is not empty, and every sentence of B_2 can be logically deduced from B_1 in conjunction with H, but not from B_1 alone.

(*b*) B is said to disconfirm H if H logically contradicts B.[31]

(*c*) B is said to be neutral with respect to H if it neither confirms nor disconfirms H.[32]

But while this criterion is quite sound as a statement of sufficient conditions of confirmation for hypotheses of the type illustrated above, it is considerably too narrow to serve as a general definition of confirmation. Generally speaking, this criterion would serve its purpose if all scientific hypotheses could be construed as asserting regular connections of observable features in the subject-matter under investigation; i.e. if they all were of the form "Whenever the observable characteristic P is present in an object or a suituation, then the observable characteristic Q will also be present." But actually, most scientific hypotheses and laws are not of this simple type; as a rule, they express regular connections of characteristics which are not observable in the sense of direct observability, nor even in a much more liberal sense. Consider, for example, the following hypothesis: "Whenever plane-polarized light of wave length λ traverses a layer of quartz of thickness d, then its plane of polarization is rotated through an angle α which is proportional to $\frac{d}{\lambda}$." — Let us assume that the observational vocabulary, by means of which our observation reports have to be formulated, contains exclusively terms referring to directly observable at-

[31] It might seem more natural to stipulate that B disconfirms H if it can be divided into two mutually exclusive classes B_1 and B_2 such that the denial of at least one sentence in B_2 can be deduced from B_1 in conjunction with H; but this condition can be shown to be equivalent to (*b*) above.

[32] The following quotations from A. J. Ayer's book *Language, Truth and Logic* (London, 1936) formulate in a particularly clear fashion the conception of confirmation as successful prediction (although the two are not explicitly identified by definition): "... the function of an empirical hypothesis is to enable us to anticipate experience. Accordingly, if an observation to which a given proposition is relevant conforms to our expectations, ... that proposition is confirmed" (*loc. cit.*, pp. 142–143). "... it is the mark of a genuine factual proposition ... that some experiential propositions can be deduced from it in conjunction with certain premises without being deducible from those other premises alone" (*loc. cit.*, p. 26).

tributes. Then, since the question of whether a given ray of light is plane-polarized and has the wave length λ cannot be decided by means of direct observation, no observation report of the kind here admitted could include information of this type. This in itself would not be crucial if at least we could assume that the fact that a given ray of light is plane-polarized, etc., could be logically inferred from some possible observation report; for then, from a suitable report of this kind, in conjunction with the given hypothesis, one would be able to predict a rotation of the plane of polarization; and from this prediction, which itself is not yet expressed in exclusively observational terms, one might expect to derive further predictions in the form of genuine observation sentences. But actually, a hypothesis to the effect that a given ray of light is plane-polarized has to be considered as a general hypothesis which entails an unlimited number of observation sentences; thus it cannot be logically inferred from, but at best be confirmed by, a suitable set of observational findings. The logically essential point can best be exhibited by reference to a very simple abstract case: Let us assume that R_1 and R_2 are two relations of a kind accessible to direct observation, and that the field of scientific investigation contains infinitely many objects. Consider now the hypothesis

$$(H) \qquad (x)((y)R_1(x, y) \supset (\mathrm{E}z)R_2(x, z)),$$

i.e.: Whenever an object x stands in R_1 to every object y, then it stands in R_2 to at least one object z. — This simple hypothesis has the following property: However many observation sentences may be given, H does not enable us to derive any new observation sentences from them. Indeed — to state the reason in suggestive though not formally rigorous terms — in order to make a prediction concerning some specific object a, we should first have to know that a stands in R_1 to every object; and this necessary information clearly cannot be contained in any finite number, however large, of observation sentences, because a finite set of observation sentences can tell us at best for a finite number of objects that a stands in R_1 to them. Thus an observation report, which always involves only a finite number of observation sentences, can never provide a sufficiently broad basis for a prediction by means of H.[33] — Besides, even if we did know that a stood in R_1 to every object, the prediction derivable by means of H would not be an observation sentence; it would assert that a stands in R_2 to *some* object, without specifying which, and where to find it. Thus, H would be an empirical hypothesis, containing, besides purely logical terms, only expressions belonging to the observational vocabulary, and yet the predictions which it renders possible neither start from nor lead to observation reports.

It is, therefore, a considerable over-simplification to say that scientific hypotheses and theories enable us to derive predictions of future experiences from descriptions of past ones. Unquestionably, scientific hypotheses do have a pre-

[33] To illustrate: a might be an iron object which possibly is a magnet; R_1 might be the relation of attracting; the objects under investigation might be iron objects. Then a finite number of observation reports to the effect that a did attract a particular piece of iron is insufficient to *infer* that a will attract every piece of iron.

dictive function; but the way in which they perform this function, the manner in which they establish logical connections between observation reports, is logically more complex than a deductive inference. Thus, in the last illustration, the predictive use of H may assume the following form: On the basis of a number of individual tests, which show that a does stand in R_1 to three objects b, c, and d, we may accept the hypothesis that a stands in R_1 to all objects; or, in terms of our formal mode of speech: In view of the observation report $\{R_1(a, b), R_1(a, c), R_1(a, d)\}$, the hypothesis that $(y)R_1(a, y)$ is accepted as confirmed by, though not logically inferable from, that report.[34] This process might be referred to as quasi-induction.[35] From the hypothesis thus established we can then proceed to derive, by means of H, the prediction that a stands in R_2 to at least one object. This again, as was pointed out above, is not an observation sentence; and indeed no observation sentence can be derived from it; but it can, in turn, be confirmed by a suitable observation sentence, such as '$R_2(a, b)$'. — In other cases, the prediction of actual observation sentences may be possible; thus if the given hypothesis asserts that $(x)((y)R_1(x, y) \supset (z)R_2(x, z))$, then after quasi-inductively accepting, as above, that $(y)R_1(a, y)$, we can derive, by means of the given hypothesis, the sentence that a stands in R_2 to every object, and thence, we can deduce special predictions such as '$R_2(a, b)$', etc., which do have the form of observation sentences.

Thus, the chain of reasoning which leads from given observational findings to the "prediction" of new ones actually involves, besides deductive inferences, certain quasi-inductive steps each of which consists in the acceptance of an intermediate statement on the basis of confirming, but usually not logically conclusive, evidence. In most scientific predictions, this general pattern occurs in multiple re-iteration; an analysis of the predictive use of the hypothesis mentioned above, concerning plane-polarized light, could serve as an illustration. In the present context, however, this general account of the structure of scientific prediction is sufficient: it shows that a general definition of confirmation by reference to successful prediction becomes circular; indeed, in order to make the original formulation of the prediction-criterion of confirmation sufficiently comprehensive, we should have to replace the phrase "can be logically deduced" by "can be obtained by a series of steps of deduction and quasi-induction"; and the definition of "quasi-induction" in the above sense presupposes the concept of confirmation.

Let us note, as a by-product of the preceding consideration, the fact that an adequate analysis of scientific prediction (and analogously, of scientific explana-

[34] Thus, in the illustration given in the preceding footnote, the hypothesis that the object a will attract every piece of iron might be accepted as sufficiently well substantiated by, though by no means derivable from, an observation report to the effect that in tests a did attract the iron objects b, c, and d.

[35] The prefix "quasi" is to contradistinguish the procedure in question from so-called induction, which is usually supposed to be a method of discovering, or arriving at, general regularities on the basis of a finite number of instances. In quasi-induction, the hypothesis is not "discovered" but has to be *given* in addition to the observation report: the process consists in the acceptance of the hypothesis if it is deemed sufficiently confirmed by the observation report. Cf. also the discussion in section 1*c*, above.

tion, and of the testing of empirical hypotheses) requires an analysis of the concept of confirmation. The reason for this fact may be restated in general terms as follows: Scientific laws and theories, as a rule, connect terms which lie on the level of abstract theoretical constructs rather than on that of direct observation; and from observation sentences, no merely deductive logical inference leads to statements about those theoretical constructs which are the starting point for scientific predictions; statements about logical constructs, such as "This piece of iron is magnetic" or "Here, a plane-polarized ray of light traverses a quartz crystal" can be confirmed, but not entailed, by observation reports, and thus, even though based on general scientific laws, the "prediction" of new observational findings on the basis of given ones is a process involving confirmation in addition to logical deduction.[36]

8. *Conditions of Adequacy for any Definition of Confirmation.* — The two most customary conceptions of confirmation, which were rendered explicit in Nicod's criterion and in the prediction criterion, have thus been found unsuitable for a general definition of confirmation. Besides this negative result, the preceding analysis has also exhibited certain logical characteristics of scientific prediction, explanation, and testing, and it has led to the establishment of certain standards which an adequate definition of confirmation has to satisfy. These standards include the equivalence condition and the requirement that the definition of confirmation be applicable to hypotheses of any degree of logical complexity, rather than to the simplest type of universal conditional only. An adequate definition of confirmation, however, has to satisfy several further logical requirements, to which we now turn.

First of all, it will be agreed that any sentence which is entailed by — i.e. a logical consequence of — a given observation report has to be considered as confirmed by that report: Entailment is a special case of confirmation. Thus, e.g., we want to say that the observation report "*a* is black" confirms the sentence (hypothesis) "*a* is black or grey"; and — to refer to one of the illustrations given in the preceding section — the observation sentence '$R_2(a, b)$' should certainly be confirming evidence for the sentence '$(Ez)R_2(a, z)$'. We are therefore led to the stipulation that any adequate definition of confirmation must insure the fulfilment of the

(8.1) *Entailment condition:* Any sentence which is entailed by an observation report is confirmed by it.[37]

[36] In the above sketch of the structure of scientific prediction, we have disregarded the fact that in practically every case where a prediction is said to be obtained by means of a certain hypothesis or theory, a considerable mass of auxiliary theories is used in addition; thus, e.g. the prediction of observable effects of the deflection of light in the gravitational field of the sun on the basis of the general theory of relativity, requires such auxiliary theories as mechanics and optics. But an explicit consideration of this fact would not affect our result that scientific predictions, even when based on hypotheses or theories of universal form, still are not purely deductive in character, but involve quasi-inductive steps as well.

[37] As a consequence of this stipulation, a contradictory observation report, such as $\{\text{Black}(a), \sim\text{Black}(a)\}$ confirms every sentence, because it has every sentence as a consequence. Of course, it is possible to exclude the possibility of contradictory observation reports altogether by a slight restriction of the definition of "observation report." There is, however, no important reason to do so.

This condition is suggested by the preceding consideration, but of course not proved by it. To make it a standard of adequacy for the definition of confirmation means to lay down the stipulation that a proposed definition of confirmation will be rejected as logically inadequate if it is not constructed in such a way that (8.1) is unconditionally satisfied. An analogous remark applies to the subsequently proposed further standards of adequacy. —

Second, an observation report which confirms certain hypotheses would invariably be qualified as confirming any consequence of those hypotheses. Indeed: any such consequence is but an assertion of all or part of the combined content of the original hypotheses and has therefore to be regarded as confirmed by any evidence which confirms the original hypotheses. This suggests the following condition of adequacy:

(8.2) *Consequence Condition:* If an observation report confirms every one of a class K of sentences, then it also confirms any sentence which is a logical consequence of K.

If (8.2) is satisfied, then the same is true of the following two more special conditions:

(8.21) *Special Consequence Condition:* If an observation report confirms a hypothesis H, then it also confirms every consequence of H.

(8.22) *Equivalence Condition:* If an observation report confirms a hypothesis H, then it also confirms every hypothesis which is logically equivalent with H.

(This follows from (8.21) in view of the fact that equivalent hypotheses are mutual consequences of each other.) Thus, the satisfaction of the consequence condition entails that of our earlier equivalence condition, and the latter loses its status of an independent requirement.

In view of the apparent obviousness of these conditions, it is interesting to note that the definition of confirmation in terms of successful prediction, while satisfying the equivalence condition, would violate the consequence condition. Consider, for example, the formulation of the prediction-criterion given in the earlier part of the preceding section. Clearly, if the observational findings B_2 can be predicted on the basis of the findings B_1 by means of the hypothesis H, the same prediction is obtainable by means of any equivalent hypothesis, but not generally by means of a weaker one.

On the other hand, any prediction obtainable by means of H can obviously also be established by means of any hypothesis which is stronger than H, i.e. which logically entails H. Thus, while the consequence condition stipulates in effect that whatever confirms a given hypothesis also confirms any weaker hypothesis, the relation of confirmation defined in terms of successful prediction would satisfy the condition that whatever confirms a given hypothesis, also confirms every stronger one.

But is this "converse consequence condition", as it might be called, not reasonable enough, and should it not even be included among our standards of adequacy for the definition of confirmation? The second of these two suggestions can be readily disposed of: The adoption of the new condition, in addition to (8.1) and (8.2), would have the consequence that any observation report B

would confirm any hypothesis *H* whatsoever. Thus, e.g., if *B* is the report "*a* is a raven" and *H* is Hooke's law, then, according to (8.1), *B* confirms the sentence "*a* is a raven", hence *B* would, according to the converse consequence condition, confirm the stronger sentence "*a* is a raven, and Hooke's law holds"; and finally, by virtue of (8.2), *B* would confirm *H*, which is a consequence of the last sentence. Obviously, the same type of argument can be applied in all other cases.

But is it not true, after all, that very often observational data which confirm a hypothesis *H* are considered also as confirming a stronger hypothesis? Is it not true, for example, that those experimental findings which confirm Galileo's law, or Kepler's laws, are considered also as confirming Newton's law of gravitation?[38] This is indeed the case, but this does not justify the acceptance of the converse entailment condition as a general rule of the logic of confirmation; for in the cases just mentioned, the weaker hypothesis is connected with the stronger one by a logical bond of a particular kind: it is essentially a substitution instance of the stronger one; thus, e.g., while the law of gravitation refers to the force obtaining between any two bodies, Galileo's law is a specialization referring to the case where one of the bodies is the earth, the other an object near its surface. In the preceding case, however, where Hooke's law was shown to be confirmed by the observation report that *a* is a raven, this situation does not prevail; and here, the rule that whatever confirms a given hypothesis also confirms any stronger one becomes an entirely absurd principle. Thus, the converse consequence condition does not provide a sound general condition of adequacy.[39]

A third condition remains to be stated:[40]

(8.3) *Consistency Condition:* Every logically consistent observation report is logically compatible with the class of all the hypotheses which it confirms.

[38] Strictly speaking, Galileo's law and Kepler's laws can be deduced from the law of gravitation only if certain additional hypotheses — including the laws of motion — are presupposed; but this does not affect the point under discussion.

[39] William Barrett, in a paper entitled "Discussion on Dewey's Logic" (*The Philosophical Review*, vol. 50, 1941, pp. 305 ff., esp. p. 312) raises some questions closely related to what we have called above the consequence condition and the converse consequence condition. In fact, he invokes the latter (without stating it explicitly) in an argument which is designed to show that "not every observation which confirms a sentence need also confirm all its consequences", in other words, that the special consequence condition (8.21) need not always be satisfied. He supports his point by reference to "the simplest case: the sentence '*C*' is an abbreviation of '*A*·*B*', and the observation 0 confirms '*A*', *and so* '*C*', but is irrelevant to '*B*', which is a consequence of '*C*'." (Italics mine.)

For reasons contained in the above discussion of the consequence condition and the converse consequence condition, the application of the latter in the case under consideration seems to us unjustifiable, so that the illustration does not prove the author's point; and indeed, there seems to be every reason to preserve the unrestricted validity of the consequence condition. As a matter of fact, Mr. Barrett himself argues that "the degree of confirmation for the consequence of a sentence cannot be less than that of the sentence itself"; this is indeed quite sound; but it is hard to see how the recognition of this principle can be reconciled with a renunciation of the special consequence condition, since the latter may be considered simply as the correlate, for the non-gradated relation of confirmation, of the former principle which is adapted to the concept of degree of confirmation.

[40] For a fourth condition, see n. 16.

The two most important implications of this requirement are the following:

(8.31) Unless an observation report is self-contradictory,[41] it does not confirm any hypothesis with which it is not logically compatible.

(8.32) Unless an observation report is self-contradictory, it does not confirm any hypotheses which contradict each other.

The first of these corollaries will readily be accepted; the second, however, — and consequently (8.3) itself — will perhaps be felt to embody a too severe restriction. It might be pointed out, for example, that a finite set of measurements concerning the variation of one physical magnitude, x, with another, y, may conform to, and thus be said to confirm, several different hypotheses as to the particular mathematical function in terms of which the relationship of x and y can be expressed; but such hypotheses are incompatible because to at least one value of x, they will assign different values of y.

No doubt it is possible to liberalize the formal standards of adequacy in line with these considerations. This would amount to dropping (8.3) and (8.32) and retaining only (8.31). One of the effects of this measure would be that when a logically consistent observation report B confirms each of two hypotheses, it does not necessarily confirm their conjunction; for the hypotheses might be mutually incompatible, hence their conjunction self-contradictory; consequently, by (8.31), B could not confirm it. — This consequence is intuitively rather awkward, and one might therefore feel inclined to suggest that while (8.3) should be dropped and (8.31) retained, (8.32) should be replaced by the requirement (8.33): If an observation sentence confirms each of two hypotheses, then it also confirms their conjunction. But it can readily be shown that by virtue of (8.2) this set of conditions entails the fulfilment of (8.32).

If, therefore, the condition (8.3) appears to be too rigorous, the most obvious alternative would seem to lie in replacing (8.3) and its corollaries by the much weaker condition (8.31) alone; and it is an important problem whether an intuitively adequate definition of confirmation can be constructed which satisfies (8.1), (8.2) and (8.31), but not (8.3). — One of the great advantages of a definition which satisfies (8.3) is that it sets a limit, so to speak, to the strength of the hypotheses which can be confirmed by given evidence.[42]

The remainder of the present study, therefore, will be concerned exclusively with the problem of establishing a definition of confirmation which satisfies the more severe formal conditions represented by (8.1), (8.2), and (8.3) together.

The fulfilment of these requirements, which may be regarded as general laws of the logic of confirmation, is of course only a necessary, not a sufficient, condition for the adequacy of any proposed definition of confirmation. Thus, e.g., if "B confirms H" were defined as meaning "B logically entails H", then the above three conditions would clearly be satisfied; but the definition would

[41] A contradictory observation report confirms every hypothesis (cf. n. 8) and is, of course, incompatible with every one of the hypotheses it confirms.

[42] This was pointed out to me by Dr. Nelson Goodman. The definition later to be outlined in this essay, which satisfies conditions (8.1), (8.2) and (8.3), lends itself, however, to certain generalizations which satisfy only the more liberal conditions of adequacy just considered.

not be adequate because confirmation has to be a more comprehensive relation than entailment (the latter might be referred to as the special case of *conclusive* confirmation). Thus, a definition of confirmation, to be acceptable, also has to to be materially adequate: it has to provide a reasonably close approximation to that conception of confirmation which is implicit in scientific procedure and methodological discussion. That conception is vague and to some extent quite unclear, as I have tried to show in earlier parts of this paper; therefore, it would be too much to expect full agreement as to the material adequacy of a proposed definition of confirmation; on the other hand, there will be rather general agreement on certain points; thus, e.g., the identification of confirmation with entailment, or the Nicod criterion of confirmation as analyzed above, or any definition of confirmation by reference to a "sense of evidence", will probably now be admitted not to be adequate approximations to that concept of confirmation which is relevant for the logic of science.

On the other hand, the soundness of the logical analysis (which, in a clear sense, always involves a logical reconstruction) of a theoretical concept cannot be gauged simply by our feelings of satisfaction at a certain proposed analysis; and if there are, say, two alternative proposals for defining a term on the basis of a logical analysis, and if both appear to come fairly close to the intended meaning, then the choice has to be made largely by reference to such features as the logical properties of the two reconstructions, and the comprehensiveness and simplicity of the theories to which they lead.

9. *The Satisfaction Criterion of Confirmation.* — As has been mentioned before, a precise definition of confirmation requires reference to some definite "language of science", in which all observation reports and all hypotheses under consideration are assumed to be formulated, and whose logical structure is supposed to be precisely determined. The more complex this language, and the richer its logical means of expression, the more difficult it will be, as a rule, to establish an adequate definition of confirmation for it. However, the problem has been solved at least for certain cases: With respect to languages of a comparatively simple logical structure, it has been possible to construct an explicit definition of confirmation which satisfies all of the above logical requirements, and which appears to be intuitively rather adequate. An exposition of the technical details of this definition has been published elsewhere;[43] in the present study, which is

[43] In my article referred to in n. 1. The logical structure of the languages to which the definition in question is applicable is that of the lower functional calculus with individual constants, and with predicate constants of any degree. All sentences of the language are assumed to be formed exclusively by means of predicate constants, individual constants, individual variables, universal and existential quantifiers for individual variables, and the connective symbols of denial, conjunction, alternation, and implication. The use of predicate variables or of the identity sign is not permitted.

As to the predicate constants, they are all assumed to belong to the observational vocabulary, i.e. to denote a property or a relation observable by means of the accepted techniques. ("Abstract" predicate terms are supposed to be defined in terms of those of the observational vocabulary and then actually to be replaced by their *definientia*, so that they never occur explicitly.)

As a consequence of these stipulations, an observation report can be characterized simply as a conjunction of sentences of the kind illustrated by '$P(a)$', '$\sim P(b)$', '$R(c, d)$', '$\sim R(e, f)$',

concerned with the general logical and methodological aspects of the problem of confirmation rather than with technical details, it will be attempted to characterize the definition of confirmation thus obtained as clearly as possible with a minimum of technicalities.

Consider the simple case of the hypothesis H: '$(x)(\text{Raven}(x) \supset \text{Black}(x))$', where 'Raven' and 'Black' are supposed to be terms of our observational vocabulary. Let B be an observation report to the effect that $\text{Raven}(a) \cdot \text{Black}(a) \cdot \sim\text{Raven}(c) \cdot \text{Black}(c) \cdot \sim\text{Raven}(d) \cdot \sim\text{Black}(d)$. Then B may be said to confirm H in the following sense: There are three objects altogether mentioned in B, namely a, c, and d; and as far as these are concerned, B informs us that all those which are ravens (i.e. just the object a) are also black.[44] In other words, from the information contained in B we can infer that the hypothesis H does hold true within the finite class of those objects which are mentioned in B.

Let us apply the same consideration to a hypothesis of a logically more complex structure. Let H be the hypothesis "Everybody likes somebody"; in symbols: '$(x)(Ey)\text{Likes}(x, y)$', i.e. for every (person) x, there exists at least one (not necessarily different person) y such that x likes y. (Here again, 'Likes' is supposed to be a relation-term which occurs in our observational vocabulary.) Suppose now that we are given an observation report B in which the names of two persons, say 'e' and 'f', occur. Under what conditions shall we say that B confirms H? The previous illustration suggests the answer: If from B we can infer that H is satisfied within the finite class $\{e, f\}$; i.e. that within $\{e, f\}$ everybody likes somebody. This in turn means that e likes e or f, and f likes e or f. Thus, B would be said to confirm H if B entailed the statement "e likes e or f, and f likes e or f". This latter statement will be called the development of H for the finite class $\{e, f\}$. —

The concept of *development of a hypothesis*, H, *for a finite class of individuals*, C, can be defined in a general fashion; the development of H for C states what H would assert if there existed exclusively those objects which are elements of C. — Thus, e.g., the development of the hypothesis H_1 = '$(x)(P(x) \vee Q(x))$' (i.e. "Every object has the property P or the property Q") for the class $\{a, b\}$ is '$(P(a) \vee Q(a)) \cdot (P(b) \vee Q(b))$' (i.e. "$a$ has the property P or the property Q, and b has the property P or the property Q"); the development of the existential hypothesis H_2 that at least one object has the property P, i.e. '$(Ex)P(x)$', for $\{a, b\}$ is '$P(a) \vee P(b)$'; the development of a hypothesis which contains no quantifiers, such as H_3: '$P(c) \vee Q(c)$' is defined as that hypothesis itself, no matter what the reference class of individuals is.

A more detailed formal analysis based on considerations of this type leads to the introduction of a general relation of confirmation in two steps; the first

---

etc., where 'P', 'R', etc., belong to the observational vocabulary, and 'a', 'b', 'c', 'd', 'e', 'f', etc., are individual names, denoting specific objects. It is also possible to define an observation report more liberally as any sentence containing no quantifiers, which means that besides conjunctions also alternations and implication sentences formed out of the above kind of components are included among the observation reports.

[44] I am indebted to Dr. Nelson Goodman for having suggested this idea; it initiated all those considerations which finally led to the definition to be outlined below.

consists in defining a special relation of direct confirmation along the lines just indicated; the second step then defines the general relation of confirmation by reference to direct confirmation.

Omitting minor details, we may summarize the two definitions as follows:

(9.1 Df.) An observation report B directly confirms a hypothesis H if B entails the development of H for the class of those objects which are mentioned in B.

(9.2 Df.) An observation report B confirms a hypothesis H if H is entailed by a class of sentences each of which is directly confirmed by B.

The criterion expressed in these definitions might be called the satisfaction criterion of confirmation because its basic idea consists in construing a hypothesis as confirmed by a given observation report if the hypothesis is satisfied in the finite class of those individuals which are mentioned in the report. — Let us now apply the two definitions to our last examples: The observation report B_1: '$P(a) \cdot Q(b)$' directly confirms (and therefore also confirms) the hypothesis H_1, because it entails the development of H_1 for the class $\{a, b\}$, which was given above. — The hypothesis H_3 is not directly confirmed by B, because its development — i.e. H_3 itself — obviously is not entailed by B_1. However, H_3 is entailed by H_1, which is directly confirmed by B_1; hence, by virtue of (9.2), B_1 confirms H_3.

Similarly, it can readily be seen that B_1 directly confirms H_2.

Finally, to refer to the first illustration given in this section: The observation report 'Raven(a) $\cdot$ Black(a) $\cdot \sim$Raven(c) $\cdot \sim$Black(c) $\cdot \sim$ Raven(d) $\cdot \sim$Black(d)' confirms (even directly) the hypothesis '(x)(Raven(x) $\supset$ Black(x))', for it entails the development of the latter for the class $\{a, c, d\}$, which can be written as follows: '(Raven(a) $\supset$ Black(a)) $\cdot$ (Raven(c) $\supset$ Black(c)) $\cdot$ (Raven(d) $\supset$ Black(d))'.

It is now easy to define disconfirmation and neutrality:

(9.3 Df.) An observation report B disconfirms a hypothesis H if it confirms the denial of H.

(9.4 Df.) An observation report B is neutral with respect to a hypothesis H if B neither confirms nor disconfirms H.

By virtue of the criteria laid down in (9.2), (9.3), (9.4), every consistent observation report, B, divides all possible hypotheses into three mutually exclusive classes: those confirmed by B, those disconfirmed by B, and those with respect to which B is neutral.

The definition of confirmation here proposed can be shown to satisfy all the formal conditions of adequacy embodied in (8.1), (8.2), and (8.3) and their consequences; for the condition (8.2) this is easy to see; for the other conditions the proof is more complicated.[45]

[45] For these proofs, see the article referred to in Part I, n. 1. I should like to take this opportunity to point out and to remedy a certain defect of the definition of confirmation which was developed in that article, and which has been outlined above: this defect was brought to my attention by a discussion with Dr. Olaf Helmer.

It will be agreed that an acceptable definition of confirmation should satisfy the following further condition which might well have been included among the logical standards of adequacy set up in section 8 above: (8.4). If B_1 and B_2 are logically equivalent observation re-

Furthermore, the application of the above definition of confirmation is not restricted to hypotheses of universal conditional form (as Nicod's criterion is, for example), nor to universal hypotheses in general; it applies, in fact, to any hypothesis which can be expressed by means of property and relation terms of the observational vocabulary of the given language, individual names, the customary connective symbols for 'not', 'and', 'or', 'if-then', and any number of universal and existential quantifiers.

Finally, as is suggested by the preceding illustrations as well as by the general considerations which underlie the establishment of the above definition, it seems that we have obtained a definition of confirmation which also is materially adequate in the sense of being a reasonable approximation to the intended meaning of confirmation.

A brief discussion of certain special cases of confirmation might serve to shed further light on this latter aspect of our analysis.

10. *The Relative and the Absolute Concepts of Verification and Falsification.* — If an observation report entails a hypothesis H, then, by virtue of (8.1), it confirms H. This is in good agreement with the customary conception of confirming evidence; in fact, we have here an extreme case of confirmation, the case where B *conclusively confirms* H; this case is realized if, and only if, B entails H. We shall

ports and B_1 confirms (disconfirms, is neutral with respect to) a hypothesis H, then B_2, too, confirms (disconfirms, is neutral with respect to) H. This condition is indeed satisfied if observation reports are construed, as they have been in this article, as classes or conjunctions of observation sentences. As was indicated at the end of n. 14, however, this restriction of observation reports to a conjunctive form is not essential; in fact, it has been adopted here only for greater convenience of exposition, and all the preceding results, including especially the definitions and theorems of the present section, remain applicable without change if observation reports are given the more liberal interpretation characterized at the end of n. 14. (In this case, if 'P' and 'Q' belong to the observational vocabulary, such sentences as '$P(a) \vee Q(a)$', '$P(a) \vee \sim Q(b)$', etc., would qualify as observation reports.) This broader conception of observation reports was therefore adopted in the article referred to in Part I, n. 1; but it has turned out that in this case, the definition of confirmation summarized above does not generally satisfy the requirement (8.4). Thus, e.g., the observation reports, B_1 = '$P(a)$' and B_2 = '$P(a) \cdot (Q(b) \vee \sim Q(b))$' are logically equivalent, but while B_1 confirms (and even directly confirms) the hypothesis H_1='$(x)P(x)$', the second report does not do so, essentially because it does not entail '$P(a) \cdot P(b)$', which is the development of H_1 for the class of those objects mentioned in B_2. This deficiency can be remedied as follows: The fact that B_2 fails to confirm H_1 is obviously due to the circumstance that B_2 contains the individual constant 'b', without asserting anything about b: The object b is mentioned only in an analytic component of B_2. The atomic constituent '$Q(b)$' will therefore be said to occur (twice) inessentially in B_2. Generally, an atomic constituent A of a molecular sentence S will be said to occur inessentially in S if by virtue of the rules of the sentential calculus S is equivalent to a molecular sentence in which A does not occur at all. Now an object will be said to be mentioned inessentially in an observation report if it is mentioned only in such components of that report as occur inessentially in it. The sentential calculus clearly provides mechanical procedures for deciding whether a given observation report mentions any object inessentially, and for establishing equivalent formulations of the same report in which no object is mentioned inessentially. Finally, let us say that an object is mentioned essentially in an observation report if it is mentioned, but not only mentioned inessentially, in that report. Now we replace 9.1 by the following definition:

(9.1*a*) An observation report B directly confirms a hypothesis H if B entails the development of H for the class of those objects which are mentioned essentially in B.

The concept of confirmation as defined by (9.1*a*) and (9.2) now satisfies (8.4) in addition to (8.1), (8.2), (8.3) even if observation reports are construed in the broader fashion characterized earlier in this footnote.

then also say that *B verifies H*. Thus, verification is a special case of confirmation: it is a logical relation between sentences; more specifically, it is simply the relation of entailment with its domain restricted to observation sentences.

Analogously, we shall say that *B conclusively disconfirms H*, or *B falsifies H*, if and only if *B* is incompatible with *H*; in this case, *B* entails the denial of *H* and therefore, by virtue of (8.1) and (9.3), confirms the denial of *H* and disconfirms *H*. Hence, falsification is a special case of disconfirmation; it is the logical relation of incompatibility between sentences, with its domain restricted to observation sentences.

Clearly, the concepts of *verification* and *falsification* as here defined are *relative;* a hypothesis can be said to be verified or falsified only with respect to some observation report; and a hypothesis may be verified by one observation report and may not be verified by another. There are, however, hypotheses which cannot be verified and others which cannot be falsified by any observation report. This will be shown presently. We shall say that a given *hypothesis is verifiable* (*falsifiable*) if it is possible to construct an observation report which verifies (falsifies) the hypothesis. Whether a hypothesis is verifiable, or falsifiable, in this sense depends exclusively on its logical form. Briefly, the following cases may be distinguished:

(*a*) If a hypothesis does not contain the quantifier terms "all" and "some" or their symbolic equivalents, then it is both verifiable and falsifiable. Thus, e.g., the hypothesis "Object *a* turns blue or green" is entailed and thus verified by the report "Object *a* turns blue"; and the same hypothesis is incompatible with, and thus falsified by, the report "Object *a* turns neither blue nor green".

(*b*) A purely existential hypothesis (i.e. one which can be symbolized by a formula consisting of one or more existential quantifiers followed by a sentential function containing no quantifiers) is verifiable, but not falsifiable, if — as is usually assumed — the universe of discourse contains an infinite number of objects. — Thus, e.g., the hypothesis "There are blue roses" is verified by the observation report "Object *a* is a blue rose", but no finite observation report can ever contradict and thus falsify the hypothesis.

(*c*) Conversely, a purely universal hypothesis (symbolized by a formula consisting of one or more universal quantifiers followed by a sentential function containing no quantifiers) is falsifiable but not verifiable for an infinite universe of discourse. Thus, e.g., the hypothesis "$(x)(\mathrm{Swan}(x) \supset \mathrm{White}(x))$" is completely falsified by the observation report $\{\mathrm{Swan}(a), \sim\mathrm{White}(a)\}$; but no finite observation report can entail and thus verify the hypothesis in question.

(*d*) Hypotheses which cannot be expressed by sentences of one of the three types mentioned so far, and which in this sense require both universal and existential quantifiers for their formulation, are as a rule neither verifiable nor falsifiable.[46] Thus, e.g., the hypothesis "Every substance is soluble in some solvent" — symbolically '$(x)(Ey)\mathrm{Soluble}(x, y)$' — is neither entailed by, nor in-

[46] A more precise study of the conditions of non-verifiability and non-falsifiability would involve technicalities which are unnecessary for the purposes of the present study. Not all hypotheses of the type described in (*d*) are neither verifiable nor falsifiable; thus, e.g., the hypothesis '$(x)(Ey)(P(x) \vee Q(y))$' is verified by the report '$Q(a)$', and the hypothesis '$(x)(Ey)(P(x) \cdot Q(y))$' is falsified by '$\sim P(a)$'.

compatible with any observation report, no matter how many cases of solubility or non-solubility of particular substances in particular solvents the report may list. An analogous remark applies to the hypothesis "You can fool some of the people all of the time", whose symbolic formulation '$(Ex)(t)\mathrm{Fl}(x, t)$' contains one existential and one universal quantifier. But of course, all of the hypotheses belonging to this fourth class are capable of being confirmed or disconfirmed by suitable observation reports; this was illustrated early in section 9 by reference to the hypothesis '$(x)(Ey)\mathrm{Likes}(x, y)$'.

This rather detailed account of verification and falsification has been presented not only in the hope of further elucidating the meaning of confirmation and disconfirmation as defined above, but also in order to provide a basis for a sharp differentiation of two meanings of verification (and similarly of falsification) which have not always been clearly separated in recent discussions of the character of empirical knowledge. One of the two meanings of verification which we wish to distinguish here is the relative concept just explained; for greater clarity we shall sometimes refer to it as *relative verification.* The other meaning is what may be called *absolute or definitive verification.* This latter concept of verification does not belong to formal logic, but rather to pragmatics [47]: it refers to the acceptance of hypotheses by "observers" or "scientists", etc., on the basis of relevant evidence. Generally speaking, we may distinguish three phases in the scientific test of a given hypothesis (which do not necessarily occur in the order in which they are listed here). The first phase consists in the performance of suitable experiments or observations and the ensuing acceptance of observation sentences, or of observation reports, stating the results obtained; the next phase consists in confronting the given hypothesis with the accepted observation reports, i.e. in ascertaining whether the latter constitute confirming, disconfirming or irrelevant evidence with respect to the hypothesis; the final phase consists either in accepting or rejecting the hypothesis on the strength of the confirming or disconfirming evidence constituted by the accepted observation reports, or in suspending judgment, awaiting the establishment of further relevant evidence.

The present study has been concerned almost exclusively with the second phase; as we have seen, this phase is of a purely logical character; the standards of evaluation here invoked — namely the criteria of confirmation, disconfirmation and neutrality — can be completely formulated in terms of concepts belonging to the field of pure logic.

The first phase, on the other hand, is of a pragmatic character; it involves no logical confrontation of sentences with other sentences. It consists in performing certain experiments or systematic observations and noting the results. The latter are expressed in sentences which have the form of observation reports, and their acceptance by the scientist is connected (by causal, not by logical relations) with experiences occurring in those tests. (Of course, a sentence which has the form of an observation report may in certain cases be accepted not on the basis of direct observation, but because it is confirmed by other observation

[47] In the sense in which the term is used by Carnap in the work referred to in n. 25.

reports which were previously established; but this process is illustrative of the second phase, which was discussed before. Here we are considering the case where a sentence is accepted directly "on the basis of experiential findings" rather than because it is supported by previously established statements.)

The third phase, too, can be construed as pragmatic, namely as consisting in a decision on the part of the scientist or a group of scientists to accept (or reject, or leave in suspense, as the case may be) a given hypothesis after ascertaining what amount of confirming or of disconfirming evidence for the hypothesis is contained in the totality of the accepted observation sentences. However, it may well be attempted to give a reconstruction of this phase in purely logical terms. This would require the establishment of general "rules of acceptance"; roughly speaking, these rules would state how well a given hypothesis has to be confirmed by the accepted observation reports to be scientifically acceptable itself; [48] i.e. the rules would formulate criteria for the acceptance or rejection of a hypothesis by reference to the kind and amount of confirming or disconfirming evidence for it embodied in the totality of accepted observation reports; possibly, these criteria would also refer to such additional factors as the "simplicity" of the hypothesis in question, the manner in which it fits into the system of previously accepted theories, etc. It is at present an open question to what extent a satisfactory system of such rules can be formulated in purely logical terms.[49]

[48] A stimulating discussion of some aspects of what we have called rules of acceptance is contained in an article by Felix Kaufmann, "The Logical Rules of Scientific Procedure," *Philosophy and Phenomenological Research* (June, 1942).

If an explicit definition of the degree of confirmation of a hypothesis were available, then it might be possible to formulate criteria of acceptance in terms of the degree to which the accepted observation reports confirm the hypothesis in question.

[49] The preceding division of the test of an empirical hypothesis into three phases of different character may prove useful for the clarification of the question whether or to what extent an empiricist conception of confirmation implies a "coherence theory of truth". This issue has recently been raised by Bertrand Russell, who, in ch. x of his *Inquiry into Meaning and Truth,* has levelled a number of objections against the views of Otto Neurath on this subject (cf. the articles mentioned in the next footnote), and against statements made by myself in articles published in *Analysis* in 1935 and 1936. I should like to add here a few, necessarily brief, comments on this issue.

(1) While, in the articles in *Analysis,* I argued in effect that the only possible interpretation of the phrase "Sentence S is true" is "S is highly confirmed by accepted observation reports," I should now reject this view. As the work of A. Tarski, R. Carnap, and others has shown, it is possible to define a semantical concept of truth which is not synonymous with that of strong confirmation, and which corresponds much more closely to what has customarily been referred to as truth, especially in logic, but also in other contexts. Thus, e.g., if S is any empirical sentence, then either S or its denial is true in the semantical sense, but clearly it is possible that neither S nor its denial is highly confirmed by available evidence. To assert that a hypothesis is true is equivalent to asserting the hypothesis itself; therefore the truth of an empirical hypothesis can be ascertained only in the sense in which the hypothesis itself can be established: i.e. the hypothesis — and thereby *ipso fac o* its truth — can be more or less well confirmed by empirical evidence; there is no other access to the question of the truth of a hypothesis.

In the light of these considerations, it seems advisable to me to reserve the term 'truth' for the semantical concept; I should now phrase the statements in the *Analysis* articles as dealing with confirmation. (For a brief and very illuminating survey of the distinctive characteristics of truth and confirmation, see R. Carnap, "Wahrheit und Bewährung," *Actes Ier Congrès*

At any rate, the acceptance of a hypothesis on the basis of a sufficient body of confirming evidence will as a rule be tentative, and will hold only "until further notice", i.e. with the proviso that if new and unfavourable evidence should turn up (in other words, if new observation reports should be accepted which disconfirm the hypothesis in question) the hypothesis will be abandoned again.

Are there any exceptions to this rule? Are there any empirical hypotheses which are capable of being established definitively, hypotheses such that we can be sure that once accepted on the basis of experiential evidence, they will never have to be revoked? Hypotheses of this kind will be called absolutely or definitively verifiable; and the concept of absolute or definitive falsifiability will be construed analogously.

While the existence of hypotheses which are relatively verifiable or relatively falsifiable is a simple logical fact, which was illustrated in the beginning of this section, the question of the existence of absolutely verifiable, or absolutely falsifiable, hypotheses is a highly controversial issue which has received a great deal of attention in recent empiricist writings.[50] As the problem is only loosely connected with the subject of this essay, we shall restrict ourselves here to a few general observations.

Let it be assumed that the language of science has the general structure characterized and presupposed in the previous discussions, especially in section 9. Then it is reasonable to expect that only such hypotheses can possibly be absolutely verifiable as are relatively verifiable by suitable observation reports; hypotheses of universal form, for example, which are not even capable of relative verification, certainly cannot be expected to be absolutely verifiable: In however many instances such a hypothesis may have been borne out by experiential findings, it is always possible that new evidence will be obtained

---

Internat. de Philosophie Scientifique 1935, vol. 4; Paris, 1936.) [Ed. note: See Carnap selection in this volume.]

(2) It is now clear also in what sense the test of a hypothesis is a matter of confronting sentences with sentences rather than with "facts", or a matter of the "coherence" of the hypothesis and the accepted basic sentences: All the logical aspects of scientific testing, i.e. all the criteria governing the second and third of the three phases distinguished above, are indeed concerned only with certain relationships between the hypotheses under test and certain other sentences (namely the accepted observation reports); no reference to extra-linguistic "facts" is needed. On the other hand, the first phase, the acceptance of certain basic sentences in connection with certain experiments or observations, involves, of course, extra-linguistic procedures; but this had been explicitly stated by the author in the articles referred to before. The claim that the views concerning truth and confirmation which are held by contemporary logical empiricism involve a coherence theory of truth is therefore mistaken.

[50] Cf. especially A. Ayer, *The Foundations of Empirical Knowledge* (New York, 1940); see also the same author's article, "Verification and Experience", *Proceedings of the Aristotelian Society* for 1937; R. Carnap, "Ueber Protokollsätze", *Erkenntnis*, vol. 3 (1932), and § 82 of the same author's *The Logical Syntax of Language* (see Part I, n. 3). O. Neurath, "Protokollsätze", *Erkenntnis*, vol. 3 (1932); "Radikaler Physikalismus und 'wirkliche Welt' ", *Erkenntnis*, vol. 4 (1934); "Pseudorationalismus der Falsifikation", *Erkenntnis*, vol. 5 (1935). K. Popper, *Logik der Forschung* (see Part I, n. 4). H. Reichenbach, *Experience and Prediction* (Chicago, 1938), ch. iii. Bertrand Russell, *An Inquiry into Meaning and Truth* (New York, 1940), especially chs. x and xi. M. Schlick, "Ueber das Fundament der Erkenntnis", *Erkenntnis*, vol. 4 (1934).

which disconfirms the hypothesis. Let us, therefore, restrict our search for absolutely verifiable hypotheses to the class of those hypotheses which are relatively verifiable.

Suppose now that H is a hypothesis of this latter type, and that it is relatively verified, i.e. logically entailed, by an observation report B, and that the latter is accepted in science as an account of the outcome of some experiment or observation. Can we then say that H is absolutely confirmed, that it will never be revoked? Clearly, that depends on whether the report B has been accepted irrevocably, or whether it may conceivably suffer the fate of being disavowed later. Thus the question as to the existence of absolutely verifiable hypotheses leads back to the question of whether all, or at least some, observation reports become irrevocable parts of the system of science once they have been accepted in connection with certain observations or experiments. This question is not simply one of fact; it cannot adequately be answered by a descriptive account of the research behaviour of scientists. Here, as in all other cases of logical analysis of science, the problem calls for a "rational reconstruction" of scientific procedure, i.e. for the construction of a consistent and comprehensive theoretical model of scientific inquiry, which is then to serve as a system of reference, or a standard, in the examination of any particular scientific research. The construction of the theoretical model has, of course, to be oriented by the characteristics of actual scientific procedure, but it is not determined by the latter in the sense in which a descriptive account of some scientific study would be. Indeed, it is generally agreed that scientists sometimes infringe the standards of sound scientific procedure; besides, for the sake of theoretical comprehensiveness and systematization, the abstract model will have to contain certain idealized elements which cannot possibly be determined in detail by a study of how scientists actually work. This is true especially of observation reports: A study of the way in which laboratory reports, or descriptions of other types of observational findings, are formulated in the practice of scientific research is of interest for the choice of assumptions concerning the form and the status of observation sentences in the model of a "language of science"; but clearly, such a study cannot completely determine what form observation sentences are to have in the theoretical model, nor whether they are to be considered as irrevocable once they are accepted.

Perhaps an analogy may further elucidate this view concerning the character of logical analysis: Suppose that we observe two persons whose language we do not understand playing a game on some kind of chess board; and suppose that we want to "reconstruct" the rules of the game. A mere descriptive account of the playing-behaviour of the individuals will not suffice to do this; indeed, we should not even necessarily reject a theoretical reconstruction of the game which did not always characterize accurately the actual moves of the players: we should allow for the possibility of occasional violations of the rules. Our reconstruction would rather be guided by the objective of obtaining a consistent and comprehensive system of rules which are as simple as possible, and to which the observed playing behaviour conforms at least to a large extent. In terms of the standard thus obtained, we may then describe and critically analyze any concrete performance of the game.

The parallel is obvious; and it appears to be clear, too, that in both cases the decision about various features of the theoretical model will have the character of a convention, which is influenced by considerations of simplicity, consistency, and comprehensiveness, and not only by a study of the actual procedure of scientists at work.[51]

This remark applies in particular to the specific question under consideration, namely whether "there are" in science any irrevocably accepted observation reports (all of whose consequences would then be absolutely verified empirical hypotheses). The situation becomes clear when we put the question into this form: Shall we allow, in our rational reconstruction of science, for the possibility that certain observation reports may be accepted as irrevocable, or shall the acceptance of all observation reports be subject to the "until further notice" clause? In comparing the merits of the alternative stipulations, we should have to investigate the extent to which each of them is capable of elucidating the structure of scientific inquiry in terms of a simple, consistent theory. We do not propose to enter into a discussion of this question here except for mentioning that various considerations militate in favour of the convention that no observation report is to be accepted definitively and irrevocably.[52] If this alternative is chosen, then not even those hypotheses which are entailed by accepted observation reports are absolutely verified, nor are those hypotheses which are found incompatible with accepted observation reports thereby absolutely falsified: in fact, in this case, no hypothesis whatsoever would be absolutely verifiable or absolutely falsifiable. If, on the other hand, some — or even all — observation sentences are declared irrevocable once they have been accepted, then those hypotheses entailed by or incompatible with irrevocable observation sentences will be absolutely verified, or absolutely falsified, respectively.

It should now be clear that the concepts of absolute and of relative verifiability (and falsifiability) are of an entirely different character. Failure to distinguish them has caused considerable misunderstanding in recent discussions on the nature of scientific knowledge. Thus, e.g., K. Popper's proposal to admit as scientific hypotheses exclusively sentences which are (relatively) falsifiable by suitable observation reports has been criticized by means of arguments which, in effect, support the claim that scientific hypotheses should not be construed as being absolutely falsifiable — a point that Popper had not denied. — As can be seen from our earlier discussion of relative falsifiability, however, Popper's proposal to limit scientific hypotheses to the form of (relatively) falsifiable sentences involves a very severe restriction of the possible forms of scientific hy-

[51] A clear account of the sense in which the results of logical analysis represent conventions can be found in §§ 9–11 and 25–30 of K. Popper's *Logik der Forschung*. An illustration of the considerations influencing the determination of various features of the theoretical model is provided by the discussion in n. 27.

[52] Cf. especially the publications by Carnap, Neurath, and Popper mentioned in n. 21; also Reichenbach, *loc. cit.*, ch. ii, § 9.

potheses[53]; in particular, it rules out all purely existential hypotheses as well as most hypotheses whose formulation requires both universal and existential quantification; and it may be criticized on this account; for in terms of this theoretical reconstruction of science it seems difficult or altogether impossible to give an adequate account of the status and function of the more complex scientific hypotheses and theories. —

With these remarks let us conclude our study of the logic of confirmation. What has been said above about the nature of the logical analysis of science in general, applies to the present analysis of confirmation in particular: It is a specific proposal for a systematic and comprehensive logical reconstruction of a concept which is basic for the methodology of empirical science as well as for the problem area customarily called "epistemology". The need for a theoretical clarification of that concept was evidenced by the fact that no general theoretical account of confirmation has been available so far, and that certain widely accepted conceptions of confirmation involve difficulties so serious that it might be doubted whether a satisfactory theory of the concept is at all attainable.

It was found, however, that the problem can be solved: A general definition of confirmation, couched in purely logical terms, was developed for scientific languages of a specified and relatively simple logical character. The logical model thus obtained appeared to be satisfactory in the sense of the formal and material standards of adequacy that had been set up previously.

I have tried to state the essential features of the proposed analysis and reconstruction of confirmation as explicitly as possible in the hope of stimulating a critical discussion and of facilitating further inquiries into the various issues pertinent to this problem area. Among the open questions which seem to deserve careful consideration, I should like to mention the exploration of concepts of confirmation which fail to satisfy the general consistency condition; the extension of the definition of confirmation to the case where even observation sentences containing quantifiers are permitted; and finally the development of a definition of confirmation for languages of a more complex logical structure than that incorporated in our model.[54] Languages of this kind would provide a greater variety of means of expression and would thus come closer to the high logical complexity of the language of empirical science.

[53] This was pointed out by R. Carnap; cf. his review of Popper's book in *Erkenntnis*, vol. 5 (1935), and "Testability and Meaning" (see Part I, n. 5), §§ 25, 26. For the discussion of Popper's falsifiability criterion, see for example H. Reichenbach, "Ueber Induktion und Wahrscheinlichkeit", *Erkenntnis*, vol. 5 (1935); O. Neurath, "Pseudorationalismus der Falsifikation", *Erkenntnis*, vol. 5 (1935).

[54] The languages to which our definition is applicable have the structure of the lower functional calculus without identity sign (cf. n. 14); it would be highly desirable so to broaden the general theory of confirmation as to make it applicable to the lower functional calculus with identity sign, or even to the higher functional calculus; for it seems hardly possible to give a precise formulation of more complex scientific theories without the logical means of expression provided by the higher functional calculus.

15 *Probability and Degree of Confirmation or Weight of Evidence*

ERNEST NAGEL

A common objection to the frequency theory of probability is that, although probability statements concerning single occasions or single propositions are often asserted and debated, it is meaningless to assert such statements in terms of the frequency theory. For example, writers like Keynes have urged that such statements as "It is probable on the evidence that Caesar visited Britain" and "The evidence makes it improbable that all crows are black" cannot be analyzed in terms of relative frequencies; and they have concluded that a conception of probability is involved in them which is different from, and "wider" than, the frequency view. Frequentists have retorted, quite rightly, that such statements *are* without meaning, if they *literally* attribute a probability in the frequency sense to a single proposition; but frequentists have also urged that such statements do have significance if they are understood as *elliptic* formulations.

There is little doubt that many probability statements which are apparently about single propositions are incomplete formulations and that, when they are suitably expanded, they conform to the conditions required by the frequency theory. On the question, however, whether *all* probability statements about single propositions are to be analyzed in this way there is considerable difference of opinion. This disagreement not only divides frequentists from nonfrequentists like Keynes but it also represents a division among those who subscribe to a frequency interpretation for the first class of statements previously mentioned.

This difference of opinion concerning the range of applicability of the calculu of probability has a long history. Earlier writers on the subject believed tha the calculus was the long-sought-for instrument for solving all problems con nected with estimating the adequacy of evidence. In particular, it was main tained that the problems associated with establishing general laws on the basi of examined instances and with obtaining some measure for the reliability c predictions (the traditional problems of induction) were part of the subjec matter of the mathematical theory of probability. Bayes's theorem and th Rule of Succession were commonly employed for these purposes, and Jevon

Reprinted from *Principles of the Theory of Probability* (International Encyclopedia of Unifie Science, Chicago, 1939, Vol. 1, No. 6, pp. 60–74.) by Ernest Nagel by permission of Th University of Chicago Press and the author. Copyright 1939 by the University of Chicago.

explicitly regarded induction as a problem in inverse probabilities. On the other hand, writers like Cournot and Venn, two of the earliest writers to propose a frequency interpretation of the probability calculus, were equally convinced, though for different reasons, that the calculus was not relevant to the problems of induction. More recently, Keynes and Reichenbach, arguing from diametrically opposite standpoints, agree on the point that the term "probable" can be given a consistently univocal meaning; and Reichenbach* has given the most complete account at present available of how to extend the frequency view to the consideration of the probability of scientific theories. But other contemporary frequentists, such as Carnap, von Mises, Neurath, and Popper, though supporting the frequency interpretation for a very large class of proability statements, do not believe such an interpretation is appropriate for every statement which contains the word "probable." This latter group of writers rejects the notion of a "logical probability" as developed by Keynes and others; but it distinguishes between "probable" employed in the sense of "relative frequency" and "probable" employed in the sense of "degree of confirmation" or "weight of evidence."

It is possible, therefore, to distinguish writers on probability according to the following schema: (1) Writers who interpret "probable" in a *univocal* sense; such writers differ among themselves according as they accept the classical view, the view of probability as a unique logical relation, or the frequency view. (2) Writers who do not believe that the term "probable" can be interpreted in precisely the same manner in every one of the contexts in which it occurs.

The present state of research, therefore, leaves the issue unsettled as to the scope of the frequency theory of probability. We shall examine the points at issue, but our conclusion will of necessity have to be highly tentative. We shall concern ourselves explicitly with statements ascribing a probability to a theory, because of lack of space; but the discussion will apply without essential qualifications to probability statements about singular statements like "Caesar visited Britain," whenever such probability statements are not analyzable as elliptic formulations involving relative frequencies. By "theory" will be understood any statement of whatever degree of complexity which contains one or more universal quantifiers, or a set of such statements.

1. *The probability of theories.*—We begin with examining the proposal to interpret probability statements about theories in terms of relative frequencies; and, since Reichenbach has expounded this proposal more fully than anyone else, we shall examine his views. Reichenbach has given two distinct but allied methods for defining "the probability of a theory." The first of these methods has received an improved formulation by C. G. Hempel, which avoids serious difficulties present in Reichenbach's own version. It should be noted that the definitions given by both methods are semantic ones.

a) Let T be some theory, for example, the Newtonian theory of gravitation. Let C_n be a class of n singular statements, each of which specifies an initial state of a system. (For from T alone, without the specification of initial con-

* [Ed. note: See the selection from Reichenbach in Section I of this volume.]

ditions, no empirically controllable consequences can be obtained; thus, the mass, initial position, and velocity of a planet must be assigned before a future state of the planet can be predicted.) From every such statement with the help of T, other statements may be derived, some of which are empirically controllable by an appropriate observation. Therefore, let E_n be the class of n such singular statements derived from C_n with the help of T. We suppose that a one-to-one correspondence is established between the elements of C_n and E_n; and without loss of generality we shall suppose that every statement in C_n is true. (From a single statement in C an indefinite number of statements belonging to E may be derived; but we can simply *repeat* a statement in C for every one of the distinct consequences drawn from it.) Let $\mathrm{nu}(E_n)$ be the number of statements in E_n which are true. The relative frequency with which a statement in E_n is true when its corresponding statement in C_n is true is given by $\mathrm{nu}(E_n)/n$. Suppose now that n increases indefinitely, so that C_n will include all possible true initial conditions for T, while E_n will include all the possible predictions which are made from them with the help of T. The numerical expression

$$\mathrm{prob}(E, C) = \lim_{n \to \infty} \frac{\mathrm{nu}(E_n)}{n}$$

will then be the probability that the consequences, obtained with the help of T from appropriate initial conditions, are true. This, in essence, is Reichenbach's first method of assigning a probability to a theory T.

Although the foregoing exposition requires supplementation in several ways, there seems to be little question that a precise definition for "the probability of a theory" can be given on a relative frequency basis. It is, however, by no means evident that such a definition formulates the concept people seem to be employing when they discuss the probability of theories.

(i) On the foregoing definition the probability of a theory is the limiting value of relative frequencies in an infinite ordered class E. This value is therefore independent of the *absolute number* of true instances in E, and is also independent of the absolute or relative number of instances in E which we know to be true *at a given time*. However, we often do say that on the basis of *definite evidence* a theory has some "degree of probability." Thus, a familiar use of this phrase permits us to say that, because of the accumulated evidence obtained since 1900, the quantum theory of energy is more probable today than it was thirty years ago. The foregoing definition is not suitable for this use of the phrase.

(ii) Because the probability of a theory is defined as the limit of relative frequencies, the probability of a theory may be 1, although the class E of its empirically confirmable consequences contains an infinite number of statements which are in fact false. This conclusion could follow even if some of these exceptions to the theory are ruled out as not being genuine negative instances (see the discussion of this point in § 7). But, according to the familiar usage of "probability of a theory" already referred to, if a theory did have an infinite number of exceptions, not only would not a "high degree of probability" be assigned to it: it would be simply rejected.

(iii) It is difficult to know how even the approximate value of the probability of a theory, in Reichenbach's first sense, is to be determined. The situation here is not quite the same as for the probability statements which occur *within* a natural science and which have been already discussed in § 7. In the present case it does not seem possible to obtain other than direct statistical evidence for an assigned numerical value; for it is not apparent how a statement about the probability of theories can be part of an inclusive system, so that the statement might possibly be confirmed indirectly, perhaps even by nonstatistical evidence. Reichenbach's proposal of a hierarchy of probabilities, according to which the probability of a probability statement may be estimated, postpones this problem by referring it to a higher level of probabilities; but postponing a problem does not solve it.

b) The second method proposed by Reichenbach for assigning a probability to a theory in a frequency sense depends upon the first method. The theory T under consideration will now be regarded as an element in an infinite class K of theories. These theories are supposed to be alike in some respects and unlike in others; and the theory T will share with a number of others in K a certain definite property P. (The following crude illustration may help fix our ideas: Suppose T is the Newtonian theory, and K the class of possible theories dealing with the physical behavior of macroscopic bodies. P may then be the property that the force functions in the theory are functions of the coordinates alone.) The probability of the theory T is then defined as the limit of the relative frequency with which theories in K, possessing the property P, have a probability in Reichenbach's first sense which is not less than a specified number q.

We can comment only briefly on this proposal.

(i) Although it is easy to introduce the reference class K and the property P in the formal definition, in practice it is by no means easy to specify them. The class K must not be selected too widely or arbitrarily, but no way is known for unambiguously grouping together a set of allegedly "relevant" theories. The difficulty is even greater in specifying the property P for a concrete case. We might wish to say, for example, that the theory of relativity is more probable than the Newtonian theory. But just what is the property P in this case on the basis of which they are to be distinguished?

(ii) We do not at present possess a sufficiently extensive collection of theories, so that appropriate statistical inquiries cannot be made with respect to them in accordance with this proposal. This proposal therefore completely lacks practical relevance. Indeed, there is some ground for suspicion that the proposal would be feasible only if, as Peirce suggested, "universes were as plentiful as blackberries"; only in such a case could we determine the relative frequency with which these different universes exhibit the traits formulated by a theory under consideration.

(iii) If we could assign a probability value to a theory according to the first of Reichenbach's two proposals, there would be little need for estimating its probability by the second method. It is consistent with these proposals that a theory which has a probability of 1 on the first method, has the probability of only 0 on the second method. But since we are, by hypothesis, interested in that *one* theory, of what particular significance is it to know that theories of such a type have almost all their instances in conformity with the facts with only a vanishingly small relative frequency? This second proposal, like the first, does not therefore formulate the sense of those statements which assign a "degree of probability" to a theory on the basis of *given* finite evidence. For this second proposal does not permit us to talk *literally* about the degree of probability which *one definite theory* has on the evidence at hand; and it is just this which is intended when the evidence for a theory at one time is compared with the evidence at another time.

2. *Degree of confirmation or weight of evidence.*—These difficulties with the two proposals for assigning a probability to a theory, in the relative frequency sense of the term, are serious enough to have led competent students to seek a different interpretation for such statements. Guided by the actual procedure of the sciences, a long line of writers have urged that a different concept is involved in such statements from the one specified by the frequency theory of probability. This concept has been designated as "degree of confirmation" or "weight of evidence," in order to distinguish it from the various interpretations given to the term "probable." We shall briefly explain what is meant by "degree of confirmation" and discuss some of the problems which center around its use.

The initial task which must be performed before a satisfactory account of "degree of confirmation" can be given is a careful analysis of the logical structure of a theory in order to make precise the conditions under which a theory may be confirmed by suitable experiments. This has been partially done by Carnap with considerable detail and refinement. We shall, however, not reproduce the results of his analyses, and shall employ distinctions inexactly formulated but which are familiar in the literature of scientific method. In particular, we shall take for granted the following, of which use has already been made: No theory (or for that matter no singular statement) can be established completely and finally by any finite class of observations. But a theory can be tested by examining its instances, that is, the singular sentences E derived with the help of the theory from the sentences C stating the initial conditions for the application of the theory. Both C and E may increase in number; but, while theoretically there are an infinite number of instances of a theory, no more than a finite number will have been tested at any given time. Indeed, a theory is said to be capable of being confirmed or verified only incompletely, just because no more than a finite number of its instances can be actually tested. The instances may be confirmed by observation, in which case they are called the *positive instances* for the theory; or they may be in disaccord with the outcome of observations, in which case they are called the *negative instances.*

We shall assume for the sake of simplicity that there are no negative instances for a given theory T. Then as we continue the process of testing T, the number of positive instances will usually increase. Now it is generally admitted that by increasing the positive instances, the theory becomes more securely established. What is known as "the weight of evidence" for the theory is thus taken to be a function of the number of positive instances. And we may accordingly state as a preliminary explanation of what is meant by "the degree of confirmation" for a theory that the degree of confirmation increases with the number of the positive instances for T.

This explanation is, of course, far from precise; but at present no precise definition for the term is available. As matters stand, the term is used in a more or less intuitive fashion in the actual procedures of testing theories. It would obviously be highly desirable to have carefully formulated semantical rules for employing the term; but there is no early prospect that the rules for weighing the evidence for a theory will be reduced to a formal schema. The following observations, however, indicate some of the conditions under which the weighing of evidence is carried on, and will contribute something to making more precise the meaning of "degree of confirmation."

a) It does not seem possible to assign a quantitative value to the degree of confirmation of a theory. Thus, at one stage of investigation a theory T may have twenty positive instances in its favor, while at a later stage it may have forty such instances. While the degree of confirmation of T at the second stage would in general be acknowledged as greater than at the first stage, it is nevertheless not appropriate to say one degree of confirmation is twice the other. The reason for this inappropriateness is that, if degrees of confirmation could be quantized, all degrees of confirmation would be comparable and be capable therefore of a linear ordering. That this does not seem to be the case is suggested by the following hypothetical situation.

Suppose that the positive instances for T can be analyzed into two nonoverlapping classes K_1 and K_2, such that the instances in K_1 come from one field of inquiry and those in K_2 from another field. For example, if T is the Newtonian theory, K_1 may be the confirmatory instances for it from the study of planetary motions, while K_2 may be those coming from the study of capillarity phenomena; each set of instances is in an obvious sense qualitatively dissimilar from the other. Now imagine the following possibilities as to the number of instances in K_1 and K_2:

	P_1	P_2	P_3	P_4	P_5	P_6	P_7	P_8	P_9
K_1	50	50	100	101	99	100	200	100	198
K_2	0	50	0	49	52	90	0	100	2
E	50	100	100	150	151	190	200	200	200

The last row of figures gives the total number of positive instances for T. These nine possibilities are arranged in order of increasing number of positive instances. Would we say, however, that this order also represents the order of increasing degrees of confirmation?

It would generally be granted that for both P_2 and P_3 the degree of confirmation is greater than for P_1, simply because of the total number of positive instances. On the other hand, many scientists would be inclined to assign a greater degree of confirmation to P_2 than to P_3, even though the total number of positive instances is the same in these cases. And the reason they would give is that in P_2 there are *different kinds* of instances, while in P_3 there is only one kind. For this reason also P_6 would be assigned a higher degree of confirmation than P_7, even though the total number of positive instances in the former case is less than in the latter case. Again, P_4 and P_5 would often be assigned the *same* degree of confirmation, even though the total number of instances is different in these cases, because the relative number of instances of each kind is approximately the same. Finally, P_8 and P_9 would often be regarded as *incomparable* with respect to their degrees of confirmation, because of the disparity in the relative number of different kinds of instances.

Variety in the kinds of positive instances for a theory is a generally acknowledged factor in estimating the weight of the evidence. The reason for this is that experiments which are conducted in qualitatively different domains make it easier to control features of the theory whose relevance in *any* of the domains may be in question. Hence, by increasing the possibility of eliminating what may be simply accidental successes of a theory under special or unanalyzed circumstances, the possibility of finding negative instances for the theory is increased. In this way of conducting experiments, the theory is subjected to a more searching examination than if all the positive instances were drawn from just one domain. A large increase in the number of positive instances of one kind may therefore count for less, in the judgment of skilled experimenters, than a small increase in the number of positive instances of another kind. It follows, however, that the degree of confirmation for a theory seems to be a function not only of the absolute number of positive instances but also of the kinds of instances and of the relative number in each kind. It is not in general possible, therefore, to order degrees of confirmation in a linear order, because the evidence for theories may not be comparable in accordance with a simple linear schema; and a fortiori degrees of confirmation cannot, in general, be quantized.

Indeed, the foregoing hypothetical situation is only a highly simplified outline of the considerations which are usually taken to be relevant in estimating the weight of the evidence for a theory. Among other factors usually considered is the precision with which the confirmable consequences of a theory are in agreement with experimental findings. Although, as has been repeatedly explained, a theory is not rejected simply because perfect agreement between predicted and experimentally determined magnitudes does not occur, the more closely the observed values center around the theoretically expected magnitudes, the greater weight is usually attached to the supporting observations for a theory. Furthermore, evidence for a theory often consists not only of its own positive instances but also of the positive instances for *another* theory, related to the first within a more inclusive theoretical system. The number of direct positive instances may in such cases be regarded as of small importance, in comparison with the fact that support is given to the theory by the accumulated positive instances for the inclusive system.

b) How large must the number and kinds of positive instances be in order that a theory can be taken as adequately established? No general answer can be given to such a question, since the answer involves practical decisions on the part of those who conduct a scientific inquiry. There is an ineradicable conventional element among the factors which lead to the acceptance of a theory on the basis of actual evidence at hand. It is always theoretically possible to demand further evidence before agreement is reached that a theory has been sufficiently well tested. However, the practical decision is in part a function of the contemporary scientific situation. The estimation of the evidence for one theory is usually conducted in terms of the bearing of that evidence upon alternative theories for the same subject matter. When there are several competing theories, a decision between them may be postponed indefinitely, if the evidence supports them all with approximately the same precision. Furthermore, the general line of research pursued at a given time may also determine how the decision for a theory will turn out. For example, at a time when a conception of discontinuous matter is the common background for physical research, a theory for a special domain of research formulated in accordance with the dominant leading idea may require little direct evidence for it; on the other hand, a theory based on a continuous notion of matter for that domain may receive little consideration even if direct empirical evidence supports it as well as, or even better than, it does the alternative theory.

In particular, the acceptance of definite numerical values for probabilities also involves practical decision, for which no general rules can be given. As already explained, such numerical values are often computed on the basis of more or less comprehensive theoretical systems, and the confidence which we have in the correctness of those values depends on the confidence we have in those systems. It may happen that we can determine the value of a probability with only small accuracy by a theory which has a relatively high degree of confirmation, while a different value may be computed with great precision by an alternative theory with an inferior degree of confirmation. The supposition that in such a case the dilemma can be resolved by a clear-cut method neglects the human and accidental factors which determine the history of science. Certainly no mathematical or logical formula can be given which would mechanically supply a coefficient of weight for the correctness of the decisions which are made in many analogous cases.

c) Assuming that these desultory observations are based on the study of actual scientific procedure, it may be asked why it is that we seem to feel that theories with a greater degree of confirmation deserve our confidence on logical grounds more than those with less — whenever such comparisons can be made. Why, in other words, should a theory be regarded as "better established" if we increase the number and kinds of its positive instances?

Perhaps a simple example will help suggest an answer. Suppose a cargo of coffee is to be examined for the quality of the beans. We cannot practically examine every coffee bean, and so we obtain some sample beans. We do not, however, sample the cargo by taking a very large number of beans from just one part of the hold; we take many relatively small samples from very many different parts of the ship. Why do we proceed in this way? The answer seems to be that our general experience is such that, when we conduct our samplings in this manner, we approximate to the distribution of qualities in the entire hold; and, in general, the larger our individual samples and the more diversified our choice of the parts of the ship from which they are taken, the more reliable (as judged by subsequent experience) are the estimates we form. It is at least a plausible view that in testing a theory we are making a series of samplings from the class of its possible instances. A theory is "better established" when we increase the number and kinds of its positive instances, because the *method* we thereby employ is one which our general experience confirms as leading to conclusions which are stable or which provide satisfactory solutions to the specific problems of inquiry. At any rate, this was the answer which Charles Peirce proposed to the so-called "problem of induction," and which has been independently advanced in various forms by many contemporary students of scientific method (e.g., M. R. Cohen, J. Dewey, H. Feigl, O. Neurath, and many others). As Peirce succinctly put the matter, "Synthetic inferences are founded upon the classification of facts, not according to their characters, but *according to the manner of obtaining them.* Its rule is that a number of facts obtained in a given way will in general more or less resemble other facts obtained in the same way; or, *experiences whose conditions are the same will have the same general characters.*" A degree of confirmation is thus a rough indication of the extent to which our general *method of procedure* has been put into operation. While no probability in a frequency sense can be significantly assigned to any formulation of our method (because it is that very method which is involved in estimating and testing such probabilities), scientific inquiry is based upon the assumption, which is supported by our general experience, that the method of science leads to a proportionately greater number of successful terminations of inquiry than any alternative method yet proposed.

Attempts to find a systematic answer to "the problem of induction" within the framework of a theory of probability, though often made, have not in general been regarded as successful. The *process* of induction has been usually conceived as the search for more or less stable and pervasive relations between properties of objects; and the *problem* of induction has been taken to be the discovery of a principle (the principle of induction) which would "justify" the various conclusions of that process. Stated in this way, it is rather difficult to know just how the "problem" is to be conceived in empirical terms. On the face of it, the "problem" seems to involve a futile infinite regress; and indeed the Achilles heel of attempted solutions of it usually has been the status of the proposed principle of induction: how is the principle itself to be "justified"? The number of different types of answers which have been given to this last question is relatively small; among them are the following: the inductive principle is a synthetic a priori proposition concerning the nature of things in general, it is an a priori proposition concerning the fundamental constitution of the human mind, it is a generalization from experience, and it is a "presupposition" or "postulate" of scientific procedure. It would take too long to examine these answers in detail. It is perhaps sufficient to note that the first two involve positions incompatible with the conclusions of modern logical research; that the third commits a *petitio principii*; and that the fourth, assuming it to have a clear meaning, cannot make of the proposed inductive principle a "justification" of the procedure of science or of its conclusions, since according to this answer the principle is simply an *instrument* of scientific procedure. The position taken in the present monograph is that no antecedent principle is required to justify the procedure of science, that the sole justification of that procedure lies in the specific solutions it offers to the problems which set it into motion, and that a *general* problem of induction in its usual formulation does not exist. Since the notion of the probability of theories (in the specific senses discussed above) has been found to involve serious difficulties, and since the degree of confirmation for a theory has been argued to indicate the extent to which the theory has been tested by the procedure of science, the problem of induction which the present writer recognizes as genuine is the formulation of the general features of scientific method — of the method which, in short, leads to a proportionately greater number of successful terminations of inquiry than the number which other methods may have to their credit.

One brief final remark: It has been customary in the traditional discussions of scientific theories to seek grounds for our knowledge of their *truth* or at least of their *probability* (in some one of the many senses previously discussed). Omitting more than mention of those students (e.g., Wittgenstein and Schlick) who have dismissed such discussions as meaningless because, according to them, theories are not "genuine" propositions since they are not completely verifiable, reference must be made to another group of writers. According to this group, the traditional discussions have not fruitfully illuminated the character of scientific inquiry because those who take part in them neglect the *function* which theories have in inquiry. When this function is examined, it has been urged, it turns out that questions of the *truth* of theories (in the sense in which theories of truth have been traditionally discussed) are of little concern to those who actually use theories. Reflective inquiry is instituted for the sake of settling a *specific* problem, whether it be practical or theoretical, and inquiry terminates when a resolution of the problem is obtained. The various procedures distinguishable in inquiry (such as observation, operation upon subject matter including the manipulation of instruments, symbolic representation of properties of subject matter, symbolic transformation and calculation, etc.) are to be viewed as instrumental to its end product. The use of theories is one patent factor in reflective inquiry. They function primarily as means for effecting transitions from one set of statements to other sets, with the intent of controlling natural changes and of supplying predictions capable of being checked through manipulating directly experienceable subject matter. Accordingly, in their actual use in science, theories serve as *instruments* in specific contexts, and in this capacity are to be characterized as good or bad, effective or ineffective, rather than as true or false or probable. Those who stress the instrumental function of theories are not necessarily committed to identifying truth with effectiveness and falsity with uselessness. Their major insight does not consist in denying the meaningfulness of certain types of inquiries into the truth of theories but in calling attention to the way theories function and to the safeguards and conditions of their effectiveness. A theory is confirmed to the degree that it performs its specific instrumental function. From this point of view, which has been developed with much detail by Dewey, the degree of confirmation for a theory may be interpreted as a mark of its proved effectiveness as an intellectual tool for the purposes for which it has been instituted.

16 A Definition of "Degree of Confirmation"

CARL G. HEMPEL AND PAUL OPPENHEIM

1. *The problem.* — The concept of confirmation of an hypothesis by empirical evidence is of fundamental importance in the methodology of empirical science. For, first of all, a sentence cannot even be considered as expressing an empirical hypothesis at all unless it is theoretically capable of confirmation or disconfirmation, i.e. unless the kind of evidence can be characterized whose occurrence would confirm, or disconfirm, the sentence in question. And secondly, the acceptance or rejection of a sentence which does represent an empirical hypothesis is determined, in scientific procedure, by the degree to which it is confirmed by relevant evidence.

The preceding remarks, however, are meant only as accounts of methodological tendencies and are not intended to imply the existence of clear-cut criteria by means of which the scientist can decide whether — or, in quantitative terms, to what degree — a given hypothesis is confirmed by certain data. For indeed, no general and objective criteria of this kind are at present available; in other words, no general definition of the concept of confirmation has been developed so far. This is a remarkable fact in view of the importance of the concept concerned, and the question naturally suggests itself whether it is at all possible to set up adequate general criteria of confirmation, or whether it may not rather be necessary to leave the decision in matters of confirmation to the intuitive appraisal of the scientist.

From *Philosophy of Science*, Vol. 12, No. 2, pp. 98–115, April, 1945.

This latter alternative would be highly unsatisfactory; for firstly, it would clearly jeopardize the objectivity — in the sense of intersubjectivity — of scientific procedure. Secondly, it would run counter to a view of confirmation which is now widely accepted; according to this view, statements about confirmation assert nothing regarding an observer's subjective appraisal of the soundness of a hypothesis; rather, they concern a certain objective relation between a hypothesis and the empirical evidence with which it is confronted; this relation depends exclusively on the content of the hypothesis and of the evidence, and it is of a purely logical character in the sense that once a hypothesis and a description of certain observational findings are given, no further empirical investigation is needed to determine whether, or to what degree, the evidence confirms the hypothesis; the decision is a matter exclusively of certain logical criteria which form the subject matter of a formal discipline which might be called inductive logic.

Of course, the widespread acceptance of this view does not prove that it is sound and that the program implicit in it can actually be carried out. The best — and perhaps the only — method of settling the issue seems to consist in actually constructing an explicit and general definition and theory of confirmation. To do this is the purpose of this article. It is intended to present in outline, and with emphasis on the general methodological issues, a theory of confirmation which was developed by the present authors jointly with Dr. Olaf Helmer.[1]

As is illustrated by the terminology used in the preceding discussion, the concept of confirmation may be construed as a metrical (quantitative) as well as a purely classificatory (qualitative) concept. These two different forms are exemplified, respectively, in the phrases "The degree of confirmation of the hypothesis H relatively to the evidence E is such and such," and "The evidence E is confirming (disconfirming, irrelevant) for the hypothesis H." The theory here to be presented deals with the metrical concept of confirmation; its objective is to construct a definition of the concept of degree of confirmation and to derive, from this definition, a number of consequences, which may be called theorems of inductive logic.[2]

[1] A detailed technical exposition of the theory is given by Olaf Helmer and Paul Oppenheim in "A Syntactical Definition of Probability and Degree of Confirmation," vol. 10, 1945, *The Journal of Symbolic Logic*.

The present issue of *Philosophy of Science* contains an article by Professor Rudolf Carnap * which likewise sets forth a definition and theory of confirmation. The approach to the problem which is to be developed in the present paper is independent of Professor Carnap's and differs from it in various respects. Some of the points of difference will be exhibited subsequently as the occasion arises. We wish to express our thanks to Professor Carnap for valuable comments he made in the course of an exchange of ideas on the two different studies of confirmation.

We also wish to thank Dr. Kurt Gödel for his stimulating remarks. [* Ed. note: This selection from Carnap is included in Section I of this volume.]

[2] For a definition and theory of the classificatory concept of confirmation, see the following two articles by Carl G. Hempel: "A Purely Syntactical Definition of Confirmation," *The Journal of Symbolic Logic*, vol. 8 (1943), pp. 122–143; "Studies in the Logic of Confirmation," *Mind*, n.s. vol. 54 (1945). [Ed. note: This selection from Hempel is included in this section.]

The technical term "confirmation" should not be construed in the sense of "verification" — an interpretation which would preclude, for example, its application to a hypothesis

2. *The language L.* — The planned definition or "rational reconstruction" of the concept of degree of confirmation in precise terms can be carried out only on the assumption that all the hypotheses to be considered and all the reports on observational data are formulated as sentences of a language, L, whose logical structure and means of expression are precisely determined. More specifically, we shall presuppose that L contains the following means of expression, which will be symbolized, but for minor and obvious changes, in accordance with the familiar notation of *Principia Mathematica:*

2.1 The statement connectives '$\sim$' ("it is not the case that"), '$\cdot$' ("and"), '$\vee$' ("or"), '$\supset$' ("if . . . then")

2.2 Parentheses

2.3 Individual constants, i.e. names of individual objects (which may be physical bodies, events, space-time regions, or the like), 'a_1', 'a_2', 'a_3', $\cdots$ The number of individual constants in L may be finite or denumerably infinite.

2.4 Some finite number p of one-place predicates, i.e. names of properties which any one of the individuals referred to under 2.3 may or may not have:

$$`P_1', `P_2', `P_3', \cdots, `P_p'$$

These predicates are undefined concepts in L; we shall therefore refer to them as the primitive predicates of L, and to their designata as the primitive properties referred to in L.

2.5 Individual variables: 'x', 'y', 'z', $\cdots$ in any number.

2.6 The symbols of universal and existential quantification, as illustrated in '$(x)P_1x$' and '$(Ey)P_1y$'.

We further assume that these symbols can be combined in the customary ways to form sentences in L[3], and that the usual rules of deductive inference govern the language L.

Briefly, then, we assume that L has the logical structure of the so-called lower functional calculus without identity sign, and restricted to property terms only. These assumptions involve a considerable oversimplification from the viewpoint of the practical applicability of the theory here to be presented, for the language of empirical science includes a great deal of additional logical apparatus, such as relation terms, expressions denoting quantitative magnitudes, etc. However, in appraising the significance of this restriction, the following points might well be borne in mind: 1. In the case of the concept of degree of confirmation, for which no explicit definition has been available at all, and for which even the theoretical possibility of a definition has been subject to serious doubt, it seems

---

about an event which is temporally posterior to the data included in the evidence. Rather, as is suggested by the root "firm," the confirmation of a hypothesis should be understood as a strengthening of the confidence that can rationally be placed in the hypothesis.

[3] Illustrations: '$(P_1a_1 \vee P_2a_1) \supset (P_3a_1 \cdot \sim P_4a_1)$' stands for "If a_1 has at least one of the properties P_1, P_2 then it has the property P_3, but not the property P_4"; '$\sim(x)P_1x \supset (Ex)\sim P_1x$' stands for "If it is not the case that all objects have the property P_1, then there is at least one object which does not have the property P_1."

to be a significant achievement if such a definition can be provided, even if its applicability is restricted to languages of a comparatively simple structure. 2. While the means of expression of L are relatively limited, they still go beyond the logical machinery which forms the subject matter of traditional Aristotelian logic. 3. The formulation of a definition for languages of our restricted type may serve as a guide in the construction of an extension of the definition to more complex language forms.

3. *Some auxiliary concepts.* — By an *atomic sentence* we shall understand any sentence of the kind illustrated by 'P_1a', which ascribes a primitive property to some individual. Any sentence such as '$(P_1a \supset \sim P_2a) \cdot P_1b$', which contains no quantifiers, will be called a *molecular sentence.*

Let 'Ma_i' be short for some molecular sentence such as '$P_1a_i \cdot (P_2a_i \vee \sim P_3a_i)$', which contains only one individual constant, 'a_i'; then we shall say that 'M' designates a *molecular property* — in the example, the property $P_1 \cdot (P_2 \vee \sim P_3)$. By a *statistic* we shall understand any sentence of the type

$$\pm Ma_i \cdot \pm Ma_j \cdot \cdots \cdot \pm Ma_t$$

where the constants 'a_i', 'a_j', $\cdots$, 'a_t' are all different from one another, and where the symbol '$\pm$' indicates that any one of the components may be either negated or unnegated. If we wish to indicate specifically the molecular property about whose incidence the statistic reports, we shall call a sentence of the above kind an *M-statistic.*

A sentence which contains at least one quantifier will be called a *general sentence;* in particular, all general laws, such as '$(x)(P_1x \supset P_2x)$', are general sentences.

By means of the p primitive predicates, we can form exactly $k = 2^p$ different conjunctions of the following kind: Each conjunction consists of exactly p terms; the first term is either 'P_1' or '$\sim P_1$', the second is either 'P_2' or '$\sim P_2$', and so on; finally, the pth term is either 'P_p' or '$\sim P_p$'. We call these expressions Q-expressions and, in lexicographic order, abbreviate them by 'Q_1', 'Q_2', $\cdots$, 'Q_k'. These Q-expressions designate certain molecular properties, which we shall call *Q-properties.* Alternatively, we may also say that each Q-expression designates a class, namely the class of all those individuals which have the Q-property in question. The classes designated by the Q-expressions clearly are mutually exclusive and exhaustive: every object belongs to one and only one of them. Moreover, they are the narrowest classes which can be characterized in L all (except for the null class, which is designated, for example, by '$P_1 \cdot \sim P_1$'); for brevity, we shall refer to them as *(L-)cells.* In intuitive terms, we may say that if for a given individual we know to which L-cell it belongs, then we know everything about that individual that can be said in L at all; it is completely determined — relatively to the means of expression of L.

4. *A model language and a model world.* — Our assumptions and definitions for L concern only the logical structure of that language and leave room for considerable variation in material content. For illustrative purposes, it will be

useful to be able to refer to a specific model L_w of such a language and to a "model world" W of which it speaks.

Let us assume that the individuals a_1, a_2, a_3, $\cdots$ of which L_w speaks are physical objects, and that L_w contains just two primitive predicates, 'Blue' and 'Round'. Then L_w determines exactly four cells, Q_1 = Blue·Round, Q_2 = Blue·∼Round, Q_3 = ∼Blue·Round, Q_4 = ∼Blue·∼Round. All the hypotheses and evidence sentences expressible in L refer exclusively to the characteristics of blueness and roundness of the objects in W. Thus, e.g., the evidence sentence E might report,in the form of a statistic, on a sample of individuals in the following manner:

4.1 E = 'Blue a_1·Round a_1·Blue a_2·Round a_2·∼(Blue a_3·Round a_3) ·Blue a_4·Round $_4a$'

and the hypothesis might be

4.2 H = 'Blue a_5·Round a_5'

In this case, E reports on four objects, three of which were found to be blue and round, while one was not; and H asserts that a fifth object, not yet examined (i.e. not referred to in E), will be blue and round. The question then arises: What degree of confirmation shall be assigned to H on the basis of E? We shall return to this case in the following section.

5. *Restatement of the problem.* — Our basic problem can now be restated as follows: To define, in purely logical terms, the concept "degree of confirmation of H relatively to E" — or briefly, '$dc(H, E)$' — where H and E are sentences in a language L of the structure characterized in section 2, and where E is not contradictory.

The restriction of E to logically consistent sentences is justifiable on pragmatical grounds: No scientist would consider a contradictory "evidence sentence" as a possible basis for the appraisal of the soundness of an empirical hypothesis. — But the same restriction is demanded also, and more urgently, by considerations of generality and simplicity concerning the formal theory of confirmation which is to be based on our definition: We shall try to define dc in such a way that the following conditions, among others, are generally satisfied:[4]

5.1 $dc(H, E) + dc(\sim H, E) = 1$.

5.2 If H is a logical consequence of E, then $dc(H, E) = 1$

But these requirements cannot be generally satisfied unless E is non-contradictory. For if E is a contradictory sentence, then any hypothesis H and its denial $\sim H$ are consequences of E, and therefore, by virtue of 5.2, both have the dc 1 with respect to E; hence $dc(H, E) + dc(\sim H, E) = 2$, which contradicts 5.1.[5]

As the illustration 4.1 suggests, it might seem natural further to restrict E by the requirement that it has to be a molecular sentence, for in practice, E will usually consist in a report on a finite number of observational findings. How-

[4] Here and at some later places we use statement connective symbols autonomously, i.e., roughly speaking, as designations of the same symbols in the "object language" L.

[5] This argument was suggested by Professor Carnap.

ever, it also happens in science that the evidence adduced in support of a hypothesis (such as Newton's law of gravitation) consists of general laws (such as Kepler's and Galileo's laws), and in the interest of the greatest possible adequacy and comprehensiveness of our definition, we shall therefore allow E to be any non-contradictory sentence in L. The sentence H, which represents the hypothesis under consideration, will be subject to no restrictions whatever; even analytic and contradictory hypotheses will be permitted; in these latter two cases, no matter what the evidence may be, the *dc* will yield the values 1 or 0, respectively, provided that *dc* is defined in such a way as to satisfy 5.1 and 5.2.

One of the guiding ideas in our attempt to construct a definition of confirmation will be to evaluate the soundness of a prediction in terms of the relative frequency of similar occurrences in the past. This principle appears to be definitely in accordance with scientific procedure, and it provides certain clues for a general definition of *dc*. Thus, e.g., in the case stated in 4.1 and 4.2, we shall want $dc(H, E)$ to be equal to 3/4. And more generally, we shall want our definition to satisfy the following condition:

5.3 If E is an M-statistic and H a sentence ascribing the property M to an object not mentioned in E, then $dc(H, E)$ is to be the relative frequency of the occurrence of 'M' in E.[6]

This rule is closely related to Reichenbach's rule of induction. This is no coincidence, for Reichenbach's theory, too, aims at giving a strictly empiricist account of the inductive procedure of science.[7] The applicability of the rule 5.3 is obviously restricted to the case where E is a statistic and H has the special form just described. And since we cannot presuppose that in science H and E are generally of this very special type, it becomes an important problem to find a rule whose scope will include also more complex forms of H and of E. In fact, this rule will have to be applicable to any H and any consistent E in L, and in cases of the special type just considered, it will have to yield that value of dc which is stipulated in 5.3. — We shall now develop, in a number of steps, the ideas which lead to a definition of the desired kind.

6. *Frequency distributions.* — We have seen that for a given language L, the p primitive predicates determine $k = 2^p$ cells $Q_1, Q_2, \cdots, Q_k$. Each one of these cells may be occupied or empty, i.e. there may or there may not be individuals having the property which characterizes the elements of that cell. Whether a given cell is empty, and if not, how many objects it contains, is of course an empirical question and not a matter to be settled by logic. At any rate, if the number of all objects is finite, say N, then each cell Q_s has a certain occupancy number (i.e., number of elements) N_s, and a certain relative frequency $q_s = N_s/N$. Obviously, $N_1 + N_2 + \cdots + N_k = N$, and

6.1 $$q_1 + q_2 + \cdots + q_k = 1$$

If the class of all individuals is infinite — and here we restrict ourselves to the

[6] On this point, see also sections 10 and 16 in Professor Carnap's article.

[7] Cf. Hans Reichenbach, *Wahrscheinlichkeitslehre*, Leiden 1935, especially §§ 75–80, and *Experience and Prediction*, Chicago, 1935, chapter V.

case of a denumerably infinite set of objects — then we shall assume that they are arranged in a fixed sequence, and by q_s we shall now generally understand the limit of the relative frequency with which elements belonging to cell Q_s occur in that sequence.

Now, while we do not actually know the values q_s, we may nevertheless consider certain hypothetically assumed values for them and develop the consequences of such an assumption. By a frequency distribution Δ in L, we shall understand any assignment of non-negative numbers $q_1, q_2, \cdots q_k$ to the cells $Q_1, Q_2, \cdots Q_k$ in such a fashion that 6.1 is satisfied. We shall briefly characterize such a distribution by thc following kind of notation:

$$\Delta = \{q_1, q_2, \cdots q_k\}$$

It follows immediately that in every Δ,

6.2 $$0 \leqq q_s \leqq 1 \quad (s = 1, 2, \cdots, k)$$

Example: In the case of L_w, one of the infinitely many possible frequency distributions is $\Delta = \{1/2, 1/3, 0, 1/6\}$, which represents the case where one half of all objects are blue and round, one third of them blue and not round, none of them round and not blue, and one sixth of them neither blue nor round.[8]

7. *Probability of a hypothesis.* — If a fixed frequency distribution Δ is given or hypothetically assumed for the cells determined by L, then it is possible to define a concept '$pr(H, E, \Delta)$' — in words: "the probability of H relatively to E according to the distribution Δ," — which we shall then use to define $dc(H, E)$.

The meaning of this probability concept will first be explained by reference to our model. Let us consider the process of establishing evidence sentences, and of testing hypotheses by means of them, in analogy to that of drawing samples from an urn and using the evidence thus obtained for the test of certain hypotheses. The latter may concern either the distribution of certain characteristics over the whole population of the urn, or the occurrence or non-occurrence of certain characteristics in objects subsequently to be drawn from the urn. For the sake of simplicity we shall assume from now on that the totality of all objects to which L refers is denumerably infinite. (This does not necessarily mean that L contains infinitely many individual constants, but it does mean that the universal and existential quantifiers occurring in the general sentences of L refer to an infinite domain.) — Now let us imagine that for our model world W we are given the frequencies associated with the four cells determined by the two predicates of L_w; let this distribution be $\Delta_1 = \{1/2, 1/3, 0, 1/6\}$. Suppose further that the hypothesis H_1 = 'Blue $a_1 \cdot$Round a_1' is under consideration. We wish to show that a definite probability $pr(H_1, E, \Delta_1)$

[8] Note that distributions cannot be characterized in L and that, therefore, they cannot form the content of any hypothesis that may be formulated in L; we speak about them in a suitable meta-language for L. In our case, this meta-language is English, supplemented by a number of symbols, such as 'H', 'E', 'q_1', 'q_2', $\cdots$, 'Δ', etc. It might be well to emphasize at this point that the definition and the entire theory of dc for L is formulated in that meta-language, not in L itself: In the meta-language, we speak about the sentences of L and about the degrees to which certain sentences confirm others.

can be assigned to H_1 with respect to any given E (with a restriction to be mentioned subsequently), according to the frequency distribution Δ_1.

I. We first consider the case where no information besides Δ_1 is available; in this case, E may be taken to be some analytic sentence, say 'Blue $a_1 \vee \sim$Blue a_1', which we shall designate by 'T'. Thus, we are concerned with an explanation of $pr(H_1, T, \Delta_1)$, i.e. the probability of H_1 according to the frequency distribution Δ_1. We shall construe the problem of defining this magnitude in strict analogy to the following question: Given the distribution Δ_1 for the population of an urn W, what is the probability that the first object drawn will be both blue and round? And since there is no discrimination among the objects except in terms of their properties referred to in L_w, this latter probability will be the same as the probability that some object, chosen at random from the urn, will be both blue and round. The latter probability, however, is uniquely determined by the given distribution: it is the relative frequency assigned to Q_1 in Δ_1. In our case, therefore, $pr(H_1, T, \Delta_1) = 1/2$. Now let H_2 = 'Blue a_1', which is logically equivalent with '(Blue $a_1 \cdot$Round a_1) $\vee$ (Blue $a_1 \cdot \sim$Round a_1)'. This sentence asserts that a_1 belongs to one of two cells whose occupancy frequencies, according to Δ_1, are 1/2 and 1/3, respectively. And since the cells are mutually exclusive, we set $pr(H_2, T, \Delta_1) = 1/2 + 1/3$. Similarly, for H_3 = '$\sim$Blue a_2', $pr(H_3, T, \Delta_1) = 1/6$. Finally, let H_4 = 'Blue $a_1 \cdot$Blue $a_2 \cdot \sim$Blue a_3'; then we set $pr(H_4, T, \Delta_1) = 5/6 \cdot 5/6 \cdot 1/6$.[9]

After these illustrations, we shall now outline a general method of determining $pr(H, T, \Delta)$ for any given H and Δ. For this purpose, we introduce an auxiliary concept. By a *perfect description*, we shall understand a conjunction each of whose terms assigns some particular individual to some definite L-cell, and in which no individual is mentioned more than once. Thus, e.g., '$Q_1a_1 \cdot Q_1a_2 \cdot Q_2a_4 \cdot Q_4a_6$' is a perfect description.

IA. Now consider first the case that H is a molecular sentence. Then H can always be transformed into a disjunction of perfect descriptions. We omit the elementary but somewhat lengthy proof of this theorem here and rather illustrate it by an example: Let L contain exactly two primitive predicates, 'P_1' and 'P_2', and let H_5 = '$P_1a_1 \cdot P_2a_2$'; then H_5 can readily be expanded into the following expression:

$$\text{`}((P_1a_1 \cdot P_2a_1) \vee (P_1a_1 \cdot \sim P_2a_1)) \cdot ((P_1a_2 \cdot P_2a_2) \vee (\sim P_1a_2 \cdot P_2a_2))\text{'},$$

which in turn is equivalent to '$(Q_1a_1 \vee Q_2a_1) \cdot (Q_1a_2 \vee Q_3a_2)$'; and this can be transformed into the following disjunction of perfect descriptions:

$$\text{`}(Q_1a_1 \cdot Q_1a_2) \vee (Q_1a_1 \cdot Q_3a_2) \vee (Q_2a_1 \cdot Q_1a_2) \vee (Q_2a_1 \cdot Q_3a_2)\text{'}.$$

Once H has thus been transformed, the determination of $pr(H, T, \Delta)$ follows simply the following two rules, which were illustrated above: (a) The proba-

[9] In the case of a finite total population, the application of the simple product rule presupposes that the objects constituting a sample are taken from the urn one at a time, and that each of them is replaced into the urn before the next one is drawn. In order to avoid complications of this sort, we assume the population to be infinite.

bility of H with respect to T and Δ is the sum of the probabilities of the perfect descriptions whose disjunction is equivalent to H; (b) The probability of a perfect description with respect to T and Δ is the product of the relative frequencies assigned by Δ to the Q-expressions occurring in the perfect description. Thus, if $\Delta = \{q_1, q_2, q_3, q_4\}$, then $pr(H_5, T, \Delta) = q_1^2 + q_1q_3 + q_2q_1 + q_2q_3$.

IB. If H is a general sentence, then two cases have to be distinguished[1]:

a) If the number N of all objects to which L refers is finite and all have names, then H can obviously be transformed into a molecular sentence. Thus, e.g., the hypothesis '$(x)(P_1x \supset P_2x) \cdot (Ey)P_3y$' is equivalent to the following molecular sentence, which will also be called the *molecular development of H for the class of individuals* $\{a_1, a_2, \cdots, a_N\}$ or, briefly, $D_N(H)$: '$(P_1a_1 \supset P_2a_1) \cdot (P_1a_2 \supset P_2a_2) \cdots (P_1a_N \supset P_2a_N) \cdot (P_3a_1 \vee P_3a_2 \vee \cdots \vee P_3a_N)$'. Now we simply define $pr(H, T, \Delta)$ as $pr(D_N(H), T, \Delta)$; and the latter magnitude can be determined according to the rules laid down in IA.

b) If the class of all individuals is denumerably infinite and ordered in a sequence $a_1, a_2, a_3, \cdots$ — and this is the case with which we are principally concerned — then we define $pr(H, T, \Delta)$ as the limit, for indefinitely increasing N, of $pr(D_N(H), T, \Delta)$. It can be shown that this limit exists in all cases. (In particular, we note that when H is a general sentence containing no individual constants the limit in question is either 0 or 1).

II. We now turn to the concept '$pr(H, E, \Delta)$', which refers to those cases where, besides the distribution Δ, some additional information E is given. To illustrate this case by means of the urn analogue and by reference to L_w: Let again $\Delta_1 = \{1/2, 1/3, 0, 1/6\}$, and let H_6 = '$\sim$Round a_5'. Then $pr(H_6, T, \Delta_1) = 1/3 + 1/6 = 1/2$. Now suppose that we are given the additional information E_1 = 'Blue a_5'. In the light of the thus enlarged total information, H_6 will acquire a different probability: Since, according to E_1, a_5 is blue, and since, according to Δ_1, the frequency of the non-round objects among the blue ones is $1/3 \div (1/2 + 1/3) = 2/5$, we shall set $pr(H_6, E_1, \Delta_1) = 2/5$.

A completely general definition of $pr(H, E, \Delta)$ can be given in terms of the narrower concept '$pr(H, T, \Delta)$':

$$7.1 \qquad pr(H, E, \Delta) = \frac{pr(H \cdot E, T, \Delta)}{pr(E, T, \Delta)}$$

This definition presupposes that $pr(E, T, \Delta) \neq 0$; when this condition is not satisfied, $pr(H, E, \Delta)$ will not be defined.

This definition is suggested by the following consideration: We wish $pr(H, E, \Delta)$, for any fixed Δ, to satisfy the standard principles of probability theory.[10], including the general multiplication principle. Now the latter demands that

$$pr(E \cdot H, T, \Delta) = pr(E, T, \Delta) \cdot pr(H, E \cdot T, \Delta)$$

In view of the fact that $E \cdot H$ is logically equivalent to $H \cdot E$ and $E \cdot T$ logically equivalent to E, this leads to 7.1.

[10] These are stated in section 10 of the present article.

It can be proved that the concept thus defined satisfies all the customary postulates of probability theory.[11]

8. *Optimum distributions relatively to given evidence.* — Our problem of defining $dc(H, E)$ could now readily be solved if it were generally possible to infer from the given evidence E the frequency distribution Δ characteristic of the L-cells in the language under consideration; for we could then simply identify $dc(H, E)$ with $pr(H, E, \Delta)$. Unfortunately, however, no evidence sentence that is expressible in L can be strong enough to permit such an inference. Nonetheless, a closely related but somewhat weaker procedure is indeed available for the definition of $dc(H, E)$. This procedure is based on the fact that while a given E does not uniquely determine a fixed Δ, it may confer different degrees of likelihood — in a sense presently to be explained — upon the different possible distributions. Under favorable circumstances it may even be possible to characterize one particular distribution, Δ_E, as the one which is most likely on the basis of E; and in this case, $dc(H, E)$ might be defined as $pr(H, E, \Delta_E)$. We shall eventually extend this idea to the case where E does not uniquely determine just one most likely distribution; but before going into the details of this method, which will be done in the subsequent section, we have first to clarify the idea of likelihood referred to in the preceding discussion.

Let us illustrate the essential points by reference to L_w and the urn analogue. Suppose that E_1 is a report asserting that among 12 objects selected at random, 6 were blue and round, 4 blue and not round, and 2 neither blue nor round. If no additional information is available, we would say that in the light of the given evidence, $\Delta_1 = \{1/2, 1/3, 0, 1/6\}$ is more likely than, say, $\Delta_2 = \{4/9, 2/9, 0, 3/9\}$, and that the latter is more likely than, say, $\Delta_3 = \{1/10, 5/10, 2/10, 2/10\}$. Precisely how is the meaning of "more likely" to be construed here? It was shown in the preceding section that on the basis of any given frequency distribution Δ, and in the absence of any further information, it is possible to assign to every sentence S of L a definite probability $pr(S, T, \Delta)$; here, S may be a hypothesis under test or any other sentence in L. In particular, we may consider the case where S is our given evidence sentence E; i.e. we may ask: What is the probability $pr(E, T, \Delta)$ which E would possess on the basis of a certain hypothetical distribution Δ, and in the absence of any other information? If E is made more probable, in this sense, by a certain distribution Δ_1 than by another distribution Δ_2, then we shall say that Δ_1 has a *greater likelihood* relatively to E than does Δ_2.

Illustration: In our last example, we have

$$pr(E_1, T, \Delta_1) = (1/2)^6 \cdot (1/3)^4 \cdot (1/6)^2$$
$$pr(E_1, T, \Delta_2) = (4/9)^6 \cdot (2/9)^4 \cdot (3/9)^2$$
$$pr(E_1, T, \Delta_3) = (1/10)^6 \cdot (5/10)^4 \cdot (2/10)^2$$

and indeed, as can readily be verified, we have here

[11] This probability concept was developed by Olaf Helmer; a detailed exposition of the theory of this concept is included in the article by Helmer and Oppenheim mentioned in footnote 1.

$$pr(E_1, T, \Delta_1) > pr(E_1, T, \Delta_2) > pr(E_1, T, \Delta_3),$$

in accordance with our earlier judgment as to the order of likelihoods involved.

Relatively to some given evidence E, therefore, the infinitely many theoretically possible frequency distributions fall into a definite order of likelihood. By an *optimum distribution relatively to* E, we shall understand a distribution Δ such that the probability $pr(E, T, \Delta)$ which Δ confers upon E is not exceeded by the probability that any other distribution would assign to E.[12] — Now it cannot be expected that every possible E determines exactly one optimum distribution: there may be several distributions each of which would give to E the same, maximum, probability. Thus, e.g. — to mention just one simple case — the probability of the evidence sentence 'Blue a_1' in L_w will clearly be maximized by any distribution which makes the frequency of the blue objects equal to 1, i.e. by any distribution of the form $\{q_1, 1 - q_1, 0, 0\}$, where q_1 may have any arbitrary value between 0 and 1 inclusive. It can be shown, however, that every E determines at least one optimum distribution; if there are several of them, then, of course, they all will confer the same probability upon E. We shall use the symbol 'Δ_E' to refer to the optimum distribution or distributions relatively to E; Δ_E is, therefore, a generally plurivalued function of the evidence E.

The determination of Δ_E for given E is a mathematical problem whose treatment will be discussed here only in outline. Consider again the model language L_w and the four cells Q_1, Q_2, Q_3, Q_4 determined by it. Let a specific evidence sentence E be given. To find Δ_E, consider the general case of a hypothetical distribution $\Delta = \{q_1, q_2, q_3, q_4\}$, where the four components of Δ are parameters satisfying the conditions

8.1 $$0 \leqq q_s \leqq 1 \quad (s = 1, 2, 3, 4)$$

8.2 $$q_1 + q_2 + q_3 + q_4 = 1$$

The probability $pr(E, T, \Delta)$ which Δ confers upon E will be a function $f(q_1, q_2, q_3, q_4)$ of the parameters, as is illustrated at the end of IA in section 6. Δ_E can now be found by determining those values of the parameters which satisfy 8.1 and 8.2, and for which $f(q_1, q_2, q_3, q_4)$ assumes an absolute maximum. These values are found by partial differentiation of the function f. By equating the partial derivatives to 0, a system of simultaneous equations is obtained whose solution (or solutions) yield the value (or values) of Δ_E for the given evidence E. Explicit formulae for the solution of such systems of equations will

[12] An alternative to this approach would be to determine, by means of Bayes' theorem, that distribution upon which E confers the greatest probability (in contradistinction to our question for that distribution which confers upon E the maximum probability); but this approach presupposes — to state it first by reference to the urn analogue — an infinity of urns, each with a different frequency distribution; and to each urn U, there would have to be assigned a definite a priori probability for the sample to be taken from U. Applied to our problem, this method would involve reference to an infinity of possible states of the world, to each of which there would have to be attached a certain a priori probability of being realized; and for such a "lottery of states of the world," as it were, it seems very difficult to find an empiricist interpretation.

be available only in special cases; but in many other cases, methods of computation can be indicated which will at least approximate the solutions. We mention here only one result of particular importance:

8.3 If E is a perfect description — as, for example, '$Q_1a_1 \cdot Q_1a_2 \cdot Q_1a_3 \cdot Q_2a_4 \cdot Q_2a_5 \cdot Q_3a_6$' in L_w — then Δ_E is unique, and its components are simply the relative frequencies with which the cells are represented in E — in our example, $\Delta_E = \{1/2, 1/3, 1/6, 0\}$.

The method which has been used here to characterize optimum distributions goes back to a procedure introduced by R. A. Fisher as the *maximum likelihood method.*[13] We shall consider later the general character of our procedure, but first we turn to the definition of *dc* in terms of the concept of optimum distribution.

9. *Definition of dc(H, E).* — In accordance with the program outlined in the beginning of the preceding section, we now define

$$9.1 \qquad dc(H, E) = pr(H, E, \Delta_E)$$

This definition embodies an empiricist reconstruction of the concept of degree of confirmation: On the basis of the given evidence E, we infer the optimum distribution (or distributions) Δ_E and then assign to H, as its degree of confirmation, the probability which H possesses relatively to E according to Δ_E.

As can be seen from 7.1, the definition 9.1 determines $dc(H, E)$ in all cases where $pr(E, T, \Delta_E) \neq 0$. Now it can be shown that this condition is satisfied if and only if E is logically consistent; so that, by 9.1, $dc(H, E)$ is defined for every non-contradictory E.

It should be noted, however, that, since Δ_E is not necessarily single-valued, $dc(H, E)$ may have more than one value.[14] Thus, e.g., when H = 'P_1a' and E = 'P_2b', $dc(H, E)$ turns out to have as its values all the real numbers between 0 and 1 inclusive. This is quite sensible in view of the fact that the given E is entirely irrelevant for the assertion made by H; E, therefore, can impose no restrictions at all upon the range of the logically possible values of the degree to which H may be confirmed.

However, $dc(H, E)$ can be shown to be single-valued in large classes of cases; these include, in particular, the cases where E is a perfect description, as can readily be seen from theorem 8.3. Also, it can be shown that in all cases of the

[13] Cf. R. A. Fisher: "The Mathematical Foundations of Theoretical Statistics," *Phil. Trans. Roy. Soc. London* 222 (1922), pp. 309–368. Also see M. G. Kendall: "On the Method of Maximum Likelihood," *Journal Roy. Stat. Soc.* 103 (1940), pp. 388–399, and the same author's work, *Advanced Theory of Statistics* (London 1943).

[14] The symbol '$dc(H, E)$' is therefore used here in a similar manner as, say, '$\sqrt{x}$' in mathematics; both represent functions which are not generally single-valued. An alternative would be to stipulate that $dc(H, E)$ is to equal $pr(H, E, \Delta_E)$ in those cases where the latter function is single-valued, and that in all other cases, $dc(H, E)$ is to remain undefined. A third possibility would be to define $dc(H, E)$ as the smallest value of $pr(H, E, \Delta_E)$; for of two hypotheses tested by means of the same evidence, that one will be considered more reliable for which that smallest value is greater. This definition, however, has a certain disadvantage, which is explained in footnote 17.

kind characterized in 5.3, our definition leads to a unique value of $dc(H, E)$, and that this value is the relative frequency stipulated in 5.3.

We shall now analyze in some detail a special example which incidentally shows that dc can be single-valued in cases other than those just mentioned. Let L contain just one primitive predicate, 'P', and let

$$E = \text{`}(Pa_1 \cdot Pa_2 \cdot \sim Pa_3) \vee (Pa_1 \cdot \sim Pa_2 \cdot \sim Pa_3) \vee (\sim Pa_1 \cdot \sim Pa_2 \cdot Pa_3)\text{'}$$

and

$$H_1 = \text{`}Pa_4\text{'}, \quad H_2 = \text{`}Pa_1\text{'}.$$

In order to determine Δ_E, we have to find that $\Delta = \{q, 1 - q\}$ which maximizes the magnitude

9.2 $$pr(E, T, \Delta) = q^2(1 - q) + q(1 - q)^2 + (1 - q)^2q = q^3 - 3q^2 + 2q$$

By equating the derivative of this function to 0 and solving for q, we obtain

9.3 $$q = \frac{3 - \sqrt{3}}{3}$$

and hence

9.4 $$\Delta_E = \left(\frac{3 - \sqrt{3}}{3}, \frac{\sqrt{3}}{3}\right)$$

Substituting from 9.3 in 9.2 yields

9.5 $$pr(E, T, \Delta_E) = \frac{2\sqrt{3}}{9}$$

We similarly compute

9.6 $$pr(H_1 \cdot E, T, \Delta_E) = \frac{2\sqrt{3}}{9} \cdot \frac{3 - \sqrt{3}}{3}$$

Hence

9.7 $$dc(H_1, E) = \frac{pr(H_1 \cdot E, T, \Delta_E)}{pr(E, T, \Delta_E)} = \frac{3 - \sqrt{3}}{3}$$

As for H_2, we note that

$$H_2 \cdot E = \text{`}(Pa_1 \cdot Pa_2 \cdot \sim Pa_3) \vee (Pa_1 \cdot \sim Pa_2 \cdot \sim Pa_3)\text{'}$$

Hence

9.8 $$pr(H_2 \cdot E, T, \Delta_E) = q^2(1 - q) + q(1 - q)^2 = q(1 - q) = \frac{\sqrt{3} - 1}{3}$$

and finally

9.9 $$dc(H_2, E) = \frac{pr(H_2 \cdot E, T, \Delta_E)}{pr(E, T, \Delta_E)} = \frac{3 - \sqrt{3}}{2}$$

After having considered some examples involving non-general hypotheses, we now turn to the case of hypotheses in the form of general sentences. Let us assume, for example, that L contains again only one primitive predicate, 'P', and let H = '$(x)Px$', E_1 = 'Pa_1', E_2 = '$Pa_1 \cdot Pa_2 \cdot \cdots Pa_t$', E_3 = '$\sim Pa_1 \cdot Pa_2 \cdot Pa_3 \cdot \cdots Pa_t$'. To compute the values of dc

for these cases, we note first that, as can readily be shown, conditions 5.1 and 5.2 are satisfied by dc as defined in 9.1, and that, as a consequence, $dc(H, E) = 0$ whenever H contradicts E. Now, if again we assume the class of all objects to be infinite, we obtain

$$dc(H, E_1) = dc(H, E_2) = \lim_{N \to \infty} 1^N = 1; \quad dc(H, E_3) = 0,$$

no matter how large t may be. The last value appears perfectly reasonable: Since E_3 contains one conjunctive term which contradicts H, E_3 itself contradicts H and thus disconfirms it to the highest degree that is theoretically possible. The value 1 in the first two cases, however, might seem counter-intuitive for two reasons: First, it seems strange that it should make no difference for the value of $dc(H, E)$ how many confirming instances for H are included in E — as long as E contains no disconfirming evidence; and second, it is surprising that even one single confirming case for H should confirm the hypothesis H — which virtually covers an infinity of such cases — to the maximum extent. The significance of these results might become clearer if we distinguish between the retrospective and the prospective aspects of what has sometimes been called the probability, and what we call the degree of confirmation, of a universal hypothesis. Taken retrospectively, the magnitude in question is to characterize the extent to which H is confirmed "by past experience," i.e. by the given evidence E; taken prospectively, it is to constitute, as it were, a measure of the warranted assertability of the hypothesis, or of the rational belief to be placed in its validity in instances which have as yet not been examined. Now clearly, in our illustration, H is confirmed to the fullest possible extent by E_1 as well as by E_2: in both cases it is satisfied in 100 per cent of the instances mentioned by E. As to the prospective aspect, it is simply an inductivist attitude which directs us to assign the dc 1^N to the hypothesis that the next N instances will conform to the hypothesis, and finally, the limit of 1^N, for indefinitely increasing N, to the hypothesis itself, i.e. to the assumption that *all* objects conform to it.

10. *Probability and degree of confirmation.* — Might $dc(H, E)$ as well be called the probability of the hypothesis H relatively to the evidence E? Partly, of course, that is a matter of arbitrary terminological decision. However, the concept of probability has come to be used with reference to magnitudes which satisfy certain conditions which, for brevity, will be called here the postulates of general probability theory.[15] We shall summarize them here in a form adapted from Janina Hosiasson-Lindenbaum's article "On Confirmation."[16]

The probability of H relatively to E, or, briefly, $p(H, E)$ is a single-valued function of two sentences, the second of which is non-contradictory. This function satisfies the following conditions:

10.1 If H is a consequence of E, then $p(H, E) = 1$

10.2 If E implies that H_1 and H_2 cannot both be true, then

$$p(H_1 \vee H_2, E) = p(H_1, E) + p(H_2, E)$$

(Special addition principle of probability theory)

10.3 $$p(H_1 \cdot H_2, E) = p(H_1, E) \cdot p(H_2, H_1 \cdot E)$$

(General multiplication principle of probability theory)

[15] On this point, cf. also section 3 of Professor Carnap's article.

[16] *The Journal of Symbolic Logic*, vol. 5 (1940), pp. 133–148.

10.4 If E_1 and E_2 are logically equivalent, then

$$p(H, E_1) = p(H, E_2)$$

The concept '$pr(H, E, \Delta)$' can be shown to satisfy, for any fixed Δ, all of these conditions. But the concept '$dc(H, E)$', which is defined by reference to it, does not. For, firstly, as we saw, $dc(H, E)$ is not always a single-valued function of H and E. As to the four postulates listed above, the following can be shown: The first, second, and fourth postulates are generally satisfied by dc provided that when dc is plurivalued, "corresponding values" — i.e. values obtained from the same Δ_E — are substituted in the formulae. The third postulate, however, is not generally satisfied; the reason for this becomes clear when in 10.3, 'dc' is replaced by its definiens. Then the left hand side turns into '$pr(H_1 \cdot H_2, E, \Delta_E)$', and as '$pr$' satisfies the general multiplication principle, we may transform the last expression into '$pr(H_1, E, \Delta_E) \cdot pr(H_2, H_1 \cdot E, \Delta_E)$'; but the right hand side of 10.3 transforms into '$pr(H_1, E, \Delta_E) \cdot pr(H_2, H_1 \cdot E, \Delta_{H_1 \cdot E})$'; and clearly, the second factors in these two expressions cannot generally be expected to be equal. However, the following restricted version of 10.3 is generally satisfied:

10.3′ "Corresponding values" of $dc(H, E)$ satisfy 10.3 in particular if the two following conditions are satisfied:
- (a) H_1 and H_2 have no individual constants in common,
- (b) At least one of the hypotheses H_1, H_2 has no individual constants in common with E.[17]

In view of the fact that dc as defined above does not satisfy all of the postulates of probability theory, we prefer not to call dc a probability.[17a]

Finally, it may be of interest to compare our way of defining dc with another method, which makes use of the concept of measure of a sentence. Briefly, this method consists in assigning, by means of some general rule, a measure $m(S)$ to every sentence S in L in such a manner that the following conditions are satisfied:

10.51 For every S, $0 \leqq m(S) \leqq 1$

10.52 If S_1, S_2 are logically equivalent, then $m(S_1) = m(S_2)$

10.53 If S_1, S_2 are logically incompatible, then

$$m(S_1 \vee S_2) = m(S_1) + m(S_2)$$

10.54 For any analytic sentence T, $m(T) = 1$

[17] In footnote 14, two alternatives to our definition of dc were mentioned. It can be shown that the concept determined by the first of these satisfies without exception the requirements 10.1, 10.2, and 10.3′, and 10.4, whereas the concept introduced by the second alternative does not. Thus, e.g., if H = 'P_1a_1', E = 'P_2a_2', then the values of $pr(H, E, \Delta_E)$ are all the real numbers from 0 to 1 inclusive, so that the smallest value is 0. The same is true of $pr(\sim H, E, \Delta_E)$; hence these two smallest values violate the principle 5.1 and thus indirectly the postulates 10.1 and 10.2, of which 5.1 can be shown to be a consequence.

[17a] The alternative term "likelihood" which suggests itself is inexpedient also, as it has already been introduced into theoretical statistics with a different meaning (cf. section 8 above). If a term customarily associated with "probability" should be desired, then "expectancy" might be taken into consideration.

The degree of confirmation of a hypothesis H with respect to a non-contradictory evidence sentence E is then defined as $\frac{m(H \cdot E)}{m(E)}$. The stipulations 10.5 leave room for an infinite variety of possible measure functions; the choice of a particular function will be determined by the adequacy of the concept of degree of confirmation which is definable in terms of it.[18] Our concept '$dc(H, E)$' can be introduced in a formally similar manner as follows: Instead of assigning to each sentence of L once and for all an a priori measure, as it is done in the method just described, we give to the sentences of L measures which depend on the given empirical evidence E. The E-measure of a sentence S in L can be defined thus:

10.6 $$m_E(S) = pr(S, T, \Delta_E)$$

In terms of this magnitude, we can express $dc(H, E)$ as follows:

10.7 $$dc(H, E) = \frac{m_E(H \cdot E)}{m_E(E)},$$

for by virtue of 9.1, 7.1, and 10.6,

$$dc(H, E) = pr(H, E, \Delta_E) = \frac{pr(H \cdot E, T, \Delta_E)}{pr(E, T, \Delta_E)} = \frac{m_E(H \cdot E)}{m_E(E)}$$

(As was pointed out in connection with 9.1, $m_E(E) = pr(E, T, \Delta_E)$ equals 0 only when E is contradictory; in this case, $dc(H, E)$ is not defined.)

11. *Concluding remarks.* — The concept of dc as it has been defined here is a purely logical concept in the following sense: Given two sentences H, E in L, $dc(H, E)$ is completely determined by the formal, or syntactical, structure of the two sentences alone, and apart from possible mathematical complications, its value can be found by an analysis of that structure and the application of certain purely deductive mathematical techniques. Nevertheless, the proposed concept is empiricist and not "aprioristic" in character; for the degree of confirmation assigned to H is determined, generally speaking, by reference to relative frequencies derived from the evidence sentence E. With reference to the alternative definition 10.6, the matter can be stated as follows: dc is defined in terms of the concept of measure of a sentence; but whereas in an aprioristic theory, the measure of a sentence is determined once and for all on the basis of a mere analysis of its logical structure, the measure used in 10.6 is empiricist in that its determination requires reference not only to the structure of the sentence, but also to the given empirical evidence E.

[18] The method characterized above is illustrated by a definition of probability which F. Waismann ("Logische Analyse des Wahrscheinlichkeitsbegriffs," *Erkenntnis*, vol. 1, pp. 228–248) has outlined following a suggestion made in L. Wittgenstein's *Tractatus Logico-Philosophicus* (New York and London 1922). Also, the regular c-functions introduced in Professor Carnap's article on inductive logic exemplify this way of defining dc. In that article, some special choices for the measure function m are presented and examined as to their suitability for the establishment of an adequate definition of the concept of degree of confirmation.

The method employed to determine $dc(H, E)$ consists essentially of two steps: First, by means of the maximum likelihood principle, a hypothetical assumption is formed, on the basis of E, as to the frequency distribution for the L-cells; second, on the basis of the hypothetical distribution thus assumed, a probability is assigned to H relatively to E. The rationale of this procedure is perhaps best exhibited by reference to a simple model case. Suppose that we are given a die about whose homogeneity and symmetry nothing is known. We have an opportunity to roll the die 20 times and are then to lay a bet on the hypothesis H that both the 21st and the 22nd throw will yield a six. The maximum likelihood principle would direct us, in this particularly simple case, to record, in a report E, the occurrence or non-occurrence of a six as the result of each of the first twenty throws, and then to form a hypothesis as to the limit of the relative frequency with which throws with the given die will yield a six. This limit is to be chosen in such a way that relatively to it, the distribution of the results found in E has a maximum probability. In the simple case under consideration, this means that we have to set the limit equal to the relative frequency with which the result six is reported in E; let this be 1/10; then the distribution $\Delta_E = \{1/10, 9/10\}$ for the cells corresponding to the results six and non-six is the optimum distribution, and on the basis of it, $dc(H, E)$ becomes 1/100; this value would be the basis for determining the rates of a fair bet on H, in the light of E.

In this special case, which is covered by the rule 5.3, the procedure dictated by the maximum likelihood principle clearly coincides with that which a "rational gambler" would use, and which is also used in statistical investigations of various kinds. It reflects an assumption which might be called the statistical version of the principle of induction, and which, stated in very crude terms, implies that relative frequencies observed "in the past" (i.e. in the instances so far examined) will remain fairly stable "in the future" (i.e. in those instances which have not as yet been examined, no matter whether they belong to the past or to the future). The maximum likelihood principle in the form in which it has been used here for the general definition of dc is but an extension of this same idea to cases more complex than those covered by rule 5.3; and we may say that it represents a generalization and rational reconstruction of the statistical version of the principle of induction.

The theory obtained by our procedure provides criteria which establish, so to speak, a fair rate of betting on a specified hypothesis on the basis of given data. (In many cases, as we saw, dc will be single-valued and the betting rate will therefore be uniquely determined; in other cases, where the evidence is insufficient in a certain sense, dc will have several values, and then, the smallest of these might be used to establish a betting rate.) The decisions, however, which a gambler has to make concern not only the betting rate but also the amount he is going to risk; and while the rate is determined, generally speaking, by the relative frequency in the past of the event on which he wishes to bet, the gambler's stake will be determined by different factors, such as, e.g., the size of the sample which represents the evidence. Analogously, the concept of degree of confirmation as it has been defined in the present article, refers only to one among several factors which enter into an objective appraisal of the soundness or reliability of an empirical hypothesis. The remaining factors include, among others, the number of tested instances which are mentioned in *E*, and the variety of those instances.[19] Our theory of confirmation is intended to account exclusively for the first of these various aspects of the evaluation of a hypothesis by means of relevant evidence, — that aspect which is analogous to the betting rate in the preceding example.

The theory of confirmation which has been outlined in this article cannot claim to be more than a first contribution to the exploration of a field in which systematic logical research is only beginning. Among various problems which are suggested by the present study, we should like to point out a few which seem to deserve special attention in future research:

(1) The next step in the development of the theory of confirmation would be the extension of the definition of *dc* to the entire lower functional calculus and possibly even to the higher functional calculus.

(2) In section 1, we distinguished the metrical concept of degree of confirmation from the classificatory concepts of confirming and disconfirming evidence for a given hypothesis. In this connection, the question arises whether the meaning of the expressions "*E* is confirming evidence for *H*" and "*E* is disconfirming evidence for *H*" is adequately definable in terms of $dc(H, E)$.

(3) In the practice of scientific research, observation reports are not all considered equally reliable; rather, their reliability will depend on certain characteristics of the observer, on the instruments of observation used, and on the circumstances under which the observation took place. Also, when general sentences are included in the evidence *E*, these might be said to have different degrees of reliability (which, for example, might be determined on the basis of their *dc* relatively to all the relevant evidence known at the time). We might try to reflect this aspect of scientific testing by assuming in our theory that each evidence sentence is assigned a numerical "weight," whose value is a real number between 0 and 1, inclusive. The problem then arises of defining $dc(H, E)$ in a manner which takes into consideration those weights attached to the evidence. The generalized definition here called for should comprehend, as one special case, our definition 9.1 (or another adequate definition of this kind); for the latter rests, as it were, on the tacit assumption that the weight of the given evidence is always 1.

[19] Cf. Ernest Nagel, "Principles of the Theory of Probability," *Internat. Encycl. of Unified Science*, vol. 1, no. 6, Chicago 1939; pp. 68–71. [Ed. note: This selection from Nagel is reprinted in this Section.] Also, see section 15 of Professor Carnap's paper, which contains a discussion of this point.

17 Degree of Factual Support

JOHN G. KEMENY AND PAUL OPPENHEIM[1]

We wish to give a precise formulation of the intuitive concept: The degree to which the known facts (the evidence) support a given hypothesis.

Perhaps the best way to clarify exactly which concept we have in mind is to relate it to another concept, the concept of degree of confirmation. This is the measure of the degree of belief a rational being would assign to a hypothesis on the given evidence. (Hence Russell's term 'degree of credibility'[2] seems to be more appropriate than 'degree of confirmation.') Let us use '*F*' as an abbreviation of our concept, and '*C*' for 'degree of confirmation (credibility).' Carnap[3] has described *C* as a measure of evidential support, and this description is fitting for both concepts. But *C* is the logical basis for induction, so we could describe it as the inductive support given by the evidence. As Carnap points out in section 46 (loc. cit.) this support depends on several factors. The most immediate factor is that of the factual support given by the evidence, our *F*. (Others are the variety of the evidence, its reliability, the simplicity of the hypothesis, etc.) In this paper we analyze this single factor. We could describe *F* as the degree to which the evidence supports the hypothesis, without any inductive considerations. Its importance lies in that it must be clarified (along with the other factors) before we can define *C*. In a given inductive judgment we must first see how favorable the facts are; some facts will support our hypothesis, while some will weigh against it, and it is our task to evaluate this — which is accomplished by *F*. Then we must take into account other factors (like the ones mentioned above) and carry out an induction, resulting in a *C*-value.

A few remarks are in order to clarify the intuitive idea we start from. A scientist uses this concept whenever he counts the number of observations favorable to his hypothesis, and compares them to the unfavorable observations. E.g., let his hypothesis be that all 150 million Americans are under 7

From *Philosophy of Science*, Vol. 19, No. 4, pp. 307–324, October, 1952.

[1] In the main the contribution of Paul Oppenheim was limited to propounding some of the fundamental ideas.

[2] Russell, Bertrand, *Human Knowledge*, New York: Simon and Schuster, 1948.

[3] Carnap, Rudolf, *Logical Foundations of Probability*, Chicago: The University of Chicago Press, 1950.

feet tall, unless they have a glandular disturbance. Then he can count all Americans who were observed to be under 7 feet tall, or were observed to have a glandular disturbance (or both) as favorable evidence; while, e.g. any report of an American over 7 feet tall, that mentioned nothing about his glandular condition, would be unfavorable. The degree of factual support weighs the favorable facts against the unfavorable ones, and weighs the result against the hypothesis. Of course, one single case of an American having no glandular disturbance, but being over 7 feet tall, would completely invalidate the hypothesis, and hence the rest of the evidence would be irrelevant. Equally irrelevant (for *factual* support) would be all evidence as to the height and gland-condition of Europeans (although this would be quite relevant from the *inductive* standpoint).

Our task is the rational reconstruction (or in Carnap's terms *explication*) of the intuitive concept of *degree of factual support*. The commonest procedure of explication is to apply a trial and error method till one arrives at an ingenious guess, and then try to find intuitive reasons to justify the proposed *explicatum*. This procedure is clearly very dangerous: The intuition of the most honest and well-trained philosopher is likely at times to become a tool for grinding an ax. Even Carnap,* who begins (loc. cit.) by setting down strict conditions of adequacy for his explicatum and arrives at the class of symmetric C-functions, finally just selects one of these, C^*, and justifies the choice by showing that C^* has satisfactory consequences. We feel that we must first put down clearly all that our intuition tells us about the *explicandum*, and then find the precise definitions that satisfy our intuitive requirements. In this sense we hope to set a standard for explications.

On the basis of this methodology we divide our work into four parts:

1. Purely formal conditions are set down, many of which are conventions; they are useful, but they do not essentially restrict the choice of the explicatum. In this part we determine what kind of a definition we are looking for.
2. We now put down as strictly as possible all that our intuition tells us about F. These material conditions, as well as the formal ones of part 1, will be conditions of adequacy for the explicatum.
3. We characterize the class of definitions which satisfy our conditions of adequacy. We should arrive either at a unique explicatum, or at a small class all of whose members are demonstrably equally well in agreement with intuition.
4. We work out some numerical examples on the basis of the (unique or several) remaining explicata, and prove a few theorems.

1. *Formal Conditions of Adequacy.* — 'Degree of factual support,' as the name suggests, is a functor. It measures a relation between a hypothesis and its evidence. Specifically we will consider the hypothesis and the evidence as stated in a formalized language. In order to avoid great technical difficulties, we will be satisfied to choose a first order functional calculus as our language. In this

* [Ed. note: See selection from Carnap included in this Section.]

language we have individual constants and variables (denoting physical objects) and predicates (denoting their properties and relations). There are the logical combinations customary for the functional calculi, and there are no restrictions on the choice of predicates — as long as they are finite in number. This last point is very important; the fact that we allow dependencies between our atomic sentences allows us to use a much richer language than the one usually considered in such papers. E.g., Carnap (loc. cit.) requires independence, and Helmer and Oppenheim[4] also require that we use only one-place predicates. If there are dependencies, these must be indicated in the form of postulates added to the usual axioms. (E.g., if we want to allow 'male' and 'father' (i.e., male parent) as predicates, we must add the postulate: $(x)(\text{Father}(x) \supset \text{Male}(x))$.) The meaningful statements of this language, i.e., the statements formed according to its rules of syntax, are as usual called 'well-formed-formulas' (abbreviate 'w.f.f.').

Thus F is a purely logical function of two w.f.f., H and E (representing the hypothesis and the evidence respectively). We can now enumerate some conditions of adequacy for our functor:

CA1. $F(H, E)$ is a functor whose two arguments are w.f.f. chosen from our first order functional calculus.[5]

The range of values of F is purely conventional. The following is a very useful convention for this:

CA2. F ranges from -1 to 1, with larger values of F indicating more support. -1 indicates the worst possible support, when the evidence shows that the hypothesis is false; 0 corresponds to evidence that is equally favorable and unfavorable (including the case of irrelevance); 1 indicates the best possible support, when the evidence proves that the hypothesis is true.

The more E supports H, the less it supports its negation $\bar{H}$. We see from CA2 that they get equal support just when F is 0, while when $F(H, E)$ is 1 (meaning that H is proved, hence $\bar{H}$ disproved) $F(\bar{H}, E)$ must be -1. The formal condition which most naturally sums up these points is:

CA3. $$F(\bar{H}, E) = -F(H, E).$$

In view of the intended meaning we must obviously have:

CA4. If $\vdash H \equiv H'$ and $\vdash E \equiv E'$, then $F(H, E) = F(H', E')$.[6]

Our next problem is to assign numbers to H and E so that we can construct the functor F. Equivalent w.f.f. must get equal numbers, and these numbers must somehow correspond to "how much H (or E) expresses." The standard way to introduce such a syntactic measure for w.f.f. is by means of a normal form. In order to save space, we will refer the reader to a text on deductive logic, or the excellent treatment of this by Carnap (loc. cit.) or the similar

[4] Helmer, Olaf and Oppenheim, Paul. "A Syntactical Definition of Probability and of Degree of Confirmation," *The Journal of Symbolic Logic*, X, 1945, pp. 25–60.

[5] This condition will be somewhat restricted later, see Part 2.

[6] '$\vdash W$' expresses that W is a theorem, i.e. that it is an analytic consequence of our dependency-postulates, or simply analytic if there are no dependencies.

approach of Helmer and Oppenheim (loc. cit.). We will simply outline the results, and indicate what changes must be made to adapt it to our approach.

We will assume for the moment that there are a finite number, n, of things in the world, i.e. that our universe of discourse has n elements. The following discussion is applicable only for a fixed value of n. Let us give a name to each of these n things in our meta-language, and let us call an *atomic statement* a statement that asserts that one of these things has a certain property, or that several things satisfy a relation; then all possible statements of our language can be represented as combinations of atomic statements. A "possible world" is as completely described as our language allows if we form a conjunction containing for each atomic statement either it or its negation. Such a conjunction is called by Carnap a *state-description* (abbreviated 's.d.'). Carnap formulates his s.d. in the object-language by requiring that all individuals have names, but this is not at all necessary. Since an s.d. describes a model world completely, every w.f.f. is either true or false *in* an s.d. Carnap shows that the meaning of a w.f.f. is expressed by the disjunction of those s.d. in which it is true. (See section 18, loc. cit.) Then Carnap introduces his regular m-functions, which assign weights to all the s.d., the sum of the weights being 1. The measure of a w.f.f. is the sum of the weights of those s.d. in which it is true. (See section 55, loc. cit.) This has to be modified slightly if there are dependencies. It is easy to see that the effect of having dependencies is that some of our s.d. contradict our postulates. So let us denote by 's.d.' only those maximal conjunctions which are consistent with our postulates. If we interpret 's.d.' in this sense, all that we said above remains true for languages with dependencies.

CA5. For fixed n, we must assign to each s.d. a *weight*, i.e. a non-negative number, the sum of the weights being 1. Then for any w.f.f. A, $m(A)$ is the sum of the weights of those s.d. in which A is true.

Such m-functions play a fundamental role in many explications. We will use an m-function to assign numerical values to the relevant combinations of H and E, and — since different relations between H and E can be expressed as relations between these numbers — they will enable us to translate all relevant information about H and E into numerical terms.

We can thus define m-functions, but in general a given definition will yield different values for the same w.f.f. for different values of n. We do not as a matter of fact know what the actual value of n is (we are not sure whether it is finite), so it is difficult to decide what value to use even for a given m-function. In spite of this difficulty there is one method that seems to be intuitively highly satisfactory.

Let us first consider the case that the number of things in the world is infinite. This case has been usually handled (e.g., by Carnap) by calculating the m-values for all finite n and taking the limit as n tends to infinity. These results, however, cannot be used, because any two universal hypotheses have the same m (namely 0) and so does any contradictory hypothesis. These theories always give counter-intuitive results for the infinite case. We must face the fact that only the m-functions for finite n are useable. The method suggested by this consideration is a method of asymptotic comparison. We say that $m(A_1)$ is greater than $m(A_2)$ if for all sufficiently high n the value of the former is greater than the one of the latter. We will discuss this method in detail later, and we will show that it is a refinement of the use of limits.

Now let us suppose that the actual number of things in the world is N, a finite number. Then the correct m-value would be obtained by letting n equal N. But we do not know what N is. Yet we know that it is a very large number, much larger than any number of things used in an experiment. The best we can do, due to our ignorance, is to require that our statements should hold for all sufficiently high n, and hope in any particular case that N is sufficiently high. (And if at some future time we get the exact or approximate value of N, we can always add a postulate to the effect that there are exactly N things in the world, and then our asymptotic comparison method will give the same results as if we had set n equal to N.)

How are we to build up F from a given m-function? F is to depend on H and E and their logical relation to each other. As we have said before, the content of the w.f.f. and their relationship can be expressed in terms of the m-values of combinations of H' and E. Fortunately, we need not consider all combinations; since the m-value of the disjunction of two incompatible w.f.f. is the sum of the m-values, it will suffice to consider the strongest conjunctions of H and E because all other combinations are expressible as disjunctions of these. So we get four basic m-values in terms of which all relevant relations are expressible:

$$(1) \qquad x = m(H \cdot E) \quad y = m(H \cdot \bar{E}) \quad z = m(\bar{H} \cdot E) \quad t = m(\bar{H} \cdot \bar{E})$$

The reader can easily check other combinations: $m(H) = x + y$, $m(E) = x + z$, $m(H \vee E) = x + y + z$, etc. And even these four values are not independent, since the disjunction of the w.f.f. is analytic,

$$(2) \qquad x + y + z + t = 1.$$

Since F is to depend exclusively on H and E and their logical relation to each other, F is a function that can be represented as depending on the quantities in (1) only.

CA6. $F(H, E)$ is a function $f(x, y, z, t)$ where x, y, z, t depend on H and E (according to (1)) and on n (since m depends on it).

We wish to state the method of comparison (see above) as it applies to F. Let us suppose that we have constructed an F-function on the basis of the selected m-function. Let us denote the value for a particular n by $F(H, E, n)$. We introduce the ordering principle:

(3) $F(H, E)$ is greater than $F(H', E')$ if there is an N such that for all n greater than N, $F(H, E, n)$ is greater than $F(H', E', n)$.

Equality and the relation of being less than are defined similarly. This definition seems to be the most rigorous and intuitive definition that we can build on our m-function. Some people may, however, find it distasteful because the values of F are functions of n, not numbers. It also has the disadvantage that if the curves of two functions intersect an infinite number of times, then the

F-values are *incomparable*. This case seems to occur only in certain unusual types of statements not used in the sciences, but it is a disadvantage. Both of these difficulties can be overcome — at a price — by passing to the limit in F.

(4) Let $F^*(H, E)$ be the limit of $F(H, E, n)$ as n tends to infinity, and use $F^*(H, E)$ in place of $F(H, E)$.

Passing to the limit in F is not quite as bad as doing the same in m, but one still gets into trouble with generalized sentences. (The reader interested in this problem should compare Carnap's corresponding results (sections 56 ff., loc. cit.).) So we have the choice between the two methods; the following obvious theorem establishes the relation between them.

THEOREM 1. If F_1 is greater than F_2 according to method (4), it is also greater according to (3).

We will show later by examples that the converse is not true: There are cases where (4) gives the same value for both F's, while (3) can distinguish between them. Hence (3) is a refinement of (4). Perhaps the best procedure is to use (4) with numerical values whenever it gives a sufficiently fine ordering, and use (3) whenever (4) gives too many equal values.

Let us sum up our formal considerations: The problem has been analyzed into two questions, the finding of a suitable measure function m, and the selection of the function f of four variables. If we have the answer to these two questions, we have our F-concept. Given an H and an E, using m we can calculate the values x, y, z, t according to (1) for any fixed n, and then $f(x, y, z, t)$ is $F(H, E, n)$. Then we proceed according to (3) or (4) in the ordering of F's.

2. *Material Conditions of Adequacy.* — Our task now is to set down all our intuition tells us about F, to be able to select an m and an f. The first six CA were really conventions; the material conditions are yet to follow. Our aim is completeness and no special attempt will be made to make conditions independent of each other. We will omit an intuitive condition only if it is immediately clear that it follows from previous conditions of adequacy.

First of all we must clarify the nature of H and E. We said that any w.f.f. is admitted. Actually we are interested in only those w.f.f. which express propositions that could possibly be of scientific interest. So in our formal development if we find exceptions to our theorems which are of no scientific interest we will simply ignore them. This is a weakening of CA1, but we do not try to state it precisely because of the difficulty of stating exactly what w.f.f. are of scientific interest. But to be safe we will ignore w.f.f. only if they are clearly uninteresting, such as analytic and contradictory w.f.f. At this time we must consider another weakening of CA1. We cannot handle a *statement of infinity*, i.e. a w.f.f. which cannot be satisfied by a finite number of individuals because it is not true in any finite s.d., so its m-function is identically 0. This means that there is no way to distinguish between it and a contradictory w.f.f. This is just one more shortcoming added to the fact that we have an oversimplified language. So we now reinterpret CA1 to apply only to such w.f.f. as are of scientific interest, and such that no combination of H and E is a statement of infinity. The remaining w.f.f. still cover a lot of ground; thus, e.g., since we allow dependencies, we have a richer language than that used by the authors writing about C.

Let us also examine more closely the meaning of our weights (p. 215). Since the number of s.d. varies with n, the weights will certainly depend on n also. Could the weights depend on E? This would mean that they are not a priori determined, but empirically. This may or may not be desirable (for example Helmer and Oppenheim require it, while Carnap rejects it); at any rate we allow it in order to give ourselves a maximum amount of freedom. But we see no possible interpretation under which the weights would depend on H.

CA7. The weights depend on n, they may depend on E, but they must be independent of H.

We now turn to some intuitive conditions about greater and lesser factual support. First of all we give material content to the part of CA2 dealing with "best possible support." The evidence definitely proves that the hypothesis is true just in case the hypothesis is a logical consequence of the evidence.

CA8. $F(H, E)$ is 1 if and only if $\vdash E \supset H$.

The evidence definitely disproves the hypothesis just if it logically implies its negation, so this corresponds to $F = -1$. But we need no new condition for this since it follows from CA8 by means of CA3.

These were extreme cases. We now turn to intermediate values of F. Let us start with H_1 and E. If we now strengthen H_1 into H_2, without any additional supporting evidence, then F_2 should be less than F_1. First of all we have that $\vdash H_2 \supset H_1$, but not conversely (meaning of 'stronger'). 'Without additional supporting evidence' could mean that E is the same in both cases, but this is not enough. It could still be that E contains some information irrelevant for H_1 but supporting H_2. So we must assure that what E and H_1 have in common is at least as much as what E and H_2 have in common. (The information two w.f.f. have in common is expressed by their disjunction.)

CA9. If $\vdash H_2 \supset H_1$ and $\vdash [H_1 \vee E] \supset [H_2 \vee E]$, but not $\vdash H_1 \supset H_2$, then $F(H_1, E)$ is greater than $F(H_2, E)$.

Let us now consider the converse case where we strengthen the hypothesis, but the new part has very good support. More precisely, let us strengthen H_1 (whose F is neither -1 nor 1) into H_2 in such a manner that the new part of H_2 (the part in H_2 and not in H_1: $H_2 \vee \bar{H}_1$) gets the best possible support from E; then F must increase.

CA10.[7] If $\vdash H_2 \supset H_1$ and $\vdash E \supset [H_2 \vee \bar{H}_1]$, but not $\vdash H_1 \supset H_2$ and not $\vdash E \supset H_1$ and not $\vdash E \supset \bar{H}_1$, then $F(H_2, E)$ is greater than $F(H_1, E)$.

[7] This CA serves to illustrate the relation between F and C. We see that F does not satisfy one of the fundamental C-principles, namely that if H_1 follows from H_2, then its C is at least as great as that of H_2 with respect to any evidence. Consider the historical example: H_1 is the bending of light-rays in a gravitational field, while H_2 is the General Theory of Relativity, and the evidence is the evidence *before* 1919. Certainly $F(H_2, E)$ is much greater than $F(H_1, E)$ since H_1 was not supported by any observation up to that time. Yet if we assigned say 80% credibility to H_2, we would have to assign at least that much to any of its conse-

Let us now turn to the middle point, where $F = 0$. According to CA2 this happens when the evidence is equally favorable and unfavorable (which very often means an irrelevant evidence). This concept is somewhat like that of the independence of two events in probability theory. Let us try to formulate an "independence condition" for H and E in this sense.

$$p(H \cdot E) = p(H) \times p(E). \tag{5}$$

But what is to take the place of p in our case? Should we choose m? But that cannot be true, because then different choices of m lead to different formulations of our condition, while the 0-values of F are intuitively fixed. So we must find a unique p-function which when inserted in (5) will give an intuitive definition of the case when the evidence is equally favorable and unfavorable.

We will derive this p-function for languages without dependencies. Consider two independent atomic sentences A and B. Two atomic statements which are logically independent cannot support each other factually since they express distinct facts; so B as evidence is irrelevant to A, and $p(A \cdot B)$ is the product of $p(A)$ and $p(B)$. Similarly we get that the p-value of the conjunction of any number of independent atoms is the product of the individual p-values.

Now let us take another example. Consider an evidence E of the form $[A \cdot B] \vee [\bar{A} \cdot \bar{B}]$. This asserts that A is equivalent to B (where B is a logically independent atom). If this is all that we know, then it is just as favorable to A as to $\bar{A}$, hence it is irrelevant. So A and E must satisfy (5). But $A \cdot E$ is equivalent to $A \cdot B$, so we get that $p(A \cdot B) = p(A) \times p(E)$. From the above we know, however, that $p(A \cdot B) = p(A) \times p(B)$, hence $p(B) = p(E)$. When we apply (5) to $\bar{A}$ and E, we get that $p(\bar{B}) = p(E)$. So an atom and its negation have the same p, which must be 1/2. Therefore the p-value of an s.d. is $(1/2)^{\text{no. of atoms}}$ which is the same for all s.d. This describes p uniquely: It is a probability function sometimes called Wittgenstein's. We will use 'p' from now on only as a name for this particular probability function which assigns equal probability to all s.d. We can now use (5) for our purpose,

CA11. $F(H, E) = 0$ if and only if $p(H \cdot E) = p(H) \times p(E)$.

Strictly speaking our argument applies only to languages without dependencies, and even then it makes use of an analogy. But we can show that there is a second approach for describing the 0-values, which applies to any language, and which leads to CA11. We prove this in the form of a theorem.

THEOREM 2. $F(H, E) = 0$ if and only if the s.d. in which H is true and the s.d. in which E is true have 0 correlation.

Proof. Take a fixed n. Enumerate all the s.d., and put a 1 under an s.d. if H is true in it, a 0 otherwise, under these put a 1 if E is true in the s.d., and 0 otherwise. We must now correlate the two rows of 1's and 0's. Let S be the total number of s.d., and h and e variables for the two rows of values. Then the correlation is

quences. Here is a case where H_1 has a high credibility (C) in spite of a very low degree of factual support (F)! The reasoning must be as follows: On the basis of its F-value and other considerations, simplicity of the hypothesis being the most important in this case, we assign by induction a high C-value to H_2, and consequently H_1 must get a C-value at least as high.

$$\frac{S\Sigma(he) - (\Sigma h \times \Sigma e)}{\sqrt{(S\Sigma h^2 - (\Sigma h)^2)(S\Sigma e^2 - (\Sigma e)^2)}} . \tag{6}$$

The sum of the h's gives us just the number of s.d. in which H is true, which can be simply written as $S \times p(H)$. (This follows from the definition of p.) Similarly the sum of the e's is $S \times p(E)$ and the sum of the he's is $S \times p(H \cdot E)$. Insert these values in (6) and simplify,

$$\frac{p(H \cdot E) - p(H) \times p(E)}{\sqrt{p(H) \times p(\bar{H}) \times p(E) \times p(\bar{E})}} . \tag{7}$$

From this we see that the correlation is 0 just when (5) holds, hence the theorem follows from CA11.

This theorem gives strong support to our claim that we have correctly reproduced our intuition in CA11, and since it applies also for languages with dependencies, we feel justified in stating CA11 as a general condition of adequacy.

Now we have considered the three basic F-values, and we have considered cases where F increases and where it decreases; the only remaining case is the one in which the value of F remains unchanged. Here we start with a fixed H, and an E_1 which will be strengthened by the addition of E_2 in such a way that F is unchanged. This happens when the new evidence is irrelevant; but irrelevant to what? We might guess that it must be irrelevant to H and E_1, but we will show that this is insufficient. Take the w.f.f. $[A \cdot B] \vee [\bar{A} \cdot \bar{B}]$, used above, as E_1, and A as H. If we strengthen the evidence by adding B as E_2 (B is irrelevant to both H and E_1), then F changes from 0 to 1 since H follows from $E_1 \cdot E_2$. The reason for this is that E_2 is not irrelevant to the conjunction of H and E_1. We see that we have to require that the new evidence be irrelevant to all combinations of the hypothesis and the old evidence. This is analogous to the condition of complete independence and can be assured by any three independent conditions. We will require that the new evidence be irrelevant to H, to the old evidence E_1, and to their conjunction.

CA12. If
$$\begin{aligned} p(H \cdot E_2) &= p(H) \times p(E_2), \text{ and} \\ p(E_1 \cdot E_2) &= p(E_1) \times p(E_2), \text{ and} \\ p(H \cdot E_1 \cdot E_2) &= p(H \cdot E_1) \times p(E_2), \end{aligned}$$
then $f(H, E_1 \cdot E_2)$ is the same as $F(H, E_1)$.

This finishes our material conditions of adequacy. Let us now see whether we have put down everything we want to require of our explicatum. Carnap has an excellent chapter (Ch. 1, loc. cit.) on the problem of explication. On page 7 he enumerates the conditions a good explicatum must satisfy: It must be similar to the explicandum (which is assured by the material CA), it must be exact (assured by the formal CA), it must be fruitful (which we will show by proving theorems and working out examples), and it must be as simple as the other conditions permit. This last point we must still assure:

CA13. The definition of F must be as simple as the other 12 CA permit.

This condition differs from all the other CA in that it is not a condition specifically for F, but for any explicatum; we list it here for the sake of completeness. While the concept of simplicity has never been precisely defined, its application is perfectly clear in many simple examples. We will make use of CA13 only when its application is non-controversial.

3. *The Definition of F.* — In the first part we showed that our problem consists in choosing the auxiliary functions m and f. In the second part we completed the list of conditions of adequacy that F must satisfy. It is now our task to use these CA to narrow down step by step the choice of m and f. We will do this by a series of simple theorems; the reader not interested in details is advised to read the theorems and skip the proofs.

A few preliminary remarks will simplify our work. First of all we will see in most of our theorems that the conditions determine the values of m and f only for certain values of the variables (those which can be obtained in actual examples). But these values are a dense set, which means that the only way m and f can be continuous is that we assume that the theorems hold for all values. Then, by CA13, we will require that this be so. Again, in some cases (e.g., theorem 11) the proof holds for practically all values, and again by simplicity we will require that the theorem should hold also for those values about which we can say nothing otherwise. Such techniques are quite general in Mathematics, and in most philosophical writings they are used without explicit mention. We state this once and for all; in the proofs we will be concerned only with establishing the theorem about sufficiently many values of the variables.

Secondly we note that whether we use (3) or (4), changing the first few values of $F(H, E, n)$ does not change the result. So we will be perfectly satisfied if our theorems hold for all sufficiently high n, and we don't even care if F is not properly defined for a few values of n. Let us apply this to H and E. Since they (and their negations) are not contradictory and not statements of infinity, they will be true in some (but not all) s.d. It is a property of the s.d. that if a w.f.f. is true in an s.d. for given n, then there is a corresponding s.d. for all higher n in which it is true. E.g., if a w.f.f. is true in 2 s.d. for some n, it will be true in at least 2 s.d. in all higher n.[8] It is very easy to see that any w.f.f. of interest to science will be true in more than one s.d. for very high n, and since we don't care what happens for a finite number of n, we may as well assume that our w.f.f. are true in more than one s.d. for each n. These considerations will simplify our proofs.

THEOREM 3. All our weights must be positive (i.e., non-zero).

Proof. Suppose some s.d. received 0 weight. Call this s.d. $\mathcal{Z}$.

Case 1. E is true in $\mathcal{Z}$. Take $E \cdot \overline{\mathcal{Z}}$ as H, and consider $F(H, E)$. Any combination of H and E differs from the corresponding combination of E and E only in being true (or false) in $\mathcal{Z}$. But $\mathcal{Z}$ has weight 0, hence all the m-values are the same as for $F(E, E)$. By CA8, $F(E, E) = 1$. So $F(H, E)$ must be 1, which contradicts CA8, since H is stronger than E.

[8] Church, Alonzo, *Introduction to Mathematical Logic — Part I*, Princeton, Princeton University Press, 1944, p. 91.

Case 2. E is false in Z. Let Z_1 and Z_2 be two s.d. in which E is true, let H_1 be $Z \vee Z_1$ and H_2 be Z_1. Then all conditions of CA10 are satisfied. (The only one that is not immediately clear is the second one, but $H_2 \vee \overline{H}_1$ is equivalent to $\overline{Z}$, which follows from E.) Hence $F(H_2, E)$ must be greater than $F(H_1, E)$. But we see again that the combinations can differ only as to being true in Z, and hence have the same m-value. This would mean that the two F's are equal, another contradiction. Hence Z cannot have 0 weight.

We have said that H and E cannot be analytic or contradictory, but their combinations could be. In the following we let B stand for a combination of H and E, and investigate the consequences of B being either analytic or contradictory.

Theorem 4. If $\vdash B$, then $m(B)$ is 1 for all n; if $\vdash \bar{B}$, then $m(B)$ is 0 for all n; otherwise the values of $m(B)$ lie between 0 and 1.

Proof. If $\vdash B$, then B is true in all s.d., hence $m(B)$ is 1 for all n, by CA5. If $\vdash \overline{B}$, then B is false in all s.d., hence its m must always be 0. If neither is the case, then B is true in some "model," and false in some other "model." [9] And if neither B nor $\overline{B}$ is a statement of infinity — which we require — then each is true in some finite "model," which can be represented by an s.d. And the same is true for all higher n. Since all weights are positive, this means that the values of $m(B)$ lie between 0 and 1 for all sufficiently high n, which is all we care about.

Theorem 5. $f(x, y, z, t)$ is a continuous function defined for all values of the variables for which $x + y + z + t = 1$, and none of the following is 0: $x + y$, $x + z$, $z + t$, $y + t$.

Proof. This theorem is mainly a summing up of previous considerations. The fact that none of the four sums can be 0 is seen as follows: $x + y = m(H)$, so by theorem 4 it is 0 only when H is contradictory, which is excluded. Similarly the other three 0-values correspond to the forbidden cases of contradictory E, and analytic H and E respectively.

Theorem 6. The values of f lie between -1 and 1.
Theorem 7. $f(z, t, x, y) = -f(x, y, z, t)$.
Theorem 8. $f(x, y, z, t) = 1$ if and only if $z = 0$.

Proof. These three theorems follow from CA2, CA3, and CA8 respectively. The first two are immediate. The last one is seen when we remember that $\vdash E \supset H$ just when $\vdash [\overline{H} \cdot E]$, then it follows from theorem 4.

Theorem 9. If x is increased and z decreased by the same amount, then $f(x, y, z, t)$ increases.[10]

Proof. We will show that this is the mathematical content of CA9. Going from $F(H_2, E)$ to $F(H_1, E)$ in this CA, E remains the same, so that $x + z$ is unchanged. The first two conditions of the CA assure that $H_2 \vee E$ is equivalent to $H_1 \vee E$, hence $x + y + z$ is

[9] A theorem due to Gödel, *ibid.*, pp. 73 ff.
[10] Theorems 9 and 10 hold, of course, only if the variables remain within the bounds specified in theorem 5.

unchanged. Therefore, t is unchanged, since the sum of the variables is 1. And if $x + z$ and $x + y + z$ are both unchanged, so is y. The first and third conditions assure that H_1 is true in more s.d. than H_2, hence $x + y$ is increased, which means that x is increased. And since the sum must remain 1, z must have decreased by the same amount. And CA9 tells us that this change results in an increase of F.

THEOREM 10. If t increases and y decreases by the same amount, then $f(x, y, z, t)$ increases; at least when x and z are both positive.

Proof. This is quite analogous to the previous proof, using CA10 in place of CA9. Passing from H_1 to H_2 in CA10 corresponds to an increase in t with an equal decrease in y; while the last two conditions in the CA mean that z and x are both positive. So the CA tells us that f must increase.

THEOREM 11. Any two s.d. in which E is true get the same weight, and any two s.d. in which E is false get the same weight.

Proof. This will be deduced from CA11. Select an H_1 so that $F(H_1, E)$ is 0. Let Z_1 be an s.d. in which E and H_1 are both true, while Z_2 and s.d. in which E is true but H_1 is false. Then $F(H_2, E)$ will also be 0 if we take $[H_1 \cdot \bar{Z}_1] \vee Z_2$ as H_2. (This follows from the fact that H_2 differs from H_1 only in that it is true in Z_2 but false in Z_1, hence all the p-values are the same.) Now let us suppose that the two s.d. got different weights, say Z_2 has a greater weight than Z_1. That means that $m(H_2 \cdot E)$ is greater than $m(H_1 \cdot E)$, while $m(\overline{H}_2 \cdot E)$ is less than $m(\overline{H}_1 \cdot E)$ by the same amount. Then by theorem 9 the two F's cannot be the same, which is a contradiction. The proof for the s.d. in which E is false is quite analogous. Constructing H_1 and H_2 as above, from Z's in which E is false, we get again that on the one hand the F's should be 0, on the other hand by theorem 10 they must be different; leading again to a contradiction if the s.d. get different weights.

This theorem is precisely the result we needed to be able to translate CA11 into a condition on f. But first we must put the theorem into a more useful form. Let us call the weights of the s.d. in which E is true, w. The other weights (those of s.d. in which E is false) are also all equal and positive, so we can call them qw, q being the quotient of the two different weights. Using the fact that the number of s.d. in which A is true is $Sp(A)$, we see that the sum of the weights is $wSp(\bar{E}) + qwSp(E)$. Since this sum is 1, we get a formula for w,

$$w = 1/S[p(E) + qp(\bar{E})]. \tag{8}$$

So if we know q, we can get w, and hence all the weights. q may, of course, depend on E and on n; but we have reduced the problem of the m-function to the finding of q. Let us denote the quantity $p(E) + qp(\bar{E})$ by D, then $w = 1/SD$. Given an arbitrary w.f.f. A, we have to break up the s.d. in which it is true into those that get weight w and those that get weight qw. There are $Sp(A \cdot E)$ of the former, $Sp(A \cdot \bar{E})$ of the latter. So we get, using (8) and then (1),

$$m(A) = [p(A \cdot E) + qp(A \cdot \bar{E})]/D. \tag{9}$$

$$(10) \qquad \begin{aligned} x &= p(H \cdot E)/D, \quad y = qp(H \cdot \bar{E})/D, \\ z &= p(\bar{H} \cdot E)/D, \quad t = qp(\bar{H} \cdot \bar{E})/D. \end{aligned}$$

Using these values we find that the equation (5) can be translated into $x = (x + y)(x + z)$. (This can be checked by a routine calculation.) And then we can translate CA11 into:

THEOREM 12. $f(x, y, z, t) = 0$ if and only if $x = (x + y)(x + z)$.

THEOREM 13. f is the ratio of two functions both homogeneous in x, y, z, t to the degree k;[11] where k is the smallest integer permissible under the first 12 CA.

Proof. Since f is a normalized function, it is simplest to take it as the ratio of two similar functions. Since x, y, z, t play analogous roles in all definitions, the functions must be homogeneous in the variables. And since the normalization of m is purely conventional, f must be unchanged if all variables are multiplied by the same number, hence the numerator and the denominator must be homogeneous to the same degree. Finally, smaller k-values give simpler functions. So this theorem is our interpretation of what AC13 tells us about f.

THEOREM 14. q, the ratio of weights of the s.d. in which E is false to those in which E is true, is independent of E and n. Hence each permissible m-function is determined by the choice of a positive constant q.

THEOREM 15. $f(xP, y + x(1 - \mathrm{P})q, zP, t + z(1 - P)q) = f(x, y, z, t)$ where P is any number between 0 and 1, and q is the number that characterizes the m-function.

Proof. Both theorems follow from CA12. Let us examine this CA precisely. It tells us that under certain kinds of changes the value of f is unchanged. We can translate the conditions of change into conditions on x, y, z, t. Let us denote the values of the variables after the change by x', y', z', t'. We can use (10) to calculate both sets of variables, they differ only in that E is E_1 in the first case, $E_1 \cdot E_2$ in the second case. Making use of the conditions in CA12, we can express the new variables in terms of the old ones; this is purely routine, and we state only the result. Let R denote the ratio of denominators, and P the value of $p(E_2)$, then

$$(11) \qquad \begin{aligned} x' = xPR \quad y' &= yRq'/q + x(1 - P)Rq' \quad z' = zPR \\ t' &= tRq'/q + z(1 - Q)Rq'. \end{aligned}$$

First of all we note that all variables have been multiplied by R, but by theorem 13 this leaves f unchanged. Cross them out. Then (11) expresses a transformation that must leave f unchanged. How is this possible? The terms in y' will be like those in y if we factor out q'/q, and similarly for t' and t. But that leaves the x' and z' terms. Somehow terms in xP must combine with terms in $x(1 - P)q'$, z being analogous. But this is impossible in general, since P depends on E_2, while q' in general depends on $E_1 \cdot E_2$. The only possible way out is that q' is independent of the evidence. That makes it possible to choose f in such a way that these terms combine in the right manner. But since the form of f is independent of n, q must be independent of n also to allow the combination. This proves theorem 14. (11) is now considerably simplified: R dropped out, and $q = q'$ is a constant. Theorem 15 states exactly that f is unchanged by this transformation, hence it follows from CA12.

[11] A function is homogeneous to degree k if multiplying its arguments by c multiplies the value by c^k.

It is interesting to note that the last theorem is the first we have which establishes different conditions on f for different choices of the m-function!

The reader can check that we have now translated our CA into conditions on m and f, in accordance with our program. Our m-functions have been determined to be the members of a small class (see theorems 3, 11, 14), each m determined by one positive constant q. Let us now try to determine the possible f's. According to theorem 13 we must find the smallest integer k such that the ratio of two homogeneous functions of degree k will satisfy the CA (which are translated in theorems 5–10, 12, 15). And since one of the conditions of f (theorem 15) depends on q, the form of the f-function may depend on the choice of m. We will now systematically consider larger and larger values of k, till we find a definition satisfying all our conditions.

THEOREM 16. k cannot be 1.

Proof. If k is 1, the numerator of f is of the form $ax + by + cz + dt$ (and the denominator is similar). This can be eliminated by a single condition. Consider theorem 12. Let us choose as sets of values for the variables: (1/2, 1/4, 1/6, 1/12); (1/2, 1/3, 1/10, 1/15); (1/2, 3/8, 1/14, 3/56); and (1/4, 1/4, 1/4, 1/4). All of these satisfy the condition of theorem 12, and hence f must be 0. So the numerator of f must vanish for these four sets of values. But simple algebra shows that this is only possible if a, b, c, d are all 0, which is forbidden.

THEOREM 17. For each m-function there is a unique f-function with $k = 2$.

Proof. If $k = 2$, f has the form

$$\frac{ax^2 + bxy + cy^2 + dxz + eyz + gz^2 + ixt + jyt + rzt + st^2}{\bar{a}x^2 + \bar{b}xy + \bar{c}y^2 + \bar{d}xz + \bar{e}yz + \bar{g}z^2 + \bar{i}xt + \bar{j}yt + \bar{r}zt + \bar{s}t^2}. \tag{12}$$

We must now try to satisfy all our f-theorems by a suitable choice of the 20 coefficients. Take theorem 7. It tells us that under a certain interchange of variables f changes its sign. This must mean that the numerator changes sign and the denominator is unchanged (since the denominator cannot be 0). This means that d and j must be 0; g, s, r, e are the negatives of a, c, b, i; and $\bar{g}$, $\bar{s}$, $\bar{r}$, $\bar{e}$ are equal to $\bar{a}$, $\bar{c}$, $\bar{b}$, $\bar{i}$ respectively. This cuts the coefficients down to 10.

Take theorems 6 and 8. If $z = 0$, f is 1, otherwise f is less than 1. (The fact that f is at least -1 follows from this by theorem 7.) Write down the formula for f, setting z equal to 0, and equate it to 1. Since this is to hold identically, we get the coefficients in the numerator equal to the corresponding ones in the denominator, and c, $\bar{c}$, $\bar{j}$ equal to 0. (Furthermore, f must be less than 1 for positive z, but this will be clearly so in (14) for positive u, so we need to add nothing.) This gives

$$f(x, y, z, t) = \frac{a(x^2 - z^2) + b(xy - zt) + i(xt - yz)}{a(x^2 + z^2) + b(xy + zt) + i(xt + yz) + \bar{d}xz}. \tag{13}$$

Take theorem 12. Work out the examples mentioned in theorem 16. They show that a and b must be 0. On the other hand whenever the condition of theorem 12 holds, $xt - yz$ is 0, so it is both necessary and sufficient to set a and b equal to 0. This reduces (13) to a simpler form. (Since i cannot be 0 now, we divide by it, putting u for $\bar{d}/i$.)

$$f(x, y, z, t) = \frac{xt - yz}{xt + yz + uxz}. \tag{14}$$

Theorem 5 is true clearly just in case u is positive. A little more mathematical checking will convince us that theorems 9 and 10 do not impose any new conditions at all (probably due to the fact that they were used indirectly in determining the form of the m-functions). Take our last theorem, number 15. Perform the transformation called for in this theorem on (14) and equate the result to (14). This equality will hold in complete generality just in case u is set equal to $2q$. So for a given m-function (hence given q) we get the unique f-function satisfying all conditions:

$$f(x, y, z, t) = \frac{xt - yz}{xt + yz + 2qxz}. \tag{15}$$

Therefore, if we use theorem 13, we must choose (15) as a definition of f. This still leaves us one choicc, the choice of q; q determines m by (10), and it also determines f by (15). Let us combine these two equations by substituting the values of the variables from (10) into (15). (We have now solved the two problems posed at the end of Part 1, and we are ready to define F.) When we make this substitution we find, to our surprise, that all quantities containing q cancel out. So it makes no difference which m-function we select, we get the same *unique* f-function. Let us sum this up:

THEOREM 18. There is a unique explicatum satisfying all the CA, namely

$$F(H, E) = \frac{p(H\cdot E)p(\bar{H}\cdot\bar{E}) - p(H\cdot\bar{E})p(\bar{H}\cdot E)}{p(H\cdot E)p(\bar{H}\cdot\bar{E}) + p(H\cdot\bar{E})p(\bar{H}\cdot E) + 2p(H\cdot E)p(\bar{H}\cdot E)}. \tag{16}$$

It may be worth-while stating an equivalent form of this. If we introduce the usual definition for a relative probability, namely $p(A, B) = p(A\cdot B)/p(B)$, we can write (16) as (we omit the routine proof):

$$F(H, E) = \frac{p(E, H) - p(E, \bar{H})}{p(E, H) + p(E, \bar{H})}. \tag{17}$$

This gives us a complete theory of the explication of *degree of factual support* for our simple language.

4. *Examples.*[12] —

Example 1. We want to illustrate the fact that it makes no difference which m-function we choose. Let H be $P(a)\cdot P(b)$, while E is $P(a)$. We choose the values 3, 1, 1/2 for q, and for each value we calculate the values of the variables by means of (10), and then F by (15). The reader is advised to write out the three f-formulas given by (15) for the three values of q. x, y, z, t equal (1/8, 0, 1/8, 3/4); (1/4, 0, 1/4, 1/2); (1/3, 0, 1/3, 1/3) respectively. In all three cases we get $F(H, E) = 1/2$.

In the remaining examples we will just calculate values of F according to one formula, a convenient equivalent form of (16). This form has the advantage that it is determined by three values: $p(H)$, $p(E)$, $p(H\cdot E)$.

$$F(H, E) = \frac{p(H\cdot E)/p(H) - [p(E) - p(H\cdot E)]/[1 - p(H)]}{p(H\cdot E)/p(H) + [p(E) - p(H\cdot E)]/[1 - p(H)]}. \tag{18}$$

[12] In order to avoid quotation marks, we will use w.f.f. as names for themselves.

The examples were selected to illustrate important theoretical points. The details of calculation will be omitted. In calculations one should consider all s.d. of the language, but this complicates matters too much. Fortunately, if a set of atomic sentences is independent of all others in the language, the result of the calculation is the same if we ignore all other atoms. So in all examples it is assumed that the atoms occurring are independent of all other atoms in the language.

Example 2. $F(P(a), P(a) \vee P(b)) = 1/3$. Weaker support than in Ex. 1.

Example 3. $F(P(a), \bar{P}(a) \cdot P(b)) = 1$. Evidence proves hypothesis is true.

Example 4. $F(P(a), \bar{P}(a) \cdot P(b)) = -1$. Evidence proves hypothesis is false.

Example 5. $F(P(a), P(b)) = F(P(a), Q(a)) = 0$. Irrelevant evidence.

Example 6. $F(P(a) \vee P(b),\ P(a)\bar{P}(b) \vee \bar{P}(a)P(c)) = 0$. The evidence is equally favorable and unfavorable.

Example 7. $F(P(a) \cdot P(b) \cdot P(c), P(a)) = .40$.
$F(P(a) \cdot P(b) \cdot P(c),\ P(a) \cdot P(b)) = .75$. Increasing the supporting evidence.

Example 8. $F(P(a) \cdot P(b) \cdot P(c) \cdot P(d), P(a) \cdot P(b)) = .67$. Compare with the previous example. We added a new unsupported hypothesis to a well-supported hypothesis, and F was reduced from .75 to .67.

Example 9. $F(P(a) \cdot P(b), P(a) \cdot Q(a)) = 1/2$. We took example 1 and added some totally irrelevant evidence.

Example 10. This is the first example where we must take account of the dependence on n. (So far the f-functions had the same value for all n.) Let H be $(x)P(x)$, E be $P(a) \cdot p(H) = p(H \cdot E) = (1/2)^n$, $p(E) = 1/2$. Substitute these values into (18); by a process of approximation we get for large n, $F(H, E) = 1/3 + 4/9(1/2)^n + \cdots$ Or if we are interested only in the limit, $F^*(H, E) = 1/3$.

Example 11. $F^*((x)P(x),\ P(a_1) \cdot \cdots \cdot P(a_k)) = (2^k - 1/2^k + 1)$. So we see that although F^* cannot be 1 if our hypothesis is universal and the evidence is singular, it approaches 1 as k increases. We note also that the *rate* of increase decreases, so that each new piece of evidence adds less to the support than the previous piece.

Example 12. $F^*((\exists x)\bar{P}(x),\ P(a_1) \cdot \cdots \cdot P(a_k)) = -(2^k - 1/2^k + 1)$. This is the converse of the previous example. The evidence is again singular, but the hypothesis is existential. While the evidence never disproves the hypothesis, F^* tends to -1 with increasing k.

Example 13. $F((x)P(x), \bar{P}(a)) = -1$. A single fact can disprove a universal hypothesis.

Example 14. $F((\exists x)\bar{P}(x), \bar{P}(a)) = 1$. A single fact can prove that an existential hypothesis is true.

Example 15. $F((x)(P(x) \cdot Q(x)), (\exists x)P(x)) = 1/2(1/2)^n + 1/4(1/2)^{2n} + \cdots$
$F((x)(P(x) \cdot Q(x)),\ (\exists x)P(x) \cdot (\exists x)Q(x)) = (1/2)^n + 1/2(1/2)^{2n} + \cdots$ This is an example demonstrating that method (3) is really stronger than method (4), see p. 311, F^* is 0 in both cases, but

according to (3) the second F is greater, since for high n (when we can neglect all but the first term) it has greater values.

Example 16. In this example we choose a two-place predicate. This is also the first example where we allow dependencies between our atomic sentences. Let H be $(x)(y)R(x, y)$, and let E be $R(a, b)$. Take first R as a general predicate: there are no dependencies. Then we get $F(H, E) = 1/3 + 4/9(1/2)^{n^2} + \cdots$. If we now take for R a reflexive predicate (the postulate $(x)R(x, x)$ being added to the logical axioms, see p. 309), then $F(H, E) = 1/3 + 4/9 \cdot 2^n \cdot (1/2)^{n^2} + \cdots$. F^* is 1/3 in each case, but by (3) the second F is greater. We can interpret this by saying that in the second case there are atomic sentences, like $P(a, a)$, which need no support since they follow from our postulate; a distinction that is lost in (4).

Example 17. Take a case of mixed operators. Let H be $(x)(\exists y)R(x, y)$, E be $R(a, b)$. Then $F(H, E) = 1/2n + \cdots$, while $F^*(H, \bar{E}) = -1/2n + \cdots$. In both cases the support is very slight (F^* is 0), favorable in the former, unfavorable in the latter.

Example 18. Let us consider a very general example; the case where all the evidence is favorable. This means that $\vdash H \supset E$. Then $H \cdot E$ is equivalent to H. Using this fact in our formula (18), we can get the simple form $\dfrac{1 - p(E)}{1 + p(E) - 2p(H)}$. If we introduce the concept: *strength* $(A) = 1 - p(A)$, we can rewrite this in the form

$$\frac{\text{strength } (E)}{2 \text{ strength } (H) - \text{strength } (E)}.$$

For a given hypothesis stronger evidence gives better support; for a given evidence the stronger hypothesis gets weaker support. This is in excellent agreement with our intuition.

Example 19. We will not discuss the problem of how statistical statements are to be expressed in our simple language. We just assume, for the sake of the example, that this can be done. Let H_r express for each n that rn of the n things has the property P (r between 0 and 1), while E_{sm} states about m things that sm of them are P's, while the others are not (s between 0 and 1, m less than n). Then

$$F^*(H_r, E_{sm}) = \frac{(2r^s(1 - r)^{1-s})^m - 1}{(2r^s(1 - r)^{1-s})^m + 1}.$$

For a given E_{sm} we find that the hypothesis given the best support is the one having $r = s$, and in general this support increases with the size of the sample, m. This is as it should be. So, for example, if we toss a coin 100 times and get 60 heads, this evidence supports the hypothesis that just 60% of all tosses will be heads best, and the support is $F^* = .77$.

Example 20. Finally we want to discuss the relation between F and the correlation coefficient (see p. 219). For this purpose we write F in the form: $[p(H \cdot E) - p(H)p(E)]/[p(H)p(\bar{H} \cdot E) + p(\bar{H})p(H \cdot E)]$. Compare this with (7). We see that they have the same numerator; hence F is positive, negative, or 0 just when the correlation coefficient is. But the latter is otherwise quite different from F; we see this already by noting that it is symmetric in H and E, while F, of course, is not. So, e.g., the correlation is 1 only if $F(H, E)$ and $F(E, H)$ are *both* 1.

5. *Summary.* — We have completed our explication of *degree of factual support* by stating in thirteen clear conditions all that our intuition told us about the concept and then showing that there is a unique F-function satisfying these conditions. This approach to the problem of explication has the great advantage (assuming that we have made no purely mathematical mistake) that any objections must be directed towards our conditions of adequacy, and hence the dispute will be clearly defined. There are two possible types of objections which we will very briefly consider.

If someone rejected one of our CA, there would be no hope for agreement. But at least we would find the root of our disagreement; and it would be his task to formulate alternate CA, and find his F-function. Then anyone wishing to use F could choose between the two sets of CA. The most we can say is that the 13 CA here stated express *our* intuition.

Someone could accept all our conditions but argue that there are other necessary conditions which do not follow from ours. Then he can use all our theorems except the last one; in place of that he will find that no function with $k = 2$ can be used, and he will have to find the lowest k for which not only our but his CA are also satisfied. Then someone wishing to use F will have to decide whether the additional conditions are important enough to warrant the greater complexity of F.

It is important, however, that these differences should not be of a trivial nature, as for example objecting to one of our conventions. If someone decided, e.g., that F should range between 0 and 1, simply replace our F by $1/2(F + 1)$. Then 0 expresses disproof, 1/2 irrelevance, and 1 still is the best possible support; but nothing essential is changed. In place of (17) we then get $p(E, H)/p(E, H) + p(E, \bar{H})$.

One line of attack against many explicata came from people who insisted that the measure-functions used must be "empirical" (m must depend on E), or conversely from the advocates of a single, fixed m-function. It is very interesting, therefore, to note that one of our m-functions is independent of E, while all others depend on E. (If q is 1, all weights are equal, hence m is p. Otherwise the weights depend on which s.d. are the ones in which E is true.) So for our purposes this whole dispute is pointless since both types of measures lead to the same explicatum.

The language-system for which we formulated F in this paper is very primitive, and the most immediate problem for future research will be the extension of our definition to higher languages. There is really only one problem in this: If we can extend the concept of *state-description* to higher languages, then p is again the measure assigning equal weights to all these s.d., and (16) will define F. Some results for higher languages will be established in a forthcoming paper by Kemeny,* replacing the concept of an s.d. by the more general concept of a finite model of the language.

Finally, it is hoped that the definition of F will be an aid in the explication of C. As we have said in the introduction, F is one of many factors influencing C, and an explication of the latter should start with definitions for all factors, and then (probably) proceed by the method of explication set forth in this paper. In this sense we hope that our paper will prove suggestive, in method as well as in content, for future work in this field.

* [Ed. note: See John Kemeny, "A Logical Measure Function," *Journal of Symbolic Logic*, XVIII, 1953, pp. 289–308.]

III
Simplicity

III
Simplicity

Introduction

It is generally agreed that the acceptance of a scientific hypothesis should depend on more than the degree of confirmation which the hypothesis has attained. It is also agreed that considerations of simplicity should play a role in the choice of hypotheses. Two questions immediately arise, however: What is the meaning of "simplicity"? What is the justification for the use of the criterion of simplicity in the choice of hypotheses?

The Meaning of "Simplicity"

The Possibility and Necessity of a Definition

It is not easy to formulate a precise definition of "simplicity" and up to the present time philosophers of inductive logic have had little success in their search for one. It may be wondered, therefore, if it is possible to formulate a definition. It has been argued, for example, that the concept of simplicity is much too vague, ambiguous, variable and subjective for it to be given any clear definition. It has been pointed out, however, that this sort of argument could have been used in ancient times against the possibility of defining "temperature" or "size."[1] The precision and objectivity which we attribute to the concepts of size and length have come about *because* of our precise definitions; they are not preconditions of it. Moreover, as S. F. Barker notes in his article which follows, just because no precise definition of a concept is yet available it does not mean that the concept is a subjective one. After all who of us can give a precise definition of "sanity?" Yet there surely is an objective difference between sane and insane people; we understand the objective meaning of the concept well enough so that we can, in general, reliably judge men as sane or insane. The same situation holds for "simplicity," Barker implies.

Now it may be argued that if Barker is correct and there is enough agreement about the application of the concept of simplicity so that we can judge correctly whether one hypothesis is simpler than another, we do not need a precise definition of "simplicity." This would be a mistake, however. In the first place, the importance of formulating a precise definition of "simplicity" no more depends

[1] Nelson Goodman, "The Test of Simplicity," *Science*, 1958, pp. 1064–1069.

upon the ease with which we make particular judgments of simplicity than does the importance of the modern systematic formulation of formal logic depend on the ease with which we make logical inferences in ordinary arguments. A systematic formulation of both simplicity and formal logic has profound theoretical importance.[2] In the second place, we should not assume that it is always easy to judge in particular cases which hypothesis is simplest. Indeed, there seem to be conflicting aspects of the total concept of simplicity that often make it difficult to come to any definite decision.[3]

In other words, simplicity may not be a single, easily discernible property at all, but rather a complex relation of several properties. If so, a precise definition of simplicity may be needed before many ordinary judgments of simplicity can be reliably made. Thus, a precise account of the notion of simplicity is sought not merely for its theoretical interest but also so that it is possible to make actual judgments.

The difficulty encountered in judging which hypothesis is the simplest is illustrated in the selections that follow by the differences of opinion between Barker and Mario Bunge. Barker argues that the theory of evolution is obviously simpler than the special creation hypothesis and that this is the main reason for preferring it. Bunge argues quite persuasively that the evolutionary theory is not simple relative to its rivals, but is preferable to them on independent grounds. Surely a clear definition of simplicity is needed in order to reconcile this disagreement.

Formal Simplicity

Scientists have used the word "simplicity" in different senses, but it is only in recent years that inductive logicians have isolated the irrelevant and unimportant senses of this term and have concentrated their analysis on those senses that seem to be most important for science.

The sense of "simplicity" that seems relevant for science has been called "formal simplicity."[4] "Formal simplicity" refers to the structural or logical properties of a language rather than to the Universe or to people's subjective reactions. In this sense of the term, the simplicity of a hypothesis presumably does not vary with the notation used.

The analysis of formal simplicity has proceeded in two different ways. One approach, taken by Nelson Goodman among others, analyzes the formal bases of descriptional systems or theories. In Goodman's case this has resulted in the analysis of the predicate bases of theories. The other approach, an older one which has been adopted in recent years by Harold Jeffreys, Karl Popper, and John Kemeny construes the problem of analyzing simplicity as one of "curve fitting."

[2] Goodman, *op. cit.*
[3] *Ibid.*
[4] See Richard Rudner, "Introduction to Simplicity," *Philosophy of Science*, 1961, pp. 109–119.

(1) An obvious approach to the analysis of the simplicity of the logical basis of a theory would seem to be through the number of postulates the theory contains. We might be inclined to say that theory T_1 is simpler than T_2, other things being equal, if T_1 has fewer postulates than T_2. But this account will surely not do. For it is always possible trivially to replace any number of postulates by one postulate: we can always form a new single postulate by taking the conjunction of the original postulates. This would mean that any theory, no matter how many postulates it has, could be replaced by another theory with an equivalent content having maximum simplicity.[5] But what is sought is an analysis of simplicity which is independent of the way the theory is codified.

Another natural suggestion would be to base simplicity on the number of undefined terms in a theory instead of basing it on the number of postulates a theory has. This proposal would be tantamount to suggesting that simplicity could be estimated by the number of predicates of the theory that were not defined in terms of other predicates. It should be clear that in this case there is no problem of alternative codifications or axiomatizations of the same theory. No matter how a theory is codified it will retain its same primitive predicates; if the primitive predicates are changed, a different theory results.

Nevertheless, a trivial replacement is always possible in this case: any number of predicates can be combined into a single predicate.[6] For example, let theory T_1 contain only two predicates; one one-place predicate and one two-place predicate:

"*Gx*" = "*x* is copper"

"*Fyz*" = "*y* is more durable than *z*"

We can form a new theory T_2 by using only the following three-place predicate:

"*Mxyz*" = "*x* is copper and *y* is more durable than *z*"

This three-place predicate of T_2 enables us to define all statements that can be formulated in T_1. Clearly no real increase of simplicity has been achieved; simpler predicates have been replaced by a more complex one, hence T_2 differs from T_1 in only the most trivial way.

Considerations of this sort might seem to suggest that an examination of the predicate basis of theories is a blind alley. This would be mistaken, however. Indeed, Goodman has developed a calculus of simplicity which takes its clue from trivial replacements of this kind.[7] Goodman's views are expounded in detail in this section by Donald Hillman.

In brief, Goodman argues that if every set of predicates of one kind is replaceable by some set of another kind, then the first set cannot be more complex than the second. He combines this principle with other principles about the re-

[5] S. F. Barker, *Induction and Hypothesis* (Ithaca: Cornell University Press, 1957), pp. 171–172.

[6] Barker, *op. cit.*, pp. 172–173; Goodman, *op. cit.*

[7] Goodman, *op. cit.*; see also, Nelson Goodman, "Axiomatic Measurement of Simplicity," *Journal of Philosophy*, 1955, pp. 709–722.

placeability of predicates of different logical types, e.g. symmetrical and reflexive. This enables him to assign different positive simplicity values to predicates of different logical types and to add the simplicity values of predicates in the bases of the theory. It has been suggested that these assignments of simplicity be thought of as depending on "the manner in which the extra-logical predicates of a theory *organize*, by virtue of such of their logical properties as reflexity or symmetry, the entities comprising the total extension of the theory."[8]

It is generally acknowledged that Goodman's calculus is a genuine contribution to a definition of "simplicity." But, as Goodman is the first to admit and as his critics have pointed out, his analysis is not the whole story. Goodman has been concerned mainly with the simplicity of terms in a theory. His analysis, however, gives no measure of overall simplicity. In particular, Goodman has not been concerned with the analysis of the curve-fitting problem. To this problem we now turn.

(2) We discussed earlier some common types of non-demonstrative inferences made in science and everyday life. There is one type of non-demonstrative inference, however, that we did not mention which, it has been argued, plays a crucial role in scientific inquiry. This type of inference involves inferring the simplest hypothesis which is compatible with the observed instances of a phenomena and which predicts correctly the occurrence of unobserved instances; hence, the phrase "inductive simplicity" is used in connection with inferences of this sort. Since simplicity of this sort is usually associated with fitting a curve to points representing the data, the problem of analyzing this sort of simplicity has been called the "curve-fitting" problem.

Suppose, for example,[9] that we have examined a large number of freely falling bodies. Let us imagine we have the following data:

All observed bodies falling freely for 1/2 second fell 4 feet.
All observed bodies falling freely for 1 second fell 16 feet.
All observed bodies falling freely for 2 seconds fell 64 feet.
All observed bodies falling freely for 4 seconds fell 256 feet.

Using the rule of inductive generalization we can infer that probably·

All bodies falling freely for 1/2 second fall 4 feet.
All bodies falling freely for 1 second fall 16 feet.
All bodies falling freely for 2 seconds fall 64 feet.
All bodies falling freely for 4 seconds fall 256 feet.

Now not only do we want to make generalizations that go beyond the data in *this* way, but we want to make generalizations that go beyond the data in another way. We want to infer how far all freely falling bodies will fall in 3 seconds, and in 5 seconds, and so on. In other words, if we were to plot our

[8] Rudner, *op. cit.*, p. 114.
[9] Our example is adopted from Barker, *op. cit.*, pp. 92–93

data on a graph, we would want to be able to infer to points on the graph between and beyond our data points. But here is the problem: There are an infinite number of generalizations compatible with the data which yield different predictions for points between and beyond our data points. For example, the following are compatible with the data and yet do not in general yield the same predictions:

(Let s = distance fallen, t = time in free fall)

$$s = 16t^2$$

$$s = (16 + \tan 2\pi t)\, t^2$$

$$s = 16(-1)^{4t}t^2$$

On which basis is one to pick a hypothesis from among these and the infinite number of other hypotheses which account for the data? As Barker notes here it does little good to say that we must wait for more data before we decide. In the first place, we must use the data that we have and make a reasonable judgment based on them. In the second place, no matter how much data we have, i.e. no matter how many points we have on our graph, there will still be an infinite number of hypotheses compatible with them.

Philosophers of inductive logic who have concerned themselves with this problem have generally agreed that the simplest curve compatible with the data should be chosen. But a question immediately arises: What does the "simplest curve" mean?

Philosophers have argued that the simplest curve is the smoothest curve compatible with the data. They do not mean that the curve must go through all the points; rather they mean that it must not deviate from them beyond a certain extent. A compromise is made between the smoothest curve and the fit of the curve to the data. But it should be clear that even if a clear definition of "compatibility" is given, the notion of the smoothest curve is no clearer than the notion of the simplest curve. The attempt to give the notion of the simplest curve some precision by analyzing it in terms of the intuitive notion of the smoothest curve is therefore no real help.

As Barker notes, Popper has attempted to give the notion of the simplest curve some mathematical precision. Briefly, Popper argues that curves can be ordered with respect to their simplicity in terms of the number of parameters they contain. Thus curves in terms of equations with one parameter are simpler than curves in terms of equations with two parameters, and so on. Kemeny uses approximately the same method as Popper although Kemeny's approach is more sophisticated.

The question is, however, whether this method of ordering is an adequate account of inductive simplicity. Ackermann says it is not and his argument in the article reprinted here should be studied carefully. If Ackermann's arguments are correct, the entire notion of inductive simplicity has been misconceived.

The Justification of Simplicity

Even if a clear analysis of the meaning of logical simplicity is obtained, the question of justifying the use of logical simplicity in science remains. One of the most natural attempts to justify simplicity is in terms of induction. It is argued that we use simple theories because these theories in the past have usually turned out to be correct and we can infer by an inductive generalization that they are likely to continue to be usually correct. This approach raises the problem dealt with in Section IV of this anthology, namely whether inductive generalizations are justified. It is also open to the kind of objection raised in this section by Barker: In making any inductive generalization we must presuppose a principle of simplicity; hence, induction cannot establish that simpler hypotheses are more likely to be correct.

Kemeny attempts to give a justification of the use of simplicity in terms of probability theory, and his argument in the pages that follow deserves careful attention. Kemeny argues that the use of a rule of simplicity makes it extremely probable that we will pick the true hypothesis. There are, according to Kemeny, only two reasons why the hypothesis chosen by a rule of simplicity may be false. First, the true hypothesis may be incompatible with the data; secondly, the true hypothesis, although compatible with the data, may not be the simplest one. Now the first problem is not serious, according to Kemeny, for we can choose a standard of compatibility that makes it extremely improbable that the true hypothesis is incompatible with the data. The second problem can be overcome, according to Kemeny, by increasing the number of experiments. As the number of experiments increases, the deviations allowed by the compatibility requirement decrease. But by the very definition of a simplicity ordering, as the interval of compatibility decreases, an interval is reached where "If the true hypothesis lies within it, no other hypothesis as simple will be in it." Since there is a very high probability that the true hypothesis does lie within that interval, it is extremely likely that given enough experiments the true hypothesis will be chosen by a rule of simplicity.

There is at least one major problem with Kemeny's approach: What assurance have we that the number of experiments needed to gain a very high probability that our hypothesis is true is not too large for practical purposes? [10] Kemeny's attempt to show that the number of experiments is not too large seems to depend on an assumption that the laws of nature are sufficiently simple.[11] But surely this assumption is just as much in need of justification as is the use of simplicity in choosing hypotheses in science.

Bunge attempts, in the selection that follows (pp. 280–309), to justify simplicity in a different way. His argument can be summarized as follows:

(1) The aim of science is to obtain truth.

[10] Cf. J. J. Katz, *The Problem of Induction and Its Solution* (Chicago: University of Chicago Press, 1962), p. 87.

[11] See footnote 9 in Kemeny, "The Use of Simplicity in Induction."

(2) A necessary but not sufficient condition for the attainment of truth is the testability of theories.

(3) A necessary but not sufficient condition for the testability of theories is the systematization of theories.

(4) A sufficient but not necessary condition for the attainment of the systematization of theories is the logical simplicity of theories.

It follows logically from (1)–(4) and from the transitivity of necessary conditions that simplicity is *not* a necessary condition for the attainment of truth. Indeed, Bunge goes on to argue that simplicity plays a very small role in science: it is justified for the attainment of systematization in certain situations only; its use must be weighed against many other factors.

It has been argued in criticism of Bunge's position that science aims at truth *and* systematization since science aims at giving an organized account of the universe, and that simplicity is a good measure of this organization.[12] But Bunge does not really deny this. He admits that systematization is a necessary condition for truth but maintains, on the one hand, that systematization is not a sufficient condition for truth and, on the other hand, that simplicity is a good measure of systematization only sometimes, i.e. that simplicity is a sufficient but not necessary condition for systematization.

Karl Popper, whose views are explained and criticized here by Barker, argues that simple hypotheses are to be preferred because they are more easily falsified. Indeed, Popper attempts to identify the degree of simplicity of a hypothesis with its degree of falsifiability. There are at least two questions that can be asked about Popper's theory, however: Is the most falsifiable hypothesis necessarily the simplest? Is the most falsifiable hypothesis always to be preferred? Barker gives a negative answer to both questions.

W. V. O. Quine's view of simplicity presented here is very similar to Popper's although it is formulated from the standpoint of the confirmability of a hypothesis rather than its falsifiability. Quine argues that a simpler hypothesis is preferable because it is more easily confirmable, i.e. because a wider range of possible findings are favorable to it. Simpler hypotheses have, in other words, a higher degree of initial probability. But surely the same sorts of questions can be asked about Quine's theory as about Popper's: Is the most easily confirmable hypothesis necessarily the simplest? Is the most easily confirmable hypothesis always to be preferred? If Barker's critique of Popper's theory is correct, a parallel one could surely be given of Quine's theory.

Barker suggests that the simplest hypothesis may sometimes be the most falsifiable and that at least at these times the most falsifiable hypothesis is to be preferred. This seems to indicate that he is using simplicity to justify the occasional choice of the most falsifiable hypothesis and is not using falsifiability to justify the choice of the simplest hypothesis. Indeed, Barker argues that the principle of simplicity is an independent principle of science — a principle whose justification cannot be reduced to any other principle, e.g. induction or falsifiability.

[12] Rudner, *op. cit.*, p. 118.

This may also be Goodman's view.[13] Goodman has argued that simplicity is a basic and essential part of science. Furthermore, his arguments suggest that he takes simplicity to be an independent principle of science, one that is not justified on other grounds.

But if the use of simplicity cannot be justified by some other scientific principles, how *can* its use be justified? Perhaps part of what is implied by saying that simplicity is an independent principle of science is that its use needs no justification; that the use of simplicity in the choice of hypotheses is simply part of what it means to make "rational" choices. Whether this sort of answer is itself free from problems cannot be considered here. It may be noted, however, that a reply of a similar sort has been given in recent years to the traditional problem of the justification of induction.[14]

[13] Goodman, "The Test of Simplicity," p. 1064

[14] See Peter Strawson's paper, "The 'Justification' of Induction," in Section IV.

18 On Simplicity in Empirical Hypotheses

STEPHEN F. BARKER

The title of this symposium,* "Formal Simplicity as a Weight in the Acceptability of Scientific Theories," to some people might seem to suggest that we are to be making positive proposals about how the concept of simplicity could be defined for formalized languages, defined so as to figure in a formalized theory of confirmation. I must confess at the start that I do not have any such ambitious object in view. I now feel, indeed, that premature formalizations have little power to illuminate the philosophically interesting questions which cluster round the problem of the role of simplicity in scientific thinking. So in this short paper I wish merely to present some elementary considerations, not very novel ones, concerning the role which simplicity seems to me to play in our non-demonstrative reasoning about matters of empirical fact. Although many writers have sought to analyze the logical character of such reasoning, little unanimity has been attained in their over-all views; thus it is that though the considerations which I wish to present are elementary, they are not wholly uncontroversial. But because these matters are elementary in nature, I do feel

From *Philosophy of Science*, Vol. 28, No. 2, 1961, pp. 162–171. Reprinted by permission of the editor of *Philosophy of Science* and the author.

* [Ed. note: See M. Bunge's and R. Ackermann's articles in this volume.]

it appropriate in discussing them to use homely examples of uncomplicated kinds, rather than elaborate examples drawn from the more sophisticated reaches of scientific theory; in doing so, I am taking it for granted that scientific inference as regards its logical character is fundamentally a refinement of everyday thinking, rather than a procedure of some essentially different nature.

1

The first point which I wish to urge is that there is indeed a type of factor which we might properly call simplicity which does play an important role in our weighing of hypotheses about empirical matters of fact. This point is not a novel one, assuredly. Flickering hints of it are to be found in some of the great philosophers of the past, and a few contemporary philosophers have sometimes insisted upon it. But it is a point which is given little prominence in most of the usual off-hand descriptions of scientific method, both as regards the establishing of hypotheses and as regards the explaining of phenomena. Uusal off-hand descriptions of the method by which the scientist establishes his hypotheses represent his method as merely a process in which testable predictions are derived from an hypothesis, and the hypothesis itself is then supposed to be regarded as established if many of these predictions are verified. And usual descriptions of the process of explaining phenomena represent it merely as a process in which the scientist invents some hypothesis from which, together with a statement of the relevant circumstances, a statement of the phenomenon to be explained is deducible. These usual descriptions assign little or no role to the notion of simplicity in scientific proof and in scientific explanation.

There is an important insufficiency, I want to suggest, in the idea that when we establish an empirical hypothesis all we are essentially doing is just to show that what the hypothesis predicts does in fact come true. And there is a correlative insufficiency, I suggest, in the idea that when we explain a phenomenon all we are doing is to find an hypothesis from which the phenomenon to be explained would follow. Consider examples.

Suppose we were investigating the electrical resistance of alloys of metals A and B. Suppose we were to find that a bar of given dimensions if composed purely of metal A has a resistance of 100 ohms, while if 20% of metal B is added the resistance becomes 120 ohms, if 40% of metal B is added the resistance becomes 140 ohms, with 60% of metal B it is 160 ohms, with 80% it is 180 ohms, and with pure metal B the bar has a resistance of 200 ohms. If we wish to base a general hypothesis upon these facts, our problem is one of curve-fitting. Our observations correspond to a limited number of points on a graph, and our problem is to find a curve which goes through these points and which represents the most reasonable conjecture regarding the general way in which electrical resistance depends upon the composition of the alloy. The obvious hypothesis in this case is that there is a linear relationship between the percentage of metal added and the increase in electrical resistance. Now, according to the usual off-hand account of how hypotheses are established, we should regard this hypothesis as established (or at any rate, appreciably confirmed), since the observed facts do fully accord with this hypothesis. Moreover, this hypothesis if true would serve (at least to some extent) as an explanation of why the observed facts are as they are.

But all is not well with this account. For of course the trouble here is that this usual off-hand account of establishing hypotheses and explaining phenomena neglects the fact that there are innumerable other quite different hypotheses with which the observed data accord. The observed data correspond to a limited number of points on a graph; through these points we can plot a straight line, yet through these points also we are able in principle to plot innumerable other curves. If we believed that all that was involved in establishing an hypothesis was to show that it fits the facts, then we should have no reason whatsoever here for choosing between the linear hypothesis and the other, more complicated ones. It may be said that each one of these more complicated hypotheses could be tested by further appropriate observations, and that we should wait for more data before attempting to reach our conclusion. Of course it is true that further observations would be bound to eliminate many of these competing hypotheses; but to say that we ought to suspend judgment and wait for more data is to miss the point, for our problem here is to use the data that we have got and in the light of them make a reasonable judgment about which hypothesis we should accept. It is inappropriate to appeal to data that are not yet obtained, for our decision always has to based upon the evidence that we have got, not upon evidence that we have not got. We never obtain more than a finite quantity of data, and no matter how excellent these data may be there will remain always innumerable different hypotheses consistent with them. We cannot forever defer our choice among the competing hypotheses, forever waiting for more data to be collected; we must be able to come to some reasonable decision in the light of a finite collection of evidence. Yet the description of the scientist's method which says merely that he accepts the hypothesis which fits the facts gives no clue as to how this decision among competing hypotheses is to be reached.

In actuality, of course, we do not feel any of this infinite hesitancy about which hypothesis to accept. In a case like this we would think it reasonable to invoke the notion of simplicity. We would choose to accept the simplest hypothesis which smoothly fits our data within the limits of experimental error. Here in this sort of case the notion of simplicity has a definitely mathematical character. But to recognize the role of simplicity in such reasoning is to go essentially beyond these usual off-hand descriptions of scientific method.

Next let us consider another case of a different kind. During the 19th century people had examined geological strata beneath the surface of the earth and there had found fossils of plants and animals of kinds not now living. What hypothesis do these discoveries tend to confirm? What hypothesis should we invoke as an explanation of these findings? The best hypothesis would seem to be that these fossils really are the remains of organisms that actually existed on earth millions of years ago. A wide range of data are consonant with this hypothesis; this hypothesis provides a possible explanation which makes a great many seemingly disparate facts fit together strikingly into a connected pattern.

Yet this is certainly not the only hypothesis consistent with the facts, not the only hypothesis which if true would explain these geological observations. A century ago when the theory of evolution was being heatedly debated in public at least one controversialist went so far as to defend the alternative hypothesis that the earth had come into existence less than six thousand years ago, geological strata and all; and that the earth was designed by an intelligent Creator whose purpose in creating fossils apparently millions of years old was merely to test our faith. This hypothesis also is perfectly consistent with the observed facts, even though it is a queerer hypothesis. Moreover, this hypothesis enables us to make predictions which we can verify; for instance, because this hypothesis conjectures that the Creator intended to equip the earth with a full supply of fossils that would seem just as if they were millions of years old, this hypothesis would lead to the prediction that fossils will be found widely spread across the globe, and that they will exhibit coherent patterns of distribution throughout the various sedimentary layers. These predictions are borne out by further investigation. Moreover, it would be improper to dismiss this hypothesis of creation as necessarily senseless just because of its supernatural aspect. Nor would it do to claim that the empirical meaning of it really is just the same as that of the other, more straight-forward hypothesis, for this is not necessarily so: the hypothesis of creation may have distinctive implications regarding what would have been to be seen had one been present six thousand years ago, and it may be linked with implications about the power of prayer, the resurrection of the dead, and the Second Coming. Although not a scientifically acceptable hypothesis, this hypothesis of creation can be a real hypothesis, and it is consonant with the so-far-observed facts.

The usual off-hand account of scientific reasoning which merely tells us to accept the hypothesis which is consonant with the observed facts gives us no clue as to a reason for preferring the one hypothesis to the other. Yet surely here again there is a clear choice to be made: the hypothesis that the fossils really are remains of primeval organisms is a better hypothesis than is the hypothesis that they are not and were created only recently. The former hypothesis is better than the latter, not because it fits more facts or enables more predictions to be elicited; it is better because it is a simpler hypothesis. Here the notion of simplicity has no mathematical connotation. Here when we describe the one hypothesis as simpler than the other, it is because the overall picture of the earth's history which it gives is smoother and less extravagant. The hypothesis of creation involves the postulation of the existence of a Being of quite extraordinary powers and nearly inscrutable motives, a Being very unlike anything we observe. Unless there is other, independent evidence in favor of the existence of such a Being, we obtain a simpler theory of history by supposing that there have existed and acted in the past only causes more or less similar to what we now observe in the world about us. Here the hypothesis which in the light of the total evidence is the simpler, more parsimonious one would be the hypothesis which it would be more reasonable to accept.

2

Even if it is granted that the notion of simplicity does have a role to play in our choosing among empirical hypotheses, however, there may be those who will still think that this notion of simplicity is not really a fundamental feature of scientific thinking. They may wish to hold that the reason why simple hypotheses are to be preferred to more complicated ones is because past experience has shown that simpler hypotheses more often turn out to be true. According to this view, the role of simplicity in non-demonstrative reasoning would be derivative, for it would depend upon pure induction for its justification.

Indeed, the majority of those philosophers who have written about the logic of our reasoning concerning matters of empirical fact have represented this reasoning as always resting fundamentally just upon some principle of induction. From Mill through Keynes to Reichenbach and Carnap, leading writers in this field almost unanimously have taken the view that induction is the fundamental type of all reasoning concerning matters of fact. That is, they take as fundamental some principle which merely enjoins us to project into the future whatever regularities we have detected in the past; or, to put it in more general form, a principle which declares that evidence of how observed cases exhibit a certain feature entitles us to infer that as-yet-unobserved cases probably will exhibit this feature also.

Presumably, then, if they acknowledge that considerations of simplicity are to be taken into account in our judging of the acceptability of hypotheses, those who regard pure induction as the fundamental type of non-demonstrative reasoning must maintain that we actually can give an inductive justification of our preference for simplicity. They must claim that we can construct an inductive argument which shows it to be probable that simpler hypotheses are true more often than are complex ones. But can such an argument be coherently constructed? Can it really be maintained that the reason why we ought to prefer simpler to more complex hypotheses is that our past experience interpreted in a purely inductive fashion yields the conclusion that simpler hypotheses more often are true than complex ones?

Reichenbach, so far as I know, is the only philosopher who actually attempted to describe how a purely inductive justification might be given of our preference for simplicity in hypotheses.[1] His argument concentrated on the problem of fitting a curve to a finite set of observed points. Reichenbach's claim was that the scientist in doing this must seek a continuous curve, but furthermore that he must seek to make the derivatives of this curve continuous also. These considerations, Reichenbach somehow thought, were sufficient to show that the preference for simplicity in curve-fitting is justified

[1] H. Reichenbach, *Experience and Prediction* (Chicago, 1938), pp. 376–380.

on the basis of purely inductive considerations. Unfortunately, his argument neglects to give us any real reason for believing that there is any purely inductive basis for our expectation that the curve and its derivatives must be continuous; nor does he take account of the fact that innumerable other curves besides the simplest always will satisfy his requirements of continuity.

Reichenbach's particular attempt to give a purely inductive justification of our preference for simplicity in hypotheses is not a success. Could such an argument be constructed at all? What would such an argument be like?

Suppose that we were to try to construct an experiment aimed at proving inductively that simpler hypotheses more often are borne out than are complex ones. We would have to proceed in some such manner as the following. We would choose some appropriate sphere of inquiry, such as, for instance, the thermal expansion of various substances at different temperatures. For each substance we would make a limited number of measurements of specimens at each of several temperatures; then for each substance we would decide what was the simplest general hypothesis about the thermal expansion of that substance which was consistent with the data so far collected; then at new temperatures we would make additional measurements of the size of each specimen so as to see whether in each case our simplest hypothesis was or was not borne out by fuller observations. If in many cases the simplest hypotheses were supported by this further investigation, then we might claim that we had made a beginning at giving an inductive proof of the thesis that simpler hypotheses are more likely to be true than complex ones.

But have we succeeded in giving a purely inductive justification of simplicity considerations? The experiments just described are compatible with the generalization that considerations of simplicity are usually successful in predictions about thermal expansion; but they are compatible also with the generalization that simplicity considerations are usually successful in predictions about thermal expansion but unsuccessful for predictions in other spheres. Or suppose that our experiments all have been conducted in small American laboratories on summer weekdays; our data then are consistent with the generalizations that simplicity works for predictions made in small laboratories but not in large ones; or in American laboratories but not in foreign ones; or in summer but not in wintertime; or on weekdays but not on Sundays and holidays. Our observations are compatible with various conflicting generalizations. Now, the principle of pure induction merely enjoins us to project into the unobserved any regularity that we have found the observed to be compatible with. But here we have various conflicting regularities with which our observed cases are compatible. One regularity is that most of the things we have observed if they are observed to be hypotheses framed in the light of simplicity considerations are observed to be hypotheses borne out by further investigations; but another regularity is that most of the things we have observed if they are observed to be hypotheses framed in the light of simplicity considerations are observed to be borne out on weekdays but not borne out on Sundays. Pure induction gives us no more reason for projecting one of these regularities than for projecting the other. It is only if we appeal to considerations of simplicity that we have any reason for projecting the simpler regularity in preference to the more complex one. And what holds in this example holds good in general; for no matter how rich and varied our data were, there would always be numerous competing regularities with which our observed cases would be compatible. Thus I conclude that it is not possible to give a purely inductive justification of our preference for simplicity in hypotheses. Inductive reasoning itself cannot proceed at all without making essential appeal to considerations of simplicity. In my opinion, simplicity must therefore be regarded as a fundamental, not as a derivative, factor in our reasoning about matters of empirical fact.

3

Suppose it be granted that a factor which may reasonably be named simplicity does have an important role to play in determining the acceptability of scientific hypotheses; and suppose it be granted that simplicity is not merely a derivative factor but is itself a fundamental and essential element in scientific reasoning. If these points be granted, where then might we turn for an account of this notion of simplicity, and of its role in non-demonstrative reasoning?

Perhaps the most interesting philosophical treatment of this notion is to be found in the writings of Popper.[2] Popper connects the notion of simplicity with the notion of empirical content. He regards one hypothesis as simpler than another if it says more about how the world is; that is, if true, it leaves less leeway open to nature. The more informative hypothesis is the one which makes a relatively big claim about what is not going to be observed; and because it makes a big claim, it lays itself open to greater possibility of refutation. Thus Popper maintains that an hypothesis is simpler the more it says, the more empirical content it has; and this he identifies with the degree of falsifiability of the hypothesis. This identification of simplicity with falsifiability, he claims, enables us to answer the epistemological question, Why should science be concerned with the simplicity of hypotheses? The answer, he maintains, is that science must aim to attain hypotheses of maximum empirical content; the empirical content of an hypothesis is a matter of how falsifiable it is; so if we identify simplicity with falsifiability we can then say that science must seek simple hypotheses because it is thereby seeking those hypotheses which really say the most about nature.

What does it mean to compare the falsifiability of two hypotheses? Popper gives two independent criteria. The first is the "inclusion" criterion, and it applies to the case where one hypothesis implies another. If H_1 implies H_2 but H_2 does not imply H_1, then any set of observations that could conceivably suffice to falsify H_2 would be included among those that could conceivably suffice to falsify H_1, but not conversely; so here H_1 must be regarded as more falsifiable than H_2. Popper's second criterion, which he calls a "dimension" criterion, is less precisely statable, but it pertains directly to those cases where

[2] K. R. Popper, *The Logic of Scientific Discovery* (London, 1959), chs. VI, VII, X.

it is a matter of comparing two different hypotheses about how a curve is to be fitted to a set of observations. Popper's example is astronomical: if we have observed certain points in the orbit of a heavenly body and wish to form an hypothesis about the over-all orbit, then our position may be that we find ourselves needing to choose between the hypothesis that the whole orbit is elliptical and other hypotheses which impute to it curves of higher degree. Popper's claim is that the ellipse-hypothesis is more falsifiable than the competing hypotheses, in this sense, that a set of three observations can be logically sufficient to refute the hypothesis that the orbit is an ellipse, whereas the hypothesis that the orbit is, say, some kind of epicycle could at the minimum be refuted only by a set of perhaps a half-a-dozen or so observations. Thus the ellipse-hypothesis is more falsifiable than the epicycle hypothesis. This is the idea of Popper's "dimension" criterion for comparing degrees of falsifiability.

The general conception which Popper offers, then, is that in science we seek the simplest, that is to say, the most falsifiable hypotheses. The more falsifiable an hypothesis is, and the more tests we make that do not refute it, the more severely the hypothesis has been tested. And the more severe the tests that it stands up to, the more highly corroborated is the hypothesis; that is, the more acceptable to science.

Now, I find Popper's conception a stimulating one. But the manner in which he presents his doctrine makes it seem as though he is claiming that in science if we have two hypotheses neither of which has been falsified, yet one of which is more falsifiable than the other, then we ought always to regard the more falsifiable hypothesis as the more acceptable one. But putting the doctrine in this sweeping form leads to trouble; if of any two unfalsified hypotheses we were always to regard the more falsifiable as the more acceptable, we should be led to absurd conclusions.

Suppose, for instance, that the maid has been acting strangely and the silver spoons are missing from their cabinet in the dining room. One hypothesis which we might entertain as a possible explanation of these observed phenomena would be the hypothesis that the maid has stolen the spoons. This hypothesis is consonant with the so-far-observed facts, and if true would explain the situation. But other more detailed hypotheses also are possible here. For instance, there is the hypothesis that the maid has stolen the spoons and pawned them to raise money which she has used in order to elope with the butler on the 10:30 plane to Acapulco. This hypothesis also is unfalsified by what we have observed, and if true it would constitute a more detailed explanation of the situation. Now, each of these two hypotheses is a potential explanation of the disappearance of the spoons; the second hypothesis embraces the first and embroiders it with more fully conjectured detail. Which of these is the more acceptable hypothesis, in the light of the disappearance of the spoons? The second hypothesis, because of its more lavish detail, clearly is the more falsifiable of the two; for anything that would falsify the first hypothesis — e.g. the discovery that the spoons actually are in the pantry, where they have been taken to be cleaned — would falsify the second hypothesis also; while there are other things which if observed would falsify the second without falsifying the first — e.g. the discovery that bad weather has caused cancellation of the 10:30 flight to Acapulco, or that the butler is confined to bed with mumps. The second is clearly the more falsifiable hypothesis. But is it clearly the more acceptable one, the one better corroborated by our data? If all the direct evidence we have is that the maid was acting strangely and the spoons are missing, then surely we must answer no. It would be a reprehensibly hasty jumping to conclusions if merely on the basis of this meager evidence we embraced the hypothesis that the spoons have been stolen by the maid, who has pawned them and eloped with the butler on the 10:30 flight to Acapulco. After all, we might with no less justice suppose that she has eloped with the cook instead. In this example the more falsifiable hypothesis surely is the one which we should normally call the less simple, and it surely is the less acceptable of the two hypotheses.

Popper leaves his readers with the impression that he thinks it the task of science always to embrace the more falsifiable hypothesis, in a head-long pursuit of empirical content. But given any hypothesis, we always can fabricate another which is more falsifiable, merely by embroidering the details. Certainly it is not the task of the scientist always to be spinning out wilder and wilder fabrications of this type. How peculiar Popper's doctrine is comes out strikingly when we find him criticizing Keynes for having maintained the implication-condition with regard to confirmation; that is, for having held that when H_1 implies H_2 but not conversely then H_2 must be more probable and more acceptable than H_1.[3] Quite the contrary, says Popper; science has got to prefer hypotheses that are more falsifiable, that take more risk. And later, he very sharply criticizes Carnap in a somewhat parallel fashion.[4]

Despite these shortcomings which flow from the unguarded aspects of Popper's doctrine, there is something challenging about his idea. He is surely wrong when he seems to maintain that science should always prefer the more falsifiable hypothesis. Yet surely too there are valuable elements in his picture of the good hypothesis as the one which has taken the risk of making a strong claim and then has withstood severe testing. As I see it, the unsatisfactory consequences of his view all come from his use of the notion of falsifiability in the "inclusion" sense. The main merit of his view seems to me to come from his use of the "dimension" criterion. Surely simplicity in his "dimension" sense is a factor contributing to the confirmation of hypotheses, even though simplicity in his "inclusion" sense is not. His own view is beclouded, I think, because he insists upon closely identifying these two essentially different senses of falsifiability.

I have been engaging in this discussion of Popper because his is almost the only attempt by a philosopher to give a serious account of the notion of simplicity in its connection with non-demonstrative reasoning. I conclude my comments on his view with the suggestion that one of his two ideas of falsi-

[3] *op. cit.*, section 83.
[4] *ibid.* Appendix ix.

fiability does have a real connection with simplicity, and that his talk about how the more falsifiable hypothesis becomes corroborated through having survived severe tests is talk that does make suggestive sense when limited to his second type of falsifiability.

4

There is one final point which I wish briefly to urge. Many writers seeing the grave difficulties which seem to lie in the way of any precise, general definition of simplicity have concluded that the notion is itself ultimately only an aesthetic one, a matter of taste. If we cannot give a rigorous definition of what it is for one hypothesis to be simpler than another, do we really know what we are talking about when we speak of simplicity? Is not the very notion itself something utterly subjective?

This sort of comment savours far too much of Platonism for my taste. Plato of all the great philosophers, was the one who most made it his habit to accuse others of not knowing what they were talking about when they proved unable to offer him rigorous general definitions of their conceptions. But this sort of Platonism is based on a mistake. A distinction may be real, and a person may understand the distinction, even though he may not be able rigorously to characterize in general terms what the distinction is. For instance, I cannot give a rigorous general definition of the difference between sanity and madness; yet this in no way shows that there is no difference, nor does it even show that I fail to understand the difference. That I do understand the difference is demonstrated by my ability to classify the men I meet as sane or mad, and my ability to do this may be quite independent of whether I can give a definition of what I am doing. And if in my classifying I must sometimes hesitate over border-line cases, then — if they are genuine border-line cases — my very hesitation itself shows the goodness, and not any weakness, of my grasp of the difference between the mad and the sane. The situation is analogous with regard to the distinction between good and bad empirical hypotheses. Even if we cannot do much by way of giving a rigorous definition in general terms of the distinction between an hypothesis that is good in the light of the evidence and an hypothesis that is bad in the light of the evidence, this in no way shows that there is no difference; nor does it even show that we fail to understand the difference. Our grasp of the distinction is proved by our ability to recognize good and bad hypotheses when we meet them; and here too if we hesitate over those cases that are genuinely border-line this only demonstrates the excellence of our grasp of the distinction.

This concluding point of mine is not that we should not try to define in general terms as rigorously as we can what the logical difference is between well and ill confirmed hypotheses. This is indeed worth trying to do. My point is that lack of success in this task of definition should not be interpreted as a sign that the confirmation of hypotheses is all a matter of subjective taste, nor as a sign that we do not know the difference between good and bad scientific reasoning.

19 On Simple Theories of a Complex World

WILLARD VAN ORMAN QUINE

It is not to be wondered that theory makers seek simplicity. When two theories are equally defensible on other counts, certainly the simpler of the two is to be preferred on the score of both beauty and convenience. But what is remarkable is that the simpler of two theories is generally regarded not only as the more desirable but also as the more probable. If two theories conform equally to past observations, the simpler of the two is seen as standing the better chance of confirmation in future observations. Such is the maxim of the simplicity of nature. It seems to be implicitly assumed in every extrapolation and interpolation, every drawing of a smooth curve through plotted points. And the maxim of the uniformity of nature is of a piece with it, uniformity being a species of simplicity.

Simplicity is not easy to define. But it may be expected, whatever it is, to be relative to the texture of a conceptual scheme. If the basic concepts of one conceptual schema are the derivative concepts of another, and *vice versa*, presumably one of two hypotheses could count as simpler for the one scheme and the other for the other. This being so, how can simplicity carry any peculiar presumption of objective truth? Such is the implausibility of the maxim of the simplicity of nature.

Corresponding remarks apply directly to the maxim of the uniformity of nature, according to which, vaguely speaking, things similar in some respects tend to prove similar in others. For again similarity, whatever it is, would seem to be relative to the structure of one's conceptual scheme or quality space. Any two things, after all, are shared as members by as many classes as any other two things; degrees of similarity depend on which of those classes we weight as the more basic or natural.

Belief in the simplicity of nature, and hence in the uniformity of nature, can be partially accounted for in obvious ways. One plausible factor is wishful thinking. Another and more compelling cause of the belief is to be found in our perceptual mechanism: there is a subjective selectivity that makes us tend to see the simple and miss the complex. Thus consider streamers, as printers

Reprinted from *Synthese*, Vol. 15, 1963, pp. 103–106 by permission of the editor of *Synthese* and the author.

call them: vertical or diagonal white paths formed by a fortuitous lining up of the spaces between words. They are always straight or gently curved. The fastidious typesetter makes them vanish just by making them crooked.

This subjective selectivity is not limited to the perceptual level. It can figure even in the most deliberate devising of experimental criteria. Thus suppose we try to map out the degrees of mutual affinity of stimuli for a dog, by a series of experiments in the conditioning and extinction of his responses. Suppose further that the resulting map is challenged: suppose someone protests that what the map reflects is not some original spacing of qualities in the dog's pre-experimental psyche or original fund of dispositions, but only a history of readjustments induced successively by the very experiments of the series. Now how would we rise to this challenge? Obviously, by repeating the experiments in a different order on another dog. If we get much the same map for the second dog despite the permutation, we have evidence that the map reflects a genuinely pre-experimental pattern of dispositions. And we then have evidence also of something more: that this pattern or quality space is the same for both dogs. But now I come to the point of my example: we cannot, by this method, get evidence of pre-experimental quality spaces unlike for the two dogs. By the very nature of our criterion, in this example, we get evidence either of uniformity or of nothing. An analysis of experimental criteria in other sciences would no doubt reveal many further examples of the same sort of experimentally imposed bias in favor of uniformity, or in favor of simplicity of other sorts.

This selective bias affords not only a partial explanation of belief in the maxim of the simplicity of nature but also, in an odd way, a partial justification. For, if our way of framing criteria is such as to preclude, frequently, any confirmation of the more complex of two rival hypotheses, then we may indeed fairly say that the simpler hypothesis stands the better chance of confirmation; and such, precisely, was the maxim of the simplicity of nature. We have, insofar, justified the maxim while still avoiding the paradox that seemed to be involved in trying to reconcile the relativity of simplicity with the absoluteness of truth.

This solution, however, is too partial to rest with. The selective bias in favor of simplicity, in our perceptual mechanism and in our deliberate experimental criteria, is significant but not overwhelming. Complex hypotheses do often stand as live options, just as susceptible to experimental confirmation as their simpler alternatives; and in such cases still the maxim of simplicity continues to be applied in scientific practice, with as much intuitive plausibility as in other cases. We fit the simplest possible curve to plotted points, thinking it the likeliest curve pending new points to the contrary; we encompass data with a hypothesis involving the fewest possible parameters, thinking this hypothesis the likeliest pending new data to the contrary; and we even record a measurement as the roundest near number, pending repeated measurements to the contrary.

Now this last case, the round number, throws further light on our problem. If a measured quantity is reported first as 5.21, say, and more accurately in the light of further measurement as 5.23, the new reading supersedes the old; but if it is reported first as 5.2 and later as 5.23, the new reading may well be looked upon as confirming the old one and merely supplying some further information regarding the detail of further decimal places. Thus the "simpler hypothesis", 5.2 as against 5.21, is quite genuinely ten times likelier to be confirmed, just because ten times as much deviation is tolerated under the head of confirmation.

True, we do not customarily say "simple hypothesis" in the round-number case. We invoke here no maxim of the simplicity of nature, but only a canon of eschewing insignificant digits. Yet the same underlying principle that operates here can be detected also in cases where one does talk of simplicity of hypotheses. If we encompass a set of data with a hypothesis involving the fewest possible parameters, and then are constrained by further experiment to add another parameter, we are likely to view the emendation not as a refutation of the first result but as a confirmation plus a refinement; but if we have an extra parameter in the first hypothesis and are constrained by further experiment to alter it, we view the emendation as a refutation and revision. Here again the simpler hypothesis, the one with fewer parameters, is initially the more probable simply because a wider range of possible subsequent findings is classified as favorable to it. The case of the simplest curve through plotted points is similar: an emendation prompted by subsequent findings is the likelier to be viewed as confirmation-cum-refinement, rather than as refutation and revision, the simpler the curve.[1]

We have noticed four causes for supposing that the simpler hypothesis stands the better chance of confirmation. There is wishful thinking. There is a perceptual bias that slants the data in favor of simple patterns. There is a bias in the experimental criteria of concepts, whereby the simpler of two hypotheses is sometimes opened to confirmation while its alternative is left inaccessible. And finally there is a preferential system of scorekeeping, which tolerates wider deviations the simpler the hypothesis. These last two of the four causes operate far more widely, I suspect, than appears on the surface. Do they operate widely enough to account in full for the crucial role that simplicity plays in scientific method?

[1] I expect that Kemeny has had all this in mind. He remarks the kinship of the rule of significant digits to that of simplicity on page 399 of 'The Use of Simplicity in Induction', *The Philosophical Review 62* (1953) 391–408. [Ed. note: See page 309 of this volume for Kemeny's article.]

20 *The Measurement of Simplicity*

DONALD J. HILLMAN *

1. The Notion of Simplicity

There is not much doubt that some version of a simplicity principle plays an important, if largely uncritical, role in our explanation of what goes on about us. If there is more than one way of accounting for some observed state of affairs, then we should normally opt for the simpler explanation. Thus, if the failure of all of my services to clear the net can be accounted for both by the explanation that my service action is at fault and also by the explanation that each of my six brand new tennis balls is a willfully manufactured oblate spheroid of non-uniform weight distribution, it is the simpler first explanation that spectators and, with perhaps more reluctance, I should prefer. Similarly, when observing a straight rod being immersed in clear water, we prefer to explain its apparent bending by invoking a simple law of refraction rather than by saying that the rod really does change shape when immersed in water, regaining its original shape only when taken out again. We reject the latter explanation because of the complications it would introduce to our descriptions of ordinary rigid bodies.

It will, of course, be said that these examples are no more than trivial reports on our everyday conduct, and that the scientist has a much more refined and sophisticated notion of simplicity. This, however, is not strictly true. In evaluating two competing hypotheses or theories, the scientist most often *does* pay regard to their relative simplicity of concepts and assumptions. And it is likely that he will choose the simpler theory as better supported by the evidence, even though both theories are equally compatible with the evidence in their favor.

Yet in spite of this, it is remarkable that a precise notion of simplicity, adequate to meet the scientist's needs, has proved so elusive to pin down. Principles of simplicity have been abundant, from Occam's Razor in fourteenth century philosophy all the way down to various twentieth-century attempts to interpret simplicity in its scientific connection. Thus Popper proffers an analysis of what he calls the *epistemological concept of simplicity.*[1] His proposal is to relate the degree

From *Philosophy of Science*, Vol. 29, No. 3, July, 1962, pp. 225–252. Reprinted by permission of the editor of *Philosophy of Science* and the author.

* I wish to thank the referees of this paper for numerous helpful suggestions as to presentation and for correcting several errors.

[1] *The Logic of Scientific Discovery*, Ch. VII, pp. 136–145.

of simplicity of a theory to its degree of falsifiability, and he supports his suggestion by arguing that simple statements "if knowledge is our object, are to be prized more highly than less simple ones *because they tell us more; because their empirical content is greater; and because they are better testable.*"[2] Other practitioners, however, feel that the notion of simplicity cannot be helpfully characterized. Simplicity is, in their opinion, much too heavily dependent on aesthetic and pragmatic considerations to be genuinely analyzable.

Both of these positions seem to be unsatisfactory. Popper's analysis, although interesting, does not appear to deal with a notion of simplicity to which we invariably appeal in our scientific and other judgments. In comparing the relative simplicity of two theories, we are concerned more with a logical than with an epistemological issue. In effect, we want to know which of the two theories has a greater logical simplicity, a greater coherence of structure and a greater economy of defining power. And the situation is hardly improved when we are told that our search is in any case fruitless, on the grounds that simplicity is a pragmatic or aesthetic notion and utterly incapable of objective characterization.

It seems to me that this last contention simply fails to take into account what we certainly *can* do, and quite often succeed in doing, when comparing the relative simplicity of competing explanations. Apart from all aesthetic or subjective considerations, we can detect a number of quite objective properties of theories that materially affect their simplicity. One theory may differ from another in its ontological presuppositions or commitments; two theories may differ with respect to the relative complexity of their conceptual schemes; and we should certainly be inclined to say that theories differing in the number and logical complexity of the statements they contain differ in simplicity. Yet even though we should be prepared to say that each of these questions has a bearing upon the simplicity of a theory, it is nevertheless clear that they constitute no sort of orderly method for coming to understand and set forth the basic principles by which we can assess and compare the simplicity measures of rival theories. For one thing, the issues raised by these questions are by no means clear. How, for example, are we to judge between the complexities of different conceptual schemes? What features of such schemes should be taken into account in making our judgment? Moreover, it could quite conceivably happen that the questions we ask lead to conflicting answers. For example, our concern with the number and complexity of the statements that make up a theory may lead us to decide that theory A is simpler than theory B, whereas our interest in the ontological presuppositions of each theory may cause us to reverse our decision. To avoid such clashes of interest, and to make clear exactly what properties of a theory determine its degree of simplicity, it is obvious that we should try to discover what notion forms the basis of all of our queries into the simplicity of theories.

This question may be brought into sharper focus by supposing that we have a set of evidential statements to be incorporated into a hypothetico-deductive

[2] *Ibid.*, p. 142.

system. In general, there will be many systems to which statements may be allocated, and the question before us is to choose the most acceptable one among them. We should, I think, normally prefer to incorporate our evidential statements in that system which is structurally more simple and logically more coherent. And this, of course, places squarely on our shoulders the burden of explaining what we mean by *structural simplicity* and *coherence*.

It is fortunate indeed that one man in particular has recognized the gravity of this task and achieved a considerable measure of success in making clear to us what features of a system determine its structural simplicity. Professor Nelson Goodman, in a series of publications,[3] has formulated and refined the issues that vex us in this difficult general problem, bringing his investigations to a logical culmination in the construction of an axiomatic method for the measurement of simplicity. The essence of Goodman's scheme is to concentrate attention upon the predicates that form the extra-logical basis of any given theory, and to propose measures for comparing the relative simplicity of different sets of such predicates. Thus, given any two suggested theories to account for a certain corpus of scientific phenomena, each framed in the language of the first-order functional calculus, we can readily determine which of the two has a structurally simpler extralogical basis by applying to each the results of Goodman's axiomatic method.

Since the method developed by Goodman can function as a criterion for choosing the simplest theory articulating a given subject matter, it is obvious that we should become fully acquainted with its principles and procedures. Accordingly, I want now to present, in order, a complete summary of the postulational basis of this method, and a statement of the most important theorems and their proofs. By way of explanation, I should add that the theorems here proved constitute a revised version of those first presented by Professor Goodman in [6], which is the basis of this paper. The revisions are to be found in [7] and consist principally of:

(1) a restatement of P3
(2) a restatement and expansion of T15
(3) amendments to definitions.

I have ordered the definitions for ease of reference, and have included others to facilitate proofs. In addition, T4′, which does not appear in [6], has been included as a useful lemma. In all other respects, the postulates, definitions and theorems of [6] appear unchanged, except for the modifications noted above.

I wish to emphasize that all of the results contained in this paper belong to Professor Goodman, so that my own contribution may be regarded as a corroboration of the authenticity of his many insights and conjectures.

2. Foundations of the Theory of Simplicity

I shall attempt, in what follows, to describe the theory of simplicity in as much detail as seems to be requisite for an adequate knowledge of its functioning.

[3] See References.

In order to avoid misunderstanding, I wish to point out that the theory has not been set up as a *fully formalized* deductive system. Accordingly, the development will not be entirely rigorous, and such metatheoretical questions as consistency and completeness will not be considered. My principal aim is to make my presentation self-contained and to acquaint the reader with current results.

It need hardly be said that the theory is not a logistic system. The symbols it employs are not formal marks but signs with their customary interpretation. Nor is any attempt made to specify a uniform proof precedure in establishing the theorems. Where standard mathematical means are available, those means are utilized in proofs. Thus the theory is pretty much a branch of ordinary mathematics in its present form, with only the addition of some methods of replacement to distinguish it from more familiar practices. This may not be entirely satisfactory from a purely formal point of view, but elegance and uniformity can be made subservient to more practical goals. It is surely enough to recognize how much our knowledge of simplicity has been increased by Goodman's studies, and to judge by its own standards the theory that embodies his results.

Bearing these comments in mind, let us now turn to a description of the logical and mathematical framework supporting Goodman's theory of simplicity. The systems to which the theory is applicable are first-order functional calculi, which, for present purposes, may themselves be regarded as formalizations of scientific theories. Such systems have the usual truth-functional connectives, quantifiers and the identity sign as logical apparatus, and contain sets of predicates of individuals as their extralogical bases. The complexity of these extralogical bases is to be assessed with the help of Goodman's theory. Thus, predicates of individuals will constitute the data of the theory.

Since we are not here concerned with the construction of a logistic system, it is unnecessary to stipulate what primitive symbols occur in the theory. Suffice it to note that the customary signs of logical sum and logical product, the summation sign of arithmetic and certain signs of group theory are used in proofs with their usual interpretations. Similarly, since our simplicity theory *is* an interpreted system, and not a system of logistic, we shall not hesitate to use the interpretation in determining the formulas we shall be working with. Each type of formula, when introduced, will be accompanied by an explanation of its use.

Our understanding of the theory of simplicity, when applied to sets of extralogical bases, depends initially on our taking into account a number of crucial refinements of logical structure.

One such refinement concerns the distinction Goodman makes between "a sequence of a predicate P" and "a place-sequence of a predicate P". For let P be an n-place predicate. Then a sequence of P is any ordered n-ad of elements, $a, b, \cdots, n$, such that $Pa, b, \cdots, n$ is true. Conversely, P has just one *place-sequence*, consisting of a sequence of distinct variables, $p_1, p_2, \cdots, p_n$, such that p_i represents the ith place of P. This distinction must be carefully observed in the construction of proofs.

Other refinements of logical structure are provided by definitions, which now follow. Certain terms appearing in definientia have been appropriated from logic and mathematics, and are here employed in their customary interpretation:

a) *Definitions concerning reflexivity*

D1. An n-place predicate P is *redundant* $=_{\text{df}}$ all sequences of P are identity sequences.
D2. An n-place predicate P is *totally reflexive* $=_{\text{df}}$ all identity n-ads are sequences of P.
D3. A sequence S of an n-place predicate is *k-variegated* $=_{\text{df}}$ S has k discrete components, for $1 \leq k \leq n$.
D4. An n-place predicate P is *irreflexive* $=_{\text{df}}$ all sequences of P are n-variegated.
D5. Let α be the set of first components of the non-identity pairs of a 2-place predicate P, β the set of second components of such pairs, and γ the set of components of the identity pairs of P. Then

i) P is *left-reflexive* $=_{\text{df}}$ $\alpha = \gamma$
ii) P is *right-reflexive* $=_{\text{df}}$ $\beta = \gamma$
iii) P is *meet-reflexive* $=_{\text{df}}$ $\gamma = \alpha \cap \beta$
iv) P is *join-reflexive* $=_{\text{df}}$ $\gamma = \alpha \cup \beta$

Predicates satisfying any of these definitions are termed by Goodman reflexively *regular;* otherwise they are irregular.

b) *Definitions concerning self-completeness*

Having dealt with reflexivity, the property of transitivity must now be examined. Just as with the former property, we find that a number of refinements are called for. Goodman has found that the customary definition of transitivity is inadequate for certain purposes of complexity measurement, and considers instead a stronger form of the property, called *self-completeness.*

Restricting our attention, initially, to two-place predicates, we say that P is transitive if $(x)(y)(z)(Px, z \cdot Pz, y \cdot \supset Px, y)$. For P, however, to be self-complete, we must have $(x)(y)(w)(z)(Px, w \cdot Pz, y \cdot x \neq w \cdot x \neq y \cdot z \neq y \cdot \supset Px, y)$. Goodman now develops the notion of self-completeness in two respects. First, the notion must be extended to apply to n-place predicates in general, and, second, there are different *levels* of self-completeness that require explanation. We can satisfy both of these requirements simultaneously in the following way.[4]

Let P be an n-place predicate, whose arguments $(x_1, x_2, \cdots, x_n)$ may be correlated one-to-one with $(p_1, p_2, \cdots, p_n)$, the place-sequence S of P. Let R be any set of mutually exclusive and jointly exhaustive subsequences of S. Representing the r members of R as $Q_1, Q_2, \cdots, Q_r$, and writing "$\vec{x}$" as an abbreviation-

[4] I am indebted to a referee for suggesting the need for such an approach. The definition that follows is based on Goodman's informal explanation in [6].

tion of "$x_1, x_2, \cdots, x_n$," we introduce $Q_i(\vec{x})$, $(1 \leq i \leq r)$, to designate that sequence obtained from $\vec{x}$ by substituting a discrete new variable y_j, $(j = 1, 2, \cdots, k)$, for each $x_i \in \vec{x}$ whose corresponding place-variable p_i is not contained in Q_i. It is easy to see that $k = n(r - 1)$, when all $Q_i(\vec{x})$ sequences are taken into account. Using this new notation, the following definition can now be constructed.

D6. An n-place predicate P is *self-complete* with respect to a set R of mutually exclusive and jointly exhaustive subsequences of its places $=_{df}$

$$(x_1)(x_2)\cdots(x_n)(y_1)(y_2)\cdots(y_{n(r-1)})\{PQ_1(\vec{x})\cdot PQ_2(\vec{x}).\cdots PQ_r(\vec{x})\cdot x_1 \neq x_2 \neq\cdots\neq x_n\cdot \supset P\vec{x}\},$$

where $PQ_i(\vec{x})$ is formed by writing $Q_i(\vec{x})$ as the arguments of P.

Thus, the four-place predicate P is self-complete with respect to the place-subsequences (p_1), (p_2, p_4) and (p_3) if and only if

$$(x_1)\cdots(x_4)(y_1)\cdots(y_8)\{Px_1, y_1, y_2, y_3\cdot Py_4, x_2, y_5, x_4\cdot Py_6, y_7, x_3, x_8\cdot x_1 \neq\cdots\neq x_4\cdot \supset Px_1, x_2, x_3, x_4\}.$$

Two more definitions may now be constructed.

D7. Q is a *partition* of a predicate $P =_{df} Q$ is a place-subsequence belonging to a set of place-subsequences with respect to which P is self-complete.

D8. M is a *minimal partition* of a predicate $P =_{df} M$ is a partition of P containing no other partition of P.

Our final definition in this Section concerns what might be termed "absolute" self-completeness.

D9. An n-place predicate P is (*first-level*) self-complete $=_{df}$ each partition of P is a one-place place-subsequence of P.

D9. is an important special case of D6. It is apparent that first-level self-completeness implies self-completeness at all higher levels.

c) *Definitions concerning symmetry*

Goodman draws a number of fine distinctions concerning the symmetrical properties of predicates that quite closely parallel his treatment of self-completeness. Thus, although a two-place predicate P is symmetrical when $(x)(y)(Px, y \supset Py, x)$, we need to furnish the apparatus for defining different *levels* of symmetry for n-place predicates. This may be accomplished as follows.

Let $Px_1, x_2, \cdots x_n$ be an n-place predicate, and $\{S_1, S_2, \cdots, S_m\}$ a set of discrete, equally long and jointly exhaustive subsequences of its places, so that m is a divisor of n. Let Q_i represent those $\frac{n}{m}$ elements of $\vec{x}$ occurring in the places of S_i. Then,

D10. An n-place predicate P is symmetrical with respect to $\{S_1, S_2, \cdots, S_m\}$, or $(S_1)(S_2)\cdots(S_m)$ symmetrical, if, whenever $Q_1, Q_2, \cdots, Q_m$ represents a sequence of P, each of the $m!$ permutations of $Q_1, Q_2, \cdots, Q_m$ also represents a sequence of P.

Thus, the predicate P is $(1, 2)(3, 4)$ symmetrical if, whenever w, x, y, z represents one of its sequences, so also does y, z, w, x.

Absolute, or first-level, symmetry may now easily be defined.

D11. An n-place predicate P is *(absolutely) symmetrical* $=_{df}$ P is $(S_1)(S_2)\cdots(S_n)$ symmetrical.

Definitions 10 and 11 do not cover all cases of symmetry, for a predicate that is not symmetrical at any level may nevertheless have *partitions* that are symmetrical at a given level. Goodman has constructed the following definition [5] to account for this.

D12. A predicate P is symmetrical with respect to a (non-exhaustive) set S of its places if, whenever P applies to any sequence q of elements, P also applies to every sequence obtained from q by permuting in any way the elements of q occurring in the places of S while holding fixed the elements of q in the remaining places of P.

Thus, a four-place predicate P is symmetrical with respect to its third and fourth places if P applies to the sequence w, x, z, y whenever it applies to w, x, y, z.

The effect of symmetry upon complexity can now be taken into account. This is complicated by the fact that symmetries of the whole predicate and of its shorter partitions must both be considered. To facilitate complexity measurement, Goodman has introduced the following auxiliary notions.

D13. S is a *first-level symmetry stretch* of a predicate P $=_{df}$ S is a set of places of P such that P is symmetrical with respect to S but is not symmetrical with respect to all the places in any S', such that $S \subset S'$.

D14. S is an *m-level symmetry stretch* of a predicate P $=_{df}$ S is a set of m-length place-subsequences of P such that no two of them intersect any lower-level stretch, and such that P is symmetrical with respect to S, but is not symmetrical with respect to all place-subsequences of any S', such that $S \subset S'$.

For convenience, let us now refer to "a symmetry" as any set of place-subsequences of a predicate P, with respect to which P is symmetrical in any of the senses defined. Then

D15. M is a *molecular symmetry* $=_{df}$ M is a symmetry all of whose place-subsequences are partitions.

D16. M is an *atomic symmetry* $=_{df}$ M is a symmetry all of whose place-subsequences are within minimal partitions.

With the help of these definitions, we may now set down the postulates. It is convenient to group these as follows

d) *Fundamental Postulates of Replaceability*

P1. If every basis of a relevant kind K is always replaceable by some basis of a relevant kind L, then K is not more complex then L (i.e., K does not

[5] Cf. [7], p. 444, footnote 23.

have a higher complexity-value than L — or, using obvious abbreviations, $vK \leq vL$).

P2. Every predicate in an extralogical basis has a positive complexity-value, and the value of the basis is the sum of the values of the predicates in it.

e) *Numerical Postulates*

P3a. If K and L are relevant kinds of *n-pl* irreflexive predicate with self-completeness at any level, differing at most in atomic symmetry, then $vK - vL = syL - syK$.

P4. If K, L, M, N are relevant kinds of *n-pl* irreflexive predicate, where $syK = syL$, $syM = syN$, $scK \leq scL$ and $scM \leq scN$, but $(vK - vL)/(vM - vN)$ is not numerically determined by P1, P2 and P3a, then $(vK - vL)/(vM - vN) = (scL - scK)/(scN - scM)$.

f) *Quantitative Postulate*

P5. Just those kinds that are determined by preceding postulates to have the same value as {1-pl} have the value 1; and every other kind has the lowest integral value consistent with this requirement and preceding postulates.

P3a and P4 involve the numerical expressions "*scP*" (read "the self-completeness measure of *P*") and "*syP*" (read "the symmetry measure of *P*"). These expressions are evaluated with the help of the following rules:

g) *Evaluative Rules*

R1. If k is the number of minimal partitions of P, then $scP = k - l$.

R2. If R is an m-level stretch that is symmetrical with respect to h m-length sequences, each having the complexity value k, then $syR = (h - 1) \cdot k$.

R3. If P is any predicate, then syP = the sum of the symmetry measures of all its stretches.

It now remains to supplement these definitions, postulates and evaluative rules with a specification of rules of procedure. These fall into two main groups. The first contains certain mathematical procedures, mostly arithmetical. More exactly, familiar lines of mathematical reasoning will be followed whenever a theorem seeks to establish a quantitative result. No effective criterion is offered for recognizing proofs. Rather, the theory presupposes an ability to recognize a valid deductive process in mathematics. The second group contains a single principle of replaceability, previously referred to in the first postulate. Goodman's own explanation of the principle runs as follows:

> ... to say that every basis of kind K is *always replaceable by* some basis of kind L, is to say not only that there always is some equivalent basis of kind L, but also that we can always find one; that is, that given any basis B of kind K, with no further information than that B is of kind K, we can define in terms of B and logic alone some basis B' of kind L such that we can redefine B from B' and logic alone. The replacement must not, for example, depend upon any existential assumption beyond the usual logical one of a non-empty universe.[6]

[6] [6], p. 710.

Some further words of explanation might be helpful regarding the application of this principle. The problem in hand is to provide the simplest adequate basis for a given system of scientific explanation. Now, any system is definable from an adequate basis, just as the basis, being contained in the system, is definable from it. This means that a given system and any of its adequate bases are interdefinable. In addition, if we wish to compare interdefinable alternative *bases* for a system, it frequently turns out that simplicity is the clue to our final decision.

Fairly obviously, we are concerned in this latter problem with *replacing* one basis for a system with another. Equally obviously, no such replacement must be of a mechanical nature, since no genuine simplification will be achieved in this manner. Consider, for example, a system whose extralogical basis consists of just three one-place predicates P, Q and R, with non-null extensions. Let us assume, further, that the system employs these predicates to describe certain facts. It is clear that we could easily devise a new system, whose extralogical basis consists of just one three-place predicate, that will be capable of describing exactly the same facts. Let S be this three-place predicate, explained as follows:

$$Sx, y, z \equiv Px \cdot Qy \cdot Rz$$

It is now obvious that each statement of the original system can be redefined in terms of S:

$$\begin{aligned} Px &= {}_{\text{df}}(\exists y)(\exists z)Sx, y, z \\ Qx &= {}_{\text{df}}(\exists y)(\exists z)Sy, x, z \\ Rx &= {}_{\text{df}}(\exists y)(\exists z)Sy, z, x \end{aligned}$$

If every statement in the new system is thus trivially obtained from statements in the old system, it is apparent that no economy has been effected. The new system, although containing fewer predicates, is certainly no simpler than the original. Any replacement procedure that will always work in this mechanical and unilluminating fashion is therefore to be rejected.

How, then, are our replacement procedures to be accomplished? It is clear that replacement of a basis B by a basis B' succeeds in substituting a less complex for a more complex basis only when bases like B cannot *always* be replaced by bases like B' in a purely routine fashion. An illustration serves to make this clear.

Suppose that Rx, y is neither irreflexive nor redundant, and that the following equivalences may be set up:

$$\begin{aligned} Qx, y &\equiv Rx, y \cdot x \neq y \\ Px &\equiv Rx, x \end{aligned}$$

Then the predicates Q and P, thus introduced, exhaust the extension of R. Let us now define R in terms of Q and P as follows:

$$Rx, y = {}_{\text{df}}Qx, y \vee Px \cdot x = y.$$

Now, this is not a merely routine replacement, as a comparison with the preceding illustration will show. It is in cases like this that we say that every basis consisting of a single two-place predicate that is neither irreflexive nor redundant is not more complex than a basis consisting of a one-place predicate and a two-place irreflexive predicate.[7]

I do not now intend to expatiate at greater length on the theory of replaceability. Enough has been said, I think, to acquaint the reader with the essence of the replaceability principle. Those interested in a fuller development of theory may be referred to the work of Svenonius.[8]

In proving the theorems of the next Section, I shall make abundant use of the principle. In so doing, I shall invoke no existence theorems for replacement predicates. The reason for this is obvious. Any replacement of one basis by another, in the sense described above, is to be regarded as a *de facto* accomplishment. To establish that a given replaceability relationship holds, it will be sufficient to produce the formulas by which the replacement is in fact carried out.

This will not be the case, of course, for predicates other than replacement predicates. That is to say, whenever an auxiliary predicate is called upon in demonstrating one of the theorems, then a proof of that predicate's existence is required if it is used *not* to replace another predicate but is utilized in some other fashion. Such proofs will be necessary for theorems 15a.2, 17 and 19.[9]

Some final words of explanation on terminology complete these preliminary remarks.

(1) A *relevant kind* of basis is characterized, first, by the number of predicates it contains and by the number of places in each of its predicates; second, by any (or no) information concerning the reflexivity, symmetry and self-completeness of these predicates, as minutely described in the definitions. It is apparent that any sum, non-null difference or non-null product of two relevant kinds is also a relevant kind. It is also assumed that each basis consists exclusively of predicates with non-null extensions, and that the complexity-value of the logical apparatus is zero. For notational convenience, the kind of basis that consists, for example, of a one-place predicate and a two-place irreflexive predicate will be referred to as "{1-pl; 2-pl irref.}".

(2) A given basis has the value of the narrowest relevant kind to which it belongs. This statement may help clarify the meaning of the expression "v{not-more-than-n-pl}" occurring in T3. The kind of basis that consists of such a predicate is obviously one composed of either an n-place predicate, *or* an (n-1) place predicate, *or . . . or* a one-place predicate. Since a relevant kind has the highest value possessed by any basis of that kind, the proof of T3 is virtually accomplished.

(3) In connection with the last sentence of (2), an expression is needed to designate the higher of two complexity-values. Accordingly, in the proofs of certain theorems, expressions such as "$H(v${1-pl; 2-pl irref}, v{1-pl})" occur.

[7] As a matter of fact, we shall see later (Cf. T7) that these two bases have an equal complexity-value.

[8] "Definability and Simplicity," *The Journal of Symbolic Logic*, Vol. 20, No. 3, 1955, pp. 235–250.

[9] This was pointed out to me by a referee.

Here, H is a single-valued function of two complexity-values, and is interpreted to mean "higher of". More specifically:

$$H(\alpha, \beta) = \alpha, \text{ if } \alpha > \beta$$

and

$$H(\alpha, \beta) = \beta, \text{ if } \beta > \alpha$$

where α and β are complexity-values. For $\alpha = \beta$, H is undefined.

(4) In T6, the expression "c" is introduced as an abbreviation of "$v\{$1-pl$\}$". c is thus a numerical quantity, determined, of course, by the postulates to be 1. I have retained the use of "c" in order that the theorems here proved correspond to those framed initially in [6].

Some important consequences of the postulates follow below. Where justification is simple, the theorem is stated without proof. In addition, where Goodman's own suggested proof is utilized, either wholly or partly, the expression "(G)" is appended to the proof in question. I should like once again to emphasize the importance of constructing these proofs, for Goodman's system, although not yet a fully formalized deductive theory, is nevertheless the most important theoretical treatment of logical simplicity yet to appear.

3. Theorems

T1. If every basis of kind K is always replaceable by some basis of kind L, and every basis of kind L is always replaceable by some basis of kind K, then $vK = vL$.

T2. If a basis B consists of some but not all the predicates of a basis B', then $vB \leq vB'$.

T3. $v\{n\text{-pl}\} = v\{\text{not-more-than-}n\text{-pl}\}$.

T4. $v\{n \text{ 1-pl}\} \leq v\{n\text{-pl}\}$.

T4 may be regarded as a special case of a more general theorem which we now proceed to establish. This latter theorem does not occur in [6], but it is included here both for its own interest and for its usefulness in enabling us to prove further theorems.

T4′. Where all predicates are applicable, a set of predicates having a total of m places may always be replaced by a single m-pl predicate.

Proof

1) Let $P_1, P_2, \cdots, P_n$ be a set of predicates such that each is a not more than $(m\text{-}n + 1)$-pl predicate, for $m \geq n$. Let s_i be the number of places in P_i. Then:

$$\sum_{i=1}^{n} s_i = m.$$

We now prove that $P_1, P_2, \cdots, P_n$ may always be replaced by an m-pl predicate by a course of values induction on the variable m.

2) *Basis of the induction*

When $m = 1$, $n = 1$. Then a single 1-pl predicate may always be replaced by another, by extensional equivalence.

3) *Induction step*

For any arbitrary m, if a set of predicates having a total of k places may always be replaced by a single k-pl predicate, for every $k \leq m$, then a set of predicates having a total of m places may always be replaced by a single m-pl predicate. Let $P_i^{s_i}$ denote the ith predicate in the set with s_i places, for $i \geq 2$. If $i < 2$, then $P_i^{s_i}$ has m places, and is always replaceable by an m-place predicate. Now the set of predicates $P_1^{s_1}, P_2^{s_2}, \cdots, P_{n-1}^{s_{n-1}}$ is replaceable by a single predicate with $(m\text{-}s_n)$ places, by the induction hypothesis. Call this predicate Q^{m-s_n}. We now prove that the set of predicates $Q^{m-s_n}, P_n^{s_n}$ is always replaceable by a single m-pl predicate R^m, so explained that:

$$R^m(x_1, \cdots, x_m) \equiv Q^{m-s}{}_n(x_1, \cdots, x_{m-s_n}) \cdot P_n^{s_n}(x_{m-s_n-1}, \cdots, x_m)$$

We then retrieve Q and P as follows:

$$Q^{m-s_n}(x_1, \cdots, x_{m-s}) =_{\mathrm{df}} (\exists x_{m-s_n-1}) \cdots (\exists x_m) R^m(x_1, \cdots, x_m)$$

$$P_n^{s_n}(x_{m-s_n-1}, \cdots, x_m) =_{\mathrm{df}} (\exists x_1) \cdots (\exists x_{m-s_n}) R^m(x_1, \cdots, x_m)$$

Thus a set of predicates having a total of m places may always be replaced by a single m-pl predicate. T4′ enables us to establish T5 immediately.

T5. If $n < m$, then $v\{n\text{-pl}\} < v\{m\text{-pl}\}$.

Proof

1) Put $m = n + q$. Then $v\{n\text{-pl};\ q\text{-pl}\} \leq v\{n\text{-pl}\}$, by T4′. But $v\{n\text{-pl}\} < \{n\text{-pl};\ q\text{-pl}\}$, by P2. Hence $v\{n\text{-pl}\} < v\{m\text{-pl}\}$, for $n < m$.

The following theorems deal with reflexive predicates.

T6. $v\{\text{2-pl redundant}\} = v\{\text{1-pl}\} = c$

Proof

1) Let P be a redundant 2-pl predicate and Q a 1-pl predicate, such that $Qx = Px, x$. We retrieve P as follows:

$$Px, y =_{\mathrm{df}} Qx \cdot x = y.$$

Thus P is always replaceable by Q.

2) We now explain P in terms of Q as follows:

$$Px, y \equiv Qx \cdot x = y$$

and retrieve Q as follows:

$$Qx =_{\mathrm{df}} Px, x.$$

Thus Q is always replaceable by P.

3) Hence $v\{\text{2-pl redundant}\} = v\{\text{1-pl}\} = c$, by T1.

T7. $v\{\text{2-pl}\} = v\{\text{1-pl; 2-pl irref}\}$.

Proof

1) Let Rx, y denote a 2-pl not irreflexive and non-redundant predicate. Then the equivalence

$$Qx, y \equiv Rx, y \cdot x \neq y$$

establishes Q to be a 2-pl irreflexive predicate.

2) Let Px denote a 1-pl predicate. Then the equivalence

$$Px \equiv Rx, x$$

establishes the applicability of P.

3) We now define R in terms of Q and P as follows:

$$Rx, y =_{df} Qx, y \vee Px \cdot x = y$$

Thus a 2-pl not irreflexive, not redundant predicate is always replaceable by a basis consisting of a 2-pl irreflexive predicate and a 1-pl predicate.

4) Now let Qx, y denote a 2-pl irreflexive predicate and Px a 1-pl predicate. Introduce a 2-pl predicate R such that:

$$Rx, y \equiv Qx, y \vee Px \cdot x = y.$$

We retrieve Q and P as follows:

$$Qx, y =_{df} Rx, y \cdot x \neq y$$
$$Px =_{df} Rx, x.$$

Since R has, by the first definition, some non-identity pairs, it is not redundant, and since, by the second definition, it also has some identity pairs, it is not irreflexive. Then a basis consisting of a 2-pl irreflexive predicate and a 1-pl predicate may always be replaced by a 2-pl not irreflexive and not redundant predicate.

5) Thus, from 3) and 4) by T1, $v\{\text{2-pl not irref, not redundant}\} = v\{\text{2-pl irref; 1-pl}\}$.

6) A 2-pl not irreflexive predicate may be redundant or non-redundant. If redundant, $v\{\text{2-pl not irref}\} = v\{\text{1-pl}\}$, by T6. If non-redundant, $v\{\text{2-pl not irref}\} = v\{\text{2-pl irref; 1-pl}\}$, by step 5).

Thus $v\{\text{2-pl not irref}\} = H(v\{\text{2-pl irref; 1-pl}\}, v\{\text{1-pl}\})$.

But $v\{\text{2-pl irref; 1-pl}\} > v\{\text{1-pl}\}$, by T2.

Hence, $v\{\text{2-pl not irref}\} = v\{\text{2-pl irref; 1-pl}\}$.

7) A 2-pl predicate may be irreflexive or non-irreflexive. If irreflexive, $v\{\text{2-pl}\} = v\{\text{2-pl irref}\}$. If non-irreflexive, $v\{\text{2-pl}\} = v\{\text{2-pl irref; 1-pl}\}$, by step 6).

Thus $v\{\text{2-pl}\} = H(v\{\text{2-pl irref}\}, v\{\text{2-pl irref; 1-pl}\})$.

But $v\{\text{2-pl irref; 1-pl}\} > v\{\text{2-pl irref}\}$, by T2.

Hence, $v\{\text{2-pl}\} = v\{\text{2-pl irref; 1-pl}\}$. (G)

T8. $v\{$2-pl regular$\} = v\{$2-pl irref$\}$.

Proof

1) Let P be a 2-pl irreflexive predicate. Then P is always replaceable by a 2-pl irreflexive predicate, by extensional equivalence.

2) Let P now be a 2-pl redundant predicate. Then P is always replaceable by a 1-pl predicate, by T6.

3) Let P now be a totally reflexive 2-pl predicate.

Introduce a 2-pl predicate Q with the following explanation:

$$Qx, y \equiv Px, y \cdot x \neq y.$$

We retrieve P as follows:

$$Px, y =_{\text{df}} Qx, y \vee x = y.$$

Then P is always replaceable by a 2-pl irreflexive predicate.

4) Let P now be a left-reflexive 2-pl predicate, and let Q be explained as in 3). We retrieve P as follows:

$$Px, y =_{\text{df}} Qx, y \vee (\exists x)(Qy, z \cdot x = y).$$

Here Qy, z supplies the non-identity pairs and $x = y$ the identity pairs of left-hand elements in Q. Thus P is always replaceable by a 2-pl irreflexive predicate.

5) Let P now be a right reflexive 2-pl predicate, and let Q be explained as in 3). We retrieve P as follows:

$$Px, y =_{\text{df}} Qx, y \vee (\exists z)(Qz, y \cdot z = y).$$

Thus P is always replaceable by a 2-pl irreflexive predicate.

6) Let P now be a meet-reflexive 2-pl predicate, and let Q be explained as in 3). We retrieve P as follows:

$$Px, y =_{\text{df}} Qx, y \vee (\exists z)(\exists w)(Qx, z \cdot Qw, x \cdot x = y)$$

Thus P is always replaceable by a 2-pl irreflexive predicate.

7) Let P now be a join-reflexive 2-pl predicate, and let Q be explained as in 3). We retrieve P as follows:

$$Px, y =_{\text{df}} Qx, y \vee (\exists z)(Qx, z \vee Qz, x \cdot x = y).$$

Thus P is always replaceable by a 2-pl irreflexive predicate. We have now dealt with each of the regularly reflexive predicates.

8) Since the value of a kind is its maximum value, $v\{$2-pl regular$\} = H(v\{$1-pl$\}, v\{$2-pl irref$\})$.

9) But $v\{$2-pl regular$\} \geq v\{$2-pl regular, self-com$\}$. Let P and Q be 1-pl predicates and R a 2-pl regular self-complete predicate such that:

$$Rx, y \equiv Px \cdot Qy.$$

We retrieve P and Q as follows:

$$Px =_{\text{df}} (\exists y)Rx, y$$
$$Qy =_{\text{df}} (\exists x)Rx, y$$

Thus two 1-pl predicates may always be replaced by a 2-pl regular self-complete predicate.

10) But $v\{\text{two 1-pl}\} > v\{\text{1-pl}\}$, by T2. Thus, $v\{\text{2-pl regular}\} \geq v\{\text{2-pl regular, self com}\} \geq v\{\text{two 1-pl}\} > v\{\text{1-pl}\}$.

Hence, $v\{\text{2-pl regular}\} > v\{\text{1-pl}\}$.

11) Thus, from 8} and 10), $v\{\text{2-pl regular}\} = v\{\text{2-pl irref}\}$. (G)

T9. $v\{\text{2-pl irregular}\} = v\{\text{1-pl; 2-pl irref}\}$.

Proof

1) Each 2-pl predicate is regular or irregular. If regular, $v\{\text{2-pl}\} = v\{\text{2-pl irref}\}$, by T8. If irregular, let $v\{\text{2-pl}\} = V$.

2) Since the value of a kind is its maximum value, $v\{\text{2-pl}\} = H(v\{\text{2-pl irref}\}, V)$.

3) But $v\{\text{2-pl}\} = v\{\text{1-pl; 2-pl irref}\}$, by T7.

4) Thus, from 2) and 3), $v\{\text{1-pl; 2-pl irref}\} = H(v\{\text{2-pl irref}\}, V)$.

5) But, by T2, $v\{\text{1-pl; 2-pl irref}\} > v\{\text{2-pl irref}\}$.

Thus, $v\{\text{1-pl; 2-pl irref}\} = V$. Hence, $v\{\text{2-pl irregular}\} = v\{\text{1-pl; 2-pl irref}\}$. (G)

The following theorems deal with self-complete predicates. T10 is an immediate consequence of T11, which is now proved.

T11. $v\{n\text{-pl irref, self-com}\} = v\{n \text{ 1-pl}\} = nc$.

Proof

1) Let $R(x_1, x_2, \cdots, x_n)$ be an n-pl irreflexive, self-complete predicate, and $P_1, P_2, \cdots, P_n$ a set of 1-pl predicates, such that:

$$\begin{aligned} P_1x_1 &\equiv (\exists x_2)(\exists x_3)\cdots(\exists x_n)R(x_1, x_2, \cdots, x_n) \\ P_2x_2 &\equiv (\exists x_1)(\exists x_3)\cdots(\exists x_n)R(x_1, x_2, \cdots, x_n) \\ &\vdots \\ P_nx_n &\equiv (\exists x_1)(\exists x_2)\cdots(\exists x_{n-1})R(x_1, x_2, \cdots, x_n) \end{aligned}$$

We may redefine R as follows:

$$R(x_1, x_2, \cdots, x_n) =_{\text{df}} P_1x_1 \cdot P_2x_2 \cdot \cdots \cdot P_nx_n \cdot (x_1 \neq x_2 \neq \cdots \neq x_n).$$

Thus, $v\{n\text{-pl irref, self-com}) \leq v\{n \text{ 1-pl}\}$, by P1.

2) Now let $R(x_1, x_2, \cdots, x_n)$ be an n-pl regular,[10] self-complete predicate and $P_1, P_2, \cdots, P_n$ a set of 1-pl predicates, such that:

$$R(x_1, x_2, \cdots, x_n) \equiv P_1x_1 \cdot P_2x_2 \cdot \cdots \cdot P_nx_n.$$

[10] Note that the notion of regularity has now been extended to n-place predicates. Although the definitions make no mention of this, because of the enormous increase thus resulting in the number of different kinds of reflexivity, Goodman has outlined the methods to be used in dealing with n place regular predicates in [6], p. 713 and [7], p. 444, footnote 23.

We redefine n 1-pl predicates as follows:

$$P_1x_1 =_{df}(\exists x_2)(\exists x_3)\cdots(\exists x_n)R(x_1, x_2, \cdots, x_n)$$
$$\vdots \qquad\qquad \vdots$$
$$P_nx_n =_{df}(\exists x_1)(\exists x_2)\cdot(\exists x_{n-1})R(x_1, x_2, \cdots, x_n).$$

Thus, $v\{n \text{ 1-pl}\} \leq v\{n\text{-pl reg, self-com}\}$, by P1.

3) It remains now to show that:

$$v\{n\text{-pl reg, self-com}\} = v\{n\text{-pl irref, self-com}\}.$$

We prove first that the value of the kind of basis consisting of an n-pl regular predicate that applies only to those k-variegated sequences of a given pattern to which an n-pl regular (self-complete) predicate applies is that of a k-pl irreflexive self-complete predicate. The proof proceeds by a course of values induction on the variable k.

a) *Basis of the induction*

When $k = 1$, $v\{n\text{-pl reg}\} = v\{\text{1-pl}\}$, since all n-ads are here identity n-ads.

b) *Induction Step*

For any arbitrary k, if an n-pl regular predicate, applying to those p-variegated sequences of a given pattern to which an n-pl regular self-complete predicate applies, has the same value as a p-pl irreflexive, self-complete predicate, for every $p < k$, then an n-pl regular predicate, applying to the k-variegated sequences of the same n-pl regular self-complete predicate, has the same value as a k-pl irreflexive, self-complete predicate.

Let S be an n-pl p-variegated sequence of a regular self-complete predicate. Then, by the induction hypothesis, $vS = v\{p\text{-pl irref, self-com}\}$. Let T be an n-pl $(k\text{-}p)$-variegated sequence of the same predicate, differing from S in exactly k places. Since $k\text{-}p < k$, for $p > 0$, then by the induction hypothesis, vT is the same as $v\{(k\text{-}p)\text{-pl irref, self-com}\}$. However, $v\{p\text{-pl irref, self-com; } (k\text{-}p)\text{-pl irref, self-com}\} \leq v\{k\text{-pl irref, self-com}\}$, by T4′. Thus, any two sequences of an n-pl regular self-complete predicate that differ in exactly k places are always replaceable by a k-pl irreflexive self-complete predicate. Moreover, each pair of sequences so defined reduces to the k-variegated primary pattern of the n-pl regular predicate of the induction step. Thus, an n-pl regular predicate having one k-variegated primary pattern, as described above, may always be replaced by a k-pl irreflexive, self-complete predicate. But, by T5, a k-pl predicate may always be replaced by an n-pl predicate, for $k < n$, so that, by T1, the value of an n-pl regular predicate that applies only to those k-variegated sequences of a given pattern to which an n-pl regular self-complete predicate applies is that of a k-pl irreflexive self-complete predicate.

If the n-pl regular predicate now applies to the n-variegated sequences of a given pattern to which an n-pl regular self-complete predicate applies, then, by

D9, it is also self-complete. It follows immediately that: $v\{n\text{-pl reg, self-com}\} = v\{n\text{-pl irref, self-com}\}$.

4) $v\{n\text{-pl}\} \leq v\{n\text{-pl irref, self-com}\}$, from steps 2) and 3).

5) $v\{n\text{-pl irref, self-com}\} = v\{n \text{ 1-pl}\} = nc$, from steps 1), 4) and T1.

T10. $v\{\text{2-pl irref, self-com}\} = v\{\text{two 1-pl}\} = 2c$.

Proof

Immediate consequence of T11.

The next set of theorems deal with symmetrical predicates. T12 is a special case of the general theorem T13, which is accordingly proved first.

T13. $v\{n\text{-pl irref, self-com, sym}\} = c$.

Proof

1) Let R be an n-pl irreflexive, self-complete and symmetrical predicate. Then, $v\{\text{1-pl}\} \leq v\{n\text{-pl irref, self-com, sym}\}$.

2) Let N be the number of elements in the range of R. Since R is irreflexive, all its sequences will be n-variegated. Since R is also (first-level) self-complete, each partition of R is a one-place place-subsequence of R. Thus, every n-variegated sequence of elements taken in order from other n-variegated sequences of R is also a sequence of R. Since each sequence contains n distinct elements, there are $\binom{N}{n}$ sets of sequences containing n distinct elements. Let M_1, M_2, $\ldots$, $M_{\binom{N}{n}}$ denote the sets of the elements contained in each sequence. Let $T(x_i) = x_j$ define a transformation of the set M_p $(1 \leq p \leq \binom{N}{n})$. Then $x_j \in M_p$ is the map of $x_i \in M_p$ by T. Since R is symmetrical, $T(x_i) = x_j$ and $T(x_k) = x_j$ only if $x_i = x_k$, i.e. all transformations are 1-1. Let $S(M_p)$ denote the set of all 1-1 transformations of M_p. Then $S(M_p)$ is the symmetric group on n elements.

For each $S(M_p)$, now define $n!$ 1-pl predicates whose extensions are the $n!$ 1-1 transformations of $S(M_p)$ taken in some arbitrary order. We obtain in this way $\binom{N}{n} \times n!$ 1-pl predicates defined in terms of all the sequences of R, or, in other words, all the true singular sentences of R.

We now redefine R as the conjunction of all the $\binom{N}{n} \times n!$ 1-pl predicates. However, in carrying out this definition, we establish for each argument appearing in any place in one of the $\binom{N}{n} \times n!$ sentences of R that it also appears in each other place in some sentence or other. Thus, all the 1-pl predicates having an element of N as argument are extensionally identical.

Hence, by tautology, R is defined as any *one* of the 1-pl predicates. Thus: $v\{n\text{-pl irref, self-com, sym}\} \leq v\{\text{1-pl}\}$.

3) $v\{n\text{-pl irref, self-com, sym}\} = v\{1\text{-pl}\}$, from steps 1) and 2) by T1. That is, $v\{n\text{-pl irref, self-com, sym}\} = c$.

T12. $v\{2\text{-pl irref, self-com, sym}\} = c$.

Proof

This follows as an immediate consequence of T13.

T14. $v\{n$-pl irref, self-com with respect to a set of k-pl partitions and sym with respect to these$\} = v\{k\text{-pl irref}\}$.

Proof

1) Let R be an n-pl irreflexive predicate. Then all of its sequences are n-variegated. Let R be self-complete with respect to a set of separate and jointly exhaustive k-pl subsequences of its places and symmetrical with respect to these. Then each partition is of equal length and the number of partitions of R is the quotient of n and k. Two cases suffice to prove the theorem.

Case 1. When n is prime, then L.H.S. of T14 $= v\{k\text{-pl irref}\}$. (The expression "L.H.S." is here used as an abbreviation for "left-hand side".)

For all n, if n is prime, then its only factors are 1 and n. Hence, as k assumes the values 1 and n, the number of partitions of R becomes n and 1 respectively.

Now, an n-pl predicate with n partitions that is self-complete and symmetrical with respect to these is self-complete and symmetrical on the first level. Hence, its value is that of a 1-pl predicate, by T13. All partitions are, moreover, 1-pl, so that: $v\{n$-pl irref, self-com with respect to a set of 1-pl partitions and sym with respect to these$\} = v\{1\text{-pl}\}$.

An n-pl predicate with one partition has all n places in that partition. It is therefore degenerately self-complete and symmetrical with respect to this partition, and its value is that of an n-pl irreflexive predicate. Thus: $v\{n$-pl irref, self-com with respect to an n-pl partition and sym with respect to this$\} = v\{n\text{-pl irref}\}$.

We have now established case 1 by enumerating all the subcases whereby R, with a prime number n of arguments, has the same value as some k-pl irreflexive predicate, when each k is determinable as 1 or n.

Case 2. When n is composite, then L.H.S. of T14 $= v\{k\text{-pl irref}\}$.

a) For all n, if n is composite, then n has p distinct factors, $k_1, k_2, \cdots, k_p$. For each k_i, where $1 \leq i \leq p$, R possesses an n/k_i-membered set of k_i-pl partitions. Moreover, no k_i is 1 or n. Thus, each k_i is less than n. Then, by T5, a k_i-pl irreflexive predicate may always be replaced by an n-pl irreflexive predicate that is self-complete with respect to a set of k_i-pl partitions and symmetrical with respect to these for each k_i.

b) Let N be the number of elements in the range of R. Then there are $\binom{N}{n}$ sets of sequences of R containing n distinct elements. Now let $M_1, M_2, \cdots, M_{\binom{N}{n}}$

denote the sets of the elements contained in each sequence. Since R is symmetrical with respect to a set of k_i-pl partitions, all transformations are 1-1 with respect to k_i-ads of elements. Let $S(M_q)$ denote the set of all such 1-1 transformations of M_q. Then $S(M_q)$ is the symmetric group on n/k_i partitions.

For each $S(M_q)$ we define $(n/k_i)!k_i$-pl irreflexive predicates as follows:

$$P_1(x_1, \cdots, x_{k_i}) \equiv (\exists x_{k_i+1}) \cdots (\exists x_n) R(x_1, \cdots, x_{k_i}, x_{k_i+1}, \cdots, x_n)$$

$$P_2(x_1, \cdots, x_{k_i}) \equiv (\exists x_{k_i+1}) \cdots (\exists x_n) R(x_{k_i+1}, \cdots, x_{2k_i}, x_1, \cdots, x_{k_i}, x_{2k_i+1}, \cdots, x_{3k_i}, \cdots, x_{n-k_i+1}, \cdots, x_n)$$

successively down to P_{n/k_i}, where the k_i-ad $(x_1, \cdots, x_{k_i})$ occupies successively the first, second, $\cdots$, and finally the n/k_ith partition.

Since there are n-k_i bound variables in each predicate falling in partitions having k_i elements each, unre are (n/k_i)-1 partitions havin bound variables. Since R is self-complete with respect to these partitions, each predicate has $((n/k_i)\text{-}1)!$ true sentences. There are n/k_i predicates. We define in this way, therefore, n/k_i predicates that are k_i-variegated. Performed on each $S(M_q)$, this operation gives us $\binom{N}{n} \times (n/k_i)!k_i$-pl irreflexive predicates, for each k_i, defined in terms of all the true singular sentences of R.

We now redefine R as the conjunction of all the k_i-pl predicates. R is irreflexive and self-complete with respect to a set of k_i-pl partitions, and is also $(1, 2, \cdots, k_i)(k_i + 1, \cdots, 2k_i)(2k_i + 1, \cdots, 3k_i) \cdots (n\text{-}k_i + 1, \cdots, n)$ symmetrical. That is to say, R is also symmetrical with respect to the partitions with respect to which R is self-complete.

We have now shown that every k_i-ad that appears in any partition in one of the true sentences of R appears also in each other partition in some sentence or other. Thus, all the k_i-pl irreflexive predicates are extensionally identical.

Hence, by tautology, R may be defined as any one of the k_i-pl irreflexive predicates. Thus, $v\{n$-pl irref, self-com with respect to a set of k_i-pl partitions and sym with respect to these$\} \leq v\{k_i$-pl irref$\}$, for all k_i.

c) If n is composite, $v\{n$-pl irref, self-com with respect to a set of k-pl partitions, and sym with respect to these$\} = v\{k$-pl irref$\}$, from steps a), b) and T1.

2) Cases 1 and 2 together establish the theorem for all integral n. We may now prove three theorems concerning irreflexive predicates that are not self-complete.

T15a. If K and L are relevant kinds of n-pl irreflexive predicate, and differ at most in molecular symmetry, then $vK - vL = syL - syK$.

Proof

1) We first prove that the value of the kind of basis consisting of an n-pl irreflexive predicate with m minimal partitions is that of the kind of basis consisting of one irreflexive predicate for each of the m minimal partitions.

Let P be an n-pl irreflexive predicate with m minimal partitions $p_1, p_2, \cdots, p_m$. Let s_i be the number of places in p_i, for $1 \leq i \leq m$.

Then

$$\sum_{i=1}^{m} s_i = n.$$

Since P is irreflexive, we may now regard each p_i as the place-sequence of an s_i-pl irreflexive predicate. We may now show:

a) $v\{m\ s_i\text{-pl irref}\} \leq v\{n\text{-pl irref with } m \text{ minimal partitions}\}$. This follows immediately from T4′, since L.H.S. of a) constitutes a set of predicates having a total of n places.

b) $v\{n\text{-pl irref with } m \text{ minimal partitions}\} \leq v\{m\ s_i\text{-pl irref}\}$. Introduce m s_i-pl irreflexive predicates thus:

$$P_1(x_1, \cdots, x_{s_1}) \equiv (\exists x_{s_1+1}) \cdots (\exists x_n) R(x_1, \cdots, x_n)$$
$$P_2(x_{s_1+1}, \cdots, x_{s_1+s_2}) \equiv (\exists x_1) \cdots (\exists x_{s_1})(\exists x_{s_1+s_2+1}) \cdots (\exists x_n) R(x_1, \cdots, x_n)$$
$$\vdots \qquad\qquad \vdots$$
$$P_m(x_{s_1+s_2+\cdots+s_{m-1}+1}, \cdots, x_n) \equiv (\exists x_1) \cdots (\exists x_{s_1+s_2+\cdots+s_{m-1}}) R(x_1, \cdots, x_n.)$$

We now redefine R as the conjunction of $P_1, \cdots, P_m$. Then, an n-pl irreflexive predicate with m minimal partitions may always be replaced by m s_i-pl irreflexive predicates, the sum of whose places is n.

c) $v\{n\text{-pl irref with } m \text{ minimal partitions}\} = v\{m\ s_i\text{-pl irref}\}$, from steps a), b) and T1.

2. Now consider two kinds, K and L, of relevant n-pl irreflexive predicate that differ at most in molecular symmetry. It follows that $scK = scL$. That is, K and L have the same number of minimal partitions.

Let V be the value K and L, when all molecular symmetries are neglected. Then, if K and L have m minimal partitions each, $V = v\{m\ s_i\text{-pl irref}\}$, where

$$\sum_{i=1}^{m} s_i = n, \text{ from step 1).}$$

3) Let K be symmetrical with respect to a set of h k-pl partitions. Then, by step 2), there exist h k-pl irreflexive predicates such that each k-ad of places in one predicate appears in each other predicate. Hence, by extensional identity, the value of these h k-pl irreflexive predicates is that of a single k-pl irreflexive predicate. That is to say, if K is symmetrical with respect to a set of h k-pl partitions, then its value is reduced by $(h\text{-}1) \cdot v\{k\text{-pl irref}\}$. But this numerical expression represents the symmetry measure of a k-level stretch, and since every molecular symmetry of h partitions, for some given h, each having the value of an s-pl irreflexive predicate, for some fixed s, reduces V by $(h\text{-}1) \cdot v\{s\text{-pl irref}\}$, we have:

(A) $$vK = V - syK$$

when the symmetry measures of all stretches of K are taken into consideration.

4) Since K and L are the same kind, neglecting all molecular symmetries, and have the same number of minimal partitions, we also have:

(B) $$vL = V - syL.$$

5) Subtracting (B) from (A), we have:

$$vK - vL = syL - syK. \qquad \text{(G)}$$

T15.a1 If K and L are relevant kinds of n-pl irreflexive predicate, that differ at most in atomic symmetry, then $vK - vL = syL - syK$.

Proof

1) Since K and L differ at most in atomic symmetry, it follows that $scK = scL$. Thus, K and L have the same number of minimal partitions. Let V be the value of K and L, when all atomic symmetries are neglected. Then, if K and L have m minimal partitions each,

$$V = v\{m\ s_i\text{-pl irref}\}, \text{ for } \sum_{i=1}^{m} s_i = n.$$

2) Consider now any minimal partition p_i of K that is atomically symmetrical. The s_i-pl irreflexive predicate corresponding to p_i is now symmetrical with respect to $q(s_i/q)$-pl subsequences of p_i, where q is either 1, s_i or a divisor of s_i. For $q = 1$, p_i has zero atomic symmetry, while for $q = s_i$, p_i is fully symmetrical. In each case the value of the s_i-pl irreflexive predicate is diminished by its corresponding atomic symmetry measure, and for all minimal partitions that are atomically symmetrical we derive:

(A) $$vK = V - syK.$$

3) But K and L are the same kind, if we neglect all atomic symmetries, and, moreover, have the same number of minimal partitions, so that by identical reasoning we derive:

(B) $$vL = V - syL.$$

4) Subtracting (B) from (A), we have:

$$vK - vL = syL - syK.$$

T15a.2 If K and L are relevant kinds of n-pl irreflexive predicate and differ at most in symmetry, then $vK - vL = syL - syK$.

Proof

1) Let P, Q, R, K and L be relevant kinds of n-pl irreflexive predicate whose symmetry measures differ in the following way:

a) P, Q and R have zero molecular symmetry
b) K has the molecular symmetry measure m_1

c) L has the molecular symmetry measure m_2
d) Q has zero atomic symmetry
e) K and P have the atomic symmetry measure a_1
f) R and L have the atomic symmetry measure a_2

On the basis of a)–f) we may now say:

i) P differs from K only in having zero molecular symmetry
ii) R differs from L only in having zero molecular symmetry
iii) Q differs from L and R only in having zero molecular and zero atomic symmetry
iv) K differs from L in both molecular and atomic symmetry, which, *ex hypothesi*, is their only difference.

2) We now show that predicates of kinds P, Q and R, respectively, exist, consistent with the above specifications.

Since predicates of kinds K and L have, *ex hypothesi*, both atomic and molecular symmetries, then they possess partitions, and, in particular, minimal partitions. Thus the theorem deals with n-place irreflexive predicates that are self-complete at some level or other. To prove the existence of P, Q and R, it suffices now to show that there exist n-place irreflexive predicates differing only from K and L in self-completeness and symmetry. This is equivalent to constructing a relevant P, Q and R whose existence is clearly compatible with the conditions imposed on K and L.

Thus, consider an n-place irreflexive predicate that is $(1, 2)(3, 4)(5, \cdots, n)$ self-complete, and such that each of its three indicated partitions is minimal. Let the predicate be $(1)(2)$ symmetrical and $(3)(4)$ symmetrical, where these are its only symmetries. Then the predicate has atomic symmetries but no molecular symmetries. Thus a relevant kind of n-place irreflexive predicate is constructible, having zero molecular symmetry and a positive atomic symmetry measure, i.e. a predicate of kind P. P, moreover, is compatible with both K and L, i.e. the conditions imposed on K and L make possible the existence of P. Thus, there is at least one predicate of kind P.

Consider now an n-place irreflexive predicate that is $(1, 2)(3, 4)(5, \cdots, n)$ self-complete and thoroughly asymmetrical. Such a predicate is clearly constructible and is of the kind Q. Thus, Q exists as a relevant kind of predicate.

Consider, finally, an n-place irreflexive predicate that is $(1, 2)(3, 4)(5, \cdots, n)$ self-complete, and such that each indicated partition is minimal. Let the predicate be $(5)(6)$ symmetrical, where this is its only symmetry. Such a predicate is of the kind R. Thus, R exists as a relevant kind of predicate.

Since predicates of the relevant kinds P, Q and R may be constructed so as to be compatible with the existence of K and L, we are entitled to assume the existence of the relevant kinds P, Q and R. Since no data pertaining to P, Q and R, other than their symmetry measures, will be used in the proof, the theorem suffers no loss of generality.

3) Since P and K differ at most in molecular symmetry, $vP - vK = syK - syP$, by T15a.

4) Since Q and P differ at most in atomic symmetry,

$$vQ - vP = syP - syQ, \text{ by T15a.1.}$$

5) By addition of 3) and 4):

$$vQ - vK = syK - syQ.$$

6) Since R and L differ at most in molecular symmetry,

$$vR - vL = syL - syR, \text{ by T15a.}$$

7) Since Q and R differ at most in atomic symmetry,

$$vQ - vR = syR - syQ, \text{ by T15a.1.}$$

8) By addition of 6) and 7):

$$vQ - vL = syL - syQ$$

9) By subtraction of 5) from 8):

$$vK - vL = syL - syK. \qquad \text{(G)}$$

The next theorem is of crucial importance.

T16. If K, L, M, N are relevant kinds of n-pl irreflexive predicate, and $syK = syL$, and $syM = syN$, and $scK \leq scL$, and $scM \leq scN$, and $(vK - vL)/(vM - vN)$ is numerically determined by P1, P2 and P3a, then $(vK - vL)/(vM - vN) = (scL - scK)/(scN - scM)$.

Proof

1) Let $scK = r$, $scL = r + s$ (for s possibly zero), $scM = p$, and $scN = p + q$ (for q possibly zero). Now it has been established in T15a and T15a.1 that the value of an n-pl irreflexive predicate is the sum of the complexity values of the k-pl irreflexive subsequences ($1 \leq k \leq n$) with respect to which it is self complete, less the sum of its atomic and molecular symmetry measures. Since K and L have the same symmetry measures, then $vK - vL$ is representable as the difference of the sums of the values of the k-pl irreflexive predicates described above. That is, $vK - vL$ equals:

$$[v\{a_0 \text{ 1-pl}\} + v\{a_1 \text{ 2-pl irref}\} + \cdots + v\{a_{n-1}\ n\text{-pl irref}\}] -$$
$$[v\{b_0 \text{ 1-pl}\} + v\{b_1 \text{ 2-pl irref}\} + \cdots + v\{b_{n-1}\ n\text{-pl irref}\}],$$

where a_i and b_i are integers ($0 \leq a_i, b_i \leq n$), such that:

$$\sum_{i=0}^{n-1} a_i = r + 1 \quad \text{and} \quad \sum_{i=0}^{n-1} b_i = r + s + 1.$$

2) Since M and N have the same symmetry measures, then, by reasoning identical to that of step 1), we may put $vM - vN$ equal to:

$$[v\{c_0 \text{ 1-pl}\} + v\{c_1 \text{ 2-pl irref}\} + \cdots + v\{c_{n-1}\ n\text{-pl irref}\}] -$$
$$[v\{d_0 \text{ 1-pl}\} + v\{d_1 \text{ 2-pl irref}\} + \cdots + v\{d_{n-1}\ n\text{-pl irref}\}],$$

where c_i and d_i are integers ($0 \leq c_i, d_i \leq n$), such that:

$$\sum_{i=0}^{n-1} c_i = p + 1 \quad \text{and} \quad \sum_{i=0}^{n-1} d_i = p + q + 1.$$

3) By collecting like terms, $(vK - vL)/(vM - vN)$ equals:

$$[v\{a_o - b_o) \text{ 1-pl}\} + \cdots + v\{a_{n-1} - b_{n-1}) \text{ } n\text{-pl irref}\}]/$$
$$[v\{c_o - d_o) \text{ 1-pl}\} + \cdots + v\{c_{n-1} - d_{n-1}) \text{ } n\text{-pl irref}\}].$$

But $(vK - vL)/(vM - vN)$ is numerically determined by P1, P2 and P3a. Thus $(vK - vL)/(vM - vN) = g$, where g is a rational. Then both numerator and denominator are representable as products whose numerically undetermined factors are the same. However, in order to perform this factorization, the ratios of the constant terms of corresponding predicates must all be identical with g.

Thus we have:

$$(a_0 - b_0)/(c_0 - d_0) = \cdots = (a_{n-1} - b_{n-1})/(c_{n-1} - d_{n-1}) = g$$

4) But if the ratios of the constant terms equal g, then:

$$\sum_{i=0}^{n-1} (a_i - b_i) \Big/ \sum_{i=0}^{n-1} (c_i - d_i) = g.$$

Moreover,

$$\sum_{i=0}^{n-1} (a_i - b_i) = \sum_{i=0}^{n-1} a_i - \sum_{i=0}^{n-1} b_i = r + 1 - (r + s + 1) = -s,$$

and

$$\sum_{i=0}^{n-1} (c_i - d_i) = \sum_{i=0}^{n-1} c_i - \sum_{i=0}^{n-1} d_i = p + 1 - (p + q + 1) = -q.$$

Hence the numerical constant $g = -s/-q = s/q$.

5) But, from step 1), $scK = r$ and $scL = r + s$, so that $s = scL - scK$. Similarly from step 1), $q = scN - scM$.

Thus, $s/q = (scL - scK)/(scN - scM)$.

6) However, from step 3), $(vK - vL)/(vM - vN) = g = s/q$.

7) Hence, from steps 5) and 6),

$$(vK - vL)/(vM - vN) = (scL - scK)/(scN - scM).$$

The remaining theorems establish numerical values for various kinds of bases, and are thus of immediate interest in computing actual, quantitative complexity values for the extralogical bases of a given theory.

T17. $v\{n\text{-pl irref}\} = 2n - 1$.

Proof

1) Let P, Q, and R be relevant kinds of n-pl irreflexive predicates with zero atomic and molecular symmetry, specified as follows:

a) P is self-complete at no level
b) Q is first-level self-complete
c) R is:

i) self-complete with respect to $n/2$ 2-pl partitions, where n is even
ii) self-complete with respect to $(n\text{-}1)/2$ 2-pl partitions and one 1-pl partition, where n is odd.

2) As in T15a.2, the existence of auxiliary predicates of the kinds Q and R may be established as follows. A predicate of kind P applies only to fully-variegated sequences of the form $x_1, x_2, \cdots, x_n$. A predicate of kind Q applies to fully-variegated sequences, but is also $(1)(2)\cdots(n)$ self-complete, i.e. every fully-variegated sequence taken in order from other sequences of Q is also a sequence of Q. It is clear that Q requires no more elements in its range than those required for P. Thus P's existence is a sufficient condition for Q's existence. By inspection of the two cases for R, it is similarly seen that P's existence is a sufficient condition for R's existence, i.e. R requires no more elements than those belonging to the sequences of P.

3) We may now establish the theorem for a), b), ci) and a), b), cii), thus establishing it for all integral n.

Case I.

Since $syP = syQ = syR = 0$, and $scP < scQ$, $scR < scQ$, then, by P4:

$$(vP - vQ)/(vR - vQ) = (scQ - scP)/(scQ - scR).$$

Let $p = v\{n\text{-pl irref}\}$ and $q = v\{2\text{-pl irref}\}$.

Then, for any even n: $(vP - vQ)/(vR - vQ) = (p - nc)/(n/2 \cdot q - nc)$, from T11 and step 1) of T15a, and $(scQ - scP)/(scQ - scR) = (n - 1)/((n - 1) - (n/2 - 1))$, from R1.

Thus, $(p - nc)/(n/2 \cdot q - nc) = (n - 1)/((n - 1) - (n/2 - 1))$.

But, by P5, $c = 1$ and $q = 3$.

Hence, $(p - n)/(3n/2 - n) = (n - 1)/(n/2)$.

Thus, $(p - n)/(n/2) = (n - 1)/(n/2)$, so that $p - n = n - 1$.

Hence, $p = 2n - 1$.

Thus, for any even n, $v\{n\text{-pl irref}\} = 2n - 1$.

Case II.

As in Case I, P, Q, and R satisfy the conditions of P4, so that:

$$(vP - vQ)/(vR - vQ) = (scQ - scP)/(scQ - scR).$$

Let $p = v\{n\text{-pl irref}\}$ and $q = v\{2\text{-pl irref}\}$.

Then, for any odd n:

$$(vP - vQ)/(vR - vQ) = (p - nc)/(q \cdot (n - 1)/2 + c - nc),$$

from T11 and step 1) of T15a, and

$$(scQ - scP)/(scQ - scR) = (n - 1)/((n - 1) - (n - 1)/2),$$

from R1.

Thus, $(p - nc)/(q \cdot (n - 1)/2 + c - nc) = (n - 1)/((n - 1)/2)$.

But, by P5, $c = 1$ and $q = 3$.

Hence, $(p - n)/((n - 1)/2) = (n - 1)/((n - 1)/2)$, so that $(p - n) = (n - 1)$ giving $p = 2n - 1$.

Hence, for any odd n, $v\{n\text{-pl irref}\} = 2n - 1$.

4) For all integral n, $v\{n - \text{pl irref}\} = 2n - 1$, from cases I and II of step 1).

T18. $v\{n - \text{pl irref, self-com}\} = n$.

Proof

Immediate consequence of T11 and P5.

T19. $v\{n\text{-pl irref, sym}\} = n$.

Proof

1) Let P be an n-pl irreflexive predicate, with zero molecular and atomic symmetries, and R an n-pl irreflexive symmetrical predicate. We show first that P and R may co-exist.

R is symmetrical in the partition consisting of all of its places; P is asymmetrical. R has a level of self-completeness. It is clear that P may also be self-complete at some level, i.e. may possess partitions such that P has no symmetries with respect to these. Thus the existence of R does not exclude the existence of the auxiliary P.

2) Since P and R differ within minimal partitions (for R constitutes its own minimal partition), they differ at most in atomic symmetry. Thus, by P3a, $vP - vR = syR - syP$.

3) Let $p = v\{n\text{-pl irref, sym}\}$.

Then, $vP - vR = 2n - 1 - p$, by T17.

4) But, $syR - syP = (n - 1) \cdot c$, from $R1$, $R2$, and step 1).

Thus, $2n - 1 - p = (n - 1) \cdot c$.

5) By P5, $c = 1$, so that $p = n$.

Hence, $v\{n\text{-pl irref, sym}\} = n$.

T20. $v\{n\text{-pl irref, self-com, sym}\} = 1$.

Proof

Immediate consequence of T13 and P5.

T21. If K is a relevant kind of irreflexive n-pl predicate, then $vK = 2n - 1 - (syK + scK)$.

Proof

1) Let V be the value of K, when all symmetry measures are neglected. Then, by T15a and T15a.1, $vK = V - svK$.

To show that $vK = 2n - 1 - (syK + scK)$, it suffices now to show that $V = 2n - 1 - scK$.

2) Let $scK = n - k$, for $1 \leq k \leq n$. Then K is self-complete with respect to $n - k + 1$ partitions. If s_i denotes the number of places in the ith partition of K, then

$$\sum_{i=1}^{n-k+1} s_i = n.$$

3) Now from step 1) of T15.a, we have: $V = v\{(n - k + 1)\ s_i\text{-pl irref}\}$.
But, from T17, $v\{s_i\text{-pl irref}\} = 2s_i - 1$.

$$\text{Hence,} \quad V = \sum_{i=1}^{n-k+1} (2s_i - 1).$$

$$\text{But} \quad \sum_{i=1}^{n-k+1} (2s_i - 1) = 2\sum_{i=1}^{n-k+1} s_i - (n - k + 1).$$

$$\text{And} \quad \sum_{i=1}^{n-k+1} s_i = n, \text{ from step 2).}$$

Thus, $V = 2n - (n - k + 1) = 2n - 1 - (n - k)$.
But $(n - k) = scK$, from step 2).
Hence, $V = 2n - 1 - scK$.

4) Since $V = vK - syK$, from step 1), we have: $vK = 2n - 1 - (syK + scK)$, from step 3).

This last theorem enables us to compute the value of *any* n-pl irreflexive predicate, and is thus of maximum generality.

REFERENCES

The development of Goodman's views on simplicity may be traced in the following writings:

[1] "On the Simplicity of Ideas," *Journal of Symbolic Logic*, 8 (1943), pp. 107–121.
[2] "The Logical Simplicity of Predicates," *ibid.*, 14 (1949), pp. 32–41.
[3] "An Improvement in the Theory of Simplicity," *ibid.*, 14 (1949), pp. 228–229.
[4] *The Structure of Appearance*, 1951, pp. 59–85.
[5] "New Notes on Simplicity," *Journal of Symbolic Logic*, 17 (1952), pp. 189–191.
[6] "Axiomatic Measurement of Simplicity," *The Journal of Philosophy*, Vol. LII, No. 24, 1955, pp. 702–722.
[7] "Recent Developments in the Theory of Simplicity," *Philosophy and Phenomenological Research*, Vol. XIX, No. 4, 1959, pp. 429–446.

21 The Weight of Simplicity in the Construction and Assaying of Scientific Theories

MARIO BUNGE

Introduction

One of the most difficult and interesting problems of rational decision is the choice among possible diverging paths in theory construction and among competing scientific theories — i.e., systems of accurate testable hypotheses. This task involves many beliefs — some warranted and others not as warranted — and marks decisive crossroads. Suffice to recall the current conflict between the general theory of relativity and alternative theories of gravitation (e.g., Whitehead's) that account for the same empirical evidence, the rivalry among different interpretations of quantum mechanics (e.g., Bohr-Heisenberg's, de Broglie-Bohm's, and Landé's), and the variety of cosmological theories (e.g., Tolman's cyclical model and the steady-state theory). They all account for the same observed facts although they may predict different kinds of as yet unknown facts; they are consequently, up to now, *empirically equivalent* theories even though they are conceptually different and may even involve different philosophical views — i.e., they are *conceptually inequivalent.*

In effect, empirically equivalent theories may differ in many respects: in the kinds of entities and properties they postulate; in their logical organization and in their explanatory and predictive power; in their empirical testability and in their conformity with the bulk of scientific knowledge and with certain philosophical principles. These and other characteristics are dealt with by certain metascientific criteria that will be investigated in the following.

The set of metascientific criteria dealing with the various traits of acceptable scientific theories is what guides the choice among competing courses in theory construction and among the products of this activity. Now, simplicity is often listed among the requirements that scientific theories are supposed to satisfy, and is correspondingly offered as a, and sometimes as the, criterion for making a rational decision of choice among empirically equivalent theories.

Yet, simplicity is not of a single kind but, on the contrary, is a complex compound; furthermore, simplicity is not a characteristic isolated from other

From *Philosophy of Science*, Vol. 28, No. 2, April, 1961, pp. 120–149. Reprinted by permission of the Editor of *Philosophy of Science*, and the author.

properties of scientific systems, and it often competes with further desiderata, such as accuracy. Therefore, in order to assess the weight of simplicity in the construction and acceptance of scientific theory, we must discuss the kinds of simplicity and their relevance to the main characteristics of scientific theory (sec. 1), as well as their relevance to the truth of scientific theory (sec. 2) and to the acceptance of scientific theories in actual practice (sec. 3).

1. Species of Simplicity and Their Relevance to Systematicity, Accuracy and Testability

1.1. *Kinds of Simplicity*

Although the question whether reality itself is simple or not is a genuine issue in ontology and in science — as may be certified by any worker in microphysics — we are here concerned with the simplicity of the theories about sections of reality, so that we may disregard the ontological problem of the complexity of reality. Complex states of affairs may be accounted for by theories with a comparatively simple basis (e.g., classical mechanics), and on the other hand there will always be room for pedants capable of expressing simple situations (or, rather, situations requiring simple descriptions) in an unnecessarily complex way: as the Viennese joke goes, "*Warum denn einfach, wenn es auch kompliziert geht?*"

Now, a system of signs, such as a theory, may be complex (or simple) in various ways:[1] syntactically, semantically, epistemologically, or pragmatically. When speaking of the simplicity of sign systems we must therefore specify the kind of simplicity we have in mind. It will not do — save as a rough indication — to say that we mean *overall simplicity*, because owing to the extreme heterogeneity of its various components it may well turn out that the degrees of complexity in the various respects are not additive; just think of the syntactical complexity of a proposition, which depends among other things on the number of places of the predicates occurring in it, and of its epistemological complexity, or degree of abstractness (in the epistemological sense), which is such a hazy notion. Even if correct simplicity measures of theories were available, the problem of the metricization of their overall simplicity would have to be solved. Let us then carefully distinguish the various ways in which a system of meaningful signs (such as a scientific theory) can be said to be simple.

Syntactical simplicity (economy of forms) depends on (1) the number and structure (e.g., the degree) of the specific primitive concepts (basic extralogical predicates); (2) the number and structure of independent postulates, and (3) the rules of statement transformation. Syntactical simplicity is desirable be-

[1] Cf. Mario Bunge, "The Complexity of Simplicity", presented to the International Congress for Logic, Methodology, and Philosophy of Science (Stanford, 1960), *Jour. Phil.* LIX, 113 (1962). For a fuller analysis, see *The Myth of Simplicity* (Englewood Cliffs, N. J.: Prentice-Hall, 1963).

cause it is a factor of cohesiveness and, in a certain sense (but not in another), of testability — as will be seen shortly. *Semantical simplicity* (economy of presuppositions) depends on the number of specifiers of meaning of the basic predicates. Semantical simplicity is valued within limits because it facilitates both interpretation of signs and fresh starts. *Epistemological simplicity* (economy of transcendent terms) depends on closeness to sense-data. Epistemological simplicity is not desirable in and of itself, because it conflicts with logical simplicity and with depth. Finally, *pragmatical simplicity* (economy of work) may be analyzed into (1) psychological simplicity (intelligibility), (2) notational simplicity (economy and suggestive power of symbols), (3) algorithmic simplicity (ease of computation), (4) experimental simplicity (feasibility of design and interpretation of empirical tests), and (5) technical simplicity (ease of application to practical problems). Pragmatical simplicity is, of course, valued for practical reasons.

No dependable measure of any of the four above-mentioned kinds of simplicity of sign systems is known at present. Even the gauges of the syntactical simplicity of predicate bases proposed so far[2] do not do justice to metrical predicates, such as 'age' and 'distance', which are in a sense "infinitely" more complex than classificatory concepts (presence/absence predicates) such as 'liquid'. And the proposal of measuring the structural complexity of equations by the number of adjustable parameters in them[3] is insufficient, since other formal properties are relevant as well, and because it involves a confusion of formal complexity with difficulty of test, with generality, and with derivativeness (as opposed to fundamentality).[4] At any rate, none of these proposals deals with systems of propositions and none of them account for the various kinds of simplicity, whence they are inadequate to cope with our problem.

Moreover, *the various kinds of simplicity are not all compatible with one another and with certain desiderata of science.* Thus, a syntactical oversimplification of the basis (e.g., a drastic reduction of the number of primitives and principles) may entail both difficulties of interpretation and lengthy deductions. A semantical oversimplification may involve the severance of the given theory with the remaining body of knowledge — i.e., a loss of systematicity in the sum total of science. An epistemological simplification, such as the elimination of transcendent (transempirical) terms is not only a guarantee of superficiality

[2] Adolphe Lindenbaum, "Sur la simplicité formelle des notions", *Actes du Congrès International de Philosophie Scientifique* (Paris: Hermann, 1936), VII, 28. Nelson Goodman, *The Structure of Appearance* (Cambridge, Mass.: Harvard University Press, 1951), ch. iii, and "Axiomatic Measure of Simplicity", *Jour. Phil.*, *52*, 709 (1955). John G. Kemeny, "Two Measures of Complexity", *Jour. Phil.*, *52*, 722 (1955). Horst Kiesow, "Anwendung eines Einfachheitsprinzip auf die Wahrscheinlichkeitstheorie", *Archiv. f. Math. Logik u. Grundlagenforschung*, *4*, 27 (1958).

[3] Dorothy Wrinch and Harold Jeffreys, "On Certain Fundamental Principles of Scientific Inquiry", *Phil. Mag. 42*, 369 (1921); Harold Jeffreys, *Theory of Probability*, 2nd ed. (Oxford: Clarendon Press, 1948), p. 100. Karl R. Popper, *The Logic of Scientific Discovery* (1935; London: Hutchinson, 1959), secs. 44 to 46, and *Appendix VIII. John G. Kemeny, "The Use of Simplicity in Induction", *Phil. Rev. 62*, 391 (1953). [Ed. note: See page 309 in this volume for the Kemeny article.]

[4] Mario Bunge, reference 1.

but also of an infinite complication of the postulate basis.[5] Finally, a pragmatical oversimplification may involve a loss of insight. Consequently, it would be unwise to recommend overall simplicity even if we had an accurate concept of overall simplicity.

Truth, however difficult may be its philosophical elucidation, is the target of scientific research; hence to truth all other desiderata — including some simplicities — must be subordinated. Now, truth is not obviously related to simplicity, but to complexity. The syntactical, semantical, epistemological, and pragmatical complexity of scientific theories usually increases with their scope, accuracy, and depth, until a point is reached where complexity of some kind becomes uncontrollable and obstrusive to further progress, and simplification in some respects and within bounds is called for.

But only those simplifications will be admitted in science which render the theory more manageable, more coherent, or better testable: no simplification will be accepted if it severely cuts down either those characteristics or the depth, the explanatory power, or the predictive power of the theory. The complexity of the task of truth-preserving simplifications — which are possible only in advanced stages of theory construction[6] — can be estimated if it is recalled that economy, not poverty, is wanted. That is, we do not want mere parsimony — which is best achieved by abstaining from theorizing — but minimization of the means/ends ratio.[7] Not a simple-minded elimination of complexities is required, but a cautious reduction of redundancies, a sophisticated simplification in some respects, under the condition that it does not detract from truth.

Let us inquire what contribution, if any, logical simplicity makes to the coherence, accuracy, and testability of scientific theory, since these are three necessary conditions for something to be a scientific theory, even before it can be regarded as approximately true.

1.2. *Relevance of logical simplicity to systematicity*

Theories are *systems* of hypotheses (corrigible propositions) containing extralogical concepts that range over a specified universe, i.e., that refer to a definite subject matter. Systems are, of course, sets of interrelated units, and the cohesion of scientific theories — in contrast with the looseness of the heaps of conjectures and data we so often find in nonscience and in underdeveloped science — is ensured by (1) exact formulation, (2) distribution of the basic concepts among the various basic propositions (axioms), and (3) economy of basic concepts. Let us be more explicit.

[5] William Craig, "Replacement of Auxiliary Expressions", *Phil. Rev.*, *65*, 38 (1956).

[6] Cf. Wilhelm Ostwald, *Grundriss der Naturphilosophe* (Leipzig: Reclam, 1908), p. 127: simple formulas to express laws of nature can be found only when the conceptual analysis of phenomena is quite advanced.

[7] Cf. Ernst Cassirer, *Determinismus und Indeterminismus in der modernen Physik* (Göteborg: Elanders 1937), p. 88, being no. 3, vol. XLII, of *Göteborgs Högskolas Arsskrift* (1936).

(1) *Logical neatness, or exact formulation of the postulates.* Loosely stated propositions can only loosely be tied together. No definite deductions are possible from vaguely worded basic assumptions; no neat distinction between axioms and observable consequences can then be made, whence no empirical datum will be strictly relevant to either. Syntactical accuracy, a prerequisite of empirical meaning and testability, is automatically achieved by mathematical formulation (this being a major and seldom noticed reason why mathematical models are sought); and semantical exactness is improved — though probably never ensured in a complete way — by the explicit and accurate statements of the rules of meaning. Where ambiguity and vagueness reign an army of scholiasts is invited to start a scholastic movement, and a manifold of theories instead of a single system readily emerge.

(2) *Conceptual connectedness, or sharing of basic concepts among postulates.* An instance of an extremely unsystematic set of mutually independent postulates would be

$$\ldots C_1 \ldots, \quad \ldots C_2 \ldots, \quad \ldots, \quad \ldots C_6 \ldots, \tag{1}$$

in which none of the basic or primitive predicates C_1 through C_6 occurs in more than one axiom. A slightly more organized system would be

$$C_1\text{–}C_2, \quad C_3\text{–}C_4, \quad C_5\text{–}C_6, \tag{2}$$

where '–' stands for ordinary and logical words tying the basic concepts together. An even better organized system would be the chain-like set

$$C_1\text{–}C_2, \quad C_2\text{–}C_3, \quad C_3\text{–}C_4, \quad C_4\text{–}C_5, \quad C_5\text{–}C_6. \tag{3}$$

An equivalent connectedness would be provided by the single postulate

$$C_1\text{–}C_2\text{–}C_3\text{–}C_4\text{–}C_5\text{–}C_6; \tag{4}$$

but, of course, such a unification at the propositional level is not always possible: it may not correspond to actual fact.

In the four cases the axioms are mutually independent on condition that the basic predicates themselves be mutually independent (as tested, for example, by Padoa's method).[8] But in the first case we have a loose aggregate of postulates, no matter how precisely they are formulated, and in the second case we have a partial connectedness of primitives, whereas in the last two cases the tightness of the conceptual connection is obvious.

Notice that increase in conceptual connectedness need not result in simplification of the postulational basis: (3) and (4) are equally coherent at the conceptual level; only postulational economy is gained by (4). In general, postulational simplification, if it preserves the predicate basis, is sufficient but not necessary for achieving conceptual cohesiveness, which is in turn necessary for having system. But postulational simplification is not a mechanical procedure: its feasibility depends on the nature of the case, i.e. on whether there

[8] Cf. Patrick Suppes, *Introduction to Logic* (Princeton: Van Nostrand, 1957), p. 169.

is in fact a direct connection among all the properties denoted by the predicates involved.

(3) *Simplicity of the predicate basis.* The less the number of primitive concepts of the theory, the larger the number of bridges among them and the derived concepts (definitions and theorems) will have to be; as a consequence, the greater will be the conceptual and propositional connectedness of the theory. (This is one reason for adopting a variational principle as the sole postulate of many physical theories: it effects maximum conceptual unification, although its interpretation and status is far from simple.) In short, economy of the predicate basis improves systematicity.[9]

Notice, however, that formal simplicity of the basis is just *one* of three *means* for achieving the desideratum of systematicity. In the second place, the simplification of the predicate basis of factual theories has a limit which is rooted to the real net of properties; thus, e.g., at the present time, at least the following properties of fundamental particles are regarded as mutually irreducible (though connected), hence as not interdefinable: location in space-time, mass, electric charge, spin, and parity. In the third place, a large number of basic concepts does not prevent an exact treatment, since mathematical techniques enable us to handle as large a number of variables as desired; moreover, it is often desirable to *increase* the number of variables to infinity in order to attain a deeper level of analysis (by handling, e.g., the Fourier transforms of the original variables, as is done in field theories). What is important is not to minimize the number of predicates — as required by phenomenalism ever since Kirchhoff — but *to keep them under control.*

In short, simplicity of the predicate basis is *sufficient but not necessary* for systematicity; moreover, simplification of the predicate bases of factual theories is limited by the richness of reality and by pragmatical (e.g., methodological) considerations.

1.3. *Relevance of logical simplicity to accuracy and testability*

Testability, a second outstanding feature of scientific theory, depends on systematicity. In effect, the latter is not merely a question of economy and elegance: a theory, whether formal or factual, has to be a tightly knit set of propositions if it is to be testable *as such*, i.e. as a unit. A dough of vague assumptions all standing on the same logical level, without strong logical relations of deducibility occurring in its body, cannot be tested the way genuine theories are: since all of the propositions of the pseudotheory are loosely related to one another, every one of them will face separately the trials of logic and/or experience. How could we test the axioms of a factual theory if we cannot spot their logical consequences? A chaotic mass of conjectures lacking logical organization — as is the case with psychoanalysis[10] — cannot be subjected to the test of

[9] Nelson Goodman, reference 2, has argued most persuasively in favor of this thesis.

[10] Cf. H. J. Eysenck, *Uses and Abuses of Psychology* (London: Penguin, 1953), ch. 12. Ernest Nagel, "Methodological Issues in Psychoanalytic Theory", in S. Hook (ed.), *Psychoanalysis, Scientific Method, and Philosophy* (New York: New York University Press, 1959), ch. 2.

experience as a whole: experience may at most confirm some of the loosely related conjectures of the pseudotheory, but no evidence will ever conclusively refute the whole set of vaguely stated *ad hoc* hypotheses — especially if they are mutually shielding. And a theory which stands no matter what experience may say, is not an empirical theory.

Logical neatness and conceptual connectedness are then not luxuries but *means for ensuring testability*, which in turn is a necessary — but, of course, not a sufficient — prerequisite for attaining approximate truth. Notice that simplicity of the predicate basis is favorably relevant to testability to the extent to which it is propitious to systematicity; but recall that this kind of simplicity, though sufficient, is not necessary for attaining systematicity, as the same goal can be attained by means of conceptual connectedness.

Again, systematicity is necessary but not sufficient to ensure testability: *accuracy* and *scrutability* of the basic predicates are necessary as well. The more exact a statement is, the easier it will be to dispose of it; vagueness and ambiguity — the secret of the success of fortune-tellers and politicians — are the best protections against refutation. Now, *accuracy demands complexity*, both formal and semantic: suffice to compare the simplicity of presystematic, ordinary, discourse with the complexity of scientific discourse; compare 'small' with 'of the order of one atomic diameter', and '$x > a$' with '$x = a$'. Not just the simplest but the simplest among *equally precise* propositions and systems is to be preferred, both because accuracy is an independent desideratum of science, and because it favors testability.

Scrutability of the basic predicates is a further, obvious, condition for testability. The basic predicates of a scientific theory need not be observable or measurable in a direct way (few of them are). Only, they must be open to public scrutiny by the method of science, and for this it is necessary and sufficient that the theory establishes exact relations among its basic predicates and observable predicates. Terms such as 'élan vital', 'infantile sexuality', 'absolute space', and the like, do not make up testable sentences, whence they must be dropped.

If desired, this norm of scrutability may be called the principle of methodological simplicity — on condition that it be realized that it is not necessarily related to other kinds of simplicity, such as formal economy of the predicate basis. A theory containing a large number of scrutable predicates will be preferable to another theory containing fewer predicates but all or part of them inscrutable, if only because the former theory will be testable, unlike the latter. The *methodological status* of the predicate basis is far more important than its logical structure and number. Thus, 'electrically charged' is both syntactically and semantically more complex than 'providential', yet it is scrutable and may consequently occur in scientific theory, whereas the latter cannot. In short, accuracy and scrutability may be consistent with logical complexity. When this is the case we are ready to sacrifice simplicity.

On the other hand, an excessive logical complexity may obstruct testability, and particularly refutability,[11] this being the reason logical simplicity is desirable as long as it does not involve loss of accuracy, scope, and depth. Irrefutability may be achieved through the mutual protection of hypotheses containing inscrutable predicates. This can be performed in a commonsensical or in a technical way. An example of the former is the theory of extrasensory perception, in which every instance unfavorable to the hypothesis of telepathic transmission can be regarded as favorable to the hypothesis of precognition, or to the hypothesis that the subject has become tired by exerting his supernatural powers. An instance of achievement of irrefutability with more impressive means is any phenomenological theory containing a number of adjustable parameters, and designed to account for phenomena *ex post facto* without risking any assumption on the mechanism involved. (Thus, e.g., the phenomenological theory of nuclear forces is allowed to introduce a number of parameters which are not independently measurable and which can be freely varied within generous limits; moreover, the observable consequences of the theory are largely insensitive to qualitative variations in the shapes and depths of the potential wells. This is one of the reasons for preferring, as a description of reality, the meson theory of nuclear forces, which involves a definite mechanism.)

The requirement of testability leads in the long run either to shave off the mutually shielding hypotheses, or to an entirely fresh start. In the former case a simplification is performed — but, then, few confirming instances may remain; in the latter case the theory ensuing from the new look may be simpler or more complex, but in any case it will be more detailed and consequently more daring than the timorous phenomenological theory (which, if empirically validated, will be useful as a control of new, deeper, theories). At any rate, the falsity of simple theories is usually easier to expose than the falsity of complex theories, on condition that they are falsifiable at all. Parsimony in the number of empirically adjustable parameters is not the seal of truth, but the abortive of falsity.

1.4. *Simplicity, likelihood, and truth*

The simpler theories are easier tested both by experience and by further theories, i.e. by inclusion in or fitting with contiguous systems. Syntactical and semantical simplification are, then, sufficient to improve testability even though they are not strictly necessary to secure it. Yet, there is as great a distance between *testable* and *tested*, as there is between a promise and its fulfilment. Syntactical and semantical simplicity are relevant to the likelihood of scientific theories in so far as they are factors of both systematicity and testability. But the assessment of the degree of *likelihood* of a theory is one thing, and the estimate of its degree of *corroboration* is another: the latter is done *a posteriori*, after certain tests have been given — and these include empirical corroboration, checking

[11] Karl R. Popper, *The Logic of Scientific Discovery* (1935; London: Hutchinson, 1959), sections 44 to 46, and *Appendix VIII.

of compatibility with the bulk of relevant knowledge, and checking of explanatory power. It is only in the *prior* estimate of the likelihood of a theory that considerations of simplicity can legitimately arise, and this in an indirect way, namely, through the contribution of simplicity to systematicity and testability.

Once a theory has been accepted as the truest available, we do not care much for its simplicity. It will not do to argue that this is because simplicity has already been built into the theory during its construction: as we have seen, epistemological simplicity is inconsistent with depth and with formal simplicity, and the latter is inconsistent with accuracy, which is not only a desideratum in itself but also a condition for testability.

Nor will probability save the thesis that simplicity is necessary for truth, as is held by the theory according to which the simpler theories are the more probable because the basis of every theory consists in the conjunction of a number of axioms, and the less the number of members that occur in the conjunction the greater will be its total probability (equal to the product of the probabilities of the single axioms). The inadequacy of this theory is patent: (1) it does not apply to theories containing at least one strictly universal law statement, since the probability of universal laws is exactly zero; (2) it is not the simplest but the more complex hypotheses which are the easier to fit with empirical data: think of a wavy line passing through or near all the dots representing empirical data on a coordinate plane, as contrasted with a syntactically simpler curve, such as a straight line; it is unlikely that a large number of empirical "points" lie on a simple curve. It is the more complex hypotheses — especially if devised *ex post facto* and *ad hoc* — which are *a priori* the more probable.[12] In short, simplicity is incompatible with a high *a priori* probability.

In summary, syntactical and semantical simplicity are, within limits, favorably relevant to systematicity and testability — not to accuracy and truth; yet, they are not necessary conditions of systematicity and testability.

Now, any number of testable systems can be invented to cope with a given set of empirical data; the question is to hit on the *truest* one — a scientific problem — and to *recognize the signs* of approximate truth — a metascientific problem. For, indeed, truth is not the unveiling of what had been occult, as the pre-Socratics and Heidegger have claimed: truth is made, not found, and to diagnose truth is as hard as to diagnose virtue. We have a working theory of the complete (not the approximate) truth of sentences involving only observational predicates,[13] but we have no satisfactory theory of the *approximate* truth of *theories.* To say that a factual theory is true if and only if its observable consequences are true and none is false, is inadequate not only because the theory may contain untestable assumptions and yet be consistent with observable facts, but also because there is no means of exhaustively testing the infinity of consequences (theorems) of quantitative scientific theories, and because the notion of approximate truth is involved in them.

[12] Cf. Hermann Weyl, *Philosophy of Mathematics and Natural Science* (1927; Princeton: Princeton University Press, 1949), p. 156, and Popper, reference 11.

[13] Alfred Tarski, "The Semantic Conception of Truth", *Phil. and Phenom. Res.*, *4*, 341 (1944).

Furthermore, we should know by now that all factual theories are, strictly speaking, false: that they are more or less approximately true. No decision procedure for recognizing the approximate truth of factual theories is available, but there are *symptoms* of truth, and the expert employs these signs in the evaluation of theories. Let us review these symptoms of truth and find out what simplicities, if any, are relevant to them.

2. Desiderata of Scientific Theory, or Symptoms of Truth

At least five groups of symptoms of the truth of factual theories can be distinguished: they may be called syntactical, semantical, epistemological, methodological, and philosophical. Each symptom gives rise to a criterion, or norm, occuring in the actual practice of weighing factual theories before and after their empirical test, in order to ascertain whether they constitute an improvement on competing theories, if any. We shall call them *assaying criteria.* They are the following twenty.

2.1. *Syntactical requirements*

(1) *Syntactical correctness.* The propositions of the theory must be well-formed and mutually consistent if they are to be processed with the help of logic, if the theory is to be meaningful, and if it is to refer to a definite domain of facts. Syntactically crippled sets of signs, on the other hand, cannot be logically handled; they cannot be unambiguously interpreted either, and if they contain internal contradictions they may lead to a sterile multiplicity of irrelevant statements. Yet, every theory is somewhat muddled in its preliminary stages; therefore, *rough* syntactical correctness, and definite *possibility* of formal improvement, are more realistic criteria than final formal neatness — which may anyhow not be attainable.

Simplicity is obviously not a factor of syntactical correctness; on the other hand, simplicity facilitates the *test* of syntactical correctness.

(2) *Systematicity or conceptual unity.* The theory must be a unified conceptual system (i.e., its concepts must "hang together") if it is to be called a theory at all, and if it is to face empirical and theoretical tests as a whole — i.e., if the test of any of its parts is to be relevant to the remainder of the theory, in such a way that a judgment can eventually be passed about the corroboration or falsification of the theory as a whole.

As we saw before (sec. 1.2), simplification of the predicate basis of the theory is sufficient to improve systematicity, but is not necessary for attaining it and cannot be forced beyond bounds which are partly set by the theory's referent (e.g., an aspect of nature). Furthermore, the historical trend of science has not been the shrinking but the expansion of the predicate bases, along with the establishment of more and more connections — mainly by way of law statements — among the various predicates. A progressive conceptual enrichment coped with an increasing logical cohesion or integration is the tendency of science — not a unification by impoverishment.[14]

[14] Mario Bunge, *Causality* (Cambridge, Mass.: Harvard University Press, 1959), pp. 290–1.

2.2. *Semantical requirements*

(3) *Linguistic exactness.* The ambiguity, vagueness, and obscurity of the specific terms must be minimal to ensure the empirical interpretability and the applicability of the theory. This requirement disqualifies theories in which terms such as 'big', 'hot', 'psychical energy', or 'historical necessity', occur essentially.

Now, the elimination of such undesirables has little to do with simplification. Clarification is more often accompanied by complication or, at least, by showing an actual complexity underneath an apparent simplicity. Hence, simplicity is unfavorably relevant to linguistic exactness, or at most irrelevant to it.

(4) *Empirical interpretability.* It must be possible to derive from the theory's assumptions — in conjunction with bits of specific information — statements that could be compared with observational statements, so as to decide the theory's conformity with fact.

Simplicity is clearly unfavorably relevant to this desideratum, since an abstract theory is simpler than an interpreted system.

(5) *Representativeness.* It is desirable that the theory represents or, rather, reconstructs actual events and processes, and not merely describes them and predicts their observable gross effects. In order to be representational — as opposed to phenomenological — a theory need not be pictorial, visualizable, or intuitable (although these characteristics warrant representativeness). It is sufficient that some of the symbols occurring in the postulates of the theory be assigned a literal meaning by being correlated with actual and essential (diaphenomenal) properties of the theory's referent. In other words, for a theory to be representational it is sufficient that some of its basic predicates be assumed to represent real and fundamental — not merely external — traits of actual entities.

In the course of the growth of science phenomenological or nonrepresentational theories have been replaced or at least supplemented by representational theories, which attempt to offer descriptions and explanations in agreement with reality (Einstein's *Realbeschreibung*). Thus, theories of action at a distance were replaced by field theories, thermodynamics was supplemented by statistical mechanics, circuit theory by electron theory, synoptic by dynamic meteorology, simple evolution theories by the theory of evolution through natural selection.

There are various reasons for preferring representational to phenomenological theories: (*a*) a major aim of investigators is not just "to save appearances" in an economical way (conventionalism, phenomenalism, pragmatism), but to attain a deep understanding of facts, both observed and unobserved — and this purpose is served better by representational than by phenomenological theories; (*b*) representational theories satisfy better the requirement of external consistency, whereas phenomenological theories are *ad hoc*; (*c*) representational theories, not being limited to the empirical data at hand, are more apt to predict facts of an unknown, otherwise unexpected, kind; (*d*) representational theories take more risks than phenomenological theories: by saying more they comply better with the requirement of refutability.

Now, a strict adherence to the rules of logical and epistemological simplicity would require us to dispense with representational theories, since these usually involve not only the predicates of the related phenomenological systems but further, more abstract, predicates of their own. We would have to drop hundreds of working theories, among them the shell model of the atomic nucleus, the spin theory of ferromagnetism, and the chromosomic theory of heredity. Here, again, simplicity is not welcome.

(6) *Semantical simplicity*. It is desirable, up to a point, to economize presuppositions; in this way empirical statements can be made and tested without presupposing the whole of science. This requirement is imposed in a moderate way and on pragmatical rather than on theoretical grounds, since it amounts to the possibility of approaching the new without having to master the old in its entirety. But external consistency, which is even weightier, competes with semantical simplicity. Thus conventional biology, which is methodologically "mechanistic", complies with external consistency and, by the same token, it is semantically complex since it presupposes physics and chemistry; on the other hand, vitalistic biology is semantically simpler but fails to be continuous with physics and chemistry.

The theoretical value of semantical simplicity lies in that it suggests the existence of objective levels of organization of reality. Thus, the mere possibility of talking meaningfully about some aspects of life, psyche, and culture, without expressly dealing with their material bases, shows that levels are to to some extent autonomous; but the requirement of depth will always end by forcing us to discover the links of events on one level to events on contiguous levels, and particularly on the lower ones.[15]

Semantical simplicity is, in short, an ambiguous rule: it may render the handling (e.g., the test) of the theory possible, but it may also be a symptom of superficiality.

2.3. *Epistemological requirements*

(7) *External consistency*. The theory must be consistent with the bulk of accepted knowledge if it is to have the support of more than just its instances, and if it is to be regarded as an addition to knowledge and not as an extraneous body. Revolutionary theories — in contradistinction to deviant or crackpot theories — are inconsistent with only a part of scientific knowledge, for the very criticism of old theories and the construction of new ones is performed on the basis of definite knowledge and in the light of more or less explicitly stated norms. Isolated heterodoxies do not imperil the bulk of established (yet provisional) knowledge; quite on the contrary, we question isolated theories in the light of accepted knowledge and rules of procedure.

[15] Cf. Mario Bunge, "Levels: A Semantical Preliminary", *Rev. Metaphys.*, *13*, 396 (1960), and "On the Connections Among Levels", *Proc. XIIth. Intern. Congr. Phil.* (Firenze: Sansoni, 1960), VI, 63.

External consistency was the strongest argument Copernicus advanced in support of his theory of planetary motions; he pointed out that, unlike Ptolemy's theory, his own accorded with the axioms of the prevailing physical theory (Aristotle's), which ruled that celestial bodies moved in circular paths[16]. The remarkable contradiction of *ESP* and other supernatural theories with the bulk of science is also — along with methodological reasons — a major ground for rejecting them.[17]

Simplicity is clearly unfavorable to external consistency, since the latter imposes a growing multiplicity of connections among the various chapters of science.

(8) *Explanatory power*. The theory must solve the problems set by the explanation of the facts and the empirical generalizations, if any, of a given domain, and must do it in the most exact possible way. To put it briefly, *Explanatory power* = *Range* × *Accuracy*. But the range of a theory cannot increase beyond every bound: a scientific theory cannot pretend to solve every problem, under penalty of becoming irrefutable.[18] In particular, a scientific theory must be single-edged, that is, it must not be capable of supporting contrary (e.g., contradictory) hypotheses or proposals, and it must not be consistent with contrary pieces of evidence. (A hypothesis, if self-consistent, and exactly formulated, cannot be compatible with contrary pieces of evidence; a pseudotheory can, provided its hypotheses are mutually shielding.) Both the theory of predestination and psychoanalysis, which offer explanations for everything human and are never embarrassed by contrary evidence, violate this condition. As regards range, the explanatory power of scientific theories is intermediate between the explanatory power of pseudoscientific theories and that of commonsensical theories.

It is clear that simplicity is unfavorable to explanatory power, because a wide range is a class of numerous subclasses, each intensionally characterized by a set of properties, and because accuracy, the second factor of explanatory power, requires complication as well (cf. 1.3). Thus, inequalities are simpler than equalities: they are simpler to define, to establish, and to test. Yet we are often ready to sacrifice simplicity for accuracy, as shown by the fact that numerical and functional equations are the more abundant the greater the severity of the standards of accuracy and testability become. In short, the demand for simplicity is incompatible with the demand for explanatory power.

[16] The compatibility of astronomy with physics was as essential to Copernicus as was the "saving of appearances", as E. Rosen rightly notes in his Introduction to *Three Copernican Treatises*, 2nd ed. (New York: Dover, 1959), p. 29. "What Copernicus desired was not merely a simpler system, as Burtt thought, but a more reasonable one" (*loc. cit.*). The unification of astronomy and terrestrial mechanics was also an unfulfilled dream of Averroes and the main drive for Galileo and Newton.

[17] See, e.g., George R. Price, "Science and the Supernatural", *Science*, *122*, 359 (1955). On the other hand C. D. Broad, in "The Relevance of Psychical Research to Philosophy", *Philosophy*, *24*, 291 (1949), accepted *ESP* while acknowledging that it would require a radical upheaval in psychology, biology, physics, and philosophy.

[18] See F. C. S. Schiller, "Hypothesis", in C. Singer (ed.), *Studies in the History and Method of Science* (Oxford: Clarendon Press, 1921), II, p. 442.

(9) *Predictive power.* The theory must predict at least those facts which it can explain after the event. But, if possible, the theory should also predict new, unsuspected, facts and relations: otherwise it will be supported only by the past. In other words, predictive power can be analyzed into the sum of the capacity to predict a known class of facts, and the power to forecast new "effects", i.e. facts of a kind unexpected on alternative theories. The former may be called *forecast power*, the latter *serendipic power.*[19] To put it in a nutshell, *Predictive power* = (*Old range* + *New range*) × *Accuracy* = *Forecast power* + *Serendipic power*. (Of course, the serendipic power of a theory cannot in turn be predicted, even after completing its construction, since we neither know in advance all the logical consequences of the theory's axioms, nor the range of unknown facts).

(Although the logical structure of prediction is the same as that of explanation, — namely, deduction of singular sentences from general laws conjoined with specific informations — explanatory power is not the same as predictive power. Pseudoscience is prolific in explanation *post factum* but barren in prediction. The theories of nuclear, atomic, and molecular physics can explain singular phenomena — or classes of possible single phenomena — but can predict collective actual phenomena only — or, alternatively, they can only predict the probabilities of singular facts. Historical theories — such as those of geology, evolution, and human society — have a high explanatory power but a small predictive power, even counting retrodictions. Besides, predictions are usually of facts and very seldom of laws, whereas explanations can be either of facts or of laws. Finally, predictions are made with the help of the lowest level theorems of a theory — the closest to experience — whereas explanations may take place on any level. These are some of the reasons for counting predictive power separately from explanatory power.)[20]

Simplicity is unfavorable to predictive power for the same reason that it is incompatible with explanatory power.

(10) *Depth.* It is desirable, but by no means necessary, that theories explain essentials and reach deep in the level structure of reality. No scientific theory is just a summary of observations, if only because every generalization involves a bet on unobserved kindred facts. But, whereas some theories just account for appearances, others introduce diaphenomenal (but scrutable) entities and properties by which they explain the observable in terms of the unobservable: it is in this sense that wave optics is deeper than phenomenological (geometrical) optics, and reflexology deeper than behavioristics.

The requirement of depth does not, of course, eliminate the less deep theories: they may well be retained along with the deeper ones if they contain useful concepts that somehow correspond to actual entities or properties. Wave

[19] The term *serendipity* (lucky accident) was coined by Horace Walpole and revived by Walter Cannon, *The Way of an Investigator* (New York: Norton, 1945), ch. iv, and by Robert K. Merton, *Social Theory and Social Structure*, rev. ed. (Glencoe, Ill.: Free Press, 1957), ch. ii.

[20] Further reasons are given in Mario Bunge, reference 14, ch. 12.

optics does not eliminate the concept of light ray but elucidates it in terms of interference, and neurophysiology is expected to elucidate behavior patterns, and not to explain them away. The requirement of depth functions as a stimulus in theory construction (e.g., the present feeling of dissatisfaction with the superficiality of dispersion relations and other phenomenological theories in physics), and in the scientific reconstruction of deep prescientific theories (e.g., Marxist sociology and psychoanalysis, both rich in deep concepts and hints, but marred by a muddled logic and a complacent methodology).

Since depth involves epistemological sophistication, it is inconsistent with epistemological and pragmatical simplicity.

(11) *Extensibility* or possibility of expansion to encompass new domains.[21] Thus, Hamilton's formulation of dynamics is preferable to Newton's because it can cope with a wider class of dynamical problems and because it can be extended beyond dynamics (e.g., into field theory); yet, it is logically and epistemologically more complex than Newton's version of mechanics: it contains twice as many equations of motion, and the concepts of generalized coordinates and momenta. The same is true of Maxwell's theory of the electromagnetic field, which it was possible to extend to optics, in relation with its rivals.

The capacity for linking or unifying hitherto unrelated domains is connected with both external consistency and serendipic power, and it depends on the depth of the concepts and laws peculiar to the theory. Hence simplicity, which is unfavorably relevant to these characteristics, is also unfavorably relevant to extensibility. On the other hand, the actual expansion of a theory produces a methodological unification, in the sense that a single method can be employed to attack problems belonging to formerly disjoint sets. But a considerable syntactical, semantical, and epistemological complexity must first be swallowed: methodological simplification is not a prerequisite but a reward for the willingness to accept certain complexities.

(12) *Fertility*. The theory must have exploratory power: it must be able to guide new research and suggest new ideas, experiments, and problems, in the same or in allied fields. In the case of adequate theories, fertility overlaps with extensibility and serendipic power. But altogether inadequate theories may be stimulating, either because they contain some utilizable concepts and hypotheses (as was the case with the caloric theory of heat and the aether theories), or because they elicit new theories and experiments designed to refute them. On the other hand, virtuous theories may be barren because nobody takes as interest in them — e.g., because they are shallow, as is the case with those theories which are little more than summaries of empirical data. This is why fertility should be counted on its own.

Here, again, simplicity is either irrelevant or unfavorably relevant.

[21] Henry Margenau, *The Nature of Physical Reality* (New York: McGraw-Hill, 1950), p. 90.

(13) *Originality*. It is desirable that the theory be new relative to rival systems. Theories made of bits of existing theories, or strongly resembling available systems, or lacking new concepts, are unavoidable and may be safe to the point of being uninteresting. The most influential theories are not the safest but those which are the more thought-provoking and, particularly, those which inaugurate new ways of thinking; and these are all deep, representational, and extensible theories, such as Newtonian mechanics, field theory, quantum theory, and evolutionism. As a noted physicist[22] says, "For any speculation which does not at first glance look crazy, there is no hope".

Now, the rules of simplicity evidently prohibit or at least discourage the framing of new, bold, constructs: the trite path is the simplest. This is particularly so in the case where theories are available which have been empirically confirmed, but which are unsatisfactory for some reason — e.g., because they are phenomenological. The policy of simplicity will in this case disavow new approaches and will thereby stop the advancement of science.

2.4. *Methodological requirements*

(14) *Scrutability*. Not only the predicates occuring in the theory must be open to empirical scrutiny by the public and self-correcting method of science (sec. 1.3), but also the methodological presuppositions of the theory must be controllable. This requirement leads to rendering suspect (*a*) evidences of a kind that only the given theory would accept, and (*b*) techniques, tests, and alleged modes of knowing which — like sympathetic understanding and essence intuition — cannot be controlled by alternative means and do not lead to intersubjectively valid conclusions, or at the very least to arguable ones.

Again, this requirement conflicts with simplicity of certain kinds, since the logically simplest theories are those speculative systems that do not care for tests. If someone should insist in introducing the term 'simplicity' in this connection, allow him to call this the requirement of methodological simplicity, but remind him that this phrase should not be construed as imposing a simplification in method in the sense of a relaxation of the standard of rigor, or of a reduction in the variety of tests, but as simplifying the task of rigorously testing the theory and the tests. Otherwise, the methodologically simplest theory would be the one validated by the "method" of navel contemplation. But, of course, no rule of simplicity enlightens us as to whether a given construct (e.g., a quantum-mechanical operator) can be regarded as representing an observable property, or not. Criteria of scrutability of predicates are not simple, and they are often controvertible.[23]

In summary, simplicity is ambiguously relevant to scrutability (see sec. 1.3).

[22] Freeman J. Dyson, "Invention in Physics", *Sci. American*, 199, no. 3, p. 80 (1958).

[23] Some variables regarded as observable in nonrelativistic quantum mechanics are no longer observable in the relativistic theory, and conditions of observability, such as reality (hermiticity), are open to criticism. It can be shown that a non-hermitian operator may represent, in a number of cases, a pair of observables. Cf. Andrés J. Kálnay, "Sobre los observables cuánticos y el requisito de la hermiticidad" (forthcoming).

(15) *Refutability*. It must be possible to imagine cases or circumstances that could refute the theory.[24] Otherwise no genuine tests could be designed, and the theory could be regarded as logically true, i.e., as true come what may — hence as empirically void.

A scientific theory may certainly contain an irrefutable premiss among its postulates, such as an existential hypothesis of the form 'There is at least one x such that x is an F' (without specifying precise location in either space or time), or a statistical law of the form 'In the long run, f approaches p'. The theory may even presuppose irrefutable metascientific principles, like "Every fact is explainable in the long run".[25] But all such irrefutable statements should be confirmable and somehow supported by the bulk of knowledge; furthermore, all the remaining premisses of the theory should be refutable and none of them should be exempt from being indicted by evidence by the interposition of shielding hypotheses; finally, none of the lower-level consequences of the theory should be indifferent to experience. In particular, no secure, uncorrigible data which "resist the solvent influence of critical reflection" (Russell) are to enter science, which is essentially corrigible knowledge.

Clearly, semantical, epistemological, and experimental simplicity are favorable to refutability. But syntactical simplicity is ambiguously relevant to it: on the one hand, refutability requires accuracy, which in turn involves complexity (see sec. 1.3); on the other hand, the fewer the predicates involved, and the simpler the relations assumed to hold among them, the easier it will be to refute the theory. But what if facts, indifferent as they are to our labors, stubbornly refuse to lend themselves to logical simplification? Forced simplification will lead to actual refutation rather than just securing testability.

(16) *Confirmability*. The theory must have particular consequences that may be found to agree with observation (to within technically reasonable limits). And, of course, actual confirmation to a large extent will be required for the acceptance of every theory. The insistence on confirmation as the sole assaying criterion (inductivism) opens the door to theories fraught with vague and inscrutable predicates (gypsy theories). Plenty of confirmation is not a guarantee of truth, since after all the evidence may all be selected, or conveniently interpreted, or else the theory may never have been subjected to severe tests. But, of course, even if insufficient, confirmation is necessary for the acceptance of theories.[26]

Now, a theory may be complicated ex profeso so as to increase its degree of confirmation; hence, simplicity is unfavorably relevant to confirmation.

(17) *Methodological simplicity*. It must be technically possible to subject the theory to empirical tests. The theory may lead to the formulation of predictions that are too difficult, or even impossible, to test empirically at the moment;

[24] Karl R. Popper, *The Logic of Scientific Discovery* (1935; London: Hutchinson, 1959), ch. iv.
[25] The legitimacy of such irrefutable statements, rejected by Popper, is defended in Mario Bunge, "Kinds and Criteria of Scientific Laws", *Philosophy of Science*, *28*, 260 (1961).
[26] Mario Bunge, "The Place of Induction in Science", *Phil. Sci.*, *27*, 262 (1960).

yet, it may be a valuable theory that may stimulate the improvement of technical media. An unpredictable number of years will pass before a single empirical test of any of the quantum theories of the gravitational field may be supplied, but the mere proliferation of theories of this kind may stimulate the design of empirical tests.

In short, methodological simplicity to a moderate extent must be required, particularly from theories designed to elude or postpone *sine die* the trial of experience; if required too sternly, it may be obstrusive.

2.5. *Philosophical requirements*

(18) *Level-parsimony.* The theory must be parsimonious in its references to sections of reality other than those directly involved. The higher levels (actual or imaginary) should not be appealed to if the lower are enough, and distant levels should not be introduced without the intermediate ones. This requirement is, of course, violated by animistic theories of matter and by mechanistic theories of mind.

The rule of simplicity is ambiguous in this connection as it is in others. In effect, level-parsimony may be regarded as an instance of the rule; yet, what can be simpler than reductionism — down, as in the case of mechanism, or up, as in the case of idealism —, which violates the rule of level-parsimony?

(19) *Metascientific soundness.* The theory must be compatible with fertile metascientific principles, such as the postulates of lawfulness and rationality, and the relevant metanomological statements [27] (such as general covariance).

Simplicity is, in the best of cases, irrelevant to metascientific soundness — unless it is arbitrarily included among the symptoms of such a soundness, despite its ambiguous relevance to the other desiderata of scientific theory.

(20) *World-view compatibility.* It is desirable that the theory be consistent with the common core of the *Weltanschauungen* prevailing in scientific circles — world-views which, anyway, do mold the very construction and acceptance of scientific theories. This requirement functions as a stabilizer: on the one hand, it leads us — along with external consistency, of which it is an extension — to reject crackpot theories; on the other hand, it may delay or even prevent revolutions in our world-view, if the latter makes no room for its own change. (Remember the cool reception given to field theory and to Darwin's theory in France one century ago.) The criterion of world-view compatibility must therefore be used with care. Anyway, it does intervene in theory assaying, and it is better to realize this than to be inadvertently dominated, in our valuation of theories, by some unscientific world-view. World-views and scientific theories should control and enrich each other.

Simplicity is, of course, as inconsistent with world-view compatibility as it was found to be with external consistency.

[27] Mario Bunge, *Metascientific Queries* (Springfield, Ill.: Charles Thomas, 1959), ch. 4.

2.6. *Further criteria?*

Alternative criteria have from time to time been proposed, such as intelligibility (psychological simplicity), elegance, practical usefulness, operational character ("definability" of all concepts in terms of effective operations), high probability, and causality. As a matter of fact these criteria often influence our valuation of theories, but they can be shown to be inadequate.

In effect, intelligibility or intuitability is beside the point, because it is largely a subjective characteristic entirely independent of truth.[28] Elegance or beauty is not an independent but a derived characteristic of some theories: a theory arouses an aesthetic feeling in us if it is logically well organized, accurate, deep, wide, and original — and if we are deeply interested in the subject. Practical applicability is rather irrelevant to truth, as shown by the heap of pseudosciences that serve a purpose beneficial to their entrepreneurs and even, occasionally, to their victims. Operational character cannot be satisfied if metrical and/or transcendent (theoretical) predicates are allowed [29] — as they must if the theory is to be exact. A high *a priori* probability is inconsistent with accuracy and universality. And causality, unless understood in a very liberal sense — as general determinism, which is committed only to the postulate "Everything is determined in accordance with law by something else" — would be as mutilating to science as overall simplicity. [30]

Further legitimate requirements may, of course, appear with the progress of metascience and with the advancement of science itself. Do not standards of rigor become more and more exacting? But the twenty above-listed criteria constitute a complex enough set — particularly for the sake of ascertaining the weight of simplicity.

3. The Acceptance of Scientific Theories: Five Case Histories

Let us illustrate the functioning of the assaying criteria listed above with a few celebrated cases. We shall concede that all the theories to be examined in the following are logically consistent and, to some extent, compatible with empirical information.

3.1. *Theory of the planetary system*

The geocentric and the heliocentric models of our planetary system are regarded by conventionalists as empirically equivalent and even as equivalent modes of speech; and it has been claimed and repeated that the sole reason for preferring the heliocentric system is its simplicity relative to the geocentric

[28] Cf. Mario Bunge, *Intuition and Science* (Englewood Cliffs, N. J.: Prentice-Hall, 1962).

[29] Carl G. Hempel, "The Concept of Cognitive Significance: A Reconsideration", *Proc. Amer. Acad. Arts and Sciences, 80*, 61 (1951). Arthur Pap, "Are Physical Magnitudes Operationally Definable?", in C. West Churchman and P. Ratoosh (eds.), *Measurement: Definitions and Theories* (New York: Wiley, 1959), ch. 9.

[30] Mario Bunge, *Causality* (Cambridge, Mass.: Harvard University Press, 1959).

image, since — so the contention runs — there is really no reason to single out one system of reference (the Copernican) to another (the Ptolemaic). Both affirmations are false: the Copernicus-Kepler system accounts for a far greater set of phenomena than Ptolemy's does, and it was not adopted because of its greater simplicity — which it does not possess in all respects — but because it is supposed to be a truer image of facts, as suggested among other reasons by its fitting with contiguous theories, whereas the geocentric system is an *ad hoc*, isolated, theory.

Specifically, the Copernicus-Kepler system satisfies the following assaying criteria (cf. sec. 2) to an extent its rival could never dream of: (*a*) *external consistency:* compatibility with dynamics, gravitation theory, and cosmology. No system of dynamics employs Ptolemy's noninertial axes (which alone could yield Ptolemy's orbits); the paths of the planets both in Newtonian and in Einsteinian theory are essentially determined by the sun; [31] and every cosmogonical theory entails the hypothesis that the earth was formed some billions years ago along with the other planets and without any special privilege (in other words, the geocentric system is inconsistent with the theory of stellar evolution). Terrestrial axes are as good as the Copernican system of reference from a *geometrical* point of view only — i.e., as regards the shape of the orbits — but they are definitely inadequate from *kinematical* and *dynamical* points of view, among other reasons because the apparent velocities of celestial bodies may take on any value (being proportional to the distance from the earth), even beyond the speed of light, and because, Ptolemy's axes being noninertial, it is not possible to apply to them the principle of relativity: they are not relativistically equivalent to the Copernican axes (they are not related by means of a Lorentz transformation); [32] (*b*) *explanatory and predictive powers:* the heliocentric system accounts for the phases of the planets (predicted and discovered by Galileo in the case of Venus), for the aberration of light (which enables us to determine both the velocity of the earth and the earth-sun distance), for the Doppler shift of the star's spectra (which leads to the determination of the recession velocity of nebulae), and for various other appearances which the geocentric system does not "save"; (*c*) *representativeness:* the heliocentric

[31] According to general relativity, the paths of bodies are determined by the gravitational field, and the latter is in turn determined by the mass distribution. The field strength being proportional to the quantity of matter (as given, e.g., by the nuclear particles), it is not possible to find a coordinate system in which the sun's field turns out to be weaker than the earth's so that the latter might be regarded as stationary and the sun as revolving around it. Gravitational fields are equivalent to accelerations, and the latter can be transformed away by means of suitable coordinate transformations, within differential spacetime volumes alone; e.g., Einstein's elevator must start from a place within the earth's field, and it finally crashes. For a criticism of the erroneous belief that general relativity permits to transform every acceleration away, see V. A. Fock, "Le système de Ptolomée et le système de Copernic á la lumière de la théorie générale de la rélativité", in *Questions scientifiques* (Paris: Ed. de la Nouvelle Critique, 1952), I, 149.

[32] For the kinematical and dynamical inequivalence of the geocentric and the Copernican reference axes according to the general theory of relativity, see G. Giorgi and A. Cabras, "Questioni relativistiche sulle prove della rotazione terrestre", *Rendic. Accad. Naz. Lincei*, IX, 513, 1929).

system is not merely a conventional calculating device but a conceptual reconstruction of facts, as Copernicus and Galileo believed, and as must now be conceded in view of the facts mentioned above; (*d*) it is *fertile:* it has prompted new astronomical discoveries (such as Kepler's laws), new developments in mechanics (e.g., the various theories of gravitation and of tides) and in optics (such as Roemer's measurement of the velocity of light), as well as the conjecturing — now fairly well established — that there is a multiplicity of solar systems (first suggested by Bruno and insisted on by Galileo upon his discovery of Jupiter's satellites); (*e*) *refutability:* it is better refutable by empirical evidence than any conventionalist system, as it does not admit an unending addition of auxiliary hypotheses aimed at saving the central assumptions; moreover, the simple Copernicus-Kepler model was refuted or, rather, improved long ago with the discovery that the real orbits are much more complex than the original ellipses, owing to the perturbations from other planets and to the finite velocity of propagation of the gravitational field; (*f*) *world-view compatibility:* the new astronomy was compatible not only with the new physics but also with the new anthropology and the new ethics, according to which the earth was not the basest place in the universe, and nature was not made to serve man.

What role did simplicity play in the choice among these two rival — but by no means empirically equivalent — theories? Copernicus, referring to the *geometrical* aspect of his theory, did employ the argument from simplicity; but, at the same time, he granted that his theory was "well-nigh contrary to common sense" or, in our terminology, that it was epistemologically more complex than the theory according to which celestial motions are such as they appear to be. But how naively simple the most complex curve Ptolemy could imagine looks as compared with the real orbits of planets as calculated with Newtonian mechanics and perturbation theory! In short, it is false to say that we retain the heliocentric system because it is the simplest: we prefer it, despite its greater complexity, because it is the truest. And simplicity did not intervene in our judgment of its truth value.

3.2. *Gravitation Theory*

Several theories of gravitation account for roughly the same observed facts as Einstein's theory does, and all of them are *simpler* than it: Whitehead's (1922), Birkhoff's (1945), Belinfante-Swihart's (1957), and others. Thus, for example, Whitehead's theory, conveniently modified, gives the same formula (not merely the same numerical value for some particular case) for the gravitational deflection of light rays as Einstein's theory does.[33] It is true that the recent measurement of the gravitational red-shift of spectral lines (due to the energy lost by photons in escaping from gravitational fields, e.g., in moving upwards in the vicinity of the earth) is in amazing agreement with the value predicted with

[33] J. L. Synge, "Orbits and Rays in the Gravitational Field of a Finite Sphere According to the Theory of A. N. Whitehead", *Proc. Roy. Soc. Lond. A*, *211*, 303 (1952).

the help of the theory.[34] Yet, the situation is not as good with regard to other empirical tests of general relativity: (*a*) the deflection of light rays in the vicinity of celestial bodies has been confirmed to within 10-15% accuracy only; (*b*) the advance of the perihelion of planets has been well confirmed in the case of Mercury alone (artificial satellites might provide further evidence); (*c*) the displacement of the perihelion owing to the sun's rotation (another effect predicted by the theory) has not been measured; (*d*) gravitational waves, also predicted by the theory, have not been detected.

Why, then, do most physicists prefer Einstein's theory of gravitation, which is so obviously complex from a syntactical and an epistemological point of view that most astronomers refuse to employ it? The reasons seem to be that, unlike its rivals, Einstein's theory of gravitation (*a*) has a *high serendipic power:* it predicts phenomena which were neither observed before nor predictable on the theories prevailing at the birth of general relativity — like the deflection of light rays and the gravitational red-shift; on the other hand, its rivals have been tailored to fit phenomena *ex post facto:* their degree of inductive character, or ad-hocness, is considerable, whereas Einstein theory's is nil; (*b*) is *extensible:* it provides a framework that might be expanded into a unified field theory; (*c*) is *representational:* it ascribes reality to the gravitational field (or space) and its sources, and contains no adjustable parameters lacking a physical meaning (as does the phenomenological linear theory of gravitation); (*d*) is *deep:* it is relevant to our views on space, time, field, force, and mass; the basic equations may even be regarded, as Schroedinger suggested, as a definition of matter; (*e*) is highly *original:* it is counterintuitive and noncausal enough to deserve attention; (*f*) is *fertile:* it has suggested new observations, some of which are still to be done.

Neither observed facts nor simplicity have played a prominent role in the construction of general relativity (notwithstanding Einstein's own statements about the value of simplicity). Rather, the complexity of the theory has been an obstacle to its acceptance by many,[35] and a major stimulus for the invention of simpler theories. In fact, the theory contains epistemologically complex predicates, such as 'spacetime curvature', and 'gravitational potential', which are not acceptable to empiricist philosophies; and the equations of the theory, though deceivingly "simple" if written in the compact tensor notation, are complex enough to obstruct and even preclude the very formulation of problems, which renders the theory unpractical. This is why many physicists, even granting that Einstein's theory is so far *the truest*, frequently employ or try alternative theories which are syntactically, epistemologically, and pragmatically simpler; but future theories of gravitation will have to be more inclusive and deeper than Einstein's (among other things, they will have to be contiguous with quantum mechanics) — whence they are likely to be even more complex than it.

[34] R. V. Pound and G. A. Rebka, Jr., "Apparent Weight of Photons", *Phys. Rev. Letters*, 4, 337 (1960).

[35] For a protest against the complexities of general relativity, see P. W. Bridgman, *The Nature of Physical Theory* (New York: Dover, 1936), pp. 89 ff.

3.3. *Beta-decay theory*

The present theory of the beta-decay of neutrons, mesons, hyperons, and other so-called fundamental particles, contains two hypotheses that it was found necessary to complicate in the course of time in order to square the theory with empirical data. One of the hypotheses refers to the existence of the neutrino, the other to certain symmetry properties of the basic equations.

The neutrino hypothesis may conveniently be expounded with reference to the mu-meson decay. If only charge conservation is taken into account, the hypothesis

$$\text{mu-meson} \rightarrow \text{electron} \qquad H1$$

will be sufficient. But it is found that electrons are emitted with a continuous energy spectrum (to the extent to which observation can suggest or test continuity!), which is inconsistent with the assumption that only two bodies are involved (if we further *assume* momentum conservation). *H*1, the simplest hypothesis, was therefore false: a more complex one had to be invented. The next simplest conjecture involves the invention of an unobserved entity, the neutrino:

$$\text{mu-meson} \rightarrow \text{electron} + \text{neutrino}. \qquad H2$$

This hypothesis is epistemologically complex; it is also methodologically complicated since the neutrino, owing to its lack of charge and its small (or zero) mass, is remarkably elusive — to the point that many physicists have disbelieved in its existence for years, especially after many independent and elaborate attempts to detect it failed. Still, *H*2 is not complex enough: it is consistent with the continuous energy spectrum but inconsistent with the hypothesis of spin conservation, found correct in other fields. This latter hypothesis is respected by introducing a further theoretical entity, namely, the antineutrino:

$$\text{mu-meson} \rightarrow \text{electron} + \text{neutrino} + \text{antineutrino} \qquad H3$$

This hypothesis is consistent with charge, energy, and spin conservation; but it involves an entity which is empirically indistinguishable from the neutrino. The decay scheme has become more and more complex syntactically, epistemologically, and methodologically.

Of course, *H*3 is not the sole hypothesis consistent with the known facts: we may frame a heap of alternative conjectures just by assuming that an arbitrary number *n* of neutrinos and antineutrinos take part in beta-decay. But there is no point in adopting any one of these more complicated hypotheses as long as we cannot distinguish experimentally among their consequences, and as long as they do not throw new light on the explanation of phenomena. It is here that we appeal to the rule of simplicity. But we do not just choose "the simplest hypothesis compatible with the observed facts", as the inductivist methodology has it: we select the simplest hypothesis of a set of *equally* *precise* assumptions all compatible with the known *facts* and with the set of *law statements* we regard as relevant and valid. And this is a far cry from unqualified simplicity: it came after a considerable sophistication and when no further complication promised to be fruitful. The rule actually used in scientific research is not just "Choose the simplest", but "Try the simplest first and, if it fails — as it normally should — gradually introduce complications compatible with the bulk of knowledge".

A second hypothesis of the theory is that the laws "governing" this kind of disintegration are not invariant under the reversal of position coordinates (i.e., under the parity transformation $x \rightarrow -x$). Until the work of Lee and Yang (1956), the simplest hypothesis had been made regarding this transformation, namely, that all physical laws are parity-invariant (i.e., do not change under the exchange of left and right). The rejection of this metanomological statement[36] made it possible to identify two kinds of particles (the theta and tau mesons) — which involved a taxonomical simplification — and led to predicting previously unsuspected facts, such as the unsymmetry of the angular distribution of decay products.

The theory, as corrected in the above sketched ways, (*a*) had *serendipic power*, (*b*) was *original* to the point of "craziness" (as both the neutrino hypothesis and the parity non-conservation hypothesis have seemed to many), and (*c*) was *deep*, to the point that it dethroned the laboriously acquired belief that no intrinsic differences between left and right could ever be found in nature.

It will not do to count the identification of the theta and tau mesons in favor of the tenet of simplicity: this small simplification introduced in the *systematics* of fundamental particles did not involve a simplification in the basic *theory* but was an assignment of simplicity to nature itself. Besides, it was overcompensated by the introduction of new, less familiar, terms (pseudoscalar and pseudovector contributions to the energy operator), which correspondingly complicated the theorems dependent on them.

Not the abidance by simplicity but the bold inventions of new, complicating, hypotheses was decisive in the building, improvement, and acceptance of the beta-decay theory.

3.4. *Theory of evolution*

What gave Darwin's theory of evolution through natural selection the victory over its various rivals, notably creationism and Lamarckism? Darwin's theory was in part logically faulty (remember the vicious circle of the "survival of the fittest"); it contained several false or at least unproven assertions ("Each variation is good for the individual", "Acquired characters, if favorable, are inherited", "Sexual selection operates universally"); it had not been tested by observation, let alone by experiment on living species under controlled

[36] For an analysis of the logical status of the parity conservation law and other metanomological statements, see Mario Bunge, "Laws of Physical Laws", *American Journal of Physics*, *29*, 518 (1961).

conditions (the development of antibiotic-resistant strains of bacteria, industrial melanism in butterflies, and a few other processes supporting the theory, were observed one century after *The Origin of Species* appeared); its explanatory power was clearly smaller than that of its rivals (irrefutable theories have the maximum *post factum* explanatory power); it had no inductive basis but was, on the contrary, a bold invention containing high-level unobservables. And, as if these sins were not enough to condemn the theory, Darwin's system was far more complex than any of its rivals: compare the single postulate that states the special creation of every species, or Lamarck's three postulates (stating the immanent tendency to perfection, the law of use and disuse, and the inheritance of acquired characters), with Darwin's system, which included among others the following axioms: "The high rate of population increase leads to population pressure", "Population pressure leads to struggle for life", "In the struggle for life the innately fittest survive", "Favorable differences are inheritable and cumulative", and "Unfavorable characteristics lead to extinction".

The characters which ensured the survival of Darwin's theory despite its complexity and its various genuine shortcomings seem to have been the following: (*a*) *external consistency:* the theory was compatible with evolutionary geology and with the evolutionary theory of the solar system; (*b*) *extensibility and fertility:* the theory was quickly, boldly, and fruitfully expanded to physical anthropology, psychology, and history, and unwarrantedly extrapolated to sociology (social Darwinism) and ontology (Spencerian progressivism); (*c*) *originality:* although the idea of evolution was old, the mechanism proposed by Darwin was new and suggested daring fresh starts in all related fields, as well as the very relation among fields hitherto disconnected; (*d*) *scrutability:* Darwin's theory did not involve inscrutable predicates like 'creation', 'purpose', 'immanent perfection', and the like, and it did not involve unscientific alleged modes of knowing (such as revelation); (*e*) *empirical refutability:* contrary to its rivals, every piece of relevant evidence was conceivably favorable or unfavorable; (*f*) *level-parsimony:* no spiritual entity was invoked to account for lower-level phenomena, and no purely physico-chemical mechanism was resorted to either; (*g*) *metascientific soundness:* in particular, compatibility with the postulate of lawfulness, violated by the hypothesis of creation — but, on the other hand, the theory was inconsistent with the inductivist methodology then dominant, and sounded suspect to some on this score; (*h*) *world-view compatibility:* definite consistency with the naturalist, agnostic, dynamicist, progressivist, and individualist outlook of the *intelligentsia* on which the recent social and cultural changes (notably 1789, Chartism, and 1848) had made a deep impression. These virtues of Darwinism overcompensated its shortcomings and made it worth correcting on several points, until it merged (only in the 1930's) with genetics.

In short, simplicity was not taken into account in the genesis and development of Darwin's theory of evolution.

3.5. *Genetic theory*

The Mendelian theory of heredity has been under attack from environmentalism, or neo-Lamarckism, since its inception. The theory of the omnipotence of the environment is attractive to many because it is so much closer to common sense, because it is causal, because (if only it were true!) it would enable us to quickly control evolution in a planned way and last, but not least, because it is superficially compatible with an optimistic and progressive view of human life, on which nurture can overcome every shortcoming of nature. On the other hand, Mendelien genetics is formally, semantically, and epistemologically much more complex; it involves theoretical terms such as 'gene'; it calls for the use of statistics; it does not so far afford a precise control of evolution; it suggests rather gloomy prospects and — at least in Weismann's version of the theory — it reinforces the anachronic ontological tenet of the existence of an unchangeable substance (the germ-plasm). Furthermore, the genetic theory does not account satisfactorily for heredity in the case of higher organisms, and many geneticists are beginning to grant a parallel though weaker intervention of the cytoplasm in the transmission of characters.

Why then is Mendelian genetics accepted by most biologists? The main reasons seem to be the following: (*a*) it is *representational:* it locates precisely each hereditary factor in a bit of matter (gene, or gene complex), and it provides a chance mechanism (gene shuffling) that explains the final outcome, whereas environmentalism is a phenomenological theory; (*b*) it is *consistent* with the theory of evolution through natural selection (as modified to meet precisely this requirement), and with biochemistry (a plausible and precise mechanism of genetic information transmission, and of gene duplication, has recently been invented); (*c*) it has *predictive power:* statistical predictions (not individual ones) are often possible in an accurate manner with the help of its laws; (*d*) it is *refutable* and *confirmable* by experiment (e.g., mutation by direct physical action of X-rays on chromosomes), whereas the environmentalist theory is confirmable only, since it speaks about vague environmental influences; (*e*) it is *compatible* with some well-grounded and widely accepted philosophical views, such as naturalism (material basis of biological traits), and atomism (existence of discrete units of some sort on every level of organization). Last, but not least, its main enemy, Lysenkoism, has been marred by fraud, dogmatism, and unpleasant associations with curtailments of academic freedom. Yet, who would deny that unacademic and unfair attitudes were apparent in both camps some years ago, just because the whole controversy was regarded as part of a holy war?

At any rate simplicity — which, incidentally, was on the part of Lysenko — played no role in the discussion as compared with ideological and political considerations.

3.6. *Test of the tests*

Five case histories have been recalled and analyzed in order to test the tests proposed in sec. 2. (No metascience is scientific if it does not test its hypotheses.) They were not just elementary cases of fitting polynomials to isolated sets of observational data — the favorite example of inductivist treatments of simplicity. The five cases selected for examination consisted of systems of testable hypotheses and were important enough to affect to some extent the modern world-view. In none of them was simplicity found to be a major factor of theory construction or evaluation: quite on the contrary, the theories ultimately chosen were in most respects remarkably more complex than their defeated rivals. Which plainly suggests the objective complexity of reality.

4. Conclusion: The Lightness of Simplicities

4.1. *Simplicity neither necessary nor sufficient*

While agreement with fact as tested by experience was regarded by metascientists as the sole test of a true theory,[37] simplicity alone seemed to provide the decisive criterion of choice among competing theories. What else could distinguish one theory from another while — in compliance with inductivism — attention was focused on empirical confirmation with neglect of all the remaining factors that as a matter of fact, consciously or unconsciously, intervene in the evaluation of scientific theories?

Gone are those days of *sancta simplicitas:* it is more and more clearly realized that the degree of truth, or degree of sustenance, of scientific theories has never been equated with their degree of confirmation. Many more requisites have always been imposed *de facto* by scientists, and have occasionally been recognized.[38] Twenty requirements — functioning at the pragmatic level as so many assaying criteria — were recognized in sec. 2, and overall simplicity was not included among them for the plain reason that a theory may be simple

[37] See, e.g., W. Stanley Jevons, *The Principles of Science*, 2nd. ed. (1877; New York: Dover, 1958), p. 510; Pierre Duhem, *La théorie physique*, 2nd. ed. (Paris: Rivière, 1914), p. 26; see, however, p. 259, where he admits that simplicity is not a sign of certainty.

[38] An early recognition of the multiplicity of requirements is found in Heinrich Hertz, *The Principles of Mechanics* (1894; New York: Dover, 1956), Introduction. Hertz listed the following: (1) logical possibility, or compatibility with the "laws of thought"; (2) predictive power; (3) maximum number of "essential relations of the object" (what I have called depth); (4) "the smaller number of superfluous or empty relations". Half a century elapsed before another scientist-philosopher dared to add non-empirical requirements: Henry Margenau, *The Nature of Physical Reality* (New York: McGraw-Hill, 1950), ch. 5, lists the following "metaphysical requirements on constructs": (1) logical fertility, (2) multiple connections, (3) permanence or stability, (4) extensibility, (5) causality, (6) simplicity and elegance. See also Mario Bunge, *Metascientific Queries* (Springfield, Ill.: Charles Thomas, 1959), pp. 79 ff., and Karl R. Popper, "The Idea of Truth and the Empirical Character of Scientific Theories", presented to the *International Congress for Logic, Methodology, and Philosophy of Science* (Stanford, 1960). In this paper Popper grants that one of the requirements for a good theory is that it "should succeed with at least some of its new predictions" — i.e., that it should be confirmed

and false, or complex and approximately true — i.e., for the simple reason that *simplicity is neither a necessary nor a sufficient sign of truth.*

It would be unrealistic to regard any of the twenty requirements, save systematicity, accuracy, and testability, as strictly necessary for calling a set of hypotheses a *scientific theory*, even though they are jointly sufficient for calling it an *approximately true scientific theory.* (The assaying criteria are consequently useful in distinguishing scientific from nonscientific systems and, in particular, in weeding out pseudoscientific theories.) The twenty requirements are rather *desiderata* of theory construction, *means* for attaining truth, and *symptoms* of truth; and, like other desiderata, they are not all mutually compatible, whence a compromise must always be sought.

Now every desideratum — here as elsewhere — can be satisfied in various degrees, and the failure of a theory to rigorously comply with *some* of the above requirements — save systematicity, accuracy, and testability, which are mandatory — should not lead one to reject a theory altogether. Thus, e.g., syntactical correctness and linguistic accuracy are always meager in the beginnings. If a theory is rich in deep transcendent and scrutable concepts, and if it promises to unify wide fields of knowledge, or to be instrumental in the exploration of new territories, it would be short-sighted to dismiss it entirely because of some formal shortcomings; the wisest course will be to work out the theory and to test it: syntactical and semantical neatness will eventually be achieved in this process. Only mature theories fulfil all the requirements in an excellent way. But, then, mature factual theories, like mature persons, are those which are about to be replaced.

What is the place of simplicity in the body of criteria that guide our evaluation of scientific theories? In order to estimate it we should recall, in the first place, that there is a variety of simplicities (sec. 1.1) and, in the second place, that simplicity of some sort is favorable to only a few symptoms of truth, and even so within limits. It was shown in secs. 1.2 and 2.2 that syntactical simplicity is favorably relevant to systematicity — though not necessary to attain it; also, moderate semantical and methodological simplicity were proposed as assaying criteria, mainly for practical reasons. On the other hand, complexity of some sort is associated with eleven other requisites: external consistency, linguistic exactness, empirical interpretability, representativeness, explanatory power, predictive power, depth, extensibility, originality, confirmability, and world-view compatibility. Finally, the rule of simplicity is ambiguous with regard to testability and to level-parsimony and, in the best of cases, it is neutral relatively to the remaining four requirements — syntactical correctness, fertility, scrutability, and metascientific soundness.

It does not seem possible to assign numerical weights to most of the requisites, and it does not seem promising to attempt to quantify the contribution — positive, negative, or nil — of simplicity to those various symptoms. If numbers have to be mentioned in this connection, let us be content with saying that simplicity does not contribute positively to 17 out of 20 major symptoms of truth. As regards most of the symptoms of truth, then, simplicity is similar to phlogiston: it is vague, elusive, and has a negative weight whenever it is not imponderable.

4.2. *The role of simplicities in research*

The role of simplicities in scientific research — as distinct from its products: data and theories — is, in summary, the following. Simplicities are undesirable in the stage of problem *finding*, since the mere discovery or invention of problems adds to the existing complexity. Simplicities of various sorts, on the other hand, are desirable in the *formulation* of problems and, much less so, in the *solution* of problems — which sometimes demands a complication of the given problem (e.g., the broadening of its setting) or the invention of new, complex concepts, hypotheses, or techniques. Then, some kinds of simplicity — notably syntactical and semantical economy — are *nolens volens* involved in *theory construction*, either because of the forced poverty of every beginning or because an unmanageable complication at a late stage has called for simplification in certain respects (usually syntactical); yet no single theory, if deep and promising, should be sacrificed to simplicity. Finally, syntactical and pragmatical simplicity are, within limits, favorable to the *test* of theories. But, then, simplicity in some regard is usually compensated by complexity in some other respect; suffice to recall the infinite syntactical complexity that must be paid for the epistemological impoverishment of theories brought about by the replacement of transcendent ("auxiliary") expressions by observational ones.[39]

The function of simplicities in scientific investigation is not, at any rate, as important as it had been imagined by conventionalists and empiricists. The main reason for the loss of weight of simplicity is this. The task of the theoretician is not merely to describe experience in the most economical way, but to *build* theoretical models (not necessarily mechanical!) of bits of reality, and to test such images by means of logic, further theoretical constructions, empirical data, and metascientific rules. Such a constructive work certainly *involves* the neglect of complexities but does not *aim* at disregarding them; rather, a desideratum of every new theory is to account for something that had been overlooked in previous views.

This is why we cannot any longer believe in the scholastic maxim *Simplex sigillum veri:* because we know that all our constructions are defective since, deliberately or not, they involve the neglect of an unknown number of factors. Factual theories apply exactly to schematic, impoverished, models or images, and only inexactly to the real referents of these pictures; the simpler the theoretical model, the coarser or more unrealistic it will be. We need not wait for empirical tests in order to discover that *all* our theories are, strictly speaking, false (cf. 1.4). We know this beforehand if only because they all involve *too many simplifications*, as shown by an analysis of the construction and application of factual theories, and by historical experience. Conceptual economy is conse-

[39] William Craig, reference 5.

quently a sign and a test of transitoriness, i.e., of falsity — to be superseded by a lesser falsity. *Simplex sigillum falsi.*

4.3. *Conclusion*

The unqualified demand for economy in every respect, or even in some one respect, is definitely incompatible with a number of important desiderata of theory construction — such as, e.g., accuracy, depth, and external consistency — whence simplicity *tout court* should neither be regarded as mandatory nor be counted as an independent criterion on a par with others — let alone above others. The rules of simplicity fall under the general norm "*Do not hold arbitrary (ungrounded) beliefs*".

If framed with all the due precautions to prevent the mutilation of scientific theory, the rule of simplicity will boil down to the norm directing us to *minimize superfluities*. But of course this rule, like every other negative injunction, is insufficient as a theory construction policy; moreover, it does not help us to recognize which elements of a theory are redundant, i.e., which ones discharge neither a logical nor an empirical function. Production is not ensured by specifying what should not be done.

Simplicity is ambiguous as a term and double-edged as a prescription, and it must be controlled by the symptoms of truth rather than be regarded as a factor of truth. To paraphrase Baltasar Gracián — "*Lo bueno, si breve, dos veces bueno*" — let us say that a working theory, if simple, works twice as well — but this is trivial. If a practical advice is wanted as a corollary, let this be: Ockham's razor — like all razors — must be handled with care to prevent beheading science in the attempt to shave off some of its pilosities. In science, as in the barber shop, better alive and bearded than dead and cleanly shaven.

I take a pleasure in thanking my students James Hullett and Robert Schwartz for their literary advice.

22 The Use of Simplicity in Induction

JOHN G. KEMENY

I. The Problem

The concept of simplicity plays a central role in inductive inferences. Given any inductive problem in which there are several "equally good" hypotheses,

From *The Philosophical Review*, Vol. 62, 1953, pp. 391–408. Reprinted by permission of the editors of *The Philosophical Review* and the author.

the scientist will choose the simplest one. In spite of the fact that this much is generally admitted, the concept of simplicity remains highly controversial in the philosophy of science.

By the "rule of simplicity" we mean a rule instructing the scientist to choose the simplest of several acceptable hypotheses. (This rule will be left vague for the time being.) Justifications for such a rule come from two diametrically opposed camps. At one extreme we find the belief that the rule involves an assumption about the "simplicity of nature"; the other extreme justifies it by saying that it is only a matter of convenience, a laborsaving device. And whatever the philosopher's attitude may be to the justification of such a rule, you will almost always find the firm opinion that no precise definition can be given for the concept of simplicity.

It is the purpose of this paper, first of all, to make a contribution to the explication (precise definition) of the concept of simplicity; secondly, to state a rule of simplicity in terms of this explicatum, and thirdly, to show the *methodological* advantages of this rule. It will be shown that such rules have a purpose deeper than mere convenience, and this will be shown without any metaphysical assumptions about nature.

The paper will first give a general discussion, and then apply the results to some well-known examples. It is convenient, however, to illustrate all the general points in terms of two simple examples. These will be included in the main body of the paper, but in order to preserve the continuity of the main line of argument, remarks referring exclusively to the illustrations will be marked off by brackets.

Although a certain amount of mathematical knowledge is presupposed in the examples, the main argument requires no such background.

II. Precise Formulation

Let us begin with a precise description of the type of inductive problems here to be considered. The scientist is confronted with some definite problem in which he will perform a series of experiments, which will culminate in the acceptance of some theory. There are two distinct steps in the technique of theory-formation: first of all, the scientist must formulate alternate hypotheses (generally there will be an infinity of alternatives considered), and secondly, the selection of one definite hypothesis on the basis of the results of experiments. It is the latter step that will be considered here. The former step is just as important, and presumably much more difficult, but it will be ignored in this paper.

We start with a given set of alternative hypotheses, and a series of experiments designed to eliminate incorrect hypotheses. The problem can be stated as follows: given the result of the first n experiments, which hypothesis shall we select?

There is some question as to the number of alternate hypotheses to be considered, and the number of experiments we should plan. Both of these will be taken to be denumerably infinite. In the case of hypotheses, in all interesting examples there will be an infinity of possible explanations (certainly in any case involving measurement), and, on the other hand, there is serious doubt whether a scientist ever *really* considers a nondenumerable infinity of possibilities. As to the experiments, we consider a series (endless in principle) of planned experiments, though, of course, at any one time we will have the results of but a finite number of them.

[The first example to be considered is the classical inductive problem of the *urn.* There is a sealed urn, with an unknown number of white and black balls in it. Through an opening you take out one ball at a time, note its color, replace it, and shake the urn thoroughly. After n draws you must decide what fraction of the balls in the urn is white. Your experiments in this case consist of drawing balls, and the result of n experiments is to tell you that m of the n drawn balls were white. Your possible hypotheses state that some fraction r of the balls in the urn is white, where r is any rational number between 0 and 1. Of course, in practice one can estimate an upper-bound for the number of balls in the urn, but for the sake of the illustration we assume that no such upper-bound is available, hence any proper fraction is possible (including 0 and 1 if we allow the cases where there are no white balls, or no black balls). On the basis of the report that m of n balls were white, we must select some r.

The second example is one involving measurements. We have two independently measurable quantities x and y, and we make a series of measurements (say for values of x between 0 and 1), and try to find how y varies as a function of x, e.g., one quantity may be temperature, the other pressure, for a gas of fixed volume. We will suppose that the scientist has selected *polynomials* with rational coefficients as his possible hypotheses. After n measurements, each one giving us an observed value of y for some preassigned value of x, we have to select some polynomial which is to describe the relation between the two quantities.]

It will be convenient to introduce a simple notation for a typical problem. Let us denote the hypotheses we must choose from by h_i, and the possible outcomes of n experiments by e_j^n. Let e^n be the actual outcome, and h^n the selected hypothesis. (We need the superscript for h, because after 100 experiments we may decide to choose a hypothesis different from the one chosen after 10 experiments.)

[In the urn example the various h_i differ only as to the number r, while e_j^n reports that j of n balls were white. If actually m of them turn out to be white, then e^n will be e_m^n, and h^n is determined by the choice of an r.

In the polynomial example the h_i are polynomials with rational coefficients, such as x or $1/2 - 1/4x + 1/3x^2 \cdot e_j^n$ reports the result of measurement at n points. Thus e^3 may tell us that at the points $x = 1/4,\ 1/2,\ 3/4$ the values $y = 1/8,\ 1/4,\ 3/8$ were observed. h^3 must then select some particular polynomial; in this case it would undoubtedly be $1/2x$.]

There are certain assumptions underlying this procedure, which we must make explicit.

Assumption 1. One (and, of course, only one) of the hypotheses is true.

Of course this assumption may be false; if the evidence indicates that the assumption is likely to be false, then the scientist looks for a new (or wider) set of hypotheses. But then the assumption will again serve as a working hypothesis for the new set of hypotheses. [In the urn example we are certain that one of our hypotheses is true.] We will use h to denote the true hypothesis.

Secondly, we need some measure as to how well the hypothesis in question agrees with the result of the experiments. For this we introduce a measure of deviation. ($m(h_i, e_j^n)$ will be used to denote the measure.) The choice of this measure will be left, to a large degree, arbitrary to allow the scientist a maximum amount of freedom. But in many examples there is a well-accepted measure of deviation. [In the urn example this would be the absolute value of the difference between m/n and the predicted r. In the polynomial case we have some choice, but we may take the average of the absolute differences between predicted values and observed values.]

Assumption 2. The deviation between a given hypothesis and the observed results tends to 0 if and only if the hypothesis is the true one.

This assumption concerns the question whether the experiments are (at least in principle) adequate for the elimination of all false hypotheses.[1]

We are now in a position to formulate the ordinary rule of induction.

Rule 1. Select a hypothesis which is as well in agreement with the observed values as possible.

This is to be interpreted in the sense that for a given e^n we must select an h^n giving us the smallest possible deviation, i.e. making $m(h^n, e^n)$ a minimum.

[For the case of the urn we get "Reichenbach's Rule" exactly.[2] The rule tells us to select the hypothesis with $r = m/n$, which is Reichenbach's posit. (In this case the deviation is 0.)

In the polynomial example we can again make the deviation 0, by selecting a polynomial going through the observed values (assuming that the measurements, as is usual, give us rational values). But here the choice is not uniquely determined — which will soon lead to trouble. Reichenbach does not even consider such problems, and we refrain from adding anything to the rule at this time.]

It is customary in such papers to base the adequacy of a rule entirely on the question of "convergence." Although this will not be our only criterion, we must consider convergence. For this we will need some measure of the difference between hypotheses. (Denote this measure by $d(h_i, h_i')$.)

For the sake of logical economy we could *define* a suitable d in terms of m. We will do this in two steps. First of all we introduce

$$d^n(h_i, h_i') = \min_j \, [m(h_i, e_j^n) + m(h_i', e_j^n)]$$

and then let

[1] We will not take into consideration the additional difficulties introduced by the Indeterminacy Principle.

[2] Hans Reichenbach, *The Theory of Probability* (University of California Press, 1949), section 87.

$$d(h_i, h_i') = \lim_{n\to\infty} d^n(h_i, h_i').$$

We must then make a special assumption about this measure, though this assumption can be satisfied in all usual cases by a suitably chosen m-function.

Assumption 3. For any two hypotheses the limit in the definition of d exists, and it is 0 only if the hypotheses are identical.

[In our two examples the method just described leads to the accepted measures of difference; the absolute difference in r's for the urn hypotheses, and the area between the curves in the polynomial example. In the latter case this is true only if the values of x are taken from "all over" the unit interval, but this is necessary if assumption 2 is to be satisfied.]

We are now supposed to be able to prove that the selected hypotheses converge to the true hypothesis, but this is not always so.

If we introduce d by definition, as above, we can easily show where the difficulty arises. It is easy to prove that $\lim_{n\to\infty} d^n(h^n, h) = 0$,[3] but what we need for convergence is that $\lim_{n\to\infty} d(h^n, h) = 0$, which does not follow.

[In the urn example we do get convergence, and this is the example usually discussed in the literature. However, in the polynomial example we get into trouble because the rule does not determine h^n uniquely. We can select any polynomial passing through the n observed points. Suppose we systematically select a polynomial which oscillates greatly between the observed values, then we can easily get a series of h^n which does not converge.]

What we need in addition to rule 1 is some assurance that the values of the hypothesis at points not observed "fit in well" with the observed values. The usual way of assuring this is to do what any scientist would do in the application of rule 1, namely to use the following rule:

Rule 2. Select a hypothesis which is as well in agreement with the observed values as possible; if there is any choice left, choose the simplest possible hypothesis.

[In the polynomial case this would direct us to choose the polynomial of lowest degree passing through the n points, and then we get convergence.]

In most applications rule 2 will result in convergence, and this is the rule that is undoubtedly in the minds of most writers when they *prove* convergence. We could have introduced it immediately, in place of the first rule, but we wanted to emphasize the point that even in the traditional rule "simplicity" comes in from purely methodological considerations.

We must now deviate entirely from the traditional approach, and start a new line of attack.

III. Finding the True Hypothesis

We have so far discussed only the question of how well the chosen hypothesis approximates the true hypothesis. We will now consider what our chances are of selecting the true hypothesis itself.

[3] By definition $d^n(h^n, h) \leqq m(h^n, e^n) + m(h, e^n)$, which in turn is at most $2m(h, e^n)$ because of the way h^n was selected. But this tends to 0 by assumption 2, hence $d(h^n, h)$ tends to 0.

We find the strange result that in the usual examples, if we use rule 2, our chance of selecting the true hypothesis gets worse and worse! And we even find that the requirements we must put on the results of experiments in order to have the true hypothesis selected are very strange indeed.

[Let there be 1/3 white balls in our urn. In order for rule 2 to select the true hypothesis, we need that $m = 1/3n$. This has the very strange consequence that a necessary condition for the selection of h is that n be divisible by 3. And even for these values of n we find that while the probability of being within a preassigned percentage of the true value tends to 1, the probability of getting the true value itself tends to 0.

The situation in the polynomial case is even more counterintuitive. We can select the true hypothesis only if all n measurements are exactly correct, the probability for which even for $n = 1$ is 0. In short, we see that while rule 2 is designed to get an h^n near h, it is also so designed that it would take a miracle to give us h itself.]

When we take these facts into account, we must realize that rule 2 somehow fails to reproduce what scientists actually do. This could also have been noted from a particular example. [If 503 out of 1000 drawn balls were white, it is most unlikely that the scientist would select the value $r = 503/1000$ instead of $r = 1/2$.[4]]

And there is a third difficulty. While we can prove convergence, we have said nothing at all about how many experiments are needed to arrive at a hypothesis close enough (for practical purposes) to the true hypothesis. Indeed in many fairly simple cases we note that the number of experiments needed is quite large, often too large from a practical standpoint. So we arrive at the following three criticisms of rule 2:

(1) The probability of selecting the true hypothesis tends to 0 as we increase the number of experiments.

(2) If we need high accuracy (h^n must be very close to h), we often have to make n too large for practical purposes.

(3) Rule 2 does not reproduce what scientists actually do.

Let us start with the last point. We note that in the examples quoted, scientists would have chosen a hypothesis different from the one selected by rule 2, even if this hypothesis was not as close to the observed values. Of course, they do not allow very large deviations, but they allow some deviation — recognizing that the results of the experiments need not be exactly the true values. They allow themselves some margin of deviation; they agree as to when a hypothesis is compatible with the evidence, and then they select the simplest one from all such compatible hypotheses.

Rule 3. Select the simplest hypothesis compatible with the observed values. (If there are several, select any one of them.)

The difficulty with this rule is that it contains two very vague terms, "simplest" and "compatible." Our immediate task is to explicate these terms.

[4] This criticism was used by Bertrand Russell in *Human Knowledge* (Simon and Schuster, 1948), p. 370.

Let us begin with the term "compatible," because in this case we have a reasonably clear usage in science. The scientist says that a hypothesis is compatible with the result of observations if these results do not definitely eliminate the hypothesis from the realm of possibilities. As has often been pointed out, this does not, in general, mean that the observations contradict the hypothesis, but only that they make the hypothesis very improbable. More precisely, for a given hypothesis we can calculate the probability of getting observational results within preassigned deviations, and we select some level of deviation such that the outcome is almost certain to fall within it; if it does not, then we eliminate the hypothesis. What this level should be is to a great degree arbitrary. For the sake of this paper we select the simple fixed level at which 99 per cent of the observations will fall within the level.[5]

Definition 1. The hypothesis h_i is *compatible* with the result e^n if, assuming the truth of h_i, there was at least a one per cent chance of getting a deviation as great as $m(h_i,e^n)$.

[In the urn example, given an h_i, i.e., given an r, it is a simple probabilistic calculation to find the compatible and the incompatible results e_j^n. Assuming that h_i is true, we can calculate the probabilities of each *possible* outcome of n experiments, and then we allow an interval around r just large enough so that the total probability of all outcomes in this interval is just 99 per cent. In the polynomial case we must invoke the theory of errors in measurement, which will tell you whether an observed deviation is within the one per cent level or not.]

So we see that under rule 3, for any e^n, there is a good deal of choice left — and we must select the simplest possible hypothesis. But which hypothesis is simplest? It is best to answer this question for examples first, and then try to give a general criterion.

[We have agreed to select 1/2 in preference to 503/1000, and we will readily agree that the selection of 1/3 is better than that of 331/1000. If we are not oversophisticated it should be pretty obvious that the simplicity in these cases lies in the fact that the simpler fractions can be expressed in terms of smaller numbers. Yet it would seem counterintuitive to select 1/3 over 2/3 because of greater simplicity. First of all, they occupy symmetric positions; secondly, 2/3 white balls is the same as 1/3 black balls; and finally, these two fractions would hardly ever be both compatible with the observations. So at least in the urn example we can safely state that simplicity consists in the smallness of the denominator of r. Of course it could be objected that the same fraction can be stated in an infinity of forms, but if we take advantage of this supposed difficulty, then we get a deeper insight into the simplicity ordering. Let us divide all fractions into classes, the kth class having all fractions with denominators $\leqq 2^k$, $k = 0, 1, 2, \ldots$ Then there are few duplications within a given class, and each

[5] Other levels of compatibility could be used as well. As a matter of fact it might be much better to use a criterion that tends to 100 per cent slowly as n increases. This would give us an improvement on the theorem which we will prove later. But since this method leads to difficulties, we will take the simpler criterion for the sake of this paper.

new class contains all the previous ones. (1/3 = 2/6 = 3/9, etc.) Thus we see that allowing greater complexity (less simplicity) coincides with allowing ourselves more freedom of description and greater accuracy.] Hence we note that rule 3 can also be stated as a warning: do not use more precision in your theories than is necessary to explain the observations. For example, in the case of a simple measurement,[6] the rule tells you to use no more digits in your summing up of results than is necessary to be within the experimental error. Hence we get the rule of significant digits!

[In the polynomial case the theory of errors allows us some deviation from the observed values, and we must fit a polynomial of lowest possible degree within this deviation, e.g., if there is a straight line compatible with the observations, we must choose it. (Of course scientists very often choose straight lines even when there is none compatible with the evidence.) So we see that simplicity in this case consists first of all in choosing the lowest exponent possible, and only if there is more than one polynomial of lowest degree compatible with the observations do we take the coefficients into account. We might do the latter by considering the largest denominator occurring in a coefficient.]

We have constructed rule 3 to bring our rules into better agreement with what scientists actually do. We are now in a position to ask: does this improved rule give us any better chance of selecting the true hypothesis? The answer turns out to be emphatically "yes."

There are two reasons why the hypothesis selected by rule 3 might not be the true one. The true hypothesis may not be compatible with the observations; or it might be compatible, but there could be a simpler hypothesis also compatible with the results. The former danger is very slight. According to definition 1 there is always a 99 per cent chance that e^n is compatible with the true hypothesis, h. This was the reason why we chose a percentage as high as 99; we wanted to be almost certain that we do not eliminate the true hypothesis. But is not there a serious danger that simpler hypotheses will also be acceptable (especially since it is so difficult to eliminate hypotheses)? This is indeed the case, but in each example this happens only for a finite number of n; from a certain value of n on it can never happen.

We must look into the reason for this. As we know from statistics, as n increases, the deviations allowed by the compatibility requirement decrease. Hence for high n we can find an interval around the observed values (an interval that can be made as small as required by increasing n) such that all compatible hypotheses lie within this interval. This, of course, is not enough; this only assures convergence under rule 3. But *the characteristic property of orderings according to simplicity* is that for any given hypothesis, even though there may be infinitely many hypotheses at least as simple, we can find an interval within which there is no other hypothesis as simple (or simpler). Hence, by making n

[6] The possible hypotheses in this case are all finite decimal expansions. We order them according to the number of decimal places. Each new class contains the previous ones, since we can always put 0's at the end of the decimal expansions. Then, e.g., if we measure .1234 ± .005, we must select .12.

large enough we can make the interval of compatibility sufficiently small so that if the true hypothesis lies within it, no other hypothesis as simple will be in it. Hence for all sufficiently high n we must select h if it is compatible with the observations. Hence for all sufficiently high n we are 99 per cent sure of selecting h. *This is the justification we offer for rule* 3.

[Let us suppose that 3/8 of the balls are white. There are only a finite number of fractions at least as simple as 3/8, hence there is a closest one. It happens to be 2/5. $2/5 - 3/8 = 1/40$. From the theory of probability we can calculate an n such that if we draw at least that many balls, then r must be within 1/80 of m/n in order to be compatible. Then, if 3/8 is compatible, none of the others at least as simple are compatible with the observations. So from this point on if 3/8 is compatible with e^n, then it must be chosen. But (by the definition of compatibility) there is always a 99 per cent chance of that. Hence from this point on we are practically certain to select the true hypothesis.

The same result holds for the polynomials, but for different reasons. Given the true polynomial, it is not true that there is only a finite number of polynomials as simple or simpler; e.g., all polynomials of lower degree are simpler, and there are infinitely many of these in general. However, it is still true that there is a lower bound (greater than 0) for the differences between the true hypotheses and other polynomials at least as simple.[7] For sufficiently many measurements (the exact number determined by the theory of errors), we can narrow the interval of compatibility sufficiently that if the true hypothesis falls within it, none of the other polynomials which are at least as simple can be compatible with the observations. Hence, from this point on we are again 99 per cent sure of selecting the true hypothesis.]

Let us summarize these results in the form of a theorem.

Theorem: If the true hypothesis is one of the hypotheses under consideration, then — given enough experiments — we are 99 per cent sure of selecting it.[8]

The proof of this theorem was given in the main text above; all that was assumed was that the simplicity ordering has one fundamental property: for each hypothesis we can find an integer such that for n at least as great as this we are assured that, if the hypothesis is compatible with the observations, no other hypothesis as simple is compatible.

We can now state precisely in what sense we propose to explicate the concept of simplicity. It will not be a unique definition, but for each inductive problem we will give a class of possible orders. This will be achieved by stating some necessary conditions for the ordering, the most important being that the order has the fundamental property just described.

But before stating the general definition, let us first see whether we have taken care of all three of the objections raised against the traditional rules. We started with the third objection, that the rules did not correspond to what

[7] The proof of this is not difficult in principle, but too long to be included in this paper.

[8] This result depends on the definition of compatibility (see footnote 5). E.g., had we selected the very common 95 per cent level, we would never be more than 95 per cent sure, but we would be that sure sooner.

scientists actually do. This was taken care of by inserting the "compatible with the observations" clause in place of "closest to the observed values," and by showing that the simplicity order corresponds to the order of going from less precision (less wealth of description) to greater precision. The former point is taken care of by the wording of rule 3, the latter by the first two conditions to be given.

Then we took up the first objection, that our chances of selecting the true hypothesis deteriorated. This is corrected by rule 3, as shown in the proven theorem. All we need for this is the fundamental property of the ordering, given in condition 3 below.

This still leaves one objection. Couldn't the "sufficiently large n" be too large for practical purposes? Actually, in many instances we can show that the n's are quite low. [In the urn example, if 1/2 of the balls are white, we are 99 per cent sure of selecting the true ratio for $n \geqq 8$.] How high this n is depends, of course, on how simple the true hypothesis is.[9] The best we can do is require that the ordering should make the required n's as low as possible. This is not so easy, since one n may be lowered at the cost of raising others. This is a question that deserves a good deal more research, but at least the formulation here given to the problem should help in finding an answer. We will be content with the vague fourth condition below.

Definition 2. Given an inductive problem (as defined in this paper), we say that the hypotheses are *ordered according to simplicity* if we have the following four conditions satisfied:

Condition 1. The hypotheses are divided into sets $H_{(a, \ldots, z)}$, where $a, \ldots, z$ are natural numbers (called the *characteristic numbers*). These sets are ordered lexicographically according to the characteristic numbers. (The hypotheses in earlier sets being called simpler than the ones occurring only in later sets.)

Condition 2. The later sets include the earlier sets in the following sense: $H_{(a, \ldots, k, \ldots, z)}$ is always a subset of $H_{(a, \ldots, k+1, \ldots, z)}$.

Condition 3. For every set H there is an integer N_H such that, if a member of H is compatible with e^n for some $n \geqq N_H$, then no member of H or of any earlier set can be compatible with this e^n.

Condition 4. N_H should in each case be as low as possible. (Or better, each h_i should belong to a set H with an N_H as low as possible.)

This completes the explication. We arrived at a characterization of orders according to simplicity. Although these conditions do not determine the order uniquely in any given problem, very often we find that there is but one natural way of satisfying the conditions. It is hoped that with the improvement of the

[9] This is the point at which an assumption about the "Simplicity of Nature" can come in. But it has to be a relation between the true laws and our ability of discovering them. It would have to take the form: The laws of nature are sufficiently simple that, following the best available inductive methods, man can in a reasonable period of time find them (or find a good approximation of them). Thus it expresses a relation between the n assigned to the true law in our inductive method, and the number of experiments we can actually carry out during some era of science. This point will be developed elsewhere.

fourth condition, and with the addition of new conditions, the explication of simplicity will be considerably advanced in the future.

It is most important to note, however, that the order defined is relative to an inductive problem! It is not true that the number 1/4 need always be simpler than 1/10. [In the urn example it is, but in the case of a simple measurement [10] the former is written as .25, the latter as .1, and hence the latter is simpler.] It should be noted, however, that the same numbers express entirely different hypotheses in different problems. This point may have been one factor that led many people to believe that no definition of simplicity can be given.

IV. Applications

So far we have only considered three extremely simple inductive problems: the urn and polynomial examples running through the text, and the simple measurement discussed in footnote 6. We are now ready to apply our method to some well-known historical problems.

Let us first take the problem of planetary motion in the time of Copernicus. Had Copernicus been familiar with the results of this paper, he could have argued as follows: the planets move in a plane closed curve around the sun. We must consider families of such curves, and order them according to their simplicity. We can in this follow the polynomial example: an ath order polynomial has $a + 1$ parameters. The polynomials were ordered first according to the number of parameters (coefficients) and then according to the values of these parameters. We also had the inclusion theorem, a first order polynomial can be written as a second order one with a 0 coefficient. We must order our curves similarly, making sure that we count only the parameters determining the shape of the path, not those locating them in space. The simplest case is the one-parameter family of circles. So the Greeks were right in trying circular paths first. But by now we see that no circle is compatible with the observed positions. They next tried adding an epicycle to the circle. This family does include circles as special cases (the radius of the epicycle being 0), but it is a three-parameter family. And when they allowed any number of epicycles, they allowed hypotheses of arbitrary complexity, which is methodologically utterly unacceptable.[11] Instead we must search for a two-parameter family of curves having circles as a special case. This family is clearly the family of ellipses (detemined by major and minor axes, circles being the special case where the two are equal). In this one step Copernicus could have anticipated Kepler's main result, *from purely methodological considerations.*[12]

So far our examples had one or two characteristic numbers: number of parameters and the complexity of the values of the parameters. In linear differ-

[10] See footnote 6.

[11] There is a theorem the author heard quoted (though he has seen no proof) that *any* closed convex curve can be approximated as closely as desired by a system of epicycles.

[12] Cf. Karl Popper, *Logik der Forschung* (Julius Springer, 1935), sections 39–46. The author wishes to acknowledge his indebtedness to this book, even though he is only in partial agreement with Dr. Popper.

ential equations we still have the number of parameters determined directly, this time by the order of differentiation. When we come to nonlinear equations, we must take both the order of differentiation and the exponents into account. The resulting order will depend on the class of equations being considered, but in general this will require the introduction of a third characteristic number. In this case the hypotheses will be ordered first according to the order of differentiation, then according to the degree, and finally according to the coefficients.[13] All of these hypotheses are stated for one variable x so far. If there are several independent variables, then we must first order laws according to the number of variables, and then according to the above three characteristic numbers. (I.e., any hypothesis with two variables is simpler than one with three independent variables.) It is according to this last principle that we understand the methodological advantage of a single unified law that can take the place of many disconnected laws; e.g., Newton's laws contain many fewer independent variables than the many unrelated laws, which we had before Newton and which can be derived from Newton's laws, had together.

And finally let us apply our method to the analysis of Einstein's thinking in passing from the Special Theory to the General Theory of Relativity.[14] There were no new facts that failed to be explained by the Special Theory. Einstein was motivated by his conviction that the Special Theory was not the simplest theory that can explain all the observed facts. In accordance with the four characteristic numbers already discussed, we see that any reduction in the number of independent variables will simplify the law, even if its form becomes otherwise more complicated. By the requirement of general covariance Einstein succeeded in replacing the previously independent "gravitational mass" and "inertial mass" by a single concept. This is sufficient to justify a change, but why just *those* gravitational equations? It is possible to show that in order that the equations explain known facts, they had to contain differentiation of at least the second order, and that at most the highest order terms could be linear. This describes a large class of simplest possible hypotheses, which are however narrowed by the condition that the results must (at least in first approximation) agree with what the well-confirmed Special Theory says. It was then shown that there is only one such hypothesis in this simplest class. Since this was the simplest hypothesis compatible with the known facts, Einstein was methodologically perfectly right in saying that this is the law we *must* accept.[15]

[13] This gives an order of ordinal type w^2. In general if we have k characteristic numbers, we get an ordering of type w^k. No examples have so far been found which require order of higher type, but there is little difficulty in extending this method to type w^w and higher types.

[14] It was a conversation with Einstein that first started the author thinking about these problems. Einstein made no metaphysical assumption, and yet simplicity played a central role in his account of his own discovery. It seemed to the author that the revolutionary success of the General Theory cannot be due to a choice whose only justification is convenience.

[15] Einstein is still following the same methodology. He is now trying to reduce the number of independent variables further, by combining Maxwell's Theory with his own, in his Unified Field Theory. He also believes that with this new theory he will be able to achieve a further simplification, namely the elimination of singularities from the laws of Physics. (This would lead to a new characteristic number(s) relating to the number and type of singularities in the law, with a continuous law being the simplest one — having 0 singularities.) If a philosopher may venture to make a comment, the present paper indicates that Einstein is again using the right method, in spite of the opinion of the majority of his colleagues.

V. Further Problems

Let us return to the question of the relation of this method to Reichenbach's posits. We have pointed out that his rule of induction agrees with rule 1 (and 2) for the urn example. He points out that instead of his posit, m/n, we could equally well have posited $m/n + c_n$, where c_n is an arbitrary function of n, tending to 0 with increasing n.[16] He believes that any choice of c_n is as good as any other, and hence he sets $c_n \equiv 0$, on grounds of "descriptive simplicity." Our posit, the simplest fraction compatible with m/n, can also be thought of as a choice of a function c_n (since the interval of compatibility tends to 0, the difference between our posit and Reichenbach's must also tend to 0), only c depends not only on n, but also on m. Hence we argue that Reichenbach is quite right in saying that the posit must be of the form $m/n + c_n$, but we argue that there is one choice of c_n superior to others (since it gives us not only convergence but an excellent chance of finding the true hypothesis), and that it is not the choice of $c_n \equiv 0$.

We must also show the relation between this paper and the work on degree of credibility (confirmation). Carnap in his recent monograph [17] treats Reichenbach's posits as estimates of the true ratio. This sounds reasonable, but when we consider the very special sense in which Carnap uses "estimate," it does not seem that he is correct in his interpretation. If he were correct, then some very reasonable posits would commit Reichenbach to a most unreasonable measure of credibility. Reichenbach, on the other hand, claims that he is not committed to any measure of credibility, and we see no reason for doubting this claim. A posit is a method of selecting one hypothesis from several possible ones, not a general method of estimation. We can find a connection if we adopt the very intuitive rule of selection: From a set of hypotheses select the one having the highest degree of credibility. Then a method of positing tells us only maximum credibility values, not all values. There are several credibility measures that would give us Reichenbach's posits, but not the counterintuitive measure that Carnap assigns to Reichenbach. If our interpretation is correct, then it is easy to show the connection between our rule and credibility. We adopted a rule of selection different from the one just stated. Ours would read: From a set of hypotheses select the simplest one having a high degree of credibility. Just how high the degree has to be depends on our definition of compatibility, and on how the particular credibility measure is constructed.

There are several problems left unsolved by this paper, and the author sincerely hopes that other people will be interested in working on these (often very difficult) questions. The most important of these is to find a precise form for the fourth simplicity-condition. The purpose of this condition is to assure fast convergence, that is to enable us to reach the 99 per cent level of certainty with as few experiments as possible. A great deal more work will have to be done in investigating the relation between the ordering of hypotheses in this

[16] *Op. cit.*, p. 447.

[17] Rudolf Carnap, *The Continuum of Inductive Methods* (University of Chicago Press, 1952), p. 44.

method, and the resulting N_H's. This is the problem on which the recent statistical methods should prove most helpful.

Another possible method of getting faster convergence is a modification of rule 3. We might try to establish a level of simplicity and then select the hypothesis on this level which is closest to the observed values (this is the converse of our rule), or try to find a criterion combining an optimum of simplicity and compatibility.[18] The former method does not give us our theorem. But the combined method may very well give us our theorem, and faster convergence.

And finally, there is the problem that our conditions allow too many different orders. We should try the method out in many more examples, and try to find additional conditions. Ultimately we should be able to prove either that the order is uniquely determined by the conditions, or that the remaining orders are in some sense equally good.

These problems are of great methodological importance, and they are intrinsically interesting; they deserve careful study, far beyond these first considerations.

[18] I am indebted to Prof. Nelson Goodman for this suggestion.

23 *Inductive Simplicity*

ROBERT ACKERMANN

The fact that simplicity has been linked with induction by many philosophers of science, some of whom have proposed or supported criteria of "inductive simplicity," means that the problem must be given some serious attention. I take "inductive simplicity" as a title, however, only by way of concession to these historical treatments, since it is precisely the burden of my paper to show that there is no such thing. So much for the conclusion. I shall spend the remainder of my time arguing for it.

A particular problem of induction, which may appropriately be called the "curve-fitting" problem, has been isolated for attention by those who claim that some rule of simplicity is an integral part of the inductive process. The problem is usually introduced by allowing experimental observations to be represented by points on a real plane, but the alternative hypotheses invoked to explain those observations to be represented by curves drawn through the plane. In this simple model a satisfactory hypothesis is represented by a curve

From *Philosophy of Science*, Vol. 28, No. 2, 1961, pp. 152–160. Reprinted by permission of the editor of *Philosophy of Science* and the author.

passing through, or very near to, each designated point in the plane. It is at once obvious that many curves can be drawn so as to satisfy this intuitive criterion. But science, so it is said, can only accept one. We may solve that problem, according to the tradition that I am referring to, by drawing *the* simplest curve through the points and accepting that as representing the hypothesis that science accepts. This is, however, but the description of a solution that can be no better than the notion of simplicity involved. It is not likely that all of the problems usually associated with induction could be dissolved by an adequate solution to the curve-fitting problem. On the other hand, it will be assumed here that an adequate account of inductive inference would have to provide a solution to this laboratory paradigm. Induction and curve-fitting, then, are related areas for any adequate philosophy of science, and we shall examine the latter here because specific proposals for inductive rules of simplicity do exist for the curve-fitting problem.

It would only be fair to examine in detail some of the specific proposals extant in the literature. This procedure, in view of the nature of this symposium, would not be optimum strategy. I would merely call your attention to the passages on simplicity in Harold Jeffreys' *Scientific Inference*, Karl Popper's *The Logic of Scientific Discovery*, and John Kemeny's "The Use of Simplicity in Induction" as representative of attempts to propose some workable rule of simplicity as a criterion for making inductive inferences.[1] In spite of the differences in notation and approach taken in these articles, they exhibit a remarkable similarity in overall strategy. It is obviously the case that a scientist can, by means of ordinary algebraic manipulations, find a curve representing a suitable hypothesis that will pass through all of the observation points. The remarkable fact to these writers is that often the curve accepted is quite different from the curve that algebraic methods would produce. For example, restricting ourselves to polynomials, often a quadratic equation might be taken as representing the acceptable hypothesis where an algebraic technique fitting all of the points would result in a polynomial of high degree. Obviously the problem is to find some compromise between simplicity and fit of the data, since the simple curve accepted does not necessarily pass through every observation point. There is no need to seek rigor here; simple laws of mechanics are not taken to be disconfirmed by the experiments conducted in sophomore lab sections, where experience quickly confirms that few sophomore experimenters ever produce observational data that coincides with what the already accepted theories of physics predict.

The approach of the authors that I have referred to is quite natural. They attempt to find a simplicity ordering of all possible scientific hypotheses which the scientist is bid to work through until he finds the simplest hypothesis in the ordering that is in some sense compatible with his data. The notion of compatibility with the data is not sufficiently clarified in any of these accounts, but that need not concern us here. It can be shown independently of that difficulty

[1] See references [6], [7] and [9].

that a simplicity ordering of the kind envisaged has not been satisfactorily accomplished. Both Jeffreys and Popper take the simplicity ordering to be in terms of the number of parameters in the equations being considered as possible hypotheses with respect to some such set of data, and in general, the scientist considers those equations with one parameter first, then those with two parameters, and so on. [2] I believe that it can be shown of both of these orderings that they are not well-defined, and that they entail the difficulty that they are hardly practical, since Galileo, for example, under one construal of these proposals, would still be leafing through a book of equations without having come to the appropriate solution to some of his specific problems. Practicality is not essential, unless a philosopher of science wishes to propose inductive rules that are to be of use to the scientist, and that is just the kind of rule that the simplicity ordering is taken to be. Kemeny is more sophisticated in his approach than either Popper or Jeffreys, and escapes some of the direct problems with their ordering by proposing, not an overall ordering of all possible candidates for scientific hypotheses, but an ordering relativized to specific experimental situations. Unfortunately, however, his proposals amount to descriptions of measure functions which would yield the ordering but which do not, as they stand, enable the scientist to find the ordering in any particular case. The only concrete examples involve functions which are ordered once again according to the number of their parameters, or similar intuitive orderings in one case of more complex functions than polynomials. Kemeny explicitly points out that he intends his article only to prepare the ground for an adequate treatment of the problem, but his own formulation contains the patent and irresolved problem that while 1/3 is earlier in one simplicity ordering than 1/10, the order of these numbers is reversed when their equivalents in terms of decimal expansions are considered. Kemeny attempts to avoid this by the obscure claim that "$f(x) = .25$" and "$f(x) = 1/4$" express different hypotheses with respect to the same problem. [3] We thus reach the point where it becomes obvious that the traditional accounts of inductive simplicity in terms of a simplicity ordering have failed to solve the problem, or at least I believe we would reach that point if we had the time to give each of these authors a careful treatment.

There is another source for information on the curve-fitting problem in the laboratory handbooks and treatises on practical analysis. But these books will not solve our problem. The scientist is greeted in their pages with something like the following: [4]

> The nature of the experiment may give us a hint as to the form of the equation which will best represent the data. Otherwise the problem is more indeterminate.

Actually, these laboratory manuals are designed to answer the following question: "Given a set of data points, and a curve form, what is the best curve of that form that can be drawn through the data within a desired degree of accu-

[2] [6], p. 39, and [9], p. 142.
[3] [7], p. 403. [Ed. note: See page 309 of this volume for Kemeny's article.]
[4] [8], p. 121.

racy?" Clearly, this is not the problem of simplicity with respect to induction with which we started. For that reason, the discussion of this kind of literature will terminate at this point. Experimental design may enable us to discriminate between hypotheses which have already been proposed, but that discrimination is on the basis of evidential fit, and not on the basis of simplicity. Let us tentatively conclude that none of the laboratory handbooks solves the problems surrounding inductive simplicity.

The observation which appears to be most damaging to optimism in connection with the problem of curve-fitting is the observation that the unsatisfactory results of previous investigations appear to have occurred in a context where certain assumptions have implicitly been made that severely restrict the potential difficulties with curve-fitting. Most of the authors concerned with the problem have proposed solutions which would completely collapse under the removal of these restrictions. Since the assumptions do not appear to be warrantable in general, their removal in an adequate philosophy of science seems imperative. In particular, three such assumptions will be mentioned at the present time: the assumption of continuity of functions, the assumption of the adequacy of measurement, and the assumption of nonstatistical assumptions.

What is here called the assumption of continuity refers to the tendency among philosophers of science to limit the functions available to the scientist in some *a priori* fashion. Certain historical accidents may account for this, such as the fact that many philosophers of science have taken classical mechanics as their paradigm case of a well-developed science. The difficulty is the following: If the results of experimentation are taken quite simply to be points in a plane, there does not appear to be any reason why the curve drawn through them should be continuous, except that most scientific laws to the present have, as a matter of fact, been continuous where they might be represented as curves through data. That continuity has been assumed in the treatments appears obvious from the measure of complexity which is taken to be related to the number of parameters in the accounts of Jeffreys and Popper. The manner in which these authors have spoken seems to indicate that they were thinking of polynomials in their treatments to the virtual exclusion of other kinds of functions. Polynomials, of course, are continuous curves, and attention to them exclusively seems to promise hope for an application of the intuitive notion of drawing the "smoothest" curve through a set of points as a possible explication of inductive simplicity. It is equally obvious that not all functions requisite to the purposes of science are polynomials. For example, the importance of transcendental functions to scientific investigation is not accounted for in any of the treatments so far discussed. Consider the simple transcendental functions "$y = \sin(x)$," "$y = \log(x)$," and "$y = e^x$." None of the simplicity orderings referred to discuss the position of these functions in a simplicity ordering. It is possible, of course, to get an approximation to them by means of power series, but that would result in taking them to be extremely complex, which is counterintuitive. On the other hand, lumping them with the simplest functions causes the embarassment to Galileo that I suggested earlier in that the early part of the ordering is so dense that it would not be practical to work through it with respect to some given scientific problem.

When the possibility of discontinuous functions is admitted, the situation becomes vastly more complicated than any extant treatment has even intimated. Even if a solution of curve-fitting that yields a unique continuous curve could be found, it seems too severe to put an *a priori* limit on scientific hypotheses to the set of equations representing continuous functions. In any given problem, it would not be known necessarily whether discontinuous functions were a possible solution, and hence there might often be no warrant for using the technique for continuous functions already described. And, of course, recent developments in science include discontinuous functions which appear as deductions from theories which are at least tentatively accepted. In an experiment to test such a theory, discontinuous curves would have to be mapped onto the laboratory data, so that at least in principle the curve-fitting problem cannot be restricted to continuous curves in an adequate philosophy of science.

By the assumption of the adequacy of measurement is meant what seems to be the supposition that enough data should, in principle, eliminate an infinite number of hypotheses, leaving only a finite number from which choice might be made by means of a modified simplicity ordering. Lurking behind this notion seems to be the old fallacy that subtraction of an infinite set from an infinite set must leave a finite set. In the case of curve-fitting, it is not enough to show, for example, that the scientist begins with an enumerable set of hypotheses and can eliminate an enumerable set of them by experiment. There can still be an enumerable set of hypotheses left to consider.

But this is only a digression: the assumption of the adequacy of measurement can be shown to have undesirable consequences on other grounds. The use of empirical measurement can only justify use of rational numbers in describing experimental results. Any theory of curve-fitting which results in the notion that a hypothesis must fit the data is not sufficient to explain why certain hypotheses with real numbers in their expressions are an integral part of science. The occurrence of π and of e, for example, cannot be easily explained on the basis of extrapolation from observational data. This obvious point in connection with the application of mathematics to scientific experiment is so well known that it is difficult to believe that philosophers who have examined the problem could have taken the position that experimental fit will rule out all but a finite number of hypotheses in conjunction with some rule of simplicity. After any number of observations, an infinite number of real-valued functions will still be compatible with the experimental results. Hence, to put it mildly, it is somewhat hasty to suppose that parameters may be decisively evaluated by a little work in the lab. This difficulty is in fact crucial, and it seems to hold the key to a fundamental error in supposing that curve-fitting may be done in terms of a simplicity ordering.

The assumption which was referred to as the assumption of non-statistical hypotheses suggests that most accounts have had a tendency to underestimate the importance of statistical data in curve-fitting. Accounts of curve-fitting in the philosophical literature have often tacitly assumed that a scientist has one set of points through which he desires to draw a curve with as little error as possible. The difficulty which arises over the point of repeated experiment, by the same scientist or other scientists, is not touched upon. Now a law, which is what these discussions have assumed the curve through the data to represent ultimately, is expected to remain the same for every such experiment. The criteria given, however, do not allow the scientist to make a very clear choice when more than one set of data confronts him, that is, when conflicting data are gathered on more than one experiment. It might be supposed that the conflict can be resolved by further experiment. But what is to be done as the result of the experiment is not at all clear. Should apparently "strange" results which have only been taken once be thrown out? This kind of abandonment of data has caused some embarrassment in scientific history, and it is a moot and extremely difficult point as to whether data incongruity should be resolved by abandoning apparently bad observations, or when the hypothesis should be made more complex to account for the apparent oddities in the data. These problems are important to any curve-fitting problem, since in practice a scientist is likely not to consider the results of experiment as points on a page, but as observations which he may have the right to interpret and juggle with before determining the result. It is true that sometimes such juggling, in the hands of an expert, results in a scientific advance. The view of the previously considered philosophers of science appears perilously close to taking the data of an experiment to be *just* a collection of points on a page, and it is not an adequate explication of scientific practice

One objection should probably be dispelled at this point. It might be supposed that in a sense *all* data are statistical. For example, it might be claimed that statements thought to be tautologous can only be shown to be so by some operation, like the truth table technique. It might be further claimed, on statistical grounds, that some statement commonly taken to be tautologous is in fact not, on the grounds that everyone constructing the truth table has always made the same mistake. This is a not uninteresting problem, but it does not have immediate application to our difficulty with inductive simplicity. Someone might claim that in principle scientific determinations could become as accurate as truth table determinations, due to refinement in measure techniques. If this were to happen, then the simplicity orderings suggested might receive a new importance, and the only talk of statistical evidence would reduce to the kind of perplexity referred to in the example of the incorrect truth table. This line of argument will not do. It can be shown, or perhaps better, described, how a truth table is constructed in an accurate manner. Each entry, for example, is either t or f. Perhaps no one has accomplished the right truth table for some given expression, but it certainly exists. This is not true of all scientific determinations. To go back to an earlier point, no experiment can discriminate between two hypotheses one of which contains a real value in its expression and the other a rational value in the same place which is arbitrarily close to the real value. It would thus appear that the problem of discriminating between analytic functions and polynomials, say, of an appropriate sort, represents an inherent limitation on curve-fitting which is not analogous to any difficulty in certain other disciplines, such as logic.

What follows from the isolation of these three assumptions as implicit limitations on the solution to the curve-fitting problem? It would appear that they have no justification within a philosophy of science, and dropping them seems to damage severely hopes for any notion of inductive simplicity along the lines of finding a simplicity ordering for the possible hypotheses of science.

There are difficulties, moreover, with the notion of inductive simplicity even should the program be completed in spite of dropping the assumptions. For example, supposing a well-ordering of scientific hypotheses is discovered along the lines that have already been suggested, and indeed, I have no *proof* that such a well-ordering could not be found, only the difficulties that I have mentioned. Given such a well-ordering, two serious problems would still confront us: the notion of simplicity invoked to justify the ordering, and the problem of its mesh with a total philosophy of science.

We have seen that some of the authors who have treated inductive simplicity have taken an ordering of polynomials in terms of increasing numbers of parameters. This, however, is far from justifying the ordering in terms of some explicit notion of simplicity. In other words, the ordering is said to be in terms of simplicity; but it is questionable what notion of simplicity is really important here. We might say to a scientist that the proper method to use when searching for a hypothesis to fit his data is to start at one end of the ordering and work to the other until some hypothesis is met which is reasonably well in accord with the data (defining "reasonably" in some fairly precise fashion, if possible). This would amount to a rather mechanical procedure designed to facilitate a planned examination of all possible laws. Any well-ordering of scientific hypotheses would serve this purpose. The question is then whether any clear notion of simplicity can be invoked to justify the ordering as a simplicity ordering. It is a reasonable contention that no such notion has been adequately discussed by the philosophers treating inductive simplicity in the past, and that no such notion is really available. If that is the case, it would appear that the use of simplicity in this connection is entirely gratuitous.

For any practical purpose, the suggestion that the scientist must work laboriously through an infinite number of hypotheses in a simplicity ordering sounds more like the temporary solution to a philosophical impasse than an adequate description of what scientists have done even in rigorous moments. It is this which leads to the suggestion that inductive simplicity does not mesh well with what would often be taken to be an adequate philosophy of science. To summarize, what is available in the way of information about the ways in which scientists actually work appears to suggest that scientists are able to work efficiently while only considering some small number of hypotheses. Scientific practice, in fact, is often concerned with the evaluation of only two or three alternate hypotheses. It would appear, therefore, that the curve-fitting problem as it is usually presented is not an adequate explication of the problem of choosing between rival hypotheses in day to day scientific practice.

Several observations may account for this discrepancy, but the most important one is concerned with what the scientist does when he experiments. The proposals for curve-fitting seemed to suppose that the scientist was only concerned with observing data without bias which he would later use to construct a hypothesis or hypotheses. As a matter of fact, the scientist rarely appears to engage in this sort of activity. More usually some hypothesis has been suggested, perhaps from some general theory by deductive inference, or even by a hunch on the part of the investigator. The experiment may then be undertaken to see whether the data predicted by the hypothesis is in close agreement with observation. An analogy to mathematics may be useful. Mathematical theorems may be found either by deduction from previously established theories, or by the subsequent discovery of some proof for a theorem which is originally considered merely as a proposal or conjecture, which, if proved, would prove interesting in some way. Part of the difficulty with the inductive approach to curve-fitting that we have been considering is that it tends to make experiment determine the theoretical structure of science to an extent which minimizes or ignores the important way in which previously considered theories and hypotheses determine experiment, and experimental interpretations in science.[5] The scientist is often not dealing with an infinite number of hypotheses in considering the results of an experiment, but with a finite number determined by the theoretical structure available to him in constructing the experiment. Experiment can thus appear to be a justification of an already conceived state of affairs rather than the basis of some type of inductive inference. It should be noted here that hypotheses to be confirmed by an experiment may occur at a number of levels. For example, a scientist may wish to determine whether a hypothesis stating that X and Y are related by a linear function is confirmable by experiment. Here any observed linear relationship would confirm the hypothesis. It is not convenient to think of the scientist as considering every linear relationship as a prior possibility, since any observed relationship of that kind will suffice to confirm, or partially confirm, the *one* hypothesis that he has in mind.

It might immediately be objected that we have just crossed to the other extreme, and that this view of the experimental situation is equally false to scientific practice. Many experiments are certainly run to *determine* a previously unknown quantity in some scientific statement. For example, theory may not suggest a value for x in the singular statement "The coefficient of expansion of this particular piece of iron is x." An experiment may be designed to find such a coefficient by observation. Such a determination, however, seems really to be the result of temporary ignorance as to some desired explanation of a wide range of events. Most such determinations, without auxiliary theory, do not suffice to permit prediction, and are consequently defective as candidates for scientific hypotheses. An extrapolation to a scientific hypothesis from data is always taken as more unsatisfactory by scientists than the confirmation in the laboratory of a hypothesis deduced from some useful theoretical structure.

One difficulty in the preceding proposals appears to be that it is implicitly

[5] This is a familiar notion in the philosophy of science. See discussions in [2] and [1].

assumed that "acceptance" of a hypothesis by scientists is a well defined notion, when as a matter of fact it is not very clear at all. Certainly *science* accepts nothing, in the sense that human beings do, and we are forced to search for some explanation in terms of what scientists do. Now the body of scientists would be a very difficult group to define in order to conform to an intuitive notion that acceptance by all scientists would constitute acceptance by science as an institution. This problem, obviously, needs attention.

Falling back on the familiar figure of speech as though it were meaningful, however, we still have problems with the notion of acceptance. It seems to be assumed in most of the traditional discussions of the philosophy of science that a given hypothesis is either accepted or not accepted by science. The advantages of such a view are numerous, but it is questionable whether these advantages are compatible with an adequate analysis. It would appear that the coefficient of expansion of iron as determined by experiment is not accepted by scientists in the same way as, say, the theory of relativity. A complete study of this problem might well show that the figure for the coefficient is always taken to be approximate, and subject to revision, while the theory of relativity may represent in scientists' minds a complete, and *simple*, explanation of all relevant cosmological data. Although this is not likely to remain a permanent view, if we regard the mortality rate of theories in the history of science, it does seem that the theory of relativity is accepted in a "different spirit" than the coefficient of expansion of iron as extrapolated from a series of experiments. Some explanation of this may be found in the way that the theory of relativity functions as a fundamental law, from which many familiar and tentatively accepted law-like statements can be deduced, while the fundamental law or laws from which coefficients of expansion can be deduced is still a desideratum for physics. Until such laws are discovered, the approximate determinations of the laboratory appear to be an *ad hoc* blemish on the theoretical structure of physics.

Any simplicity ordering of the kind envisioned by the proponents of inductive simplicity thus appears to be an arbitrary device for selecting one extrapolation out of an infinite number of alternative hypotheses compatible with the experimental data. It would thus appear that curve-fitting treatments leave untouched a great many important and crucial experiments in science by leaving unexplained the relationship of theory to the hypotheses being tested by experiment, while they do deal only with experiments which yield provisional determinations of quantities until such time that they can be incorporated into science as deductions from higher level hypotheses.

The conclusions to this probe of inductive simplicity are thus rather negative. Taking the special problem of curve-fitting, it has been suggested that no simplicity ordering of the kind desired has been developed, and that there are strong arguments, although not a proof, militating against the completion of any such proposal. It would further seem that the notion of inductive simplicity along the lines explored in connection with the curve-fitting problem accounts for only a small portion of actual scientific practice, and that it fails to account satisfactorily for an experiment designed to confirm a hypothesis or to choose among a finite set of already proposed hypotheses. Indeed, the difficulties with the notion of inductive simplicity force attention to the notions of simplicity as related to scientific systems, where experiments are designed to test the deductive consequences of these systems. Simplicity of systems, which has been explored by Nelson Goodman among others, has received fairly precise explication, and it seems that hopes for a clear and useful notion of simplicity may well lie in that direction.[6]

[6] Goodman's notion is developed in [3], [4], and [5]. References to other proposals are to be found in [4].

REFERENCES

[1] Braithwaite, Richard B., *Scientific Explanation*, Cambridge, 1955.
[2] Duhem, Pierre. *The Aim and Structure of Physical Theory*. Princeton, 1954.
[3] Goodman, Nelson. "Axiomatic Measurement of Simplicity. *The Journal of Philosophy*, LII(1955), pp. M09–722.
[4] Goodman, Nelson. "Recent Developments in the Theory of Simplicity." *Philosophy and Phenomenological Research*, XIX, (1959), pp. 429–446.
[5] Goodman, Nelson. *The Structure of Appearance*. Cambridge, 1951.
[6] Jeffreys, Harold. *Scientific Inference*. Cambridge, 1957.
[7] Kemeny, John G. "The Use of Simplicity in Induction." *Philosophical Review*, LXII (1953), pp. 391–408.
[8] Lipka, Joseph. *Graphical and Mechanical Computation*. London, 1921.
[9] Popper, Karl R. *The Logic of Scientific Discovery*. New York, 1959.

IV
The Justification of Induction

IV
The Justification of Induction

Introduction

Hume's Problem

The problem of the justification of induction was first explicitly posed by David Hume and it can be put rather simply: Reasoning about matters of fact is non-demonstrative reasoning for we cannot logically infer from the existence of one thing to the existence of another. But if there is no logical connection between matters of fact, how are we to justify those inferences that we draw when we are reasoning about matters of fact in science and ordinary life? It is to no avail to say that such reasoning is probable. The argument that some future occurrence of an event is probable on the basis of past occurrences of a similar event *presupposes* that the future will resemble the past. But this presupposition is an assumption about matters of fact, hence it is not a necessary truth. How then is it to be established? Surely not on the basis of experience. Arguments from experience themselves presuppose that the future will resemble the past; thus they cannot be used to establish this matter of fact.

Most philosophers have found Hume's answer to this problem hard to accept. Hume maintained that we cannot in any way *show* that the future will resemble the past. Our belief in the reliability of reasoning about matters of fact is based upon custom or habit and has no rational foundation.

Attempts to Answer Hume

Hume's attack on inductive reasoning, if correct, seems to undercut all of science and common sense. It is hardly surprising, therefore, that inductive logicians have devoted a great deal of energy to the attempt to refute him. In this section we shall discuss a number of different approaches to the justification of induction. We have grouped them under the following headings: (1) inductive justifications (2) metaphysical justifications (3) *a priori* justifications (4) pragmatic justifications (5) dissolutions of the problems by linguistic analysis.

Inductive Justifications

One of the most natural approaches to the justification of induction proceeds along inductive lines. It is argued that past inductive inferences have been successful and it is inferred on the basis of these past successes that future inductive inferences will probably be successful. As Hume points out, however, this approach can easily become circular.

Consider a rule *R* that would permit singular predictive inferences: "If 'Most *A*'s so far examined in a wide variety of circumstances have been *B*,' and '*X* is *A*,' then we can infer probably '*X* will be be *B*.' " The question now arises how rule *R* is to be justified. The answer forthcoming is "by induction." This presumably means that the future use of rule *R* would be justified by past successful uses of rule *R*, i.e. that if past inferences made by means of rule *R* from true premises usually had true conclusions, then it would be probable that the next inference made by means of rule *R* from true premises would have a true conclusion. But it would seem that rule *R*, the very rule to be justified, would have to be used in this inductive justification of rule *R*. For how else could one infer from "Most uses of *R* so far examined in a wide variety of circumstances have been successful" and "This is a use of *R*" to probably "This use of *R* will be successful"?

The controversy over an inductive justification of induction is by no means dead, however. Arguments over this issue are still waged in philosophical periodicals.[1] One of the most sophisticated attempts to justify inductive inferences by induction is that of R. B. Braithwaite. It should be noted that Braithwaite, whose views are presented in the pages that follow, is keenly aware of the problem of circularity and takes great pains to avoid it. As Robert C. Coburn in his critique of Braithwaite points out, however, Braithwaite may have given a non-circular argument for an inductive justification of inductive inferences at the cost of making his position completely unsatisfactory and even paradoxical.

Metaphysical Justifications

Some inductive logicians, skeptical of ever finding an adequate inductive justification of induction, have turned to metaphysics. Certain metaphysical assumptions about the world, it is argued, will give induction all the support it needs. Different inductive logicians have given different accounts of the metaphysical assumptions needed to justify induction. In the selections that follow, the views of two inductive logicians are presented. John Stuart Mill argues that the uniformity of nature must be presupposed and Bertrand Russell argues that five postulates of scientific inference are needed.

Two basic questions can be asked about this kind of approach to the justification of induction:

(1) Are the writer's assumptions sufficient for establishing the inductive inferences we want to establish?
(2) How are these assumptions themselves to be established?

[1] See Peter Achinstein, "The Circularity of Self-Supporting Inductive Arguments," *Analysis*, Vol. 22, No. 6, 1962, pp. 138–141; Max Black, "Self-Support and Circularity: A Reply to Mr. Achinstein," *Analysis*, Vol. 23, No. 2, 1962, pp. 43–44; Peter Achinstein, "Circularity and Induction," *Analysis*, Vol. 23, No. 6, 1963, pp. 123–127.

(1) There is reason to think that neither the assumptions made by Mill nor by Russell are sufficient for establishing our ordinary inductive inferences. We have already seen that Mill's eliminative type of induction must presuppose some restriction on the number of possible laws of nature. Mill presupposes the principle that nature is uniform, but Cohen and Nagel argue in their critique of Mill that the Principle of the Uniformity of Nature is by no means sufficient to establish general statements and that its vague formulation prevents its application to any specific situation.

Bertrand Russell is aware of many of the problems inherent in the views of Mill and others who have approached the justification of induction in this way and tries to overcome these by means of his five postulates of scientific inference. William Hay argues in his critique of Russell that it is doubtful whether these postulates are either sufficient or necessary for the justification of inductive inferences. According to Hay, Russell's postulates do not give one the right to believe that a *particular* regularity he may observe will continue into the future; at best they give him the right to believe that *some* regularity or other will continue. It should be clear that this is little help in justifying a particular generalization.

(2) Even if we were to grant that the assumptions introduced by Mill and Russell in order to justify induction were adequate to their task, it is not clear how they themselves could be established. Mill argues that the Principle of the Uniformity of Nature is to be established by induction; the problem is whether this can be done without using this very assumption.

Hay argues that Russell's five postulates face the same problem as does Mill's Principle of the Uniformity of Nature: We are not given any good reason to believe them and any attempt to establish them by scientific or common sense procedures would have to assume them.

A priori Justifications

The first difficulty faced by metaphysical justifications of induction, namely that the assumptions made are not adequate to their task, can be easily solved: new assumptions can be added until the set of assumptions is sufficient to justify the inductive inferences we want to make. The second problem, however, seems to be without a solution: the assumptions made, unless they are to be taken on faith, must be established by induction; yet induction must presuppose them.

This dilemma naturally suggests another approach to the justification of induction. If some premises of an inductive argument can be established *a priori*, then these premises together with evidential premises would justify conclusions that go beyond the evidence. This approach would not face the problem of the metaphysical approach: inductive inferences would not be required in order to establish any premises of the argument. In a selection that follows, Donald C. Williams argues that induction can indeed be justified in just such an *a priori* fashion.

Williams argues that the following statement can be established *a priori* by means of the mathematical theory of permutations and combinations: In a finite population most of the samples of *n*-members, if *n* is large, differ very little from the statistical make-up of the population. This purely *a priori* and necessarily true statement provides the major premise for what Williams calls a statistical syllogism.

Consider, for example, the following argument:

(1) At least 95% of 2500-member samples of Bostonians differ not more than 2% from the whole population in regard to the fraction of their members that are Irish.

(2) This sample which is 70% Irish is a 2500-member sample of Bostonians.

(3) Therefore, it is highly probable that this sample differs not more than 2% from the whole population in respect to the fraction of its members which are Irish.

Williams emphasizes that the major premise in this kind of argument is not a factual premise but an *a priori* statement which can be established by mathematical reasoning. The minor premise is established by observation. Hence if we accept the statistical syllogism, we appear to have good grounds for inferring from a sample drawn from a population to the statistical make-up of the population; we seem to need no more than observation and the mathematical theory of permutations and combinations to go beyond observation. In short, we seem to have a solid answer to the problem posed by Hume: the argument is not circular and no metaphysical presuppositions are necessary.

Crucial questions can be raised about Williams' argument, however: (1) Is the statistical syllogism a legitimate mode of inference? (2) Does Williams' argument rest on an implicit factual assumption?

(1) It has been argued that the answer to the first question is "No"; that the statistical syllogism can lead to inconsistencies. Consider an example given by S. F. Barker in *Induction and Hypothesis.*[2] Assume that Jones is a Texan and that 99 per cent of Texans are millionaires. Then by means of the statistical syllogism we can argue:

99 percent of Texans are millionaires.
Jones is a Texan.
Therefore it is highly probable that Jones is a millionaire.

Assume also that Jones is a philosopher and that only 1 percent of philosophers are millionaires. Then we can argue:

1 percent of philosophers are millionaires.
Jones is a philosopher.
Therefore it is highly improbable that Jones is a millionaire.

Thus the statistical syllogism leads from true premises to incompatible conclusions.

[2] S. F. Barker, *Induction and Hypothesis* (Ithaca, N. Y.: Cornell University Press, 1957), pp. 75–78.

It might be suggested that the incompatibility can be prevented by taking account of the total evidence available. But, as Barker points out, this would be tantamount to giving up arguments which take the form of a statistical syllogism. The statistical syllogism can contain only two statements as premises, but usually our total evidence does not consist of just two statements.

(2) According to Dickinson Miller in his critique of Williams' views included here, the answer to the second question is "Yes." Miller argues that Williams must assume, at the very least, that the sample mentioned in the minor premise of a statistical syllogism is a member of a class of samples of an *existing* larger population mentioned in the major premise. Unless this is assumed the supposedly analytic, hence factually empty, major premise can provide no support for the inferences which go beyond the evidence stated in the minor premise. Thus to return to our example, it must be assumed that the sample of Boston Irish mentioned in the minor premise is a member of a class of samples of an *existing* larger population of Boston Irish before the conclusion can be said to follow. But the major premise in a statistical syllogism is supposed to be a purely analytic statement and it is well-known that nothing existential follows from such a premise. Hence, the purely analytic major premise in conjunction with the factual minor premise cannot yield a factual conclusion that goes beyond the minor premise.

Pragmatic Justifications

The problems inherent in the inductive, metaphysical and *a priori* approaches to the justification of induction have suggested to some inductive logicians that in an important sense of the term "justified" induction cannot be justified. Hume was quite right, they argue; past evidence gives us no reason to *believe* the conclusions of inductive arguments. But this is no cause for despair. Inductive inferences can be justified in another sense; such inferences can be justified on *practical* grounds. We have good practical reasons, they say, for the use of inductive principles, for *if* knowledge of the future is to be had, *then* the method of induction will produce such knowledge. It may be asked, however, why this is so? How can we actually know that inductive methods will give us knowledge of the future provided there is knowledge to be had?

Reichenbach's pragmatic justification of induction is presented in the pages that follow. On his theory, it is true *a priori* that if knowledge of the future is to be had, inductive methods will produce it; it is true simply by virtue of the meaning of the terms involved, in particular by virtue of the meaning of "probability." In this respect Reichenbach's justification is similar to an *a priori* justification of induction. But he does not purport to show *a priori* that if we *use* inductive reasoning, successful prediction will be obtained (or will probably be obtained). Rather, he purports to show *a priori* that *if* successful predictions can be obtained, then inductive reasoning can obtain them.

The main problem with Reichenbach's "justification" of induction, according to John Lenz, is that it is trivial and unhelpful. It is trivial because after analysis this important sounding *a priori* truth can be seen to be the barest tautology; it is unhelpful because we can never have any right to believe here and now on the basis of the evidence the conclusion of an inductive argument.

Dissolution of the Problem

In recent years an even more radical approach to the problem of induction than the pragmatic approach has emerged: inductive logicians have begun to believe that Hume's problem is not a real problem after all. They claim that the doubts raised by Hume are not to be answered by some straightforward "solution" of the sort presented above. Such traditional attempts to answer Hume are thought to be misconceived from the start for the simple reason that they presuppose that Hume has actually posed a problem. It is argued that the way to answer Hume is to show that his problem is senseless, hence it makes no sense to seek a solution.

In short, these inductive logicians argue that Hume's problem is to be dissolved, not solved. In their view, the problem of induction, like many other traditional philosophical problems, can be dissolved by means of the techniques of linguistic analysis as they have been developed by such philosophers as Ludwig Wittgenstein and John Austin. Since philosophical problems are said to arise from certain confusions in ordinary linguistic usage, philosophers need only straighten out such linguistic errors. Once this is done, "philosophical peace," as Wittgenstein once called it, will be achieved.

Included here is a selection in which Peter Strawson uses linguistic analysis in an attempt to show that the traditional problem of induction is not a problem; that under analysis Hume's problem dissolves. Strawson argues that the use of inductive procedures is simply part of what is meant by "being rational." He claims that there is no more sense in asking for the justification of inductive procedure *in general* than there is in asking for the justification of deductive procedure *in general*. No significant answer can possibly be given to either of these questions. To be sure, one can ask for the justification of a *particular* inductive or deductive inference. In this case a significant answer is available in terms of the commonly accepted canons of induction and deduction.

The New Problem of Induction

Whether or not one is convinced by the arguments of Strawson, it is important to realize that insofar as he has "dissolved" the old problem of induction, he has left us with a new problem of induction. The new problem of induction can be stated even more easily than the old: Suppose we grant that part of what is meant by "rational" is the use of rules of induction. What are these rules? The usual formulation of these rules leads to inconsistent and paradoxical conclusions.[3] The new problem of induction consists then, in giving an account

[3] For further discussion of these inconsistencies see C. G. Hempel, "Inductive Inconsistencies" in *Logic and Language* (Dordrecht-Holland: D. Reidel Pub. Co., 1962).

of the rules of inductive inference which is at once precise and coherent and free from inconsistencies and paradoxes.

In an essay that follows, Israel Scheffler brings to light the problems inherent in the usual formulations of inductive rules. Scheffler, in explaining the views of the inductive logician Nelson Goodman, shows that the most commonly accepted rule of induction — what Scheffler calls the "generalization formula" — leads to paradoxical conclusions; he then outlines Goodman's solution to the problem.

In this respect at least philosophy parallels the sciences: a proposed solution to an old problem generates new problems that in their own way are just as stimulating and challenging as the old. And what could be more stimulating and challenging than the problem of the rationality of our inductive beliefs?

24 *An Abstract of a Treatise of Human Nature*

DAVID HUME

It is evident that all reasonings concerning *matter of fact* are founded on the relation of cause and effect, and that we can never infer the existence of one object from another unless they be connected together, either mediately or immediately. In order, therefore, to understand these reasonings we must be perfectly acquainted with the idea of a cause; and in order to do that, must look about us to find something that is the cause of another.

Here is a billiard ball lying on the table, and another ball moving toward it with rapidity. They strike; and the ball which was formerly at rest now acquires a motion. This is as perfect an instance of the relation of cause and effect as any which we know either by sensation or reflection. Let us therefore examine it. It is evident that the two balls touched one another before the motion was communicated, and that there was no interval betwixt the shock and the motion. *Contiguity* in time and place is therefore a requisite circumstance to the operation of all causes. It is evident, likewise, that the motion which was the cause is prior to the motion which was the effect. *Priority* in time is, therefore, another requisite circumstance in every cause. But this is not all. Let us try any other balls of the same kind in a like situation, and we shall always find that the

From *An Inquiry Concerning Human Understanding*, The Library of Liberal Arts, Oskar Piest, General Editor; Edited with an Introduction by Charles W. Hendel. The Bobbs-Merrill Company, Inc., New York, 1957, pp. 186–189. Reprinted by permission of The Bobbs-Merrill Company, Inc.

impulse of the one produces motion in the other. Here, therefore, is a *third* circumstance, viz., that of a *constant conjunction* betwixt the cause and effect. Every object like the cause produces always some object like the effect. Beyond these three circumstances of contiguity, priority, and constant conjunction I can discover nothing in this cause. The first ball is in motion, touches the second, immediately the second is in motion — and when I try the experiment with the same or like balls, in the same or like circumstances, I find that upon the motion and touch of the one ball motion always follows in the other. In whatever shape I turn this matter, and however I examine it, I can find nothing further.

This is the case when both the cause and effect are present to the senses. Let us now see upon what our inference is founded when we conclude from the one that the other has existed or will exist. Suppose I see a ball moving in a straight line toward another — I immediately conclude that they will shock, and that the second will be in motion. This is the inference from cause to effect, and of this nature are all our reasonings in the conduct of life; on this is founded all our belief in history, and from hence is derived all philosophy excepting only geometry and arithmetic. If we can explain the inference from the shock of the two balls we shall be able to account for this operation of the mind in all instances.

Were a man such as Adam created in the full vigor of understanding, without experience, he would never be able to infer motion in the second ball from the motion and impulse of the first. It is not anything that reason sees in the cause which makes us *infer* the effect. Such an inference, were it possible, would amount to a demonstration, as being founded merely on the comparison of ideas. But no inference from cause to effect amounts to a demonstration. Of which there is this evident proof. The mind can always *conceive* any effect to follow from any cause, and indeed any event to follow upon another; whatever we *conceive* is possible, at least in a metaphysical sense; but wherever a demonstration takes place the contrary is impossible and implies a contradiction. There is no demonstration, therefore, for any conjunction of cause and effect. And this is a principle which is generally allowed by philosophers.

It would have been necessary, therefore, for Adam (if he was not inspired) to have had *experience* of the effect which followed upon the impulse of these two balls. He must have seen in several instances that when the one ball struck upon the other, the second always acquired motion. If he had seen a sufficient number of instances of this kind, whenever he saw the one ball moving toward the other, he would always conclude without hesitation that the second would acquire motion. His understanding would anticipate his sight and form a conclusion suitable to his past experience.

It follows, then, that all reasonings concerning cause and effect are founded on experience, and that all reasonings from experience are founded on the supposition that the course of nature will continue uniformly the same. We conclude that like causes, in like circumstances, will always produce like effects. It may now be worth while to consider what determines us to form a conclusion of such infinite consequence.

It is evident that Adam, with all his science, would never have been able to *demonstrate* that the course of nature must continue uniformly the same, and that the future must be conformable to the past. What is possible can never be demonstrated to be false; and it is possible the course of nature may change, since we can conceive such a change. Nay, I will go further and assert that he could not so much as prove by any *probable* arguments that the future must be conformable to the past. All probable arguments are built on the supposition that there is this conformity betwixt the future and the past, and therefore [he] can never prove it. This conformity is a *matter of fact*, and if it must be proved will admit of no proof but from experience. But our experience in the past can be a proof of nothing for the future but upon a supposition that there is a resemblance betwixt them. This, therefore, is a point which can admit of no proof at all, and which we take for granted without any proof.

We are determined by *custom* alone to suppose the future conformable to the past. When I see a billiard ball moving toward another, my mind is immediately carried by habit to the usual effect, and anticipates my sight by conceiving the second ball in motion. There is nothing in these objects — abstractly considered, and independent of experience — which leads me to form any such conclusion: and even after I have had experience of many repeated effects of this kind, there is no argument which determines me to suppose that the effect will be conformable to past experience. The powers by which bodies operate are entirely unknown. We perceive only their sensible qualities — and what *reason* have we to think that the same powers will always be conjoined with the same sensible qualities?

It is not, therefore, reason which is the guide of life, but custom. That alone determines the mind in all instances to suppose the future conformable to the past. However easy this step may seem, reason would never, to all eternity, be able to make it.

25 The Predictionist Justification

RICHARD B. BRAITHWAITE

This justification of induction was first explicitly proposed by C. S. Peirce in 1877–8;[1] it has in the last quarter century gained many adherents among

From *Scientific Explanation*, Cambridge University Press, New York, 1959, pp. 264–291. Reprinted by permission of the Cambridge University Press and the author.

[1] "Illustrations of the Logic of Science", six articles which appeared first in *Popular Science Monthly*, reprinted in *Chance Love and Logic* (London, 1923) and in *Collected Papers of Charles Sanders Peirce*, vols. 2, 5, 6 (Cambridge, Mass., 1932–5). *The Philosophy of Peirce*, ed. J. Buchler (London, 1940), contains the first, second and fourth articles entire, most of the third and part of the fifth. These works will be denoted by *CLL, CP* and *PP* respectively.

logicians. In order to discuss it we must express it more precisely than so far has been done.

What is meant by speaking of a policy as being "predictively reliable"? Peirce in 1878 gave a criterion in terms of the proportion among the inferences from true premisses covered by the policy of those inferences which lead to true conclusions. Peirce finds the germ of this doctrine in Locke, who having spoken of a man who assents to a mathematical theorem on the authority of a mathematician without taking "the pains to observe the demonstration", went on to say: "In which case the foundation of his assent is the probability of the thing, the proof being such as, for the most part, carries truth with it."[2] Peirce takes this use of Locke's 'probability' to be the criterion of inductive validity: "in a logical mind an argument is always conceived as a member of a *genus* of arguments all constructed in the same way, and such that, when their premisses are real facts, their conclusions are so also. If the argument is demonstrative, then this is always so; if it is only probable, then it is for the most part so. As Locke says, the probable argument is '*such as* for the most part carries truth with it'."[3] And in the following article in the series he says that, in the case of synthetic inferences (inductions), unlike that of analytic inferences (deductions), "we only know the degree of trustworthiness of our proceeding. As all knowledge comes from synthetic inference, we must equally infer that all human certainty consists merely in our knowing that the processes by which our knowledge has been derived are such as must generally have led to true conclusions."[4]

I am sure that this account of Peirce's of the trustworthiness of inductive inference as the criterion of its validity is along the right lines — in that it makes inductive validity depend on some objective fact about the principles in accordance with which the inference is made. But to make this dependence a dependence upon the proportion of inferences covered by the policy which lead to true conclusions is to put it in a form which is, in two ways, badly suited for our purpose.

In the first place, since the conclusion of an induction is a general hypothesis, there is no time at which it is conclusively proved. The hypothesis may, of course, be established by the induction, but its establishment at one time will not prevent its refutation at a later time if contrary evidence occurs. It is desirable that our criterion should be such that known evidence will have conclusively proved that the criterion held of some at least of the inductions that have been made in the past.[5] That the criterion will also hold of some inductions which will be made in the future will, of course, be a proposition that cannot be proved but

[2] John Locke, *An Essay concerning Human Understanding*, Book IV, Chapter 15, § 1.

[3] *CLL*, p. 67; *CP*, § 2.649; *PP*, p. 158.

[4] *CLL*, p. 105; *CP*, § 2.693; *PP*, p. 188.

[5] The past participles in my second quotation from Peirce may show that he had this consideration in mind. Why Peirce did not explicitly treat of this point may be because he intended his criterion to cover inferences with non-general conclusions, and thus, by taking the class of reference to be all possible inferences of the sort in question, to connect the Locke-Peirce 'probability' with a Limiting-Frequency view of probability of events. See *CLL*, p. 68; *CP*, §§ 2.650 f.; *PP*, p. 159.

will be one which is only capable of being established for inductive reasons. But knowledge that the criterion held in the past we wish to be independent of inductive considerations. This can be secured if we substitute for the 'true conclusions' in Peirce's criterion 'conclusions which up to now have been confirmed in experience but never refuted'.

Expressed more exactly, the criterion for the reliability of the inductive policy Π will run: At any time *t*, more than half of the hypotheses which have been established by the use of Π at a time earlier than *t* have the joint property (1) of not having been empirically refuted at any time between the time of establishment and *t*, (2) of having been empirically confirmed at least once at a time between the time of establishment and *t*.

But this criterion is not yet satisfactory. What we want is a criterion which we can be fairly confident has held of inductions made in the past by the use of some, at least, of the reputable scientific inductive policies. But can we be certain, of any of these policies, that more than half of the hypotheses established by the use of this policy have been empirically confirmed and have not been empirically refuted since their establishment? It would be an extremely rash historian who would venture to maintain such a proposition. To make it at all plausible it would be necessary to diminish the class of reference from being that of all inferences made in the past which were covered by the policy in question to that of all such inferences made by a reputable scientist after the scientist had tried out a large number of alternative hypotheses which experience had then refuted. For it is one of the best-known facts in the history of science — a fact as notorious as the predictive success of science — that scientific discovery (i.e. the well-establishment of scientific hypotheses) is largely a matter of patience and perseverance in invention, and that there are very few fields in which the scientist expects the first hypothesis which he has thought of to cover the known facts to survive after confrontation with new facts. And even with this qualification we should not have sufficient historical evidence to justify an assertion that most of the hypotheses invented by scientists after many disappointments have been confirmed and not refuted. Moreover, a limitation of the class of reference to include only such hypotheses is far too arbitrary a limitation to be used as a satisfactory criterion for the reliability of an inductive policy.

The escape from this difficulty is to be found, I believe, by the abandonment in Peirce's criterion of the requirement that a *majority* of the hypotheses established by use of the inductive policy should be confirmed and unrefuted. Instead of this requirement all that will be demanded will be that *many* of such hypotheses should be confirmed and unrefuted; however, since this would be satisfied if a bunch of such hypotheses established in the past had this property while newly established hypotheses failed to have it, it is necessary to require that there should be many of these confirmed and unrefuted hypotheses established during each period of time since some fixed date. The criterion thus has to take the somewhat complicated form:

Of every time *t* later than a fixed time t_o, and of every interval of time of a fixed length of years *d* lying within the interval $[t_o, t]$, it is true that many of the hypotheses established by the use of policy Π during the interval of d years (unless there are no such hypotheses) have the joint property (1) of not having been empirically refuted at any time between the time of establishment and t, (2) of having been empirically confirmed at least once between the time of establishment and t.

In this criterion there are three arbitrary elements. The first is the fixed time t_o, which can be taken as the date of Babylonian astronomy or of Archimedes or of Galileo according to taste; it is inserted in order that historical evidence may be sufficient to establish the truth of this criterion as applied to the reputable inductive policies. The second is the fixed length d of the intervals, which might be one year or ten years. The third is the meaning of the vague word "many". The second and the third of these arbitraries are related in that, the shorter the interval, the smaller will have to be the least number covered by "many" in order that the criterion, restricted to past times, shall be known to have held of scientifically reputable policies.

There is also an implicit arbitrary element in the class of persons using the policy for whom the truth of the criterion in the past has been established. This class may be taken to be all human beings or all those with a scientific education or some other limited class of persons; and the other arbitrary elements will have to be adjusted to be appropriate to this class.

To save words, let us call a policy satisfying this criterion (suitable values having been assigned to the arbitrary elements) an *effective* policy, and let us call one satisfying the same criterion with "Of every time t not later than the present time and" substituted for "Of every time t" an *effective-in-the-past* policy. It is a historic fact that the inductive policies of good scientific repute are effective-in-the-past policies; it is a general hypothesis that they are effective as well as being effective-in-the-past.

There are two ways in which a policy, Π, may fail to be effective in the future. One way is if enough of the hypotheses established during some period in the past by the use of Π are refuted to contradict the statement that many will not be refuted. The other way is for these old-established hypotheses to continue to be confirmed and unrefuted, but for enough of the new hypotheses established by the use of Π in the future to be refuted to contradict the statement that many of them will not be refuted. An inductive policy, that is, may fail in the future either by its past successes turning out to be failures after all or by its failing to have future successes.

This possibility of refutation in the future dispels the suspicion, which might otherwise be entertained, that the design of the effectiveness criterion in such a way that the inductive policies of good repute are known at present to be effective-in-the-past may have resulted in the effectiveness of a policy being a logical consequence of the policy's effectiveness-in-the-past, so that the reputable inductive policies would as certainly be as effective in the future as they have been in the past. But, although the word "many" is vague, if no old-established hypotheses were unrefuted in the future, or if no newly established hypotheses were unrefuted after their establishment, the inductive policy concerned would be discovered empirically by future facts not to be effective. So the effectiveness of an inductive policy is an empirical proposition which does not logically follow from the policy's effectiveness-in-the-past.

If an inductive policy, Π, is found not to be effective in the future, this does not imply that at some time it will then be unreasonable to believe a hypothesis the only reason for believing which is its establishment by the use of Π. It will not be reasonable to believe the hypothesis in the sense of "reasonable" for which the effectiveness of the policy is the criterion; but it may well be reasonable in some other way. Or rather, the truth is that, if a policy Π which is at present effective-in-the-past turns out in the future not to be effective-in-the-past so that it is not effective, we just shall not know what to say as to the reasonableness or unreasonableness of belief in the hypotheses established by the use of this policy. If the failure in effectiveness of Π were not due to the refutation of hypotheses established by its use in the past, but were due to the refutation of new hypotheses established by its use, there would be an inclination to say that it was still reasonable to believe in the old hypotheses, but that it would be unreasonable to believe new hypotheses established by its means. This state of affairs might be expressed by saying that the old successful inductive policy had done all that it could do in wresting her secrets from Nature, but that it was now played out and new policies must be discovered and used. The state of affairs would appear not so much as a breakdown of a particular policy as an exhaustion of its field of profitable application. On the other hand, there would also be an inclination to say that the failure of the inductive policy to yield new unrefuted hypotheses showed that we had been unjustified in using it in the past, and that its supposed past successes had been just lucky coincidences. We have no satisfactory way of choosing between these two opposing considerations. There would be similar opposed tendencies as to what should be said if the failure in effectiveness of Π were due to the refutation of hypotheses established by its use in the past while it continued to yield confirmed hypotheses in the future.

If the inductive policy broke down in both these ways at once so that neither the old nor the new hypotheses established by its means continued to be unrefuted, there would be a strong inclination to say that it would then be positively unreasonable to believe these hypotheses. But suppose that all the inductive policies broke down simultaneously. It would then, of course, not be reasonable in the sense which used the criterion of effectiveness, or in the modified senses described in the last paragraph, to believe an inductive hypothesis; but it might well be called "reasonable" in some new sense of the word. The sense of "reasonable" as applied to belief in inductive conclusions is different from the sense of "reasonable" as applied to belief in logically necessary propositions; the former use, in connexion with policies of inductive inference, was developed exactly because these policies were found to have been effective-in-the-past. A discovery that these policies were not effective would remove the occasion for applying the epithet "reasonable" to beliefs in hypotheses established by their means; but another use might then be found for the epithet as applied to an inductive hypothesis, and another rationale for that use. It is futile to speculate as to what inductive beliefs we should call "reasonable" and what "unreasonable" if all our present inductive policies proved ineffective; our language is fixed on the assumption of their effectiveness, and if they are all ineffective we have no criterion for the application of the term.

The situation can be inadequately expressed by saying that the criterion we have been expounding for the validity of an inductive inference and for the reasonableness of belief in its conclusion — the criterion of the effectiveness of the inductive policy concerned — is a *sufficient*, but not a *necessary*, criterion. Why this is an inadequate way of expressing the situation is that this way of talking presupposes that there is a necessary criterion for the reasonableness of belief in an inductive hypothesis. And this would be equivalent to being a sufficient criterion for the unreasonableness of a hypothesis — which it would be rash to take as being given by the ineffectiveness of the inductive policy concerned.

The thesis maintained in this chapter is that the effectiveness of the inductive policy concerned is a sufficient condition for the adjective "valid" to be applied to an inductive inference from known evidence and for the adjective "reasonable" to be applied to belief in the conclusion of the inference. But, if this condition — the effectiveness of the inductive policy — fails, we do not necessarily use this failure as a sufficient condition for the adjective "invalid" to be applied to the inference or the adjective "unreasonable" to belief in the conclusion; we may, if this situation ever occurs, make use of some new criterion unthought-of at present. Books on logic have almost always considered only definitions of terms where the definition holds whatever the facts may be. Here we are concerned with a partial definition, in the form of a sufficient criterion, where the applicability of this partial definition depends upon the truth of an empirical matter of fact. If policy Π is effective, then the use of policy Π in inferring an inductive conclusion from empirical data makes the inference a 'valid' one and the belief in the conclusion a 'reasonable' belief. But if policy Π is not effective, then here nothing is said. A justification of induction requires a criterion for the validity of an inductive inference; it does not require one for the invalidity of such an inference.

The Weakness of the Effectiveness Criterion

The Locke-Peirce criterion for the trustworthiness of an inference in terms of a majority of inferences of a certain sort being confirmed has been abandoned in favour of a criterion which substitutes "many instances" for the "most instances" of the Locke-Peirce criterion. This new criterion constitutes a very much weaker condition than the Locke-Peirce one. And, even though we have strengthened it into the requirement that there should be many confirmed and unrefuted hypotheses established during every fixed interval of time since a fixed date in the past, the criterion may still be criticized for being too weak. The criticism may be put in the form that, although "valid" and "reasonable" can, if we like, be defined in this way, this definition will make the concepts so weak as to be pragmatically valueless. What a man wants, it will be said, is to use the adjective "reasonable" in such a way that its application to belief is related to its application to action, so that it will be reasonable for him to do an action which it is reasonable for him to believe is a means to a goal at which he is aiming. But if all that can be said in favour of using an inductive policy is that it frequently predicts successfully, is this a justification for basing actions upon beliefs obtained by such a policy? Other policies for obtaining beliefs might be more predictively successful; in which case surely it would be better to use them rather than the inductive policies, or at any rate to prefer them to the inductive policies when there is a conflict of results.

The reply to this criticism is that why it is possible plausibly to propose such a weak condition as effectiveness (as specified in this chapter) for the validity of inductive inference is because no policy for establishing scientific hypotheses other than the scientifically reputable inductive policies is effective in even this very weak sense. It is not as if there were competitors to the inductive policies in the predictive-reliability race so that it would be unreasonable to prefer the inductive policies unless we could depend on their swiftness in the race. The non-inductive policies are not starters. There is no general policy other than an inductive policy which there is good reason to believe has been effective in the past, i.e. has, during every interval of time of a fixed length since some fixed date in the past, established many hypotheses which have been confirmed and not refuted — the fixed lengths of the intervals and the fixed past date being the same as those used in the specification of the effectiveness criterion according to which there is no doubt that the reputable scientific inductive policies have been effective in the past.

Some logicians of the Peircean school (e.g. William Kneale[6]) say that there is no other way, or at least no other systematic way, of attempting to make true predictions except by pursuing an inductive policy. This, I think, is too sweeping; we can *try* to make true predictions by a policy of consulting a soothsayer selected in some predetermined way or by a policy of deep breathing followed by free-association or by any other systematic non-inductive policy we fancy. But experience has taught us that we shall not succeed by any of these ways, that none of these non-inductive policies are effective-in-the-past, and so none of them are effective. The case for employing the recognized inductive policies is thus not the negative fact that there is no other systematic way of *trying*, but the negative fact that there is no other way of *succeeding* in making true predictions, combined with the positive fact that pursuing inductive policies frequently does succeed. The justification for the use of an inductive policy in terms of its effectiveness must be read in the context of other predictive policies being known to be ineffective.

It may be objected to this line of thought that it involves supposing that the inductive policies of good repute among scientists at present are the only policies

[6] *Probability and Induction*, pp. 234, 235, 259.

that it ever will be reasonable to think effective. But this is not the case. That policy Π is effective is an inductive hypothesis to be established by induction according to a principle of simple enumeration on the basis of its effectiveness-in-the-past. A policy which has never been tried before may be tested for its ability to yield confirmed and unrefuted hypotheses; if many of the hypotheses which it yields are confirmed and not refuted, then it will satisfy the criterion for effectiveness-in-the-past and its introduction into our inductive repertoire for establishing hypotheses can be justified by the effectiveness of the policy being established in accordance with an effective inductive policy of simple enumeration. For example, suppose that in the first instance I do not accept hypotheses on the strength of their being asserted by Savant *M*, but, through curiosity perhaps, record the hypotheses he asserts throughout a period of time. If many of these hypotheses are confirmed and unrefuted during this period, the simple-enumerative inductive policy may make it reasonable for me to believe hypotheses asserted by *M* on the grounds that they have been asserted by *M*; and I shall thereby have obtained a new predictive procedure which will be good while it lasts. To say that in fact no predictive policy other than the recognized inductive policies is at present known which is effective-in-the-past does not imply that no such policy will be discovered. Indeed, the eliminative inductive policies and the policy of establishing functional laws have been so discovered, the latter only some 350 years ago; the justification for their use is their effectiveness, which was in each case established by a simple-enumerative policy. Similarly, a simple-enumerative policy may establish the effectiveness of new predictive policies in the future; if it does so, these new policies will enter into competition with the present inductive policies of good repute, and we shall be compelled to choose as to which policy to use if they lead to conflicting results. But at present there is no competition.

The Alleged Circularity in the Predictionist Justification of Induction

The thesis of this chapter may be expressed not quite precisely by saying that the justification for inductive inference consists in the fact that a policy of passing, in accordance with an inductive principle, from true beliefs to beliefs in general hypotheses frequently enables us to accept hypotheses which are confirmed and not refuted by experience. This thesis is thought by many philosophers to involve a viciously circular way of looking at the matter. Their argument runs as follows: On the predictionist thesis the reason for believing an inductive conclusion consists in two premisses, one being the evidence for the conclusion appropriate to the inductive principle concerned, the other being the proposition that the policy of making inferences in accordance with the inductive principle concerned is an effective one. And reasonableness of belief in the conclusion is due to the reasonableness of the belief in each of these premisses. But, so it is said, this second premiss is itself a general hypothesis, reasonableness of belief in which can only be established by another inductive argument. This second induction will similarly require as premiss the proposition that the policy of making inferences in accordance with the inductive principle used in it is an effective one; and this premiss will again be a general hypothesis which will require justifying by a third inductive argument. Thus, either there will be an infinite regress with an infinite series of inductive policies the establishment of the effectiveness of each policy in the series requiring the establishment of the effectiveness of the succeeding policy in the series, or we shall arrive, in ascending the series, at one inductive policy the establishing of whose effectiveness will require the establishment of its own effectiveness.

Since the reason that could be given for the effectiveness of any inductive policy except those of induction by simple enumeration would be that it had frequently been predictively reliable in the past, i.e. that it had proved to be effective-in-the-past, the establishment of the effectiveness of any other policy would require the establishment of the effectiveness of a simple-enumerative inductive policy. (For the purpose of this argument it is unnecessary to distinguish different simple-enumerative policies; so they will be referred to in the singular as the policy of induction by simple enumeration.) Thus to establish the effectiveness of the policy of induction by simple enumeration would require its own effectiveness to be taken as a premiss; and the circularity born of the dilemma would be the one upon which we should be impaled. If we care to use the word "presupposition" the argument against the predictionist justification may be expressed by saying that, according to it, the validity of every inductive inference *presupposes* the validity of induction by simple enumeration, and the validity of induction by simple enumeration *presupposes* its own validity; and this, it is alleged, is a viciously circular justification for induction.

Before trying to answer this charge of vicious circularity, the predictionist may be permitted a *tu quoque* retort. The accusation of circularity does not lie solely against the predictionist justification of induction but lies equally against any account of the validity of induction which makes such validity depend upon a premiss which can only be established inductively. Keynes's attempt to justify induction by means of a theory of probability falls into this class. On Keynes's theory inductive confirmation serves only to increase the probability of a hypothesis by multiplying it by another probability, so that if the hypothesis has a 'prior probability' of zero its 'posterior probability' remains zero, however much evidence there may be for it. And the only way to secure that every hypothesis should have a prior probability greater than zero is to assign some probability greater than zero to a proposition which limits the number of possible hypotheses (e.g. Keynes's Principle of Limited Independent Variety).[7] But such a proposition is itself an empirical hypothesis, which calls for an inductive justification. So Keynes's justification for induction is viciously circular — unless one cuts the circle by the improper expedient of 'postulating' the empirical hypothesis required.

The fact, however, that many other attempted justifications of induction are

[7] J. M. Keynes, *A Treatise on Probability*, Chapter XXII.

open to the accusation of vicious circularity does not excuse the predictionist from trying to show that the charge does not lie against his account. This rebuttal must now be attempted.

The first move in the rebuttal is that the proposition 'presupposed' in the predictionist justification of an inductive inference does not function in the inference as an additional premiss. The inductive inference to the proposition that induction by simple enumeration is an effective policy does not make use of this proposition as a premiss, and so is not circular in the *petitio principii* sense of professing to infer a conclusion from a set of premisses one of which is the conclusion itself.

This point is so important that it is desirable to make it as precisely as possible. What we are concerned with is the sort of circularity, if any, involved in the establishment of the validity of induction by simple enumeration by means of an induction by simple enumeration. A few symbols will abbreviate the discussion.

Let Π be the inductive policy of adding belief in a hypothesis h to belief in a set of propositions which collectively constitute π-evidence for h, i.e. adequate evidence for inferring h in accordance with the principle of inference π, π being the principle of induction by simple enumeration.[8]

Let e be the proposition that the policy Π is effective.

Now to say that the truth of e is the justification for employing the inductive policy Π is not to say that the principle π of induction by simple enumeration requires that e should be added as an additional premiss to the otherwise adequate evidence; were this to be the case, the inference of e by means of the principle π would require the inclusion of e itself among the premisses believed. The alleged inference would then not be an inference at all, let alone a valid inference, since it would be professing to establish belief in a proposition which was already one of the believed premisses. But since e does not function in the argument as a premiss which has to be believed along with the other premisses, the argument by means of the principle π from the π-evidence for e to e does not commit the fallacy of *petitio principii*, and it is a genuine inference in which belief is acquired in a new proposition which was not believed before.

The circularity in the argument is of a more sophisticated character. It is the circularity involved in the use of a principle of inference being justified by the truth of a proposition which can only be established by the use of the same principle of inference. To express the matter in the symbols we have used:

The truth of e justifies the use of policy Π; i.e. for every h the truth of e justifies an addition of belief in h to reasonable belief in π-evidence for h.

From which there follows, by the substitution of e for h: The truth of e justifies an addition of belief in e to a reasonable belief in π-evidence for e. In other words, if e is true, an addition of belief in e to reasonable belief in π-evidence for e is justified.

I do not wish to deny that there is a sort of circularity involved in this statement, but it is a peculiar sort of circularity whose viciousness is by no means

[8] The Greek capital letter Π has been used earlier in this chapter to denote any inductive policy. It will henceforth be restricted by this definition to denote only the simple-enumerative inductive policy.

obvious. The statement does not commit the fallacy of *petitio principii* as would have been the case had it said that, *if e were reasonably believed*, an addition of belief in *e* to the believer's body of reasonable belief would be justified. For in the statement the sufficient condition for the addition of belief in *e* is, not that a premiss is believed, but that an empirical proposition is true. The peculiar circularity consists in the *truth* of the conclusion of an inference being a sufficient condition for the validity of the inference. Let us call this type of circularity "effective circularity", since in the cases in which we are interested it is the effectiveness of the inferential policy which is the sufficient condition. The question before us is whether or not the presence of effective circularity renders an inference invalid, or whether it prevents an inference from being a genuine inference at all?

At this point it is worth remarking that there are deductive inferences in which a sufficient condition for the effectiveness of the principle of inference is exactly that proposition which is the conclusion of the inference itself.[9] But here the proposition which is the condition for the effectiveness of a deductive principle of inference must be a logically necessary proposition; and though, in the case we are considering, this logically necessary proposition is supposed to be established by being deduced from other logically necessary propositions within a pure deductive system which uses as principle of inference a principle the condition for whose effectiveness is the logically necessary proposition itself, yet this proposition could always be established in ways which do not involve this effectiveness. For there is no necessary order in the deducing of logically necessary propositions from one another. However, in our inductive case, the proposition stating the effectiveness of the induction-by-simple-enumeration policy is a logically contingent proposition which can be established in no other way than by the use of an induction-by-simple-enumeration policy.

Now for a consideration of 'effective circularity'. Is there anything wrong in the effectiveness of a policy of inference being a justification for the inference to this effectiveness as conclusion? Is there anything wrong in obtaining a belief in a proposition by inference according to a principle whose validity as a principle of inference is attested by the proposition which is itself the conclusion of the inference? In order to answer these questions it is necessary to consider what exactly we mean by "inference" and by an inference being "valid".

The Conditions for Valid Inference and for the Reasonableness of an Inferred Belief

Inference is the passage of thought from belief, or rational belief, in a set of propositions, collectively called the *premiss* of the inference, to belief, or rational belief, in a proposition called the *conclusion* of the inference, the premiss and the

[9] An example of this would be the deduction within a deductive system of the proposition $(p(p \supset q)) \supset q$ from the two propositions

$$(p(p \supset q)) \equiv pq, \quad ((p(p \supset q)) \equiv pq) \supset ((p(p \supset q)) \supset q)$$

by the use of an 'implicative' detachment principle the condition for whose effectiveness is the necessary truth of $(p(p \supset q)) \supset q$.

conclusion being related in accordance with some principle of inference. The question of the validity of a process of inference is the same as the justification for adding a belief in the conclusion to the believer's body of reasonable beliefs (his 'rational corpus'), in the case in which the premiss of the inference forms part of this rational corpus, or for associating a belief in the conclusion with the belief in the premiss, in the case where this belief is ont part of the believer's rational corpus, in such a way that belief in the conclusion will be inferentially supported by the belief in the premiss. And vice versa the question of the reasonableness of a belief, except in the case in which the reasonableness of the belief consists in the proposition believed being known directly to be true, is that of the validity of an inference by which the belief could be supported.[10]

Different sorts of criteria can be given for the validity of an inference, or for the reasonableness of an inferentially supportable belief. In order to avoid complications due to differences of nuance in the meaning of the words concerned, these different possible sets of criteria will be considered in the first instance in the form of an abstract classification.

The two relevant propositions are the premiss p of the inference and the proposition r asserting the effectiveness of the inferential policy which uses the principle of inference concerned in passing from the premiss p to the conclusion q. The possible criteria for the validity of an inference from p to q are obtained by considering the possible combinations of a belief in p, or a rational belief in p, with the truth of r, or with a belief in r, or with a rational belief in r. Possible combinations with the truth of p will not be considered, since the truth of the premiss is not relevant to the validity of an inference from it, though it is relevant to the question as to whether or not an inference to a conclusion constitutes a *proof* of the conclusion.[11]

There are ten possibilities for sufficient criteria for the validity of an inference by a person B of the conclusion q from the premiss p in accordance with a principle of inference the effectiveness of whose use is asserted by the proposition r: [12]

I B believes p and believes r;
II B believes p and reasonably believes r;
III B believes p, and r is true;
IV B believes p and believes r, and r is true;
V B believes p and reasonably believes r, and r is true;

VI B reasonably believes p and believes r;
VII B reasonably believes p and reasonably believes r;
VIII B reasonably believes p, and r is true;
IX B reasonably believes p and believes r, and r is true;
X B reasonably believes p and reasonably believes r, and r is true.

[10] Not 'has been supported', for a belief may be reasonable if the believer would support it by an inference if the reasonableness of his belief were to be disputed, although in fact he had not arrived at it by inference.

[11] My treatment of the validity of inference, which owes much to W. E. Johnson's discussion in his *Logic, Part II* (Cambridge, 1922), Chapter I, disagrees with him here.

[12] Criteria sufficient, that is, except for the possibility of a vicious circularity to the discussion of which this classification is preliminary.

Criteria VI–X are possible criteria for the validity of an inference regarded as justifiably adding a belief in *q* to *B*'s body of reasonable beliefs; criteria I–V are possible criteria for the validity of an inference regarded as justifiably carrying a belief in *q* along with *B*'s belief in *p*. Which of the five criteria in each case is chosen as *the* criterion for the validity of the inference is to some extent a matter of taste. The usage of the expression "valid inference" and "reasonable belief" is not sufficiently fixed by common usage for any of the possibilities to be excluded from the outset.

But some of these possibilities will make some inferences circular, and these possibilities will have to be excluded for the case of these inferences; otherwise these inferences will be invalid, not in failing to satisfy one of the criteria, but in involving a vicious circularity. The inferences that will be invalid through circularity will be those satisfying any of the conditions

I–X if *B*'s belief in *p* includes a belief in *q*.
I, II, IV, V, VII and X if *B*'s belief in *r* includes a belief in *q*.

It is important to notice that *B*'s belief in *r* may include a belief in *q* without making inferences satisfying conditions VI and IX circular, for these inferences are allegedly adding *q* to *B*'s body of reasonable beliefs, and the fact that *q* is already a proposition which *B* believes does not invalidate an inference which proposes to move *q* from *B*'s body of *beliefs* to his body of *reasonable beliefs*.[13]

Let us now turn to the case of inductive inference. Here *p*, the evidence for the inductive hypothesis *q*, is assumed to be reasonably believed; so the criterion for the validity of the inference will be one of the possibilities VI–X. Suppose that the conclusion *q* of the inference is the proposition stating the effectiveness of a policy of induction by simple enumeration, and that it is according to induction by simple enumeration that the inference is being made. Then the inference will be invalid through circularity only if its condition for validity is taken to be either VII or X. For it is only in these two cases that *B*'s reasonable belief in the conclusion of the inference will be part of his reasonable belief in the effectiveness of the inferential policy. So if any one of the other three possible criteria for the validity of an inference is taken, i.e. any one of VI, VIII or IX, an inference to a conclusion stating the effectiveness of the inferential policy will be valid without any circularity.

Having reduced the number of possibilities to three, we can conveniently give them specific names. Let us call an inference (leading to reasonable belief in a conclusion) "subjectively valid" if it satisfies condition VI (i.e. if VI is a sufficient condition for its validity), "objectively valid" if it satisfies condition VIII and "both subjectively and objectively valid" if it satisfies condition IX. To justify the use of the policy of induction by simple enumeration by its effectiveness, as we have done, is to use criterion VIII for the objective validity of the inference to the hypothesis of its effectiveness. The inference made by a person *B* is then

[13] Some accounts of inference would limit it to being a passage of thought leading to belief in a proposition not previously believed; but this would seem to involve an undesirably narrow definition of inference.

objectively valid in that B reasonably believes the evidence for the hypothesis and that the hypothesis justifying the principle of inference is itself true; no question of his belief, reasonable or non-reasonable, in the hypothesis itself is part of the condition for the validity (the 'objective validity') of the induction.

It may, however, be felt that such objective validity is not enough, and that an inference cannot be a properly valid inference unless the inferrer is in some way cognizant of the principle according to which he is making the inference and of the propriety of the principle for this purpose. Whether or not objective validity is thought to be enough depends upon whether the validity of the inference is being considered, as it were, from the outside or from the inside. When considered from the outside the person making the inference is being regarded as a reasoning machine. The machine would first have fed into it a set of propositions which together make up π-evidence for e, and would thus take up a 'position' which would correspond to having a reasonable belief in this π-evidence for e. The machine would then be put in operation according to its principle of working, and would acquire a new position which would correspond to a reasonable belief in the proposition e. Obviously there is nothing objectionable in the machine arriving at a new position which corresponds to having a reasonable belief in a proposition asserting some general property of the method of working of the machine. From the external point of view the machine is making 'valid inferences' if it is working according to its working 'principle of inference' starting with a 'reasonable' position, and it can quite well arrive by such working at a position which corresponds to having 'validly inferred' a proposition which asserts some general property of its working 'principle of inference'.

Similarly, from an external point of view, a man may be considered to be making valid inferences from reasonably believed premisses if his policy of inference is in fact an effective one, quite independently of whether or not he believes or knows that it is effective; and in this case there is no vicious circularity in his arriving by a valid process of inference at the conclusion that the policy of using the principle of inference according to which he is making this inference is an effective one.

An inference will be valid in the sense of being *objectively valid* (in the sense explained) if the inference proceeds from reasonably believed premisses to a conclusion according to a policy of inference which is in fact effective, whether or not the inferrer knows or believes that it is effective or indeed whether he considers the question of its effectiveness at all. The inferrer, that is, is acting like a machine which works according to certain principles without being cognizant of these principles. He is not assumed to be wholly a machine, since he is supposed to start with a reasonable belief in the premisses and to end with a reasonable belief in the conclusion, but the process by which he passes from his original reasonable belief to his final reasonable belief is supposed to be one which does not require his cognitive participation. This process may be regarded as analogous to the free-association used in adding up a column of figures, where the adder has consciously thought of the number written at the head of the page and again consciously thinks of the number to be written at the bottom of the page but does not consciously think of the arithmetical relationships which justify his calculating from the one to the other. The result of a calculation obtained in this automatic way may well be a statement which asserts the effectiveness of the method of calculation.

But if the machine becomes self-conscious and critical of its mode of working, it will not be satisfied with a criterion for the validity of inference which depends upon the effectiveness in fact of the method by which it is working, but will demand a condition, either as an alternative or as an addition, which states its belief in this effectiveness. From the inside, that is, criteria VI or IX will seem more appropriate criteria for the validity of an inference than the criterion VIII giving 'objective validity'. Since criterion IX combines the conditions of criteria VI and VIII, it is criterion VI that needs to be considered. It substitutes the requirement that the thinker should believe that the policy of induction by simple enumeration is effective for the fact that it is effective; in the terms we have used it ascribes 'subjective validity' rather than 'objective validity' to the inference leading to the conclusion that the policy is effective. Though belief in the effectiveness of this policy is one of the conditions for the subjective validity of an inference yielding a reasonable belief in such effectiveness, this fact does not (as we have seen) make the inference *ipso facto* circular, for the thinker is passing from a mere belief in this effectiveness to a reasonable belief in it. He is, as it were, moving it within his body of beliefs into the privileged position of being one of his body of reasonable beliefs.

So a critic who finds the objective validity criterion inadequate, in that it gives no place for the thinker's consciousness of the principle according to which he is making the inference, can be offered instead, without fear of vicious circularity, either the subjective validity criterion or the subjective-and-objective validity criterion for the validity of his inference. In none of these three cases is there any vicious circularity.

At this point, however, the question may well be raised as to whether either of the criteria VI or VIII are at all appropriate criteria for the validity, in any proper sense, of the inductive inference. The objector may perfectly well say that for an inference to yield a new reasonable belief the inferrer must not merely *believe* that the policy represented by the principle of inference is effective, but must *reasonably believe* this proposition. And he can point out that we have required reasonable belief, and not only belief, in the premiss in order that an inference may yield reasonable belief in the conclusion.

On the face of it this objection seems a very cogent one. To obtain a reasonable belief by inference, it says, we must have reasonable belief all along the line, reasonable belief in the effectiveness of the policy of inference no less than reasonable belief in the premiss. But the rejoinder can be made that such a requirement would invalidate the majority of inferences, deductive as well as inductive, that are actually made in the course of reasoning. For the requirement would admit only deductions in which the proposition authenticating the principle of inference used was either seen directly to be true or was seen directly to be a logical consequence (in a chain of proof sufficiently short to be taken in at one glance) of a proposition seen directly to be true. Any other way of attaining belief in the effectiveness of the policy of deduction, e.g. by citing authority, or by remembering that one had satisfied oneself of its truth in the past, would involve inductive steps, and would thus not permit the belief to be 'reasonable', since the inference by which it had been obtained, or upon which it could be based, would not satisfy this stringent condition for validity. So to insist that an inference is only valid, and a belief in the conclusion of the inference only reasonable, if the inferrer's belief in the effectiveness of a policy of inference is already a reasonable one would exclude a great number of the inferences, and a great many of the beliefs, which would normally be considered to be valid or to be reasonable.

The objector may, of course, say at this point that he is not concerned with the application of the terms "valid" and "reasonable" in our ordinary slovenly everyday language; what he is concerned with is a purified use of these terms after the user of them has been purged by a course of treatment with methodological doubt. In a purified sense the objector may decline to admit valid inferences in which the effectiveness of the policy of inference is not reasonably believed — even if this were to exclude most so-called 'valid' inferences. But then it is difficult to see what the argument is about. It started presumably because the objector wished to dispute the justification of induction by simple enumeration in terms of the effectiveness of this policy, the ground of his objection being that such an attempted justification was circular. We then replied that this justification would not be open to this criticism if the criterion of valid inference did not require reasonable belief in the effectiveness of the policy of inference, but only required alternatively either the fact of this effectiveness or belief in this effectiveness. And we maintained that a reasonable belief in this effectiveness was not an essential part of the criterion for validity of the sorts of passages of thought which are normally thought of as valid inferences. If the objector has decided beforehand to decline to admit as a valid inference any inference in which the effectiveness of the policy is not reasonably believed, his valid inductive inferences will be bound to suffer from circularity (unless, indeed, he takes the desperate course of regarding the effectiveness of the policy as a logically necessary truth). But the vicious circularity will be of the objector's own making.

A Comparison with Different Senses of "Rightness"

It is illuminating to compare the senses in which we have called inferences "objectively valid", "subjectively valid" and "both objectively and subjectively valid" with various senses in which an action may be said to be "right".

Whether the rightness of an action is held to consist in its fittingness to a certain situation or in its having a certain characteristic or producing effects having that characteristic or in some blend of these two, it will in all cases be possible to distinguish two senses of rightness — one an objective sense, when the action in fact is fitting to the situation or in fact has the characteristic or produces effects having the characteristic, whether or not an action is right in this sense being entirely independent of whether or not the agent believes it to be right; the other a subjective sense in which what determines the rightness of the action is whether or not the agent believes the action to be fitting to the situation or to have the characteristic or to produce effects having the characteristic, i.e. whether or not the agent believes the action to be right in the first, objective sense of the word. And a third sense of rightness can then be given in which an action is right if it is both obejctively right and subjectively right.[14]

The objective sense of rightness of an action may be compared with the objective sense of validity of an inference, that in which the policy of inference is in fact effective; the subjective sense of rightness of an action may be compared with the subjective sense of validity of an inference, that in which the policy of inference is believed to be effective. The third, composite sense of rightness may then be compared with the sense of validity of an inference which is both objective and subjective. And there would similarly be comparable senses of reasonable belief in a proposition which had either been derived by inference or would be defended against criticism by citing an inference by which it might have been derived. An objectively reasonable belief, associated with an objectively valid inference, would be compared with an objectively right action; a subjectively reasonable belief, associated with a subjectively valid inference, would be compared with a subjectively right action; and there would be a similar comparison in the case of a belief which was both objectively and subjectively reasonable.

The enlightenment produced by making these comparisons seems to me to be as follows. Whatever be the sense of rightness appropriate to describing other moral situations, it is almost undisputed that the sense of rightness which is appropriate to the imputation of moral praise or blame is the subjective sense of rightness. A man, that is, is not considered blameworthy for doing an action which is objectively wrong provided that, at the time of doing it, he believed it to be objectively right, nor is he considered praiseworthy for doing an action which is objectively right if he believed it to be objectively wrong.

Now to say of a man that he is reasonable in holding a belief q, or that his belief in q is reasonable, is in many contexts to make a judgment which is either a moral judgment or closely resembles one. It is a moral judgment if reasonably holding beliefs is regarded as one of the modes of moral goodness of a man; it is closely related to a moral judgment if reasonably holding beliefs is regarded, not as itself a manifestation of moral goodness, but as a positive symptom for moral goodness in a man. In either case to say of a man that he is unreasonable in holding a belief q is to make, or to imply, a hypothetical moral criticism of him. For it is to imply that the man would be morally better were he not unreasonably

[14] Further distinctions can be made for the cases in which an action is subjectively right without being objectively right according as the agent's erroneous belief as to the objective rightness of his action is due to his being in error on a matter of fact (as to the nature of the situation or as to what effects the action will in fact have) or in his moral evaluation. Such further distinctions are not relevant for the purpose of our comparison.

to hold the belief *q*. It does not imply that he ought not unreasonably to hold the belief, for it may not be in his power either to hold it reasonably or to abandon the belief. But, whether these possibilities are in his power or not, the fact that he unreasonably holds the belief makes him worse than would be the case were he not unreasonably to hold it.

In any context in which reasonableness is ascribed with this moral implication, to the extent that the reasonableness of a man's belief is derived by a valid process of inference, this reasonableness must depend not upon the actual effectiveness of the policy of inference but upon the man's belief in this effectiveness. For otherwise a man would be regarded as blameworthy for holding a belief in a scientific hypothesis which he had inferred from reasonably believed evidence by following an inductive policy which, although the man believed it to be effective, was not in fact an effective one. And he would be regarded as praiseworthy for holding an inductive belief which he had inferred by a policy which was in fact effective, even though he did not believe that it was effective. Such judgments would be contrary to our moral sense as displayed in our use of moral language, which makes "unfortunate" and "fortunate" more appropriate epithets than "blameworthy" and "praiseworthy" to ascribe to these two cases. So, in the contexts in which reasonableness is associated with praiseworthiness and unreasonableness with blameworthiness (and these are the most frequent contexts), what we have called the subjective sense of reasonableness will have to be taken — just as it is the subjective sense of rightness that has to be associated with praiseworthiness.

This comparison with subjective rightness further supports the view that the sufficient condition for the subjective reasonableness of an inductively supported belief, so far as the effectiveness of the inductive policy is concerned, is simply the belief that this policy is effective, without the qualification that this belief should be a reasonable one. For we think that a man is acting rightly if he does what he believes to be the objectively right action, irrespective of whether or not this belief of his is a reasonable one. If we think that his belief is an unreasonable one, and that he might, for example, by a previous more diligent study of the facts of the situation, have prevented himself from having this unreasonable belief, and instead have acquired a different and reasonable belief, we may blame him for his past sin of omission in not having taken the steps he might have taken to acquire a more reasonable belief. But we do not blame him for acting on his present belief, whether this be reasonable or unreasonable. Similarly, we should consider a man reasonable in following an inductive policy which he believed to be effective, independently of the question as to whether or not his belief was a reasonable one. Thus, in the sense of reasonableness which is comparable with subjective rightness, it is belief in the effectiveness of the inductive policy, whether or not this belief is well grounded, that is a condition for the validity (in the subjective sense) of the inductive inference and for the reasonableness (in the subjective sense) of belief in the inductive conclusion.

But may not this comparison with subjective rightness be pushed further so that the reasonableness of belief in the premiss is as irrelevant to the reasonableness of belief in the inductive conclusion as is the reasonableness of belief in the effectiveness of the inductive policy? If so, the criterion for the reasonableness of an inductive belief would be criterion I, namely, that the thinker believes both the premiss of the inductive inference and that the inductive policy is effective. In defence of selecting this criterion it might be argued that a man might defend himself against criticism for holding an inductive belief *q* by saying that he believed the evidence from which he derived his belief in *q* by following an inductive policy in whose effectiveness he believed, without thinking it necessary to maintain that his belief in the evidence was a reasonable one. But I do not think that this would be a good defence. If the reasonableness of a belief is to be defended by the belief's having been inferred or being able to be inferred from other beliefs, these other beliefs must themselves be reasonably held. The process of obtaining new reasonable beliefs by inference is one of adding new beliefs to the thinker's body of reasonable beliefs (his rational corpus) on the basis of some of the beliefs already in this corpus. If the beliefs to which the new belief is added by the inference fall within the body of the thinker's beliefs but not within his rational corpus, the inference may well be valid in the sense of justifiably supporting his belief in *q*, but the inference does not justify him in including *q* in his rational corpus.

The situation in the criterion for reasonable belief in an inductive conclusion is thus different in respect of the roles played by belief in the inductive premiss and by belief in the effectiveness of an inductive policy pursued. The former belief has to be a reasonable one, in order that the inference should build upon a stable foundation. But what is required of the latter proposition — that the inductive policy pursued is effective — is, for the subjective sense of reasonable, that this proposition should be believed, for the objective sense of reasonable, that this proposition should be true. In neither the subjective sense nor the objective sense nor the combined sense is a reasonable belief in the policy's effectiveness a requirement for a belief which has been obtained by the use of the inductive policy from a reasonably believed premiss to be a reasonable belief.

The result of this discussion is, I hope, to uphold the thesis that there are three proper criteria yielding three proper senses for the 'validity' of an inductive inference made by a man *B*, and also three corresponding senses for the 'reasonableness' of *B*'s belief in a conclusion arrived at, or that would be based upon, an inductive inference. All three criteria agree in requiring that the premiss of the inference — the inductive evidence — should be reasonably believed by *B*; they agree in requiring something which is concerned with the effectiveness of the inductive policy pursued. They differ as to what is this something required. The objective criterion requires that the proposition asserting the effectiveness of the inductive policy should be true, the subjective criterion requires that this proposition should be believed by *B*. The both-objective-and-subjective criterion requires both that the inductive policy should in fact be effective and that its effectiveness should be believed by *B*. Let us now re-examine the accusation of vicious circularity in the light of this triple distinction.

Circularity Re-Examined

The conditions for it to be subjectively valid for a man to infer *e*, the proposition that the policy Π of induction by the principle π of simple enumeration is effective, from π-evidence for *e*, and correlatively that this belief obtained or supportable by this inference is a subjectively reasonable belief are, first, that he should reasonably believe the evidence for *e*, and secondly, that he should believe *e*. Since neither of these conditions includes the requirement that his belief in *e* should be a reasonable one, there is no explicit circularity in his reasoning. Nor is there any implicit circularity, since he can quite well reasonably believe both that he is reasonable in believing the π-evidence for *e* and that he is believing *e* without reasonably believing, or indeed believing, that he is reasonable in thus believing *e*. The critic will thus be compelled to withdraw his charge of circularity. But, of course, he will fall back upon saying that this criterion for the validity of an inductive inference and for the reasonableness of an inductive belief is too weak a one.

In which case the critic can be offered the stronger criterion for the man's inference to be both subjectively and objectively valid and for his inductive belief to be both subjectively and objectively reasonable. This criterion adds a third condition to the two conditions for subjective validity, namely, that *e* should in fact be true. Since this third condition no more than the other two includes the requirement that the man should reasonably believe *e*, there is again no explicit circularity. But the critic will then insist that here there is an implicit circularity in that to have a reasonable belief in this third condition for the validity of the inference requires an inference of exactly the same sort to establish it.

There is one consideration which is worth mentioning at this point, since it may perhaps serve to mitigate this implicit circularity. Let us consider the new inference whose premiss is the conjunction of the three conditions for the both subjective and objective validity of the inductive inference whose conclusion is *e*, i.e. whose premiss is the conjunctive proposition

(*B* reasonably believes the π-evidence for *e*) and (*B* believes *e*) and (*e* is true),

and whose conclusion is the proposition that it is both subjectively and objectively reasonable for *B* to believe *e*. Since with this sense of "reasonable" it is a logically necessary proposition that the premiss in this new inference is a sufficient condition for the conclusion, this new inference is a deduction. Now think of this new inference, not as adding a belief in the conclusion to *B*'s body of reasonable beliefs but as carrying with it *B*'s belief in the conclusion by deducing the conclusion from a premiss which *B* believes. Criteria I–V (p. 354) then become the relevant criteria for validity; and, if *B* believes the conjunctive premiss, belief in which is equivalent to a conjunction of three beliefs held by *B* — a belief that he reasonably believes the π-evidence for *e*, a belief that he believes *e*, and a belief in *e* — this triple belief justifiably carries with it a belief that it is both subjectively and objectively reasonable for *B* to believe *e*, provided that, if criteria I, II, IV or V are used, *B* believes that the conjunctive premiss is logically a sufficient condition for the conclusion, and, if criteria II or V are used, that this belief of *B*'s is a reasonable one. So *B*'s second-order belief that he is both subjectively and objectively reasonable in believing *e* is a belief justifiably carried along with a first-order belief in *e*, together with a second-order belief that he has this belief, a second-order belief in the reasonableness of a belief in the π-evidence for *e* and — in the case of some of the criteria — a belief or a reasonable belief in a logically necessary proposition. If we take the second-order belief that he has a belief in *e* as going along automatically with a belief in *e*, and if we take for granted the second-order belief in the reasonableness of a belief in the π-evidence for *e* and the belief or reasonable belief in the logically necessary proposition, what we have said can be reduced to the statement that, if a man believes *e*, this belief justifies his holding along with it the second-order belief that he is both subjectively and objectively reasonable in believing *e*. Thus a belief in *e* is self-rationalizing — not, of course, in the sense that believing *e* makes this belief itself reasonable, but in the sense that believing *e* carries along with it a belief that this belief in *e* is reasonable.

The critic may object that all this farrago is like taking in one another's washing, and goes no way to producing any argument which is not circular for a belief in *e* to be reasonable in a sense of "reasonable" which is not merely subjective. I can say no more than that the account of objective validity of an inference which has been given is in terms of the right working of an inference-machine, and that the implicit circularity only arises from the inference-machine becoming self-conscious about the way in which it operates. The predictionist can offer to the circularity-mongering critic two alternatives — a weak subjective sense of reasonableness with no suspicion of circularity, or a stronger sense of reasonableness, objective as well as subjective, with no explicit circularity but with an implicit circularity which depends essentially upon the inferrer being regarded as an inference-machine and the validity of his inference depending upon his operating, *qua* inference-machine, according to an efficient mode of operation (with the rider that, if the inferrer believes that he, *qua* inference-machine, is operating efficiently, that belief is self-rationalizing in the way explained in the last paragraph). If neither of these alternatives, nor the third alternative of the purely objective sense of reasonableness, satisfies the critic, and if he is not prepared to be satisfied by one sense of reasonableness in some contexts and another in other contexts but still demands a method of establishing the effectiveness of an inductive policy which is not to be obtained by following an inductive policy, he must be told outright that what he is demanding is that the effectiveness of an inductive policy should not be an empirical proposition. But if so, induction would be deduction, there would be no inductive problem to puzzle our heads over, and this chapter tediously worrying at the problem would have been altogether unnecessary.

26 *Braithwaite's Inductive Justification of Induction*

ROBERT C. COBURN

One of the recurrent temptations in theory of knowledge is to try to provide an inductive justification for employing the principles of inductive inference. The purpose of the present paper is to suggest that this approach is misguided by exposing the deficiencies of what appears to be the most carefully constructed attempt of this kind which has thus far been made. I refer to the attempt made by R. B. Braithwaite in his *Scientific Explanation.*[1]

Braithwaite begins his argument by defining an "inductive policy" as a policy "for establishing general hypotheses in accordance with inductive principles of inference on the basis of empirical data" (p. 261). Then he suggests the following criterion for the "reliability" of an inductive policy Π, and a fortiori for the "validity" of any inference it occasions and the "reasonableness" of belief in any hypothesis it sanctions (cf. p. 264):

> Of every time t later than a fixed time t_o, and of every interval of time of a fixed length of years d lying within the interval $[t_o, t]$, it is true that many of the hypotheses established by the use of policy Π during the interval of d years (unless there are no such hypotheses) have the joint property (1) of not having been empirically refuted at any time between the time of establishment and t, (2) of having been empirically confirmed at least once between the time of establishment and t" (p. 267).

The precise form of this criterion and the argument adduced in support of it need not concern us here. The important point is merely that for a policy Π to be reliable it must have what Peirce referred to as "truth-producing virtue".

Following his explication of this Peircean notion, Braithwaite defines an "effective" policy as one which satisfies this criterion of reliability ("suitable values having been assigned to the arbitrary elements"), and an "effective-in-the-past" policy as one which satisfies the criterion which results when "of every time t not later than the present time and" is substituted in the above for "of every time t" (p. 268).

From *Philosophy of Science*, Vol. 28, No.2, 1961, pp. 65–71. Reprinted by permission of the editor of *Philosophy of Science* and the author.

[1] (Cambridge, England, 1955), chap. VIII. All page references in parentheses refer to this book. [Ed. note: Our selection from Braithwaite is taken from the 1959 edition; pages 264–291.]

And finally, after noting that "the effectiveness of an effective policy is an empirical proposition which does not logically follow from the policy's effectiveness-in-the-past" (p. 269), and that the inductive establishment of policies other than (and including) the policy of simple enumeration in fact proceed by the use of the latter policy, Braithwaite advances certain considerations to show the non-circularity (in the vicious sense) of the following argument justifying the use of the policy of simple enumeration:

ARGUMENT A: (1) Policy Π is effective-in-the-past;
Therefore,
(2) Policy Π is effective,

where Policy Π is the policy of inferring in accordance with a principle of simple enumeration, and where the principle governing the inference is this same principle of simple enumeration.

The first of these considerations is that *A* obviously does not have among its premises proposition (2) and accordingly is not circular "in the *petitio principii* sense of professing to infer a conclusion from a set of premises one of which is the conclusion itself" (p. 276). However, as Braithwaite himself concedes, this observation alone is hardly adequate to put down the charge of vicious circularity. There remains the difficulty involved in the use of an inferential policy to establish its own effectiveness (cf. *ibid.*). To surmount this difficulty, Braithwaite proceeds to argue that provided (1) in *A* is reasonably believed,[2] the argument will be both valid[3] and exempt from the charge of vicious circularity if any of the following conditions is satisfied:

I. (2) is merely believed (and not reasonably believed), or
II. (2) is true, or
III. (2) is both believed (though not reasonably believed) and true.

His attempt to substantiate this claim begins with the following rather obscure point. From an "external point of view," Braithwaite says, all that is required for inferential validity in addition to reasonable belief in the premises of the argument is the truth of the proposition asserting the effectiveness of the principle governing the inference. For when considered from this point of view, the person making the inference is regarded simply as a reasoning machine; and "obviously," he continues, "there is nothing objectionable in [such a] machine arriving at a new position which corresponds to having a reasonable belief in a proposition asserting some general property of the method of working of the machine" (p. 281). Moreover — as he says in another place —

> it is quite plausible to maintain that such an external, naturalistic, semi-behaviourist way of looking at inductive thinking is the proper one, and that *inductive behavior* . . . rather than inductive belief is the fundamental concept. [And] when looked at in this way the onus of proof changes. It is no longer up to the logician to give reasons for

[2] Where the reasonableness of a belief is said to consist in the proposition believed being either "known directly to be true" or capable of valid inference from a proposition "known directly to be true" (p. 278).

[3] In the sense that the conclusion can justifiably be added to the inferrer's body of reasonable beliefs (p. 280). Hereafter, I shall use the words "valid" and "validity" in this sense.

inferring inductive conclusions; it is up to the critic to give reasons for abandoning inductive behaviour.[4]

Now the force of these considerations, I confess, eludes me. It is true, of course, that a machine doubtless could be constructed in such a way that when "fed" certain propositions, it would "arrive" at the proposition that its "principle of working" was effective. Accordingly, there is nothing "objectionable" in the conception of such an occurrence. But why this is relevant to the question whether human beings can legitimately consider warranted those of their beliefs which are inferred in accordance with inferential principles not themselves known (or "reasonably believed") to be effective, is extremely difficult to see. And to say that human beings can plausibly be viewed as inductive machines, or that "inductive behaviour" is a more "fundamental concept" than "inductive belief," hardly helps matters. Human beings are, after all, very unlike machines. And one feature of this dissimilarity is just their ability to question the status of beliefs inferred from reasonably believed premises by principles of inference whose effectiveness is not similarly reasonably believed. And if to say that the concept of inductive behavior is more fundamental than that of inductive belief is just to say that the "external point of view" is the proper one, isn't this just to beg the question at issue?

Braithwaite is not unaware, however, of the difficulties of this line of argument. For directly after developing the machine analogy, he writes: "But if the machine becomes selfconscious and critical of its mode of working, it will not be satisfied with a criterion for the validity of inference which depends upon the effectiveness in fact of the method by which it is working" (p. 282). And accordingly, being a machine of this latter sort, Braithwaite turns to an attempt to defend the view that it is sufficient for the validity of an inductive argument that the inferrer have reasonable belief in the premises of the argument together with belief, though not reasonable belief, in the effectiveness of the principle of inference employed.

His defense has three parts. First: it is claimed that if reasonable belief, rather than belief *simpliciter*, in the effectiveness of the policy employed in an inference were a condition of such an inference's validity, then the majority of deductive inferences would be invalid as well as inductive inferences. For this requirement

> would admit only deductions in which the proposition authenticating the principle of inference used was either seen directly to be true or was seen directly to be a logical consequence (in a chain of proof sufficiently short to be taken in at one glance) of a proposition seen directly to be true. Any other way of attaining belief in the effectiveness of the policy of deduction, e.g. by citing authority, or by remembering that one had satisfied oneself of its truth in the past, would involve inductive steps, and would thus not permit the belief to be "reasonable," since the inference by which it had been obtained, or upon which it could be based, would not satisfy this stringent condition for validity (pp. 283–284).

[4] R. B. Braithwaite, "Probability and Induction," *British Philosophy in Mid-Century*, C. A. Mace, ed. (New York, 1957), p. 149. (Italics his.)

Second: it is pointed out that to say of a man that he is reasonable in holding a particular belief "is in many contexts to make a judgment which is either a moral judgment or closely resembles one" (p. 286). And this is so because "to say of a man that he is unreasonable in holding a belief *q* is to make, or to imply, a hypothetical moral criticism of him" (p. 286). But, Braithwaite continues, "the sense of rightness which is appropriate to the imputation of moral praise or blame is the subjective sense of rightness" (p. 286), where what determines the rightness of an action in this sense is "whether or not the agent believes the action to be fitting to the situation or to have . . . or to produce effects having" a certain characteristic (p. 285). Hence, the argument concludes, in any context in which reasonableness is ascribed to a man with a moral implication, "to the extent that the reasonableness of a man's belief is derived by a valid process of inference, this reasonableness must depend not upon the actual effectiveness of the policy of inference but upon the man's belief in this effectiveness" (pp. 286–287).

Third: it is argued that belief in the proposition *e* that a certain inferential policy (Π say) is effective is "self-rationalizing — not, of course, in the sense that believing *e* makes this belief itself reasonable, but in the sense that believing *e* carries along with it a belief that this belief in *e* is reasonable" (p. 291). The argument is as follows. Consider the inference from the premises:

(1) *B* reasonably believes the Π-evidence for *e*
(2) *B* believes *e*
(3) *e* is true,

to the conclusion

(4) It is both subjectively and objectively reasonable for *B* to believe *e*,

(where it is both subjectively and objectively reasonable to believe a certain proposition when that proposition has been inferred from premises which are reasonably believed, in accordance with a principle of inference which is both effective and believed to be effective.) This is plainly a deductive inference. Now, Braithwaite continues,

if *B* believes the conjunctive premiss, belief in which is equivalent to a conjunction of three beliefs held by *B* — a belief that he reasonably believes the Π-evidence for *e*, a belief that he believes *e*, and a belief in *e* — this triple belief justifiably carries with it a belief that it is both subjectively and objectively reasonable for *B* to believe *e*, provided that, if criteria I, II, IV or V are used, *B* believes that the conjunctive premiss is logically a sufficient condition for the conclusion, and, if criteria II or V are used, that this belief of *B*'s is a reasonable one.[5] So *B*'s second-order belief that he is both subjectively and

[5] Criteria I–V are certain possible sufficient criteria for the validity of an inference by a person *B* of the conclusion *q* from the premise *p* in accordance with a principle of inference the effectiveness of whose use is asserted by the proposition *r*, where by "validity" is meant "justifiably carries a belief in *q* along with *B*'s belief in *p*" (p. 280). They are as follows:

I. *B* believes *p* and believes *r*;
II. *B* believes *p* and reasonably believes *r*;
III. *B* believes *p*, and *r* is true;
IV. *B* believes *p* and believes *r*, and *r* is true;
V. *B* believes *p* and reasonably believes *r*, and *r* is true (p. 279).

objectively reasonable in believing *e* is a belief justifiably carried along with a first-order belief in *e*, together with a second-order belief that he has this belief, a second-order belief in the reasonableness of a belief in the Π-evidence for *e* and — in the case of some of the criteria — a belief or a reasonable belief in a logically necessary proposition (pp. 290–291).

Unfortunately, none of these considerations, as far as I can see, come anywhere near to being compelling. To begin with, even if we overlook the highly debatable contention that remembering involves "inductive steps" in some way relevant to Braithwaite's first argument, clearly this argument would founder in any case upon the fact that it is so obviously subject to reversal. That is, if reasonable belief in the effectiveness of the policy of deduction did rest upon inductive arguments, and induction did have the character Braithwaite suggests, I should think it would be at least as reasonable to question the validity of the majority of deductive arguments as to conclude, *à la* Braithwaite, that induction must be a valid process.

And the second argument Braithwaite gives is even less convincing. In the first place, the argument proves too much. If it follows that because we praise men for doing what they merely believe to be right, we ought therefore to give men equally high marks for holding beliefs inferred via inferential policies they merely believe to be effective; why does it not also follow that we ought to give the same marks to men for holding beliefs inferred from premises in which they merely believe? Now Braithwaite, it must be conceded, anticipates this objection. "May not this comparison with subjective rightness," he asks, "be pushed further so that the reasonableness of belief in the premiss is as irrelevant to the reasonableness of belief in the inductive conclusion as is the reasonableness of belief in the effectiveness of the inductive policy?" (p. 288). But in reply to this embarrasing query, he merely reiterates the commonsense position. "If the reasonableness of a belief is to be defended by the belief's having been inferred or being able to be inferred from other beliefs," he asserts, "these other beliefs must themselves be reasonably held" (p. 288). Unfortunately, this reply misses the force of the objection entirely. For exactly the same sort of reply could be made by one insisting that the effectiveness of inductive policies be reasonably believed; and if such a reply is adequate in the one case, it is surely *as* adequate in the other. In either case, what the reply amounts to is a rejection of the alleged relevance of the conditions of moral praise and blame to the question concerning the conditions of inferential validity.

In addition to the above difficulty, the second argument is also weak on two other counts. First: though it is true, as Braithwaite says, that to say of a man that he is reasonable in holding a certain belief is "to make a judgment which is either a moral judgment or closely resembles one" (p. 286); it is also true, I submit, that like judgments ascribing courage and kindness, judgments of reasonableness carry a fairly constant and well-defined descriptive sense as well as an evaluative one. This is clear from the fact (e.g.) that it is not self-contradictory to say: "It is reasonable to believe *p*, but you ought not to believe it nonetheless." Whether Braithwaite would wish to deny this observation is not evident. But, in any case, he has certainly provided no reason whatever for thinking this difference between judgments of reasonableness and *certain* types of moral judgment is *not* a crucial one relatively to his argument. And second: this argument, like the first, would appear to be also liable to reversal. That is, why could it not be as plausibly argued that (1) if, as Braithwaite seems to recognize, we ordinarily think that reasonable belief in the effectiveness of an inferential policy is a necessary condition of the validity of inferences governed by that policy; and (2) if further it is true that judgments of reasonableness are like moral judgments in the ways that matter for Braithwaite's argument; that (3) it is probably a mistake to think it proper to ascribe praise and blame on the basis of the presence or absence of mere belief (as opposed to reasonable belief) that a certain line of conduct was objectively right? I confess I see no reason whatever; and Braithwaite has certainly provided none.

As far as Braithwaite's third argument is concerned, despite its prolixity a word is sufficient to dismiss it. And the reason is that the conclusion of the argument, viz., that belief in *e* carries along with it a belief that this belief in *e* is reasonable, is irrelevant to the problem at issue. For what is required is an argument which shows that an inference can plausibly be viewed as valid despite the fact that no reasonable belief in the effectiveness of the principle governing the inference is possible. But by virtue of the fact that the senses in which one's belief that one's belief in *e* is reasonable according to Braithwaite's argument are the "subjective" and "objective" senses; all that Braithwaite's argument shows is that if one believes in *e*, then one necessarily has a belief concerning the reasonableness of one's belief in *e* of the same kind that one will have concerning the reasonableness of one's belief in the conclusions of inferences governed by principles of inference which are in fact effective, which are believed in, but which are not reasonably believed in. But to have shown this will hardly satisfy anyone who is not much impressed by this kind of "reasonableness."

Thus far I hope to have shown that Braithwaite has in fact provided no good reasons for thinking that Argument *A* can be both valid and exempt from the charge of vicious circularity apart from a reasonable belief in the effectiveness of Policy Π. By way of conclusion, I should like to indicate certain considerations which show that even if Braithwaite's arguments were more powerful than they are, we should still have very good reason for hesitating to accept his conclusions.

Let us suppose that Braithwaite is right in holding that it is sufficient for an argument's validity that the premises of the argument be reasonably believed and that the proposition asserting the effectiveness of the principle of inference governing the argument should be either true or believed to be true or both. In this case, provided (1) is reasonably believed and (2) is believed, true, or both, the following argument would be valid:

Argument B: (1) Policy Φ is not effective-in-the-past;
Therefore,
(2) Policy Φ is effective,

where Policy Φ is some counter-inductive policy such as that whenever two characteristics have invariably been conjoined in the past, the hypothesis that they will not occur (or perhaps not generally occur) in conjunction in the future "is to be treated as being well established" (p. 260). But if this argument really is valid under the conditions indicated, then since we can reasonably believe (1), it seems to follow that in order to get support for (2) on the basis of past experience all that we (or anybody) need do is to believe (or start believing) (2). But surely this is a wildly paradoxical conclusion; surely it would be wrong-headed in the extreme to think that empirical support could be gained in behalf of counter-inductive procedures by virtue of some psychological change within the inquirer(s).

An even more perplexing consequence of thinking ARGUMENT *B* valid follows from the fact that, again since we can reasonably believe in (1), we might be in possession of empirical support for (2) without being aware of it. This would be the case if (2) were true, though not believed by anybody to be true. And this fact, in turn, entails that it is logically possible that we might possess empirical support for both (2) of ARGUMENT *B* and (2) of ARGUMENT *A*, i.e., for the truth of the proposition which asserts the effectiveness of Φ and for the truth of the proposition which asserts the effectiveness of Π. This would be so provided either (a) we believed *A*(2) while *B*(2) was in fact true, or (b) we believed *B*(2) while *A*(2) was in fact true. But again, surely this possibility is not one which it is intelligible to think actually obtains.

27 *Of the Ground of Induction*

J. S. MILL

Induction properly so called, as distinguished from those mental operations, sometimes, though improperly, designated by the name, may, then, be summarily defined as Generalization from Experience. It consists in inferring from some individual instances in which a phenomenon is observed to occur, that it occurs in all instances of a certain class; namely, in all which *resemble* the former, in what are regarded as the material circumstances.

In what way the material circumstances are to be distinguished from those which are immaterial, or why some of the circumstances are material and others not so, we are not yet ready to point out. We must first observe, that there is a principle implied in the very statement of what Induction is; an assumption

From *A System of Logic*, Harper & Brothers, New York, 1895, Book III, Chapter III, Sections 1, 2. 8th Edition. Reprinted by permission of Harper & Row, New York.

with regard to the course of nature and the order of the universe; namely, that there are such things in nature as parallel cases; that what happens once, will, under a sufficient degree of similarity of circumstances, happen again, and not only again, but as often as the same circumstances recur. This, I say, is an assumption, involved in every case of induction. And, if we consult the actual course of nature, we find that the assumption is warranted. The universe, so far as known to us, is so constituted, that whatever is true in any one case, is true in all cases of a certain description; the only difficulty is, to find what description.

This universal fact, which is our warrant for all inferences from experience, has been described by different philosophers in different forms of language: that the course of nature is uniform; that the universe is governed by general laws; and the like. One of the most usual of these modes of expression, but also one of the most inadequate, is that which has been brought into familiar use by the metaphysicians of the school of Reid and Stewart. The disposition of the human mind to generalize from experience — a propensity considered by these philosophers as an instinct of our nature — they usually describe under some such name as "our intuitive conviction that the future will resemble the past." Now it has been well pointed out by Mr. Bailey, that (whether the tendency be or not an original and ultimate element of our nature), Time, in its modifications of past, present, and future, has no concern either with the belief itself, or with the grounds of it. We believe that fire will burn to-morrow, because it burned to-day and yesterday; but we believe, on precisely the same grounds, that it burned before we were born, and that it burns this very day in Cochin-China. It is not from the past to the future, as past and future, that we infer, but from the known to the unknown; from facts observed to facts unobserved; from what we have perceived, or been directly conscious of, to what has not come within our experience. In this last predicament is the whole region of the future; but also the vastly greater portion of the present and of the past.

Whatever be the most proper mode of expressing it, the proposition that the course of nature is uniform, is the fundamental principle, or general axiom, of Induction. It would yet be a great error to offer this large generalization as any explanation of the inductive process. On the contrary, I hold it to be itself an instance of induction, and induction by no means of the most obvious kind. Far from being the first induction we make, it is one of the last, or at all events one of those which are latest in attaining strict philosophical accuracy. As a general maxim, indeed, it has scarcely entered into the minds of any but philosophers; nor even by them, as we shall have many opportunities of remarking, have its extent and limits been always very justly conceived. The truth is, that this great generalization is itself founded on prior generalizations. The obscurer laws of nature were discovered by means of it, but the more obvious ones must have been understood and assented to as general truths before it was ever heard of. We should never have thought of affirming that all phenomena take place according to general laws, if we had not first arrived, in the case of a great multitude of phenomena, at some knowledge of the laws themselves; which could be done no otherwise than by induction. In what sense, then, can a principle, which is so far from being our earliest induction, be regarded as our warrant for all the others? In the only sense, in which (as we have already seen) the general propositions which we place at the head of our reasonings when we throw them into syllogisms, ever really contribute to their validity. As Archbishop Whately remarks, every induction is a syllogism with the major premise suppressed; or (as I prefer expressing it) every induction may be thrown into the form of a syllogism, by supplying a major premise. If this be actually done, the principle which we are now considering, that of the uniformity of the course of nature, will appear as the ultimate major premise of all inductions, and will, therefore, stand to all inductions in the relation in which, as has been shown at so much length, the major proposition of a syllogism always stands to the conclusion; not contributing at all to prove it, but being a necessary condition of its being proved; since no conclusion is proved, for which there can not be found a true major premise.

The statement, that the uniformity of the course of nature is the ultimate major premise in all cases of induction, may be thought to require some explanation. The immediate major premise in every inductive argument, it certainly is not. Of that, Archbishop Whately's must be held to be the correct account. The induction, "John, Peter, etc., are mortal, therefore all mankind are mortal," may, as he justly says, be thrown into a syllogism by prefixing as a major premise (what is at any rate a necessary condition of the validity of the argument), namely, that what is true of John, Peter, etc., is true of all mankind. But how came we by this major premise? It is not self-evident; nay, in all cases of unwarranted generalization, it is not true. How, then, is it arrived at? Necessarily either by induction or ratiocination; and if by induction, the process, like all other inductive arguments, may be thrown into the form of a syllogism. This previous syllogism it is, therefore, necessary to construct. There is, in the long run, only one possible construction. The real proof that what is true of John, Peter, etc., is true of all mankind, can only be, that a different supposition would be inconsistent with the uniformity which we know to exist in the course of nature. Whether there would be this inconsistency or not, may be a matter of long and delicate inquiry; but unless there would, we have no sufficient ground for the major of the inductive syllogism. It hence appears, that if we throw the whole course of any inductive argument into a series of syllogisms, we shall arrive by more or fewer steps at an ultimate syllogism, which will have for its major premise the principle, or axiom, of the uniformity of the course of nature.

It was not to be expected that in the case of this axiom, any more than of other axioms, there should be unanimity among thinkers with respect to the grounds on which it is to be received as true. I have already stated that I regard it as itself a generalization from experience. Others hold it to be a principle which, antecedently to any verification by experience, we are compelled by the constitution of our thinking faculty to assume as true. Having so recently, and at so much length, combated a similar doctrine as applied to the axioms of mathematics, by arguments which are in a great measure applicable to the present case, I shall defer the more particular discussion of this controverted point in regard to the fundamental axiom of induction, until a more advanced period of our inquiry. . . .

In order to obtain a better understanding of the problem which the logician must solve if he would establish a scientific theory of Induction, let us compare a few cases of incorrect inductions with others which are acknowledged to be legitimate. Some, we know, which were believed for centuries to be correct, were nevertheless incorrect. That all swans are white, can not have been a good induction, since the conclusion has turned out erroneous. The experience, however, on which the conclusion rested, was genuine. From the earliest records, the testimony of the inhabitants of the known world was unanimous on the point. The uniform experience, therefore, of the inhabitants of the known world, agreeing in a common result, without one known instance of deviation from that result, is not always sufficient to establish a general conclusion.

But let us now turn to an instance apparently not very dissimilar to this. Mankind were wrong, it seems, in concluding that all swans were white: are we also wrong, when we conclude that all men's heads grow above their shoulders, and never below, in spite of the conflicting testimony of the naturalist Pliny? As there were black swans, though civilized people had existed for three thousand years on the earth without meeting with them, may there not also be "men whose heads do grow beneath their shoulders," notwithstanding a rather less perfect unanimity of negative testimony from observers? Most persons would answer No; it was more credible that a bird should vary in its color, than that men should vary in the relative position of their principal organs. And there is no doubt that in so saying they would be right: but to say why they are right, would be impossible, without entering more deeply than is usually done, into the true theory of Induction.

Again, there are cases in which we reckon with the most unfailing confidence upon uniformity, and other cases in which we do not count upon it at all. In some we feel complete assurance that the future will resemble the past, the unknown be precisely similar to the known. In others, however invariable may be the result obtained from the instances which have been observed, we draw from them no more than a very feeble presumption that the like result will hold in all other cases. That a straight line is the shortest distance between two points, we do not doubt to be true even in the region of the fixed stars. When a chemist announces the existence and properties of a newly-discovered substance, if we confide in his accuracy, we feel assured that the conclusions he has arrived at will hold universally, though the induction be founded but on a single instance. We do not withhold our assent, waiting for a repetition of the experiment; or if we do, it is from a doubt whether the one experiment was properly made, not whether if properly made it would be conclusive. Here, then, is a general law of nature, inferred without hesitation from a single instance; a universal proposition from a singular one. Now mark another case, and contrast it with this. Not all the instances which have been observed since the beginning of the world, in support of the general proposition that all crows are black, would be deemed a sufficient presumption of the truth of the proposition, to outweigh the testimony of one unexceptionable witness who should affirm that in some region of the earth not fully explored, he had caught and examined a crow, and had found it to be gray.

Why is a single instance, in some cases, sufficient for a complete induction, while in others, myriads of concurring instances, without a single exception known or presumed, go such a very little way toward establishing a universal proposition? Whoever can answer this question knows more of the philosophy of logic than the wisest of the ancients, and has solved the problem of induction.

28 The Doctrine of the Uniformity of Nature

MORRIS R. COHEN AND ERNEST NAGEL

The claim that the experimental methods are capable of demonstrating with complete certainty universal, invariable connections rests on a belief that "nature is uniform." Induction, according to Mill, consists in inferring from a finite number of observed instances of a phenomenon, that it occurs in *all* instances of a certain class which resemble the observed instance in certain ways. But according to Mill, the very statement of what induction is requires an assumption concerning the order of the universe. The assumption is that "there are such things in nature as parallel cases, that what happens once, will, under a sufficient degree of similarity of circumstances, happen again."[1]

This assumption may be expressed in various ways: that nature is uniform, that the universe is governed by general laws, that the same cause will under similar circumstances be accompanied by the same effect. In *some* form, however, so the claim runs, it is required for induction. Every induction may be thrown into the form of a syllogism, and the principle of the uniformity of nature will then appear as the "ultimate major premise of all inductions."[2]

Mill puts the matter as follows: "The induction, 'John, Peter, etc., are mortal, therefore all mankind are mortal,' may . . . be thrown into a syllogism by prefixing as a major premise (what is at any rate a necessary condition of the

From *An Introduction to Logic and Scientific Method* by Morris R. Cohen and Ernest Nagel, pp. 267–269, copyright, 1934, by Harcourt, Brace & World, Inc., renewed ©, 1962, by Ernest Nagel and Leonora Cohen Rosenfield. Reprinted by permission of the publishers and Ernest Nagel.

[1] *A System of Logic*, Vol. I, p. 354.

[2] *Ibid.*, p. 356.

validity of the argument) namely, that what is true of John, Peter, etc., is true of all mankind. But how came we by this major premise? It is not self-evident; nay, in all cases of unwarranted generalization, it is not true. How, then, is it arrived at? Necessarily either by induction or ratiocination; and if by induction, the process, like all other inductive arguments, may be thrown into the form of a syllogism. This previous syllogism it is, therefore, necessary to construct. There is, in the long run, only one possible construction. The real proof that what is true of John, Peter, etc., is true of all mankind, can only be that a different supposition would be inconsistent with the uniformity which we know to to exist in the course of nature. Whether there would be this inconsistency or not, may be a matter of long and delicate inquiry; but unless there would, we have no sufficient ground for the major of the inductive syllogisms. It hence appears, that if we throw the whole course of any inductive argument into a series of syllogisms, we shall arrive by more or fewer steps at an ultimate syllogism, which will have for its major premise the principle, or axiom, of the uniformity of the course of nature." [3]

We shall not discuss whether the principle of the uniformity of nature is true or whether some such principle is required for making inductive inferences. We wish simply to determine whether the principle *if it were true* would in fact help to demonstrate the existence of some particular instance of a supposed causal relation. We must carefully note the following.

1. The principle is stated in an extremely vague form — "what happens once, will, under a sufficient degree of similarity of circumstances, happen again." But what is a sufficient degree of similarity? The principle does not tell us. In any particular investigation we must rely on other criteria, if there are any, to determine what are the circumstances material to the occurrence of a phenomenon.

2. In the second place, the minor premise of an inductive syllogism, even according to Mill, is a *particular* proposition. Therefore even if we employ a universal major premise, such as the principle of uniformity of nature, the premises are insufficient to *demonstrate* a universal conclusion.

3. Finally, the principle does not affirm that *every* pair of phenomena are invariably related. It simply states that *some* pairs are so connected. To appeal to the doctrine in a particular investigation is therefore useless. If we suspect that tight-fitting hats are the cause of baldness, we employ the canons to eliminate as many circumstances other than tight hats as we can. But no finite number of observed cases of tight-fitting hats followed by baldness can demonstrate a law which is to hold for an *indefinite* number of cases. The principle of uniformity of nature does not help us. It does not say *which* of the innumerable causal connections between phenomena are invariable; it merely asserts that *some* are. But the task of the particular inquiry is to show that a *designated* pair of phenomena are in causal relation.

[3] *A System of Logic*, Vol. I, pp. 357–358.

29 *Postulates of Scientific Inference*

BERTRAND RUSSELL

As the outcome of the discussions in previous chapters of this Part, I suggest that the postulates required to validate scientific method may be reduced to five. It is highly probable that they can be further reduced, but I have not myself succeeded in doing so. The five postulates to which previous analyses have led us may be called:

a. The postulate of quasi-permanence.
b. The postulate of separable causal lines.
c. The postulate of spatio-temporal continuity in causal lines.
d. The postulate of the common causal origin of similar structures ranged about a center, or, more simply, the structural postulate.
e. The postulate of analogy.

Each of these postulates asserts that something happens often, but not necessarily always; each therefore justifies, in a particular case, a rational expectation which falls short of certainty. Each has an objective and a subjective aspect: objectively, it asserts that something happens in most cases of a certain sort; subjectively, it asserts that, in certain circumstances, an expectation falling short of certainty in a greater or less degree has rational credibility. The postulates collectively are intended to provide the antecedent probabilities required to justify inductions.

A. The Postulate of Quasi-Permanence

The chief use of this postulate is to replace the common-sense notion of "thing" and "person," in a manner not involving the concept "substance." The postulate may be enunciated as follows:

Given any event A, it happens very frequently that, at any neighboring time, there is at some neighboring place an event very similar to A.

A "thing" is a series of such events. It is because such series of events are common that "thing" is a practically convenient concept. It is to be observed

From *Human Knowledge, Its Scope and Limits*, Simon and Schuster, New York, 1962, pp. 487–496.

that in a series of events which common sense would regard as belonging to one "thing," the similarity need only be between events not widely separated in space-time. There is not very much similarity between a three months' embryo and an adult human being, but they are connected by gradual transitions from next to next, and are therefore accepted as stages in the development of one "thing."

It will frequently happen — for example, in the case of a drop of water in the sea — that there are, at a given neighboring time, many neighboring events similar to A. We can pass by gradual transitions from any one drop in the sea to any other. Our postulate neither affirms nor denies the multiplicity of such events similar to A at a given time; it contents itself with asserting that there is probably at least one such event. Our next postulate, that of causal lines, will enable us to say that when there are many such events at a given time, there is usually one which has a special connection with A, of the sort which makes us regard it alone as part of the history of the "thing" to which A belongs. This is essential if we are to be able to say that a drop of water in the sea at one time, rather than any other drop, is the "same" as a certain drop at another time. Our present postulate does not suffice to enable us to say this, but gives us a part of what we require.

Our postulate has a subjective and an objective aspect. Suppose you have been looking at the sun, and you then close your eyes. Your subjective condition changes rapidly, but not discontinuously; it passes through the stages of akoluthic sensation, immediate memory, and gradually fading true memory. The sun, we believe, goes through no analogous changes; its changes also, we believe, are gradual, but of quite a different sort. Physical and psychological continuity — for example, that of motion and that of fading memory — have different laws, but both exemplify our postulate.

B. The Postulate of Separable Causal Lines

This postulate has many uses, but perhaps the most important is in connection with perception — for example, in attributing the multiplicity of our visual sensations in looking at the night sky to a multitude of stars as their causes. The postulate may be enunciated as follows:

It is frequently possible to form a series of events such that from one or two members of the series something can be inferred as to all the other members.

The most obvious example is motion, particularly unimpeded motion such as that of a photon in interstellar space. But even in the case of impeded motion, so long as the phenomena can be interpreted as a "thing" changing its position, there is an intrinsic causal law, though it tells us less than when the motion is unimpeded. For instance, we can recognize a billiard ball throughout a game of billiards; its motion is continuous, and its changes of appearance are slight. We recognize the billiard ball by means of laws of change which are intrinsic, in the sense that they do not require that we should take account of the effects of other things upon it.

A series of events connected with each other in the manner suggested in the postulate is what I call a "causal line." What makes the inference possible is a "causal law." The first law of motion is an example, if we give it empirical content by adding that there are many motions in nature which, to a first approximation, are unaffected by outside forces. The motion of light rays is the most obvious illustration.

Our postulate is involved, however, in the very concept of "motion." This concept requires that something should preserve its identity while changing its position. When we dispense with substance, the "something" will have to be a series of events, and the series must have some characteristic which facilitates the common-sense interpretation as a "thing" with changing states. I suggest that the required characteristic is an intrinsic causal law, i.e. a law which enables us to say something about unobserved members of the series without having to take account of anything else in the world.

As we have seen, when two causal lines interact — for example, in the collision of two billiard balls — we need no fresh postulate, but can content ourselves with observation and induction.

Our postulates, with the partial exception of the first, all involve the concept of "cause." I cannot accept the view that causation is merely invariable sequence. This opinion cannot be maintained except with an addendum (which is never made) to the effect that a "cause" must not be too narrowly defined. A statement of the form "A is invariably followed by B" requires that "A" and "B" should be general terms, such as "lightning" and "thunder." But it is possible to multiply the general terms applicable to a given event, or to define them with quantitative precision, until "A" and "B" are descriptions each only applicable to one event in the history of the world. In that case, if A is the earlier, A is invariably followed by B, but in general we should not regard A as the "cause" of B. We only think that A is the cause of B if there are many instances of its being followed by B. In fact, I think, these instances are regarded as evidence of something more than sequence, though not, in general, as conclusive evidence.

Between any two events belonging to one causal line, I should say, there is a relation which may be called one of cause-and-effect. But if we call it so, we must add that the cause does not *completely* determine the effect, even in the most favorable cases. There is always *some* influence, which is also causal, though in a slightly different sense, of the environment on the causal line. A photon in interstellar space is slightly deflected by gravitation from its rectilinear path, and in general the disturbing effect of the environment is much greater than in this case. What our postulate asserts may be restated as follows: A given event is very frequently one of a series of events (which may last a fraction of a second or a million years) which has throughout an approximate law of persistence or change. The photon preserves direction and velocity of motion, the billiard ball preserves shape and color, a foetus develops into an animal of the appropriate species, and so on. In all these cases there is spatio-temporal continuity in the series of events composing a causal line; but this brings us to our third postulate.

C. The Postulate of Spatio-Temporal Continuity

This postulate is concerned to deny "action at a distance," and to assert that when there is a causal connection between two events that are not contiguous, there must be intermediate links in the causal chain such that each is contiguous to the next, or (alternatively) such that there is a process which is continuous in the mathematical sense. When a number of people all hear a speaker, it seems obvious that there is a causal connection between what the different auditors hear, and it also seems obvious that since they are separated in space, there must be a causal process in the intervening regions, such as sound waves are considered to be. Or when you see a given person on a variety of occasions, you do not doubt that he has had a continuous existence during the times when you were not seeing him.

This postulate presupposes causal lines, and is only applicable to them. If you know two twins, A and B, whom you cannot tell apart, and you see one on one occasion and one on another, you cannot assume that a continuous chain connects the two appearances until you have satisfied yourself that it was the same twin on both occasions.

This postulate is not concerned with the evidence for a causal connection, but with an inference in cases in which a causal connection is considered to be already established. It allows us to believe that physical objects exist when unperceived, and that it is in virtue of continuous processes in intervening space that percipients in the same neighborhood have perceptions which appear to be causally interconnected, though not directly caused the one by the other. It also has applications in psychology. For example, we may recollect a given occurrence on various occasions, and in the intervening times there is nothing observable that belongs to the same causal line as the recollections, but we assume that there is *something* (in the brain?) which exists at these intervening times, and makes the causal line continuous.

A great many of our inferences to unobserved occurrences, both in science and in common sense, depend upon this postulate.

D. The Structural Postulate

This postulate is concerned with certain circumstances in which inference to a probable causal connection is warranted. The cases concerned are those in which a number of structurally similar occurrences are grouped about a center. The phrase "grouped about a center" is intentionally vague, but in certain cases it is capable of a precise meaning. Suppose a given object to be simultaneously seen by a number of people and photographed by a number of cameras. The visual percepts and the photographs can be arranged by the laws of perspective, and by the same laws the position of the object seen and photographed can be determined. In this instance the sense in which the percepts and photographs are "grouped about a center" is precisely definable. When a number of people hear the same sound, there is an equally precise definition if there is an accurate method of determining when they hear it, for it is found that the times when they hear it differ from a given time by amounts proportional to their distance from a certain point; in that case, the point at the given time is the space-time center or origin of the sound. But I wish to employ the phrase also in cases (such as smells) where no such precision is possible.

Of the three-fold postulate enunciated in Chapter VI, part has been absorbed into our third postulate, and part is not at present relevant. What remains is as follows:

When a number of structurally similar complex events are ranged about a center in regions not widely separated, it is usually the case that all belong to causal lines having their origin in an event of the same structure at the center.

We say that this is "usually" the case, and the inference in a given instance is therefore only probable. But the probability can be increased in various ways. It is increased if the structure is very complex (e.g. a long printed book). It is increased if there are many examples of the complex structure, e.g. when six million people listen to the Prime Minister's broadcast. It is increased by regularity in the grouping about a center, as in the case of a very loud explosion heard by many observers, who note the time when they hear it.

It seems likely that the above postulate could be analyzed into several simpler postulates, and that the above ways of increasing probabilities would then become demonstrable. But though I believe this to be possible, I have not succeeded in doing it.

The uses of this postulate have been sufficiently set forth in Chapter VI.

E. The Postulate of Analogy

The postulate of analogy may be enunciated as follows:

Given two classes of events A and B, and given that, whenever both A and B can be observed, there is reason to believe that A causes B, then if, in a given case, A is observed, but there is no way of observing whether B occurs or not, it is probable that B occurs; and similarly if B is observed, but the presence or absence of A cannot be observed.

In connection with this postulate, it is necessary to recall what was said on the subject of observed negative facts in Part Two, Chapter IX. By looking out of the window you can observe that it is not raining; this is different from not observing that it is raining, which can be achieved by shutting the eyes. The postulate is concerned with the second kind of non-observation, not with the first, and there must be some reason for supposing that the unobserved fact, if it occurs, will be unobservable. Suppose, for example, that a barking dog is running after a rabbit, and for a moment is hidden by a bush. The bush accounts for your not seeing the dog, and allows you to infer that the bark, which you still hear, is still associated with what you saw a moment ago. When the dog emerges from the bush, you think your belief is confirmed.

The non-perception of other minds is more analogous to that of the dog in the bush than is generally thought. We do not see an object if an opaque body is between it and us, i.e. if no causal line leads from it to our eyes. We feel a touch on any part of the body because causal lines travel along the nerves to the brain from the part touched. If the nerves are cut, we feel nothing; the effect is exactly analogous to that of an opaque body in the case of sight. When someone else's body is touched we feel nothing, because no nerves travel from his body to our brain. Probably in time physiologists will be able to make nerves connecting the bodies of different people; this will have the advantage that we shall be able to feel another man's tooth aching. In the meantime, there are understandable reasons for the impossibility of observing the bodily sensations of others, and therefore the fact that we do not observe them is no reason for supposing that they do not occur. It is only in cases where some such reason for non-observability exists that our postulate can legitimately be applied.

Let us take as an illustration of our postulate the connection of certain kinds of visual appearance with the expectation of hardness. There is a certain kind of tactile sensation which leads us to call the body touched "hard." The word "hard" is a causal word: it denotes that property of an object in virtue of which it causes a certain kind of tactile sensation. Our previous postulates enable us to infer that there is such a property, which bodies possess while they are causing the appropriate sensations. But our previous postulates do not enable us to infer that bodies sometimes have this property when they are not being touched. But now we find that when a body is both seen and touched, hardness is associated with a certain kind of visual appearance, and our postulate allows us to infer that hardness is probably associated with this visual appearance even when the body concerned is not being touched.

As appears from the above discussion, this postulate has many uses in addition to that of allowing us to infer mental occurrences connected with bodies other than our own.

The above postulates are probably not stated in their logically simplest form, and it is likely that further investigation would show that they are not all necessary for scientific inference. I hope and believe, however, that they are sufficient. There are certain epistemological problems connected with them, which I shall consider in the next chapter; these problems do not depend upon the exact form of the postulates, and would remain the same even if the postulates were much modified.

The postulates, in the form in which I have enunciated them, are intended to justify the first steps toward science, and as much of common sense as can be justified. My main problem in this Part has been epistemological: What must we be supposed to know, in addition to particular observed facts, if scientific inferences are to be valid? In dealing with this problem, it is not science in its most advanced and technical form that we have to examine, for advanced science is built on elementary science, and elementary science is built on common sense. The progress of science is from generalizations that are vague and liable to exceptions to others that are more nearly precise and have fewer exceptions. "Unsupported bodies in air fall" is a primitive generalization; the Psalmist noted that sparks are an exception, and nowadays he might have added balloons and airplanes. But without this crude and partly untrue law, we should never have arrived at the law of gravitation. Premises for theory of knowledge are always different from premises for logic, and it is premises for theory of knowledge that I have been trying to discover.

In what sense can we be said to "know" the above postulates, or whatever substitutes may hereafter be found preferable? Only, I think, in a sense which takes account of the discussion of kinds of knowledge in Chapter I of this part. Knowledge of general connections between facts is more different than is usually supposed from knowledge of particular facts. Knowledge of connections between facts has its biological origin in animal expectations. An animal which experiences an A expects a B; when it evolves into a primitive man of science it sums up a number of particular expectations in the statement "A causes B." It is biologically advantageous to have such expectations as will usually be verified; it is therefore not surprising if the psychological laws governing expectations are, in the main, in conformity with the objective laws governing expected occurrences.

We may state the matter as follows. The physical world has what may be called "habits," i.e. causal laws; the behavior of animals has habits, partly innate, partly acquired. The acquired habits are generated by what I call "animal inference," which occurs where there are the data for an induction, but not in all cases where there are such data. Owing to the world being such as it is, certain kinds of inductions are justified and others are not. If our inductive propensities were perfectly adapted to our environment, we should only be prone to an induction if the case were of the sort which would make the induction legitimate. In fact, all except men of science are too prone to induction when one of the characters concerned is interesting, and too little prone to it when both characters are not easy to notice. When both characters are interesting, the popular mind finds the impulse to induction irresistible: comets foretell the death of princes, because both are felt to be noteworthy. But even in animal induction there are elements of validity. The inference from smell to edibility is usually reliable, and no animal makes any of the absurd inductions which the logician can invent to show that induction is not always valid.

Owing to the world being such as it is, certain occurrences are sometimes, in fact, evidence for certain others; and owing to animals being adapted to their environment, occurrences which are, in fact, evidence of others tend to arouse expectation of those others. By reflecting on this process and refining it, we arrive at the canons of inductive inference. These canons are valid if the world has certain characteristics which we all believe it to have. The inferences made in accordance with these canons are self-confirmatory and are not found to contradict experience. Moreover they lead us to think it probable that we shall have mental habits such as these canons will on the whole justify, since such mental habits will be biologically advantageous.

I think, therefore, that we may be said to "know" what is necessary for scientific inference, given that it fulfills the following conditions: (1) it is true, (2) we believe it, (3) it leads to no conclusions which experience confutes, (4) it is logically necessary if any occurrence or set of occurrences is ever to afford evidence in favor of any other occurrence. I maintain that these conditions are satisfied. If, however, anyone chooses to maintain solipsism of the moment, I shall admit that he cannot be refuted, but shall be profoundly skeptical of his sincerity.

30 *Bertrand Russell on the Justification of Induction*

WILLIAM H. HAY

"Nay I will go farther, and assert, that he could not so much as prove by any *probable* arguments, that the future must be conformable to the past. All probable arguments are built on the supposition, that there is this conformity betwixt the future and the past, and therefore can never prove it. This conformity is a *matter of fact*, and if it must be proved, will admit of no proof but from experience. But our experience in the past can be a proof of nothing for the future, but upon a supposition, that there is a resemblance betwixt them. This therefore is a point, which can admit no proof at all, and which we take for granted without any proof."

David Hume, *An Abstract of a Treatise of Human Nature*, p. 15

1. In *Human Knowledge, Its Scope and Limits*, Bertrand Russell recognizes and attempts to deal with what is one of the central questions of philosophy since Descartes, "The relation between individual experience and the general body of scientific knowledge." [1] He states that his purpose is "to discover the minimum principles required to justify scientific inferences." [2] The search for such principles arises from his belief that "data are private and individual." [3] He has only scorn for those who, "finding these problems distasteful" have "tried to deny that these problems exist." [4]

Russell takes the question of the justification of inference from sense-data to physical objects to be the same kind of question as that of induction in the sciences. We may ask for justification for believing that the sun will rise tomorrow at 4:34 a.m. on the evidence of the past behavior of physical objects.

From *Philosophy of Science*, Vol. 17, No. 3, July 1950, pp. 266–277.

[1] *Human Knowledge, Its Scope and Limits*, Simon and Schuster. New York, 1948, p. xi. (All later references by page alone are to this book.)

[2] P. xiii. Cf., G. H. von Wright, *Logical Problem of Induction*, Helsinki, 1941, for a clear-headed and detailed discussion of the question.

[3] P. xii.

[4] P. xii.

We may ask for the justification of using the sights of furry shapes and the sounds of mewing as evidence of a cat. In either case the question concerns an inference from something already accepted to some as yet unaccepted thing.

When Russell asks for justification of such inferences, he does not suppose that in every case an act of inference has in fact occurred. Rather most beliefs simply occur unaccompanied by any conscious act of inference. Russell calls such beliefs, conditioned reflexes or animal inductions. "Whenever A has, in the animal's past experience, been frequently associated with B, where B is something of emotional interest, the occurrence of A tends to cause behaivor appropriate to B." [5] The question that then may be asked is whether such inductions can ever be justified, that is, exhibited as valid inferences from true premises.

Such is the problem. We have beliefs which seem in some sense capable of being supported by other beliefs which are themselves completely certified by the completely known occurrence of the facts they describe. This support takes the form of showing that states of kind B can be inferred from those of kind A, although they may not in fact have been inferred. The relation between these premises and the conclusion of the induction is found, however, not to be deductively valid, unless some further premises not themselves completely evidenced for are added. Russell has put the point in this way: "since in deductive logic one fact or collection of facts cannot imply any other fact," [6] "scientific inferences, if they are in general valid, must be so in virtue of some law or laws of nature, stating a synthetic property of the actual world, or several such properties." [7]

2. Russell makes very strong claims for the necessity of finding such principles if we are not to conclude that "science is moonshine," [8] and that we are limited to a "solipsism of the moment." [9] Russell is not prepared to believe that science is moonshine. He claims over and over again that the alternative to such principles is that "inductive methods of inference . . . are only to be believed, if at all, because they seem indispensable in reaching conclusions we all accept," [10] (In the light of the postulates Russell offers, I do not see that is an alternative) or that induction is "merely a habit that makes us comfortable." [11] We shall want to see whether Russell's postulates, if true, would deliver us from such a painful position. Further we shall want to know what evidence Russell offers us for the truth or probability of his postluates.

This is very much the same formulation of the problem that Russell gave in *Problems of Philosophy* (1912). There too he was looking for an answer in terms of certain laws or principles which would justify scientific inference. At that time he proposed the inductive principle as such as a solution. He held that we

[5] P. 183.
[6] P. 506.
[7] P. 418. Cf. pp. 336-337.
[8] P. 505.
[9] P. 181.
[10] P. 456.
[11] P. 359. (One is reminded of Hume's statement: "If we believe fire warms . . . it is because it costs us too many pains to think otherwise," p. 270, *Treatise*. Selby-Bigge Edition.)

might know such a principle to be self-evidently true in the same way in which we knew "other logical principles." [12] However, "the inductive principle has less self-evidence than some of the other principles of logic." [13] Inferences to the physical world he held to have the self-evidence of the relations of universals. "The principle that sense-data are signs of physical objects is itself a connection of universals." [14] As late as "The Limits of Empiricism" (1935),[15] Russell is still suggesting that the recognition of connections of universals might be sufficient to establish the inductive principle.[16]

In Part V of this volume Russell abandons the view that an inductive principle in the form of simple enumeration would alone be sufficient to give more than a small probability to a generalization. His argument, which follows Keynes,[17] runs as follows: Suppose we ask whether all members of a class, α, are members also of a class, β. Let us further assume that, since information is absent, it can be said to be equally likely before we look that each member of α is or is not a member of β. Suppose we examine n members of α and find that each is in fact a member of β. Even if the class α is finite, containing N members, the "induction has only a probability $\frac{n+1}{N+1}$, which is usually small." [18]

Russell proposes to improve on this by following the lead of Keynes in his proposal "to seek for principles . . . such that given certain data not of the form: This *A* is a *B*, the generalization "All *A* is *B*" has a finite probability." [19] Then, given a generalization and principles which give it an initial probability prior to the examination of instances, "induction can make the generalization increasingly probable." [20]

The principle which Keynes offered was what he called the Principle of Limited Variety, which is similar to what has sometimes been called the Principle of Natural Kinds. This is roughly the principle that "the amount of variety in the universe is limited in such a way that there is no one object so complex that its qualities fall into an infinite number of independent groups." [21] Russell rejects this on three counts:

1) There is no evidence that the number of independent groups of properties, even if it is finite, is small enough that the number of favorable instances can give any generalization an appreciable probability.[22]

2) The Principle of Limited Variety does not apply to attempts to discover the probability of quantitative laws of functional correlation.[23]

[12] *Problems of Philosophy*, p. 175.
[13] *Ibid.*, p. 184.
[14] *Ibid.*, p. 232.
[15] Pp. 131–150. *Proceedings of the Aristotelian Society*, vol. 36.
[16] For another statement of this see W. E. Johnson, *Logic*, Vol. II, Ch. VIII.
[17] P. 407.
[18] P. 407.
[19] P. 436.
[20] P. 436.
[21] J. M. Keynes, *Treatise on Probability*, p. 258.
[22] P. 409.
[23] P. 444.

3) It does not seem to him to be "discoverable, by analysis, as implicit in arguments which we all accept." [24]

In place of the Principle of Limited Variety, Russell offers his own postulates.* He devotes Part Six of the book to an exposition of the five following Postulates of Scientific Inference, which he believes will, if true, confer an initial probability on certain generalizations, and not on others, prior to the examination of instances.

A. Postulates of Quasi-Permanence: Given any event, *A*, it happens very frequently that, at any neighboring time, there is at some neighboring place an event very similar to *A*.[25]

B. Postulate of Separable Causal Lines: It is frequently possible to form a series of events such that from one or two members of the series something can be inferred as to all the other members.[26]

C. Postulate of Spatio-Temporal Continuity: Whenever a system of structurally similar events is found to be connected with a center in the sense that the time when each event occurs differs from a certain time by an amount proportional to the distance of the event from this center, there is an appreciable probability that all the events are connected with an event at the center by intermediate links having spatio-temporal contiguity with each other.[27]

D. The Structural Postulate: When a number of structurally similar complex events are ranged about a center in regions not widely separated, it is usually the case that all belong to causal lines having their origin in an event of the same structure at the center.[28]

E. The Postulate of Analogy: Given two classes of events *A* and *B*, and given that, whenever both *A* and *B* can be observed, there is reason to believe that *A* causes *B*, then if, in a given case, *A* is observed, but there is no way of observing whether *B* occurs or not, it is probable that *B* occurs; and similarly if *B* is observed, but the presence or absence of *A* cannot be observed. [29]

When you look at these postulates, it is surprising how little they seem to have to do with scientific inference. Russell replies by reminding us that these are intended to justify us "in adhering to the common-sense belief in a common world of mental and physical objects." [30] He claims that if we can show that we are justified in those beliefs we can easily determine the degree of probability possessed by scientific laws. But when you look again at the postulates with *this* in mind, it is surprising how little they seem to have to do with the common sense world and how suspiciously they characterize the world as it was described by nineteenth-century physics with the use of differential equations.

3. Russell offers these postulates as synthetic statements. He states that on

[24] P. 439.
* [Ed. note: See Russell's selection, "Postulates of Scientific Inference," in this Section.]
[25] P. 488.
[26] P. 489.
[27] P. 471.
[28] P. 492. Cf. p. 471, #1.
[29] P. 493.
[30] P. 462. Cf. pp. 458, 471, and 484.

this account he doesn't expect that we can know them to be certain. He does propose that they may be seen to be rationally credible. Russell tells us very little about what he means by speaking of rational credibility. He explicitly distinguishes it from subjective credibility or degree of belief. He distinguishes it equally from mathematical probability of a proposition, which, however, "measures its degree of credibility." [31] This undefined term occupies a vital spot in his scheme, since the degree of credibility possessed by the postulates is said to be the reason for believing them. With the little we are told about rational credibility it is difficult to see that it gives us any reason for believing the postulates to be true. Russell does not tell us how to determine what is evidence for rational credibility. We are only told that "in relation to any proposition about which there is evidence there is a corresponding degree of credibility." [32]

We shall have to pass on then from the question of whether or not "rational credibility" is intended by Russell to name some feature identifiable in experience. We may look at the more easily settled question of what kind of assurance such a property could give about the future instances in induction. For it either does or does not make a claim about instances as yet unobserved. If it does make such a claim, the presence of rational credibility cannot be evidence for it, as Hume so coolly observes, but upon a supposition that there is a conformity betwixt the future and the past. Hence, rational credibility is no evidence for this conformity.

Now Russell saw this fairly clearly in *Problems of Philosophy*. There he is prepared to say that though we believe something about the future we have no assurance that our predictions will prove true. He is, I take it, using "probable" in the sense of his later "rationally credible" when he says: "The fact, therefore, that things often fail to fulfill our expectations is no evidence that our expectations will not *probably* be fulfilled in a given case or a given class of cases. Thus our inductive principle is at any rate not capable of being *disproved* by an appeal to experience." [33] If, then, to say that something is rationally credible makes no claim about what will happen, but only about what it is credible will happen, Russell has not given scientists the "grounds for trusting the inference before it is verified" [34] that he is looking for. Oddly enough Russell has noticed this himself in this volume. In his discussion of the relation between induction and probability he comments:

> If 'probability' is taken as an indefinable, we are obliged to admit that the improbable may happen, and that, therefore a probability proposition tells us nothing about the course of nature. If this view is adopted, the inductive principle may be valid, and yet every inference made in accordance with it *may* turn out to be false; this is improbable, but not impossible. . . . If the principle is to serve its purpose, we must interpret 'probable' as meaning 'what in fact usually happens'; that is to say, we must interpret a probability as a frequency.[35]

[31] P. 381.
[32] P. 343.
[33] *Problems of Philosophy*, pp. 105–106.
[34] P. 451.
[35] P. 402.

Apart from the consideration of whether we may know these postulates to be true, Russell offers some considerations based on our conviction that scientific statements are true. These appear in what Russell lists as three requisites of a postulate.[36]

1) "They must be sufficient, from a purely logical point of view, to do the work that is asked of them." [37]

2) "They must be such that some inferences which depend on them for their validity are, to common sense, more or less unquestionable." [38]

3) They must be "discoverable, by analysis, as implicit in arguments which we all acccpt." [39]

1) claims they must be *sufficient* to the truth of scientific statement. 3), by claiming they must be found to be implicit in arguments we accept, might be supposed to claim that a postulate must also be *necessary* to the conclusion. I find further evidence for this in another passage where Russell tells us that he is looking for postulates that are "necessary for scientific inference." [40] There Russell maintains that we may be said to know what is necessary

1) if it is true
2) if we believe it
3) if it leads to no conflicting experiences
4) "if it is logically necessary if any occurrence or set of occurrences is ever to afford evidence in favor of any other occurrences." [41]

We may take it, then, that Russell's claim is that these postulates are both necessary and sufficient to scientific inference. This claim rests on two others. 1) They are both necessary and sufficient to inference to the common sense world. 2) Inference to the common sense world is both necessary and sufficient to scientific inference. As he says: "further investigation may show that these postulates are not all necessary for scientific inference. I hope and believe, however, that they are sufficient." [42] It is odd that he worries only about whether the postulates are necessary and not whether they are sufficient. One would have thought it easier to establish that a certain set of statements were necessary to the truth of another than that they were sufficient. Perhaps what Russell has in mind is that these postulates might turn out to be all necessary to provide a set of sufficient conditions. But he does not discuss so complex a relationship.

We shall want to see whether a close examination of the postulates bears out these claims. There is, however, a further question which appears only from time to time in Russell's discussion. Is *knowledge* of these postulates necessary and sufficient to inference to the common sense world? Is *knowledge* of the common sense world necessary and sufficient to scientific inferencc? These are very

[36] P. 439.
[37] P. 438.
[38] Pp. 438-439.
[39] P. 439.
[40] P. 496.
[41] P. 496.
[42] P. 494.

different, though not unrelated, questions from those about the necessity and sufficiency of the *truth* of these postulates. A lake full of carp and carp alone is sufficient to make true my predictions about the kind of fish the summer visitor will catch. It is not necessary that I know the species of each individual fish in the lake in order to predict correctly. Nor is it necessary that all the fish in the lake be carp for the truth of my prediction that every fish he catches, assuming he catches any, will be a carp. For there may well be statements which must be true if I am to guess successfully, and yet I may guess successfully without the necessity of *knowing* that the statements are true.

Before we attempt to answer these questions it would be well to fix our attention on the notion of *necessary to* and *sufficient to.* The phrases are in very common use in mathematics and purely formal science. Their senses are, I take it, roughly these:

S_1 *is necessary to* S_2 is to say that S_2 *and not* S_1 *is self-contradictory*
S_1 *is sufficient to* S_2 is to say that S_1 *and not* S_2 *is self-contradictory*

Thus to say that a set of postulates is sufficient to a given set of theorems is to say that the theorems can be deduced from the postulates. To say that a postulate is necessary to a given set of theorems is to say that the postulate in question can be deduced from the theorems. Some statements which are necessary have, however, a very trivial air, given the rules of the logical calculus, i.e., Given $(\exists x)$ *x is green and x is round* it follows that $(\exists x)$ *x is green*, so that $(\exists x)$ *x is green* is necessary to $(\exists x)$ *x is green and x is round*. Even more trivial is the discovery that $(\exists x)$ *x is green* is necessary to *a is green.* There may be some suspicion that Russell's postulates are somewhat of this character.

1) Suppose Russell were right and that the truth of such postulates were logically *necessary* to common sense beliefs. That, however, is only to say that, given statements at present accepted, we could deduce Russell's postulates. Is it so very instructive, however, to learn such things, for example, that given that every pitch has some loudness, (x) *x is a pitch* $\supset$ *x is a loudness*, we can deduce that there are a pair of properties such that if any thing possesses one property, then it possesses the other, $(\exists\phi)(\exists\psi)(x)\ \phi x \supset \psi x$? Russell has said that the truth of these postulates is necessary if any occurrence or set of occurrences is to provide evidence in favor of any other occurrence. That claim does not follow from the necessity of such postulates to present common sense beliefs. For example, it is necessary to the truth of the present physical law of acceleration of falling bodies that there are some laws in which "from one or two members of the series something can be inferred as to all the other members," which is a weakened form of Postulate B. This weakened postulate is plainly not necessary to the truth of qualitative laws, such as "the melting point of silver is 960 degrees C." Further, knowledge of the postulates, even if they can be shown to be necessary to common sense statements, is not of any great importance, since their necessity to *true* statements could be known only after the fact of discovery of the truth of the statements to whose truth they are necessary. Hence it cannot be *necessary* to know the postulates beforehand.

2) Suppose the truth of certain common-sense statements were necessary to the science of the present. The considerations we have just reviewed make plain how empty a discovery that would be, and how unnecessary for discoveries of science. For if the scientific laws which came to be recognized were quite different in character, we would then discover that quite different postulates would be true. For example, these postulates assert that action at a distance is rarely, if ever, found in scientific laws. Surely this is simply a reflection of science as Russell finds it to be, and not any guarantee of the character of any possible science. Further, as in (1) the knowledge of the truth of such postulates would not be necessary to the discovery of scientific laws, nor to their proof.

3) Suppose the truth of such postulates were *sufficient* to guarantee that there are some laws about common sense objects that are true. Even in this case the *knowledge* that these postulates were true or probably true would not be *sufficient* to identify *which* laws were true or probable. Hence the knowledge of the truth or probable truth of these postulates would not be *sufficient* to the knowledge of the common sense world. For the knowledge of the postulates would not guarantee that any recognized regularities would be continued indefinitely in further cases, but only that *some* regularities (whether among those already recognized or not) would continue. In order to give a convincing account of the justification of statements about the physical world Russell would need to show in terms of his postulates and the data two things. First he would have to show how we identify the contemporaneous properties of physical objects as belonging to one and the same object. Secondly, he would have to show how we identify regularities in the behavior of any identified physical object. One would expect Russell to deal with these questions by detailed discussions of the kind Professor Price gives in his book, *Perception*. Russell makes no attempt to show how the postulates are of any use in reconstructing inferences.

4) The truth of common sense statements is certainly not *sufficient* to the science of the present day. The most obvious evidence that this is not so is that in the sciences words occur that designate theoretical entities and do not directly name any empirical quality nor occur at all in the language of common sense. Consequently *knowledge* of the truth of common sense statements would not be sufficient to the discovery of scientific statements.

We have seen that the claims for the necessity and sufficiency of knowledge of the truth of these postulates are not satisfied. We may ask, however, whether in fact Russell thinks we know these postulates to be true or probably true. Russell does not seem to be consistent on this point.

a) In some places he says that we cannot know these postulates even with probability.[43]

b) In other places he claims that certain of the postulates can acquire a high probability.[44]

We can extricate Russell from this painful state of self-contradiction if we take seriously his quip in the preface: "The Prophet announced that if two texts

[43] P. 507.
[44] P. 314, p. 458.

of the Koran appeared inconsistent, the later text was to be taken as authoritative, and I should wish the reader to apply a similar principle in interpreting what is said in this book." [45] If we assume "later" to mean a page of the book with a higher number, we can take (a) to be his final position, since on Page 507, which is the highest numbered page not in the index, Russell says:

> These principles, if assumed, lead to results which are in conformity with experience, but this fact does not logically suffice to make the principles even probable.[46]

4. Some readers might be prepared to take these criticisms of Russell's views as an indication that the whole problem may be dismissed as meaningless. That would be an easy way out, but it would be unjustified by anything we have said. The problem in hand has bothered many philosophers. Perhaps few scientists ask themselves the question. That would not demonstrate that there is no question. Why should we believe that the future will resemble the past? Why should we believe that any prediction has any chance of being true? Why should we believe that already obtained samples indicate anything about what will be found in other samples? The sceptic who asks these questions deserves an answer, even if the answer to some of them consists in getting him to see that the question is unanswerable because it assumes as true what is a wrong answer to another question.

Faced with the difficulties in Russell's answer, we may try to see whether there might not be something mistaken in the way that he and others conceived of the question. If our answer is to meet the conditions we have accepted in the examination of Russell, we must recognize that gold may not all be ductile, that the next peach pit I let go of may fly up and hit me in the face. Is that to say that it is rational to believe that the next piece of gold will shatter like glass when I strike it with a hammer or that the next peach pit I drop will fly up and hit me in the face? Quite obviously we all have evidence of peach pits, prune stones, and so on, which we have dropped and which have fallen to the ground. Without any further knowledge there is one possible belief about the next peach pit which is uniquely selected, namely, "It will fall to the ground." For the evidence is that there were peach pits that were observed to fall to the ground and none that were observed to fly up into the air. How different if we should believe that the next peach pit would have a long rubber band attached to it the other end of which were fastened above and slightly behind my head. Then I should get ready to duck.

We do believe something about what will be found in as yet unobserved cases. Yet we have no guarantee that our belief is correct. The belief which is considered rational is that which those generalizations that are true of known instances enable us to infer about the as yet unknown. What do we mean when we call this "rational"? Do we mean the same as we mean by saying that "Given $(x)\phi x \supset \psi x$ and $(\exists x)\phi x$, it is rational to believe $(\exists x)\psi x$? Obviously not, for in that case it would be self-contradictory to accept such premises and to deny

[45] P. vi.
[46] P. 507.

$(\exists x)\psi x$. Any *particular* case of an induction is said to be rational because it has evidence of a kind that has a high rate of past success. Why pick the kind of evidence with a high rate of success rather than palmistry which has a low rate of success? The only answer is that we prefer to make up our minds in a way which would have been the most successful in the past. It is a kind of method that enables us to modify our expectations in the light of our failures. These modifications in the past have led us with greater predictive success than if we had not altered our beliefs. It is hard to make out what "rational" means. It does seem to presuppose that in Hume's vague words the future must be conformable to the past. So to call induction reasonable either tells us nothing but that it *has* been successful, or else begs the question by asserting that it will continue to be successful.

Other writers have made this point. Many of them, however, go on to use rational in a sense in which they say it is *rational* to trust inductive methods. Professor Feigl, in what is now a classic statement, says: "Any other 'method' (like expecting systematic deviations from past regularities or not employing all available experience) would be 'madness,' because it would not in any typical sense be distinguished from an indefinite number (a continuum, virtually) of equally arbitrary methods." [47] On the other hand, "the justification of the inductive procedure lies precisely in the uniqueness (extreme character) of the only rational method capable (but not guaranteed) of success." [48]

If we are alert to the pitfalls in the discussions of induction, we will already have pricked up our ears at the words, "madness," "uniqueness," "the only rational method capable of success." Let us see if these have a sense which does not violate the empirical stand. Suppose we find a scientist whose work has been acclaimed and now has begun to expect systematic deviations from past experience. He might propose that from a certain time on the gravitational constant will be double the present value. Can we find any evidence for his madness which does not presuppose that inductive procedure will continue to be successful? I think not. Is there any sense in which his prediction is unique and the only rational method where "unique" and "rational" do not presuppose the inductive principle? I think not. However, the mention of an extremum character does point to the very important characteristics we have found in the past use of inductive methods as compared with others. Russell mentions this feature in one passage, where he speaks of "a criterion of the excellence (hitherto) of any suggested rules of induction." [49] He is so intent on his search for principles that will give initial probability to certain generalizations that he has no more to say about this.

What we have is evidence which is sheer matter of fact about past inductions. In a recent, short paper Professor Max Black maintains the irrelevance of the demand for a deductive justification of induction, i.e. "that the inductive

[47] H. Feigl, "The Logical Character of the Principle of Induction." Reprinted from *Philosophy of Science*, vol. I in Feigl and Sellars, *Readings in Philosophical Analysis*. New York, 1948, p. 303.

[48] *Ibid.*, p. 304.

[49] P. 360.

methods characteristic of science have worked better than other methods *in the past* is a reasonable ground for confidence in their applicability in the future."[50] Again we prick up our ears. Is there any sense in which this claim of "a reasonable ground" does not presuppose the general maxim of induction? We ordinarily consider any given induction as justified if the known cases support it providing we have taken pains to look for counter-evidence. We might then consider a method justified on the basis of its past use. What is there that is reasonable about that? Only that it is what is meant by "reasonable" as applied to accepting generalizations.

It is very important to call attention to the relative success in the past of inductive methods compared to other methods. It is on these grounds that specific inductions are chosen. Hence we can say that induction as used in the past worked better than other methods. If it is true that it *has* worked better, that is an extremum character. There is still no evidence that there is an argument with knowable premises which justified picking this general pattern. We do see its special character in the observed cases. We may adopt it as a principle of action, or we may not.

The special importance of the comparison of various methods is apparent, when we consider the position of a man who is not acquainted with many cases of the application of inductive procedures. How foolish it is to blame Plato for holding the opinions he did about knowledge. He did not know what degree of success has attended various methods for the simple reason that he did not know of many people who had tried them very elaborately. How natural for him to esteem mathematics, when its credentials were so good compared to others. *We* as the result of the last three hundred years of experimental and observational science, have very different evidence about the past success of inductive methods from what Plato had. This extremum character of induction is something which has been revealed by trying out the methods.

We have admitted that the character of the inductive principle is such as to make it hopeless to get evidence for or against it. It is, then, possible to understand why Professor Feigl says that "the principle of induction . . . is not a proposition . . . but rather is an operational rule."[51] But is it no more than a rule? The point of calling it an operational rule is that we can and do act as if we believed an inductive generalization were true, although we have no guarantee of its truth, or, for that matter, even of any probability of its truth in the frequency sense. We may not even be aware, at the time, that we are accepting the statement. That is no evidence that the inductive generalization is not a proposition, but only that it makes claims about which it is difficult to get conclusive evidence. Nor does this give evidence that the inductive *principle* does not express a proposition about what use of evidence will lead us to generalizations that will turn out to be true. So that while the inductive principle is at least a rule, it is also a proposition.

[50] M. Black, "The Justification of Induction," *Library of the Xth International Congress of Philosophy*. Amsterdam, 1948, vol. I, p. 59.

[51] *Op. cit.*, p. 302.

It is the very great degree of restraint that is required in giving an answer to the sceptic that makes the answer only rouse the doubts again. The philosopher keeps feeling that we surely must have better grounds than these we have described. Alarm arises on hearing a philosopher say: "we are not justified in believing that the sun will rise tomorrow." For it suggests that this induction is not as well supported by the past as we thought it was. As Professor Black points out, our alarm will be lessened when we realize that this philosophic doubt is a type of warning that is always appropriate. Our alarm will be still further lessened if we notice that the philosopher does not mean that we are justified in believing that the sun will *not* rise tomorrow. What the philosopher calls to our attention is that we cannot rightfully treat our beliefs about the world as completely justified. We are constantly gathering new evidence which is relevant to our general beliefs. Sometimes we can get evidence that will be sufficient to show their falsity. That is not to say that present evidence together with the assumption of the truth of inductive principles does not point to the sun's rising at 4:34 a.m. It does emphasize that the kind of claim is such that important new evidence may come to light, which on inductive principles would lead us to a quite different belief.

We have said nothing about the other part of Russell's problem, the inference from private data to physical and public objects of the common sense world. The answer we have given to the inductive questions of science does not give any obvious assistance. As Hume said: "We may observe a conjunction or relation of cause and effect between different perceptions, but can never observe it between perceptions and objects." [52] That makes plain that on Russell's formulation of the problem we could never by determining the proportion of favorable empirical instances increase the probability of a generalization about the properties of physical objects allegedly guaranteed by his postulates.

The solution may lie in abandoning altogether so simple a scheme of the relation between evidence and conclusion in inductive inquiries. This would require a consideration of what have been called "theoretical entities" in certain branches of science. In an examination of induction in science we find that science does not consist solely of an assortment of independent generalizations about empirical objects. It also contains words which name no empirical objects. Notable examples are those of molecules in the kinetic theory of heat and genes in genetics.[53] A detailed study of the sciences with this in mind would disclose a very important place played by such entities and axioms about them.

The solution of the question of the justification of inferences to the common sense world would then take the form of considering whether the common sense world cannot be treated like a theoretical system, bearing the same relation to statements about the private data that the physical world does to the common

[52] David Hume, *Treatise of Human Nature* (Selby-Bigge ed.), p. 212.

[53] Cf. N. R. Campbell, *Physics: the Elements*. Cambridge, 1920. F. P. Ramsey, "Theories" in *Foundations of Mathematics*. London, 1931. G. Bergmann, "Outline of an Empiristic Philosophy of Physics," *American Journal of Physics*, vol. 11, pp. 248–258 and 335–342. E. Nagel, "The Meaning of Reduction in the Natural Sciences" in *Symposium on Science and Civilization*, ed. R. C. Stauffer, Madison, Wisconsin, 1949.

sense world. If this can be exhibited, Russell would be correct, in contrast to Hume, at least in thinking that the question of induction in science and inference to a public world are the same kind of problem. I shall not attempt to work this out in this article.

These suggestions for the reformulation of Russell's questions show that the philosopher's interest in induction does not close with the admission that Hume is correct in maintaining that proof (deductive proof, that is) is impossible. There is, on the contrary, a great deal of constructive and enlightening analysis to be done on the logical structure of theories.

I have been severe in my criticism of this book. That should not obscure these two points. First, I owe a great deal of the ability to reach some clarity in these criticisms to the great advances in logic that Whitehead and Russell have taught all of us. Second, the constructive work on the problems discussed in the book will have to come through the greater "fertility in imagining abstract hypotheses as a result of the advances in logic"[54] that Russell suggested in the eloquent conclusion to *Our Knowledge of the External World.* It is unfortunate that Russell and Whitehead have made so little use of their own creation. It is, however, a mark of a great discovery that the next generation is able to go further along the lines opened up by the work of their teachers.

[54] *Our Knowledge of the External World*, 2nd ed. New York, 1929, p. 259.

31 The Probability of Induction

DONALD C. WILLIAMS

In what we may call 'the inductive situation' we are interested in a class, genus, or population, M, say the class of rabbits, and we wish to know the composition of that class with respect to some property, P, say whiteness. That is, we wish to know the proportion of rabbits which are white, or the ratio of the number of white rabbits to the total number of rabbits. Using the convention that "$[M]$" stands for *the number of the class M*, we may put it that we wish to ascertain the ratio $\frac{[MP]}{[M]}$. What we have to go on is a knowledge of the composition, in the specified respect, of a subclass, species, or sample of that class, MQ. That is, what we know is the ratio $\frac{[MQP]}{[MQ]}$. So far as logic is concerned the sub-

Reprinted by permission of the publishers and the author from Donald C. Williams, *The Ground of Induction*, Cambridge, Mass.: Harvard University Press, Copyright, 1947, by The President and Fellows of Harvard College, pp. 77–104.

class MQ may be any class included in the class M. The kind of subclass, however, on which our empirical knowledge, in fact, eventually rests is the *observed* part of the class M — the subclass of those rabbits, for example, which have sufficiently come under our eye so that by a summary or perfect induction we have ascertained directly the proportion which are white. (Since virtually all material knowledge rests on induction, and all induction rests on summary or perfect induction, it is a graceless error to describe perfect induction as in some invidious sense 'trivial'). The problem of induction is the problem of finding the exact nature and the logical warrant of the inference which concludes to the composition of the population (rabbits) from the premises or evidence afforded by the same (examined rabbits).

The rule of induction normally followed is to ascribe the *same* composition to the population as is discovered in the sample. That is, we proceed as if on the principle that, probably and approximately,

$$\frac{[MP]}{[M]} = \frac{[MQP]}{[MQ]}.$$

Given that 20 per cent of the observed rabbits are white, we infer that in all likelihood about 20 per cent of all rabbits are white. When occasionally we infer that the population differs from the sample in a specifiable way, as when we infer that the apples in the bottom of the barrel will be inferior to those on top, this is because of previous wider inductions, inductions about merchandising methods, for instance, which do proceed on the principle that populations are like their samples. Apparently then, any specific induction involves (1) a general over-all premise, common to all inductions, that samples 'match' their populations, and (2) specific premises peculiar to the induction immediately concerned, that the presented class (say of observed rabbits) is a sample of a population (say of rabbits) and that its composition with respect to a specified property (say whiteness) is so-and-so (say 20 per cent). Given these premises, it follows demonstratively that, probably and approximately, the proportion of rabbits which are white is 20 per cent. Of the premises thus utilized, the last one, concerning the composition of the sample, is established by observation. The next to the last, that the class of observed rabbits is a subclass of the class of rabbits, is an analytic truism, an instance of the logical law of subsumption, that any class product PQ necessarily is contained in either of the component classes, say P. All that remains then to justify an induction of this form is to establish the first and most abstract premise, that any population will probably and approximately match, in any statistical respect, any of its samples — or at any rate that it will do so under certain verifiable conditions. If this, which may be called 'the inductive principle', can be exactly stated and can be proved analytically and demonstratively, like the principle of the syllogism, and not merely inductively, it will provide at least one sufficient solution of the problem of induction. The sole *material* premise then required for a valid induction is a statement of the size and composition of the sample.

In effect, the solution of the problem of induction which I here defend is a statement and proof of the above inductive principle. We shall understand its significance better, however, and make surer that it grows out of a fair canvass of the problem, if we return to the concrete demands of the inductive situation and work it out from there.

No demonstrative principle, either the Aristotelian syllogism or the latest dodge of the mathematical logician, will avail us, we know, to infer directly from the composition of *MQ* to the composition of *M*. Given that 99 out of 100 *MQ*s are *P*, we cannot with certainty deduce anything about what proportion of *M*s are *P* except that the sheer number of *M*s which are *P* must be at least as great as the number of *MQ*s which are *P*. It remains logically possible that none of the rest of the *M*s is *P* and that all of them are and that any intermediate proportion are. We must be content then with a probability, preferably a high probability, if we are to ground any inference from the composition of a sample to the composition of its population.

It is equally apparent, however, that the ordinary proportional syllogism will not furnish directly the required probability. Given our premise that 99 per cent of *MQ* is *P*, we can state syllogistically the probability that any particular member of *MQ*, say *a*, is *P*, and by means of the additive and multiplicative laws we can reckon the probability that any selected group of members of *MQ*, say the sub-subclass *MQR*, will all be *P*, or that half will be *P*, and so forth, but all these inferences are purely explicative. They tell us about individuals and classes *included in* the sample *MQ*; they tell us nothing about the object of our ampliative induction, the population *M*, which includes but is not included in *MQ*.

There is a clue for us here nevertheless. If we imagine the inductive situation reversed, so that instead of knowing already the composition of the sample *MQ* and trying to infer the composition of the population *M*, we know the composition of the population *M* and try to infer what will be the composition of a sample *MQ* drawn from it, the proportional syllogism with its auxiliaries will do the job. For simplicity's sake let the population *M* be a bagful of marbles. (We shall see later that induction is, if anything, more difficult to justify in these artificial situations than on the wider stage of concrete scientific inquiry, so that whatever we can establish with respect to the simple bag of marbles will be valid *a fortiori* for more cumbrous populations of atoms, planets, labor unionists, and so forth.) Let *MP* be the red marbles, and let the sample *MQ* be a handful of marbles scooped from the bag. Now, if we knew that all the marbles in the bag were red, i.e. that

$$\frac{[MP]}{[M]} = 1,$$

or that none was red, i.e., that

$$\frac{[MP]}{[M]} = 0,$$

we could infer by the traditional *dictum de omni et nullo*, in a demonstrative syllogism, that the same must be true of the handful *MQ*. That is, if all the marbles in the bag are red, and the handful consists of marbles in the bag, then all the handful must be red, and if none of the marbles in the bag is red, certainly none of the handful can be red. These are old-fashioned syllogisms in the moods Barbara and Celarent with universal minor premises instead of the singular ones with which we were made familiar by Chapter 2. If now some intermediate proportion of the marbles in the bag are known to be red, if 2/3 are red, let us say, we must resort to a proportional instead of a categorical syllogism, and be content with a probability. By itself, to be sure, the proportional syllogism, with its singular minor premise and singular conclusion, enables us under the circumstances only to state the probability that any one marble in our handful will be red. Since every member of the handful (*MQ*) is a member of the bagful (*M*), and since the proportion of red marbles in the bagful is 2/3, the probability that any specified member of the handful will be red is 2/3. By means of the multiplicative and additive laws, however, which are rules for deriving the probabilities of compound propositions from the probabilities of simpler ones, we can under certain conditions use this knowledge to calculate exactly the probability that the handful will contain any stipulated proportion of red marbles, either 2/3 (the same as the proportion in the bagful) or any other proportion we care to name. One condition required for the reckoning is that we know the number of the handful, [*MQ*], which is generally easy; another is that we either know the total number of marbles [*M*] and the number of red marbles [*MP*], or know that these numbers are so great that the withdrawal of the handful *MQ*, whatever *its* composition may be, cannot appreciably affect the composition of what remains — or that we replace each marble before drawing the next so that our total selection cannot make any difference to the population composition. Let us suppose for a moment that one or the other of the last two conditions, which are arithmetically equivalent, is realized. The former is not a very plausible supposition with regard to a bagful of marbles, but it is a safe one with respect to the great natural populations, of rabbits, stars, or what not, with which induction is usually concerned. If for convenience' sake we consider a 'handful' of only 3 members, the probability that *all* will be red is, by the multiplicative law, $2/3 \times 2/3 \times 2/3$, or $(2/3)^3$, or 8/27. In general, the probability that all of a sample *MQ* will have the character *P* is equal to $\left(\frac{[MP]}{[M]}\right)^{[MQ]}$: that is, it is equal to the probability of any one *M*'s being *P*, multiplied by itself to a number of terms equal to the number of *MQ*s. Now, if the proportion of red marbles in the bag is 2/3, the proportion of non-red marbles must be $1 - 2/3$, or 1/3, and the probability that any specified marble will be non-red is 1/3. The probability that none of the marbles in the handful of 3 will be red is accordingly $(1/3)^3$, or 1/27. Figuring the probability that just two of the three will be red and the other non-red, so that the proportion of red in the handful will be the same as in the bagful, is a little more complicated. The probability that any designated two marbles in the handful will be red and the third not red is equal to 2/3 × 2/3 × 1/3, or 4/27. But this, of course, is not the only allotment of red and non-red among the three marbles which will give a total of two red and one not red. There are in fact three such allotments: any one of the three marbles may be the non-red one while the other two are red. Each of these allotments has the same probability, 4/27, so that by the additive law the probability of obtaining some one or other of them is equal to 4/27 + 4/27 + 4/27, or 4/27 × 3, or 4/9. This is less than an even chance, but we can note already that it is greater than the probability of any one other composition. The probability of getting one red marble and two non-red ones, for example, is only (2/3 × 1/3 × 1/3) × 3, or 2/9.

If now we give up our handy fiction that the population *M* (marbles in the bag) is virtually infinite, and suppose that it contains, say, 60 members, of which 40 are red, we find not a less but a greater probability that the proportion in our tiny sample will match it. The probability that the first marble in the sample will be red is 40/60, but the probability then that the next marble is red is 39/59, while the probability that the third marble is non-red is then 20/58. Thc probability that *some* two marbles will be red, then, and some one non-red, is equal to (2/3 × 39/59 × 10/29) × 3, or 2340/5133. Decimally, this is .456, whereas 4/9, our previous fraction, is only .444. In general, as the reader may be sufficiently persuaded by these examples, the effect of assuming a virtually infinite population where in fact the population is finite, is to determine a smaller probability for a matching sample than a more accurate procedure would yield. Since a calculation using the precise number of *M* is more complicated, and since we very seldom know the number [*M*] anyhow, and since furthermore the difference between the results is insignificant as soon as [*M*] is five or six times as great as [*MQ*], as always happens in the sort of situations with which we shall be concerned, we may safely employ the simpler method. In any case the true proabability cannot be less then we state.

A sample set *MQ* of only three members is grotesquely small. Scrutinizing our illustration, however, we hit on some general rules. Given a set or sample *MQ*, taken from a population *M*, the probability that any specified subset or part of *MQ*, of number *n*, will be *P*, is equal to the *n*th power of the proportion of *P*s among the *M*s, i.e., to $\left(\frac{[MP]}{[M]}\right)^n$. The probability that the remaining $[MQ] - n$ members of *MQ* will be *non-P* is $\left(1 - \frac{[MP]}{[M]}\right)^{[MQ]-n}$, or, if we write "$\bar{P}$" for the class or property *non-P*, it is $\left(\frac{[M\bar{P}]}{[M]}\right)^{[MQ]-n}$. The probability of the conjunction, that one specified subset in *MQ*, with *n* members, will be *P* and the rest will be *non-P*, is equal to the product of these two quantities, that is, to

$$\left(\frac{[MP]}{[M]}\right)^n \times \left(\frac{[M\bar{P}]}{[M]}\right)^{[MQ]-n}.$$

We are now interested, however, not in the probability that one particular subset of n MQs will be P and the rest not P, but in the probability that just some, that is, one or another, subset of n MQs will be P and the rest not P. The number of subsets of n members each which exist in a class MQ is the number of mathematical 'combinations' of $[MQ]$ things taken n at a time, ${}^{[MQ]}C_n$. The probability, then, that just n members of the sample MQ will be P and that the other $[MQ] - n$ members will be not P is equal to:

$$\left(\frac{[MP]}{[M]}\right)^n \times \left(\frac{[M\bar{P}]}{[M]}\right)^{[MQ]-n} \times {}^{[MQ]}C_n.$$

Rulcs for reckoning the number of combinations of r things taken n at a time are included in the algebra books. One is provided by the equation

$${}^rC_n = \frac{r \times (r-1) \times (r-2) \times \cdots \times ((r-n)+1)}{n \times (n-1) \times (n-2) \times \cdots \times 1}.$$

That is, for the numerator we multiply r by the next smaller number than r and so on down till we have multiplied together n numbers in all. For the denominator, we multiply n by the next less number than it and so on down to 1. Since to pick n things out of a collection of r things is at the same time to single out another set of things, whose number is $r - n$, to be left behind, the rule holds that ${}^rC_n = {}^rC_{r-n}$. When n is greater than $r - n$, therefore, we can save trouble by figuring on the latter rather than the former. In our first simplified example, above, we employed the fact that ${}^3C_2 = {}^3C_1 = 3$; the numbers of combinations involved in more ordinary instances will be enormously greater.

The notion of 'combinations' is fundamental to our whole program and must be grasped with intuitive sureness if we are to get anywhere. A combination is often referred to as a 'selection' or 'possible selection' of things. Perhaps the most familiar example of it is the notion of a hand of cards. Any given bridge hand of 13 cards is a selection from a class of 52 cards, and is one of the some billions of possible selections or combinations of 52 cards taken 13 at a time.

Now if we know again that 2/3 M is P but if we take 9 individuals to compose the selected group MQ instead of only 3, the probability that just 2/3 of *them*, or 6, will be P, is equal to $(2/3)^6 \times (1/3)^3 \times {}^9C_3$. (${}^9C_3$, we remember, is the same as ${}^9C_6$.) This works out as $\frac{64}{729} \times \frac{1}{27} \times \frac{9 \times 8 \times 7}{3 \times 2 \times 1}$, or $\frac{64}{19683} \times 84$, or .273. The result is a little disconcerting because it is less than the probability of getting a match with the smaller sample of 3, which in decimals was .444. In point of fact, the larger the sample the less likely it is to match the population *exactly*. When a sample is more than the merest handful, however — and this covers all cases of inductive importance — we are not interested in the probability of an exact match, which may indeed be impossible since the sample may not be exactly divisible in the ratio $\frac{[MP]}{[M]}$. We want to know the probability that the sample composition will not vary from the population composition by more than a certain percentage or proportion, and this always does increase as the sample increases. Our sample of 9 is still far too small to be typical but even with it we can reckon the probability of not missing the 'true' proportion by more than 11.1 per cent, i.e., one individual, one way or the other. The probability that 7 instead of 6 of the 9 members of MQ will be P is $(2/3)^7 \times (1/3)^2 \times {}^9C_2$, or $128/19683 \times 36$, or .234. The probability that only 5 will be P is $(2/3)^5 \times (1/3)^4 \times {}^9C_4$, which figures out to .205. The probability of each of the two nearly-matching compositions for MQ is less than the probability of the exactly matching composition, 6-and-3. The probability however of getting *some one* of these three compositions which either match or nearly match is (by the additive law) equal to .273 + .234 + .205, or .712. Even with a tiny sample of 9, therefore, drawn from a virtually infinite population, M, of which 2/3 are P, the probability that the proportion of Ps in the sample will not vary from what it is in the population, namely 2/3, by more than 11.1 per cent, is .712. As we consider larger samples, a near match (in terms of percentage) becomes rapidly more probable, or — what comes to the same thing — the probable disparity between sample and population becomes rapidly less. By 'Bernoulli's theorem' it is accordingly always possible to specify a sample sufficiently large so that there is as great a probability as we please that the sample matches the population as closely as we please. This is true for a population divided in the ratio 2/3; it is true for populations divided in other ratios, though the probabilities of a given degree of approximation for samples from differently divided populations are different. By a common mathematical procedure the statisticians have calculated from principles such as we have been observing an over-all rule, for virtually infinite $[M]$ and large $[MQ]$, the formula for 'the standard error of sampling', $\sigma\%$:

$$\vdash: \sigma\left(\frac{[MQP]}{[MQ]}\right) = \sqrt{\frac{\frac{[MP]}{[M]} \times \frac{[M\bar{P}]}{[M]}}{[MQ]}}.$$

The standard error or 'standard deviation' got by this rule is the degree of approximation attached to the 'standard' probability, .6826. That is, there is a probability of .6826 that the composition of the sample, $\frac{[MQP]}{[MQ]}$, will not differ or 'deviate' from the composition of the population, $\frac{[MP]}{[M]}$, by an amount (i.e., by a percentage or proportion) greater than the value of σ thus computed. It is provable, furthermore, that there is a probability of .9545 that the sample will not deviate by more than $2 \times \sigma$, and a probability of .9973 that it will not diverge more than $3 \times \sigma$. Given a large population (M) of marbles, say, in which the proportion of red marbles (MP) is 2/3 and the proportion of non-red marbles is accordingly 1/3, and given a fairly large sample of 600 marbles, say, then $\sigma = \sqrt{\frac{2/3 \times 1/3}{600}}$, or $\sqrt{.000370370}$, or a little less than .02. This means that there is a probability of .6826 (the chances are about 2 to 1) that the proportion of red marbles in the sample will not differ from the proportion in the population (2/3, or 66.7 per cent) by more than 2 per cent. There is that probability, in other words, that the proportion of red marbles in the sample will lie between 64.7 per cent and 68.7 per cent. There is a probability of .9545 that the sample will not differ by more than 4 per cent, and a probability o .9973 that it will not differ by more than 6 per cent.

The deviation corresponding to a probability of .6826, called "sigma", is taken as standard only because of some important arithmetical peculiarities and because of its comparative simplicity of calcluation. There are tables by which from this base there can be figured the deviation corresponding to any other probability, or the probability corresponding to any other deviation. The 'probable error' ('P.E.'), for example, is the deviation corresponding to a probability of 1/2. It is equal to $.6745 \times \sigma$.[1] With the deviation formulas at hand the statisticians are accustomed to calculate, for any composition of population, and for a sample of any size, the probability that the sample will match the population with any desired accuracy.

Of what use, however, we may ask, is all this? In the inductive situation we don't know the composition of the population on which all this depends — that's just what we are trying to learn. And we aren't trying to find out the composition of the sample — that's just what we know already. Practical statisticians, to be sure, commonly ignore the difference and recommend that, not knowing the composition of the population, we write for the $\frac{[MP]}{[M]}$ and $\frac{[M\bar{P}]}{[M]}$ required by the sampling formula the values observed in the sample for $\frac{[MQP]}{[MQ]}$ and $\frac{[MQ\bar{P}]}{[MQ]}$ respectively. "Standard error" is often defined to mean just this quantity. That its use is a begging of the question does not need laboring. It puts us in the position of asking absurdly, "If we assume that the population has the same composition as the sample, what is the probability that the sample will have the same composition as the population?"

The statistician's trick nevertheless gives us another important clue. In the first place, although the inferring of the composition of the population from the composition of the sample is not logically the same as the converse process of inferring the composition of the sample from the composition of the population, both inferences could be made valid by the single general principle that given any population and any (largish) sample thereof, it is highly probable that the

[1] There is no special significance for our purpose in the similarity between the standard probability .6828 and the quantity .6745 which occurs in the equation relating σ to P.E. There is no significance at all, of course, in the simliarity between both of these and our illustrative population composition .667 (i.e., 2/3). The σ probability is always and by definition .6826 (and a bit more), and the P.E. is always $.6745 \times \sigma$ (a bit less). A population composition of 2/3 serves as illustration only because 2/3 is a neat and easy sort of fraction. It should be clear, incidentally, that when we speak of a "percentage deviation" we mean a percentage of the whole population or sample and not a percentage of the composition. The sigma formula itself is an idealization which actual instances only approach, but this is not a detriment because its discrepancy is only such as to overestimate the error.

sample matches the population (and hence that the population matches the sample). In the second place, the latter general principle may be proved to be true by no more intricate method than considering *the whole range of possible population compositions* and observing that although the probability of a matching sample of a stipulated size is different for different compositions, the probability of a matching sample is always greater than the probability of any other kind of sample, and if the sample is large, then *no matter what the population composition may be*, the probability is very great.

To bring this out clearly, let us look again at the sampling formula and ask how much we can say about its various terms even though we do not yet know the actual composition of the population. We know $[MQ]$, the number of the sample. We can usually make it as great as we like, and the formula indicates that the greater it is, the more nearly the sample is likely to match the population. Of the other quantities we do not know $\frac{[MP]}{[M]}$ and $\frac{[M\bar{P}]}{[M]}$, the composition of the population with respect to P and to *non-P* respectively. By pure logic and arithmetic, however, we know something about them. We know that $\frac{[M\bar{P}]}{[M]}$ must be equal to

$$1 - \frac{[MP]}{[M]},$$

and we know the range within which both must lie, and hence the range of the required product,

$$\frac{[MP]}{[M]} \times \frac{[M\bar{P}]}{[M]}.$$

In the extreme cases, the proportion of Ps among the Ms, $\frac{[MP]}{[M]}$, is 1 or 0; that is, all M is P or no M is P; and the proportion of *non-P*s among the Ms will accordingly be 0 or 1, respectively. In either of these circumstances, any sample, no matter what its size, *must* match. In the sampling formula, this result appears as the fact that σ, and every multiple of σ, is then 0, while our quantity

$$\left(\frac{[MP]}{[M]}\right)^{[MQP]} \times \left(\frac{[M\bar{P}]}{[M]}\right)^{[MQ\bar{P}]} \times {}^{[MQ]}C_{[MQP]}$$

then must reduce to $1 \times 1 \times 1$. (The 0th power of any number is 1.) It is plainest, of course, by the *dictum de omni et nullo* of the categorical syllogism.

On the other hand, the probability of matching is least, and the probable deviation σ is the greatest, when the composition of the population is midway between the two extremes 0 and 1, that is, when just half of M is P and half accordingly is *non-P*,

$$\frac{[MP]}{[M]} = \frac{[M\bar{P}]}{[M]} = \frac{1}{2}.$$

In other words, the product of $1/2 \times 1/2$, namely, $1/4$, is greater than the product of any other two numbers whose arithmetical sum is 1, as the reader may satisfy himself by a few experiments, and it determines accordingly the greatest, and 'worst', value of σ. What happens then in this worst of all conceivable situations for the probability of the sample's matching the population? We might easily expect a very great deviation indeed, or a correspondingly low probability. If the best possible situation, with a parent composition of 0 or 1, makes it certain that the sample will have the matching composition, we could pessimistically conjecture, for instance, that the worst possible situation, with a parent composition of 1/2, if it did not make a matching sample impossible, would make it at any rate no more probable than any other variety of sample. If such were the case, we should have got nowhere by all this inquiry. Emphatically, however, it is not the case: *the worst possible situation is still a very favorable one.* No matter what the composition of the population — even if it is half and half — the sample not only is more likely to have the matching composition than to have any other composition; it is, if it is fairly large, *very* likely to have very nearly the matching composition — a nearly matching composition, that is, is then much more probable than all the other possible compositions put together.

Filling in the σ formula with the worst possible values of $\frac{[MP]}{[M]}$ and $\frac{[M\bar{P}]}{[M]}$, and writing "$\overline{\overline{<}}$" to mean *is equal to or less than* (i.e., *is no greater than*) we have the principle,

$$\vdash: \sigma \overline{\overline{<}} \sqrt{\frac{.5 \times .5}{[MQ]}}\,.$$

The crucial right-hand expression may of course be written also more simply as $\frac{.5}{\sqrt{[MQ]}}$. If $[MQ]$, the number of the sample, is 2500, for example, then the standard deviation *cannot* be more than $\frac{.5}{\sqrt{2500}}$, or .01. That is, there must be a probability of .6826, at the very least, that the sample composition does not differ from the population composition by more than 1 per cent, and a probability, at the very least, of .9545 that it does not differ by more than twice this, or 2 per cent, and so forth. The probability that the composition of the sample does not differ from that of the population by more than 2 per cent, however, is identical with the probability that the composition of the population does not differ from that of the sample by more than 2 per cent. If now we take the actual observed composition of the sample, say 2/3 *P* and 1/3 *non-P*, it follows that there is a probability of *at least* .9545 that the proportion of *P*s in the population does not differ from 66 2/3 per cent by more than 2 per cent; i.e., there is that probability that the proportion of *P*s in the population lies between 64 2/3 per cent and 68 2/3 per cent. If this is not a high enough probability, or a small enough possible deviation, the remedy is at hand: we need only add to the sample. We cannot in this fashion reach unmitigated certainty, and since our rule connects the reliability of the inference, not directly with the number of the sample but with the square root of the number, we must continually add more generously to the sample in order to bring about a stipulated amount of increase in the reliability. We can in theory, nevertheless, approach certainty within any assignable margin, however small, and we can in practice rapidly attain a 'moral certainty' humanly indistinguishable from the result of a strict deductive demonstration (which in spite of its ideal impeccability is always subject to error due to the inadvertence of the deducer).

Here, I take it, is in main principle a solution of the problem of induction. We wished to prove that an inference from $\frac{m}{n}$ *MQ is P* to $\frac{m}{n}$ *M is P* has a genuine probability or logical credibility of the sort described in Chapter 2, and that when *MQ* is fairly numerous it has a large probability of that sort. What we have to work with in an inductive situation consists of two kinds of knowledge: the number of the sample, and its composition, which are facts of observation; and the principle that no matter what the population is like, any sample, of considerable size, will very probably be very similar to it, this being an *a priori* law of classes, demonstrable by logical analysis. Putting together these two pieces of knowledge, and taking advantage of the fact that to say that a given sample of 2502 marbles, say, of which 2/3 are red, is very probably very similar in a statistical way to the total content of the much larger bagful from which it was taken, is equivalent to saying that the total bagful is very probably very similar to the sample, we conclude that in the total bagful very probably very nearly 2/3 of the marbles are red. We have in fact done better: we have provided no method of laying down *exactly* how probable is any assignable degree of approximation between population and sample, but we are able to lay down a little indeterminately the minimum possible probability for any stipulated degree of approximation, or conversely the maximum possible divergence for any stipulated degree of probability, by the *a priori* principle

$$\vdash : \sigma \lesseqgtr \frac{.5}{\sqrt{[MQ]}}.$$

To most of us, this odd margin of indeterminateness about the inductive probability will be some earnest of the *bona fides* of the whole calculation. Not only do we seldom or never want to know exactly the probability of an inductive argument; we should be suspicious, rightly or wrongly, of any scheme which could adduce an exact probability for one. What we want, and the most we are inclined to credit, is a whacking big probability, objective and rigorously provable, even though somewhat indeterminate.

The probability which our formula assigns, we recall, is a minimum in two respects, corresponding to the two respects in which, in the inductive situation, we lack the definite knowledge of the population required for an exact reckoning. We don't know the number of the population, so we reckon the probability on that assumption on which the probability is the least possible, namely, that the number is virtually infinite. We don't know the composition of the population, so we state the probability which would ensue on the least favorable of all compositions, half-and-half. The point is that even then the resultant probabilities are satisfactory ones, and comport closely, indeed, with the degrees of credibility which the most thoughtful inquirers have intuitively assigned to the inductions they make. We can afford to be generous: we have probability to burn.

Some persons may still be dubious just because of the indefiniteness of our results, which hence seem to them somehow subjective, lacking in logical rigor. Even if the indefiniteness proves altogether irremediable, however, their delicacy is a mistake. A somewhat indeterminate logical conclusion like ours is just as real and objective, just as 'absolute', and just as rigorously certified, as any could be. It is no less objective and necessary that the number 6 is greater than 3 (a relatively indeterminate truth) than that 6 is twice 3 (a more determinate one). If any distinction at all could be made among logical necessities, the former, since it follows '*a fortiori*' from the latter, is more thoroughly necessary, more absolutely rigorous, than the latter. More specifically, we saw on page 42 that the principle of the proportional syllogism provides no less for approximative probabilities like *q is more probable than r*, or *q is very probable*, than for exact ones like *q is probable to the degree* $\frac{m}{n}$.

The argument which we have been pursuing, however, although it stays as close as may be to the beaten path of concepts most likely to be familiar to anyone who has had anything to do with statistical arithmetic, is for the logical philosopher awkward and roundabout, unlikely to fill his bosom with the ardor of living conviction. It has relied, furthermore, on the additive and multiplicative laws which we found a little suspect. There is another way of formulating the solution which may be stated more briefly, which may carry more concrete understanding and confidence, and which puts the probability of an induction directly in terms of one objective ratio of real frequencies and one corresponding proportional syllogism without relying on any ulterior principles. In brief, its principle is this: Any sample, $\mathfrak{a}$, which we may have drawn from a population is itself one of a large class, $\mathfrak{M}$, of possible samples, to wit, the multitude of groups or sets, each of the same size as $\mathfrak{a}$, which are included in the population, and among these the overwhelming majority have the property ($\mathfrak{P}$) of matching the population. Hence, by the proportional syllogism, it is overwhelmingly probable that the actual sample $\mathfrak{a}$ is one of those which match ($\mathfrak{P}$), and hence it is probable that the population matches *it*, that is, has approximately the same composition which we may now discern in the sample.

Consider again, therefore, what we can know *a priori* of any population M, consisting of marbles in a bag, stars in the sky, rabbits all over the earth, or anything else, anything whatever. We know in the first place that M has some one definite number, and that just one definite proportion of M must have the property P (any property we care to specify, say whiteness). Either all the marbles (or the rabbits or the stars) are white or none is white or half are white or some other fraction between 1 and 0 are white. Now, we know also, *a priori*, by pure logic, that there exist in the population a definite number of smaller groups, sets, or subclasses of any size we care to specify.[2] Thus in a population of 4 marbles there are 6 sets of 2 marbles each — the number of combinations of 4 things taken 2 at a time, ${}^{4}C_{2}$, is 6. With larger populations and with large sets, the number of sets of any specified size is very great — immensely greater, of course, than the number of members of the population. But if the number in the population of individuals (M) is finite, so is the number in any 'hyperpopulation' ($\mathfrak{M}$) of sets of any specified size, n, contained in it. There exist, for example, in the total population of marbles, of stars, or of rabbits (or of all three together), just so many sets with 100 members each, so many with 1000 each, so many with 3724, and so forth. Every set, in turn, must contain the specified property P in some one definite proportion — in every set of 100 marbles, or rabbits, for example, either all are white, or none is white, or some intermediate proportion are white. In some of these sets, of the specified size, the proportion of P will be the same, or approximately the same, as the proportion in the original population M: among all the sets of 100 rabbits each which exist in the total rabbit population, some sets will have very nearly the same proportion of white rabbits (20 per cent, 5 per cent, 95 per cent, or whatever it may be) as the whole rabbit population. That is, a certain proportion of the hyper-class ($\mathfrak{M}$) of sets must have the property ($\mathfrak{P}$) of matching the original population, M. If all M is P or if no M is P, then every set must exactly match. If 1/2 M is P, the number of matching sets will be the least. But, and this again is the nub of the affair, *whatever* the composition of M with respect to P, more sets will have approximately that composition than any other composition, and if the sets are large, the overwhelming majority of them must have approximately that composition. This too is *a priori*, a law of logic.

Formally, the total number of the hyperpopulation of sets of the size $[MQ]$ which are included in a population M is ${}^{[M]}C_{[MQ]}$. The number of those sets which contain n Ps and $[MQ] - n$ *non-P*s is ${}^{[MP]}C_{n} \times {}^{[M\bar{P}]}C_{[MQ]-n}$. The *proportion* of the hyperpopulation which contain n Ps and $[MQ] - n$ *non-P*s is accordingly

$$\frac{{}^{[MP]}C_{n} \times {}^{[M\bar{P}]}C_{[MQ]-n}}{{}^{[M]}C_{[MQ]}}.$$

The inductive principle now is the logical law that this proportion is greatest when $\frac{n}{[MQ]}$ is as nearly as possible equal to $\frac{[MP]}{[M]}$, that is, when the composition of the set matches the composition of the population, and that when $[MQ]$ is large (a few hundred, say), the number of the sets in which $\frac{n}{[MQ]}$ is approximately equal to $\frac{[MP]}{[M]}$ is much greater than of all the other sets put together.

[2] "Group," "set," and "subclass" are here taken as synonyms. "Group" is perhaps unduly suggestive of 'grouping', as though all the members of any group had to be segregated in one place. That is not intended. What we call "a group" is just a possible selection, a 'combination' in the mathematical sense above defined. "Set" is perhaps the safest and most colorless term.

There is a difficulty here for the logical imagination because when sets are large enough so that the population-matching sets are in a great majority, there are so many of them that they defy conception except in abstract and symbolic terms. No one can envisage, for example, the whole hyperpopulation of sets of 2500 members each which are embedded right now in a population, say, of 140 million, nor even treat of its number by the resources of common arithmetic. The contemplation of highly simplified examples, however, with conveniently small populations, small sets, and small hyperpopulations of sets, will be of some assistance. In the accompanying diagram is represented *in toto* the hyperpopulation of sets of 3 members each which are contained in a population of 9 (balls, let us say). The number of such sets is given arithmetically by the equation

$$^{9}C_{3} = \frac{9 \times 8 \times 7}{3 \times 2} = 84.$$

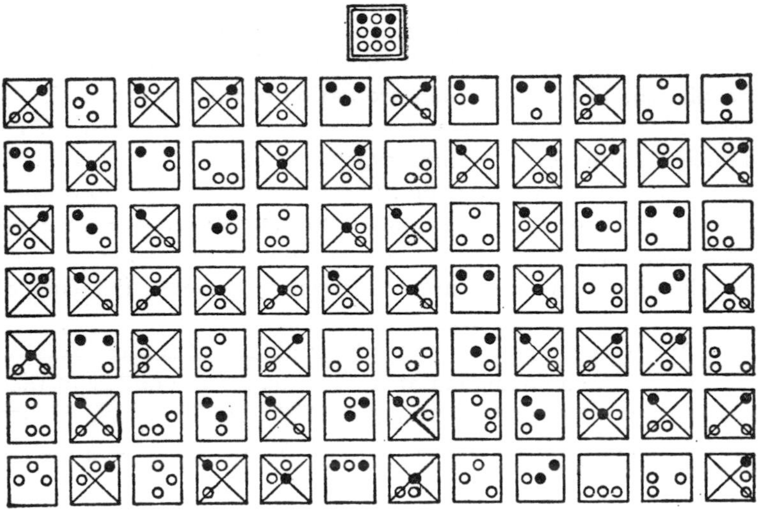

MATCHING SAMPLES

The figure at the top of this diagram represents a population of 9 balls, of which 1/3 are black and 2/3 non-black. Each of the 84 squares below it represents one of the samples, sets, or selections, of 3 balls each, which are included in that population. The sets or samples indicated by the check marks are those which have the same composition as the population: that is, each of them is 1/3 black and 2/3 non-black. There are 45 — a clear majority — of such matching samples. It is a universal principle, provable by pure arithmetic, that, no matter what the composition of the population, and no matter what the size of the sample, more samples of that size must have (as nearly as possible) the same composition as the population than have any other composition. If the samples are large, then no matter how great the population, the vast majority of them must have approximately the same composition as the population. Given a fair-sized sample, then, from any population, with no further material information, we know logically that it very probably is one of those which match the population, and hence that very probably the population has a composition similar to that which we discern in the sample. This is the logical justification of induction.

Representing the population as divided 2/3 white and 1/3 black, the diagram also shows which of the sets are divided in the same proportion and which are not. Arithmetically, the number of sets of 3 members each in which there are 2 white and 1 black (the matching composition) is figured by noting that the subset of 2 white in any such set must be selected from the 6 white in the population, thus providing for ${}^{6}C_{2}$ possibilities, while the subset of 1 black must be chosen from the 3 black in the population, providing for ${}^{3}C_{1}$ possibilities more. Since any one of the white subsets may be conjoined with any one of the black subsets, the total number of matching sets contained in the indicated population is therefore ${}^{6}C_{2} \times {}^{3}C_{1}$, or 15×3, or 45. On the other hand, the number of sets (of 3) in which the composition is the reverse of that of the population, being 1 white and 2 black, is ${}^{6}C_{1} \times {}^{3}C_{2}$, or 6×3, or 18. The number in which all are white is ${}^{6}C_{3} \times 1$, or 20, and the number in which none is white is ${}^{3}C_{3}$, or 1. Even with so small a selection, we observe, the proportion of matching sets is 45/84, or 53.5 per cent. This is a large proportion of exact matches, and with so small a group as 3 it is futile to ask for near matches. If we consider now larger sets, we shall find a smaller relative number of exactly matching ones but a greater relative number which either exactly or nearly match. Taking, for example, a population of 24 balls, in which 16 are white, and considering sets of 6, we note that the number of sets which match the population, that is, in which 4 are white and the other 2 non-white, is ${}^{16}C_{4} \times {}^{8}C_{2}$, or 1820×28, or 40,960 (already far too many to diagram). The number of sets in which the number of whites is one more than the matching number, i.e. in which the number of whites is 5, is ${}^{16}C_{5} \times {}^{8}C_{1}$, or 34,944. The number of sets in which the number of whites is one too few, namely 3, is ${}^{16}C_{3} \times {}^{8}C_{3}$, or 31,360. The total number of sets in which the composition does not vary from the composition of the population by more than one individual, or 16.7 per cent, therefore, is 40,960 + 34,944 + 31,360, or 107,264. The total number of sets of 6 members each which are included in a population of 24 is ${}^{24}C_{6}$, or 134,596. The proportion of those sets which exactly match the population is then only 40960/134596, or .30, but the proportion of sets which do not differ from the population by more than 16.7 per cent is 107264/134596, or .80.

Now, the relevance of all this to the justification of induction is plain enough. When we have laid hands or clapped eyes on an inductive sample *MQ* drawn from a population *M*, we have chosen one set out of an enormous hyperpopulation of sets or 'protosamples' of the size [*MQ*] which are included in the population *M*. Concerning this hyperpopulation there can be proved by pure logic and arithmetic, in a manner suggested though of course not carried through by our elementary formulas and examples, that if the number [*MQ*] is at all large, the vast majority of protosamples must approximately match the population *M* with respect to its proportion of the property *P*, whatever the latter may be. By the ordinary proportional syllogism we were assured that if we know, for example, that the great majority of marbles in a bag are red, it is highly probable that any marble we may draw or have drawn is red. By the same principle, on a higher logical level, since we know *a priori* that the great majority of sets or protosamples which are choosable from a population are statistically similar to that population, it is highly probable that the group which we actually draw as a sample is statistically similar to it, and hence that the population is statistically similar to the sample. Given empirically now that, let us say, 2/3 of the sample are in fact *P*, it is highly probable that very nearly 2/3 of the population are *P*. Without knowing exactly the size and composition of the original population to begin with, we cannot calculate, as in the artificial examples of the preceding paragraphs, exactly what proportion of our 'hyper-marbles' have the quality of nearly-matching-the-population, but we do know *a priori* that most of them have it. Before we choose one of them, it is hence very probable that the one we choose will be one of those which match or nearly match; after we have chosen one, it remains highly probable that the population closely matches the one we have, so that we need only look at the one we have to read off what the population, probably and approximately, is like.

Every sample, in other words, is like a chip, marked with a fractional number, drawn from a bucket of chips among which we know most of the chips are marked with the true composition of the population in which we are interested. It is by thus treating the whole sample *MQ* as a single chip or counter or hyper-marble in a bagful of the same that we have been able to formulate the validity of induction in terms of one straight-forward syllogistic probability instead of by the enormous combination of probabilities to which we resorted in an earlier part of this chapter. The fact that such a reduction is possible will bring home forcibly to the student who has read elsewhere on these subjects that our result is a plain 'direct' probability, and not an 'inverse' probability of the kind usually appealed to by theories which employ the laws of large numbers to justify induction, and that it accordingly does not require the questionable assumption, utilized by the latter, that the moot population is antecedently as likely to have one composition as another. It does, to be sure, presuppose that any one sample, or chip, or counter, is antecedently as likely to be selected as any other, or at any rate that there is no evidence that the principle of selection is relevant to the quality of the sample, but this, as we observed in Chapter 3 and shall observe again in Chapter 6, is an innocent truism.

Although we have now avoided the complication of probabilities which we earlier employed, our new probability is in fact, of course, equal to the probability yielded before, and its calculation must proceed by similar mathematical steps. It has accordingly the same kind of indeterminateness as our previous results. We cannot assert exactly what proportion of protosamples match the population. We know, however, that if they are large, most of them do; we know that the proportion of matching is the least when the population is virtually infinite and is divided half and half. We know how great is the preponderance of matching protosamples, of any specified size, under these worst possible conditions, and hence can assert what is the least possible probability that a sample of a given size will match to any specified degree of approximation. All this can be read off again, nearly enough, from the formula for the standard error of sampling, and from the supplementary tables, and is indeed the way in which the formula is commonly explained in statistical texts. The fact that with a sample of 2500, σ equals or is less than .01, may be now interpreted to mean that of all the possible samples of 2500 members apiece which are included in any given population, the proportion which match the sample within 1 per cent must be *at least* .6826, while the proportion which match within 2 per cent cannot be less than .9545, and so forth.

At the beginning of this chapter, we desiderated as 'the inductive principle', adequate to justify induction, the proposition that any sizable sample very probably matches its population in any specifiable respect. We have provided this, and more, by the more exact and definite sampling formula,

$$\vdash: \sigma \lesseqqgtr \frac{.5}{\sqrt{[MQ]}},$$

which we now interpret to mean that the proportion of samples that match within the margin expressed by the right-hand term cannot be less than .6826, and so forth. To make perfectly plain, however, the manner in which any particular induction is to be reduced to a proportional syllogism of the form made familiar by our Chapter 2, we must acquire a major premise of the familiar form by logically 'specifying' the sampling law by supplying the numbers discoverable in the case in question. We shall then have, for example: *At least 68 per cent of the sets of 2500 members each which are included in the population of rabbits do not vary in composition from the population itself by more than .01.* From the data we obtain the minor premise, *The observed sample is a set of 2500 members included in the population of rabbits.* Thus there follows, with a probability of at least .68, *The observed sample does not differ in composition from the population by more than .01*, or, what is equivalent, *The composition of the rabbit population is equal to a quantity between 1 per cent less than the composition of the sample and 1 per cent greater than it.* From the data now we supply the value .20, let us say, for *the composition of the sample.* Simple arithmetic then furnishes the final answer, with the indicated probability: *The composition of the rabbit population lies between .19 and .21.*

I have persistently repeated, with numerous minor variations, the main topics of our argument, and have labored the simple arithmetical steps which it needs, for the benefit of readers unaccustomed to the arithmetical theory of classes, who may be suddenly illumined by one turn of phrase where they have been stubbornly opaque to others. The actual process of making inductions is extraordinarily familiar to us, while the manner of thought required for its abstract justification, though simple and fundamental in principle, is off the beaten track of our ordinary discourse. In particular, it is hard for most of us to keep in mind without confusion the various interlocking and overlapping classes, and classes of classes, and their arithmetical ratios, which the scheme involves. We must distinguish: the population M, and the proportion of P in M, which is the object of our inductive quest; the actual sample MQ, and the proportion of P in MQ, which is the datum of our induction; and the hyperpopulation, $\mathfrak{M}_{[MQ]}$, of groups of the size $[MQ]$ which are included in M, and the proportion of this hyperpopulation which match the population M with respect to the proportion in which they evince the character P. In our diagram a few pages back, the population M is represented by the single figure at the top; the hyper-population of groups or sets (protosamples) of 3 which are included in M is represented by the rest of the figure.[3]

The cardinal syllogism on which hinges the validity of an inductive inference, though cogent in exactly the same way as any other proportional syllogism, is peculiar in certain respects which may be distracting. (1) Its reference class $\mathfrak{M}$ is a class of classes, and the major premise is accordingly a statistical proposition of the second level. (2) Its major term $\mathfrak{P}$ is an oddly relational property of classes, namely, (*a*) 'matching the population' (whatever the latter may be), (*b*) within a certain range of approximation. (3) The composition of $\mathfrak{M}$ with respect to $\mathfrak{P}$ is not statable exactly but only approximately — 'at least .95', etc. (4) The major premise is analytic and *a priori*, a principle of the logic and arithmetic of classes, or a specification thereof.

None of these oddities militates against the validity of the inductive syllogism. In the respects which are relevant to the syllogism, a character like 'approximately matching the population' behaves exactly like the simple quality red, for example. The margin of indeterminateness in assigning the composition of $\mathfrak{M}$ and the consequent probability is a trait which the inductive syllogism shares with many others. The analytic necessity of the major premise is just what the validity of induction requires if it is not to rest, circle-wise and futilely, on induction itself. Although as a principle of logic, or an exemplification of one, the supreme premise need not be expressed, any more than the principle of Barbara need be stated in a valid demonstrative syllogism, but may be thought of as simply the principle of inference by which we pass from the other premise to the conclusion, nevertheless it perfectly well may be expressed. It is true, and the conclusion follows validly from it, and by expressing it we achieve what we set out to accomplish, a clear proof that an induction has a high degree of the kind of credibility which is yielded by a proportional syllogism at its best.

The cardinal principle that most of the possible samples selectable from any population must statistically match the population, in any assignable respect, naturally is nothing new, for all that it has been so much ignored by philosophical logicians and so seldom expressed and utilized in the way which we have just carried through. Works on probability and statistics abound with *a priori* laws of large numbers which are varied editions of it. In using the principle we have been content to take it in its narrowest form, as it applies one by one to any given population and a certain sized sample thereof. We can in fact, of course, say more: that of *all* largish samples, of mixed sizes, contained in any population, the vastly larger number match the population in the stipulated respect; and indeed that in the whole stupendous hyper-class consisting of all the combinations of populations, sets, and predicate properties in the world, that is, the hyper-class each of whose members consists of one population, one set from

[3] Logically, the groups or sets are *members* of the hyperpopulation $\mathfrak{M}$, which is a class of classes. They are not members of, but are subclasses or species logically included in, the population M.

that population, and one property *P*, the overwhelming majority are such that the 'set' matches the population with respect to the property.[4] Whenever we fix upon any one triad of population, sample, and predicate, therefore, it is highly probable that what we have is one of the matching sets. There is some value in reflecting on such statistical vastitudes in order to appreciate how the validity and success of induction are only the glittering iceberg-tip of an all-pervasive and inevitable logical marshaling of the universe. They are cumbersome, however, and unnecessary to our argument, which proceeds more simply and determinately by confining attention to the rules establishing a definite statistical relation among just the populations, samples, and predicates with which we may deal. We can continue to speak of 'a sample' matching 'its population' because, although every set, of course, is a sample of innumerable populations, in innumerable respects, we suppose 'the' population and 'the' respect in question to be stipulated along with the selection of the sample.

Our incorporation of the logical law of large numbers into a sort of inductive syllogism makes plain how an induction satisfies what is perhaps the most convincing prescription for an inference with a high degree of logical credibility, namely, that it belong to a class of possible inferences in which the great majority of those with true premises have true conclusions. The composition of every protosample included in any population provides a true possible premise for an inductive inference to the conclusion that the composition of the population is approximately the same, and the conclusions of most of those inferences necessarily are true. Any actual inference, from an observed sample, is a realization of one of those possible inferences, and hence very probably has a true conclusion. *Quod erat demonstrandum.*

[4] Purists will be pleased to emend this statement to restrict its generality, so that the idea of 'all populations' shall not incur the paradoxes of the idea of the class of all classes. We can cope well enough with all populations whose members are low-level individuals.

32 *Professor Donald Williams Versus Hume*

DICKINSON S. MILLER

Why can't we settle anything in philosophy? Even when the clear, final, inescapable facts have been long ago thrust upon our attention?

From *The Journal of Philosophy*, Vol. XLIV, No. 25, December 4, 1947, pp. 673–684. Reprinted by permission of *The Journal of Philosophy*.

Hume pointed out that from past and present data we can not *deduce* any prophecy of the future; not even a merely probable prophecy. Professor Donald Williams in his brilliant book, *The Ground of Induction*,[1] maintains that we can; that from uniform data in experience we can prove a probability that the uniformity will continue. And this on strictly deductive principles.

Professor Williams, in spite of all his care and power of reasoning, seems not fully to have noted how deep Hume's argument cuts. We can not infer deductively from the existence of one thing the existence (even only probable) of another or quality. The thought may be thrown into this form: we can not deduce one particular from another — no matter how extensive our first particular may be — even if it consists of a multitude of particulars. Such a deduction would have to be an "immediate inference," an inference with but one premise, the conclusion of which was a proposition about something not mentioned in the premise! The sanction of logic has been claimed for many a monstrosity, but it will hardly be claimed for this. Hume's thesis therefore stands. And Professor Williams's is inconsistent with it.

It is inconsistent because he starts with particulars, invokes no factual generalization that could serve as major premise, and ends with particulars (as well as generalization) — in a probable form. He does not oppose Hume's argument in direct collision, but he would seem to find his way round it — by a course of reasoning of a captivating ingenuity. From anyone interested in all attempts to confute Hume on this topic the book can not fail to command signal attention.

For the sake of simplicity and clearness in a subject so easily thrown into complexity, I may be permitted to approach the author's argument by steps or stages.

I

The commonest reply to Hume is this: we know that if the same event occurs again under precisely the same circumstances it must produce the same: if its nature is identical how can it produce something different? This argument seemed cogent, for example, to both Bradley and Bosanquet. Yet it is a mere trick with words. To produce is to cause; you are saying that the event was a cause, and by the definition of the word "cause" or "produce" the same cause or productive agency must always have the same effect. But how do you know that the event *was* a cause, that it has a right to the name, that it always will be followed by the same sequel? That is an implication of the term, not of the event. Hume pointed out that what we call the cause and what we call the effect are two distinguishable events, that we can think of each by itself, that is, apart from the other, that the one, taken simply as an event, does not imply the other, that it is only from experience we learn that the one may be expected to usher in the other. The verbal trick begs the whole question. From this evasive fallacy Professor Williams's book is wholly free.

[1] Cambridge: Harvard University Press. 1947. ix + 213 pp. [Ed. note: Page numbers are to Williams' book. Pages 77–104 are included here.]

II

The species of argument employed in the book is the mathematical calculation of probabilities. Let us begin, as an introduction, merely to illustrate the conditions of any such calculation and without any reference whatever to the book's argument, with some of the simplest examples that Professor Williams happens quite incidentally to mention.

> If, for example, the conditions of a race (p) entail that just one of six horses must win ($q_1, q_2, \cdots q_6$), and if there is no other relevant information, then the credibility of any one horse winning is 1/6. [Pp. 34–35.]

Over the "logic of chance" or "theory of probability" a great illusion has for many minds long hovered: the illusion that pure deductive reason can extract a probability solely from "the possibilities of the case." Out of this has grown the dream that we can found induction and natural science upon such a procedure of pure deductive reason. But you can not extract a probability from mere possibilities. The idea of probability is not contained in the idea of possibility or possibilities and can not be conjured out of it.

In the example just given there is specified a definite fact (not a mere possibility) which is the foundation of all that follows, namely, that a certain event will take place: the race will be run. In real life, if a race is announced and expected, this is a high probability arising from experience; in a hypothetical case like the present it is part of the hypothesis. But this event that is going to happen may take any one of several forms, that is, one or another of the horses may win. Each of these forms of the outcome is rightly called possible, but they are simply possible alternative forms of something which is not merely possible but certain or highly probable. This certainty or high probability they divide up between them. Thus we are *not* dealing with mere possibilities but with probabilities each of a low degree. In a race in real life each of these low probabilities (that a particular one of the horses will win) is 1/6 of a high probability (namely, that some horse will win); in a hypothetical case each is 1/6 of a hypothetically imagined certainty. If we did not have our probability or assumed certainty at the outset — that the race would be run and one of the horses win — we should have no emergent probability at all. And this applies to every case of a mathematically computed likelihood of this order. We might reason forever about mere possibilities and arrive at no fact or probable fact.

And there is another requisite, of course, besides mere possible cases, namely, the limitation of their number; in this case the known fact that *only* six horses will compete. That is not a possibility but an ascertained or definite assumed fact, without which the inference would be impossible.

Look at another of Mr. Williams's incidental examples.

> . . . to aver that the premise that a bag of marbles contains 9,999 white and 1 black gives no rational support to the belief that a marble abstracted from it will be white, is strictly absurd.

Certainly; we have no reason, when we take out one, to expect that any particular marble more than another will be the one taken. Hence we must be prepared to the degree of 999/1000 to see one-or-another-of-the-white-marbles, and be prepared to the degree of 1/1000 for the black.

Here the event that it is assumed will take place is the drawing of a marble from the bag — the revelation of the color of some one of the marbles, like the revelation of the comparative speed of one of the horses. There are one thousand forms, so to speak, in which this may take place, since there are one thousand different marbles each of which may be the one drawn. The probability that any particular marble will be drawn is a thousandth part of the assumed certainty that the event will occur.

So let us formally set down the following as the first and second of certain principles governing our subject.

1. *Calculation under the Theory of Probability is based on an initial certainty or probability that something exists or will exist; there is, however, more than one form or embodiment in which it may exist, and the number of alternative forms or embodiments is known.*

2. *Probability can never be extracted from mere possibilities, the former idea not being contained in the latter.*

Suppose now we try as an experiment to reason inductively, that is, from experience, as nearly as possible after the fashion of these two examples. *I am not connecting this with any procedure of Professor Williams's.* I try it as a preliminary for the light it sheds on the whole subject. Suppose, for instance, having always found that "water wets and fire burns," we ask: On the occasion when next we encounter fire or water how shall we reckon on deductive principles the probability that it will burn or wet? That occasion would be intended to correspond with the race and with the discovery of the color of a particular marble. At once we see that there is no parallelism. Deductively, we do not know that there will be any such occasion. Deductively, we know nothing at all about any future events. We expect them, owing to our experience, but not on deductive grounds. We have no information from that source limiting the number of forms in which our event may occur, or showing us that objects will retain the properties they now have. Hence the entire basis of procedure in the two examples is lacking and no ground remains for deductive procedure at all.

III

We come now to Professor Williams's own manner of proceeding in offering a basis for induction. It consists in passing from the calculation of what a sample will probably be when we know something about the whole class to the calculation of what the whole class will probably be when we know a sample. It is the latter that induction requires — the sample being our data of a certain kind or class up to the present. And the misfortune of the argument is that we can not effect such a passage; that which enables us to make the calculation in the first instance is the very thing that is completely absent in the second; we have nothing from which to draw a conclusion. In the first case at the outset we have a knowledge of the whole class and to that extent a knowledge of the sample, which is part of it. In the second case we have a knowledge of the sample and none whatever of the rest of the class.

I am not, of course, seeking dogmatically to exclude Professor Williams's view in advance; I am saying that this is how the matter appears when we look it deliberately in the face. If there is any logic that will deliver us from this apparent *impasse* we shall certainly salute it as a marvelous discovery.

If we try to extricate ourselves from our ignorance of the rest of the class by considering *all possible* members of it, and what alone they *could* be or must be, then we encounter at once two broad considerations: (1) we have no deductive means of knowing anything whatsoever about what the rest of the class could, must, or will be; and (2) if we had we still should not know deductively that any more of the class existed or would exist. We have no deductive knowledge that the universe or any part of it will continue to exist beyond this moment.

Of course we are constantly inferring with regard to the future from uniform facts already in hand; what Hume said was this is another kind of inference; it is not deduction.

It seems entirely clear that if we are going to draw deductive conclusions of any sort about the nature of the rest of the class — what properties further things of that kind will turn out to have — we must begin by making some sheer factual assumption about it. We can not draw conclusions from nothing. We can not distil them from utter ignorance. But, granted an arbitrary assumption of one sort or another, we can proceed to base conclusions upon it. Now to make an assumption which in fact is arbitrary about the actual composition of a class, in advance of our knowledge of any part of it but our data, and then to base deductions upon this arbitrary assumption, is, I think, exactly what we shall presently find Professor Williams doing. We have our sample, we have nothing more; in some manner an element of fact about the unknown remainder must be imported into the matter if we are to seem to reach any probability.

The appeal of his book is to "the fundamental law of large numbers, that most samples [for instance our data] match their populations [the membership of their class]." ". . . this is an analytic law of logic" (p. 153). But where does he argue the matter, where do we find the nerve of his actual proof of this law as a basis for induction, what is the piece of reasoning which has the resoponsibility upon it of being the one means of escape from Hume's conclusion? We are manifestly intended to find it in the chapter on "The Probability of Induction." There on page 91 we read: "Here, I take it, is in main principle a solution of the problem of induction." What has preceded? An attempt, as already said, to pass from the calculation of what a sample will be when we know something about the whole class to a calculation of what the whole class will probably be when we know a sample; to calculate the latter in a comparable manner *and with comparable warrant* (the thing that I suggest is impossible).

What we have to work with in an inductive situation consists of two kinds of knowledge: the number of the sample, and its composition, which are facts of observation; and the principle that no matter what the population is like, any sample, of considerable size, will very probably be very similar to it, this being an *a priori* law of classes, demonstrable by logical analysis. [P. 91.]

What, then, are the steps of the argument?

In the first place, although the inferring of the composition of the population from the composition of the sample is not logically the same as the converse process of inferring the composition of the sample from the composition of the population, both inferences could be made valid by the single general principle that given any population and any (largish) sample thereof, it is highly probable that the sample matches the population (and hence that the population matches the sample). In the second place, the latter general principle may be proved to be true by no more intricate method than considering *the whole range of possible population compositions* and observing that although the probability of a matching sample of a stipulated size is different for different compositions, the probability of a matching sample is always greater than the probability of any other kind of sample, and if the sample is large, then *no matter what the population composition may be*, the probability is very great. [P. 88.]

"*To bring this out clearly*," he says — the emphasis is my own — "let us look again at the sampling formula and ask how much we can say about its various terms even though we do not yet know the actual composition of the population." He points out what "the extreme cases" would be: if *all* the class had the character in question, all the class would in that respect resemble any sample; if none of the class had the character in question again all the class would in that respect resemble any sample. True.

On the other hand, the probability of matching is least, and the probable deviation σ is the greatest, when the composition of the population is midway between the two extremes 0 and 1, that is, when just half of M is P and half accordingly is non-P. . . . What happens then in this worst of all conceivable situations for the probability of the sample's matching the population? . . .*the worst possible situation is still a very favorable one.* That is, there must be a probability of .6826 at the very least that the sample composition does not differ from the population composition by more than 1 percent., and a probability, at the very least, of .9545 that it does not differ by more than twice this, or 2 percent., and so forth." [P. 89.]

This seems a strangely artificial approach to the question, How do we know that the data we have are any guide to the future? Our situation in induction is not that of contemplating academically a merely conceived class and considering upon what hypotheses as to its composition any possible sample will be likeliest or least likely to be in a certain respect a true specimen of the whole class. Our situation is that of having an actual specimen already in hand (our data) and desiring to know what prospect there is that the rest of the class will in the respect in question be like it. And "the probability of matching is least "if *none* of the rest are like it. *That* is "the worst possible situation." To say that at least half the class must resemble the sample is to make an arbitrary factual assumption about the rest of the class; it is just here that we find the author doing this. Inasmuch as in the cases that arise in induction the possible other members of the class are for us wholly uncertain in existence and, if existent or so to be, wholly unknown in character beyond being members of the class, we have no assurance, not even any degree of probability, in the matter. I speak, of course, from the strictly deductive point of view, which alone is here in question. From that point of view our data are no clue to anything. Which is just what Humc pointed out.

To be sure, the assumption that one-half of the class have the character in question is midway between assuming that all have it and that none have it. That none have it we know to be false because our data have it. That all have it we possess, of course, no deductive means of knowing. But he has shown us nothing that obliges us, from our actual point of view, to deem the midmost situation between these particular extremes the worst possible. He has shown us nothing that obliges us to make any assumption at all.

When the author invokes "the law of large numbers" he must not forget that its substantiation as supporting induction has been effected *through* the reasoning just quoted, and apparently depends upon that reasoning. That seems to be the bottleneck of the argument. If the law can be substantiated as supporting induction apart from that reasoning, he must show us just how.

It does seem to be this very argument just cited that is offered as "in main principle a solution of the problem of induction." True, he mentions at least one other "way of formulating the solution" (p. 93), but it is briefly and dogmatically stated, without rendering clear the one essential, the nerve of proof. What we need to know is the innermost logic of his solution, explicitly, completely stated, and if we do not find this in the passage quoted above, where do we find it? If I have missed the pith of his argument my only desire is that my eyes shall be opened and that I may see it set palpably before us. I am pathetically ready to be convinced, to recant, and to become an advocate of his thesis. If he has supplied a logical confutation of Hume he has given us the most momentous production on the subject since that philosopher wrote. Attempts by others at confutation up to the present have signally failed. But it would seem that Professor Williams has a liability to be carried away by the technics of symbolic logic out of sight of first principles and first needs. These technics have been and are, of course, invaluable. But it is a healthful exercise, every little while, to translate them into Ehglish, and had he done so he would probably have avoided some of the reasonings presented in this book.

Needed: a formulation of the law of large numbers as basis for induction which does not require any arbitrary assumption about the unknown. Needed for the author's position but apparently impossible. If possible it is, might it not be stated in full, without dependence on allusions, taking nothing for granted?

In the absence of such a formulation may we not now say:

3. *There is no means possible or conceivable by which from given specimens of a class could be deduced the probable character of its other members. For the reason that in the nature of any existent or existents no implication is present as to the nature of any other. From concrete particulars we may gather empirical probability, yes, but implication, no.*

4. *While the deductive inference of probabilities depends always upon definite knowledge or assumption of an antecedent probability or certainty which it can not transcend, the*

inductive inference of probabilities, on the other hand, depends upon data which it is its very function and essence to transcend.

This is in effect what Hume laid down.

IV

We turn now to the philosophic background of the work.

In drawing an inductive inference from our data to further particulars, if we could supply a major premise, such as the Law of Causation or "the Uniformity of Nature," and certify it apart from experience, our inference would become deductively valid. But we can not. And Professor Williams offers at the outset no principle respecting the sequence of events in nature. Any such general proposition would be "synthetic," and he maintains that no such is required. "Induction presupposes nothing."[2] He does invoke "a principle," "the law of large numbers," but it is "an analytic law of logic" (p. 153), "an analytic truism" (p. 139), "an *a priori* law of classes, demonstrable by logical analysis" (p. 81). "Since the principle is purely logical, presupposing nothing about its data or its objects except that they be members of classes — a status that no conceivable entities could avoid — it makes induction quite independent of any supposed maxim of causation, uniformity, or sufficient reason" (p. 202).

If the nature of our data in induction involved membership in a class that must include other members, *existent or to be existent*, than the data themselves, then their nature would prove the existence of other particulars, and Hume would be wrong. Or if their nature involved that the possible other members of the class would probably if they existed have a further quality like that of the data, besides belonging to the class, then again their nature would prove a superadded fact respecting existence, though a conditional fact and a fact of probability alone; their implication would stretch out into the world of reality beyond themselves. But plainly neither of these suppositions is or could be true. It is other *possible or conceivable* members and qualities only that the class must contain to which they belong. And to this Hume could have no objection, for it does not contravene his thought.

Yet it is the idea that they are members of a class from which the author derives his whole theory of the basis of induction. The class-idea is the hat out of which he gets the rabbit.

The broadest comment to be made on Professor Williams's philosophy of induction is the following: if the only element you introduce into the reasoning besides your data is an explicative or "analytic" proposition, it can never enable you to infer any existent or probable existent, even if it be only a quality. If your major premise had said, "This kind of fact is always coupled with a certain other" (a synthetic proposition), then you could have concluded, I repeat, to further fact — a real induction. But if it only says, "This kind of fact always contains a constituent attribute of this kind of fact" (an analytic proposition),

[2] A chapter-heading.

you are not enabled to go further; you are left with your data and nothing else on your hands. Upon such a major premise induction can never be founded. What is apparently deemed the strength of the argument, its economy of philosophical assumption and immunity in that respect from scepticism, consisting in its having dispensed with all but analytic, that is, self-evident foundations, turns out to be its weakness. This is simply one aspect of a truth that we may submit as a fifth among the principles that the book obliges us to recall.

5. *We can not prove from the definition of terms, no matter what they are, nor from any analytic proposition, that something will exist or probably exist; nor can we even when the proposition is taken in conjunction with concrete data.*

(If the principle and warrant of our empirical knowledge, the saving and governing knowledge of our life, arose out of the depths of "identical" and merely verbal propositions, what a singular logic would be ours!)

Coming a step closer to the specific argument of the book we may add, therefore,

6. *No law of numbers, no mathematico-logical laws, can prove the existence or probable existence of particular units in nature or particular qualities of such units.*

As Hume would put it, we can not in inference pass from "relations of ideas" to "matters of fact." In other words, we can not infer from the relations of implication amongst abstract terms of thought that anything concrete exists. *Even granted that certain units (our data) exist,* we can not deduce from such relations that other units exist — either certainly or probably. Terms imply according to their definition. There are two cases possible. Either our term implies another existent, as "husband" implies a wife, in which case we must have separate and empirical evidence of the other existent before we know that the term is applicable; or it does not imply another existent, in which case it can not be used to prove that there is any other. In neither case does our datum *plus* a definition or *plus* any analytic proposition prove the probable existence of anything else, nor even a probable existent quality of it, in case the thing itself does exist.

And when we watch Professor Williams at work basing induction on the law of large numbers we find him obliged, as we have seen, to make a factual assumption about the whole class with which he is dealing, namely, that at worst one-half are like the sample, which assumption is not analytic and not a truism and not deducible from any truism.

V

In conclusion may be mentioned Mr. Williams's treatment of logical implication as if it had degrees. He speaks of "a degree of implicative connection intermediate between strict entailment and inconsistency" (p. 47). Again, "a non-demonstrative logical implication" (p. 134). Again, "a relation analogous to entailment, albeit of an intermediate degree" (p. 46). Etc.

Surely there can not be such a thing as a degree of implication. A degree of probability — yes; but not a degree of implication. Implication is entire and absolute or it is not what is meant by the term. If the conclusion does not strictly follow from the premises then it does not follow at all. To follow means to be true if the premises are true. It may be said that in some cases it is only probable if the premises are true. But then the probability does follow, and unreservedly. A probability may be implied as truly as a certainty; all depends on the content of the premises.[3] But in that case the conclusion is certainly true if the premises are, the conclusion being that a probability obtains.

He formulates "the proportional or statistical syllogism" thus: if m/n M is P, and a is M, then there is a probability of m/n that a is P. And he tends to treat it as in a sense or degree deficient or falling short, in that it issues in a probability only, which accrues, as a substitute that we must put up with, in place of a conclusion that is certain.

The shortcoming, however, is not in the probative force of the syllogism but in the knowledge with which it sets out. Granted that knowledge, granted that we understand the premises in their completeness, the logical force of the argument is in no respect short of absolute implication and coercion. Once more, the conclusion as conclusion from those premises is certain and not merely probable, though it is only the assertion of a probability. And better than certain the inference could not be. Probability is not a growth that germinates in the cracks and gaps of a deficient syllogism. I am not offering objection to any artifices of procedure that prove convenient for mathematical logic. What I am saying is that it is only by a confusion of thought that we can assert degrees of implication.

Mr. Williams writes: "What we require is an 'ampliative' inference (to use Peirce's phrase), proceeding in accordance with abstract principles whose validity is evident or demonstrable in the same way as the rule of the syllogism, from factual premises . . . to something *further*" (p. 11).

But if it passes to something further, if it passes beyond the exact contents of its premises, it is not deduction. If it does not pass beyond it is not "ampliative." When is deduction not deduction? When it is "ampliative." It is the whole essence, warrant, claim, and soul of deduction to be explicative. What Mr. Williams would have to do, what fundamentally he is trying to do, is to seek a rational support for induction by an explicative process. (This term is used just here, of course, like Peirce's term, in a wider sense than the established one, namely, as the opposite of the latter.)

So the last of our relevant principles is:

7. *There are no intermediate degrees between following from premises and not following from them. There is no such thing as half-following or quarter-following.*

This is not, of course, a review of the book. Here I am concerned with but one thing, the thread of proof that runs through it. There is much in the book

[3] Mr. Williams explicitly discusses this matter just as he explicitly discusses Hume and just as he discusses or approaches other matters of principle put forward here. In this brief article I can not attempt to enter into all the indentations of his coastline, but I steer a course which I hope subtends them.

that awakens high admiration. But it does leave a deep regret that rare capacities and knowledge should have been devoted to an enterprise that Hume exposed as impossible two hundred years ago: the laying of a deductive foundation for induction. The more plausible such an attempt is made, the more it interferes with the advance of philosophy, which is wholly dependent on the recognition of distinctions once they are discovered.

33 *The Justification of Induction*

HANS REICHENBACH

The first to criticize the inference of induction by enumeration and to question its legitimacy was David Hume.[1] Ever since his famous criticism, philosophers have regarded the problem of induction as an unsolved riddle precluding the completion of an empiricist theory of knowledge. In Hume's analysis it does not appear as a problem of probability; he includes it, rather, in the problem of causality. We observe, Hume explains, that equal causes are always followed by equal effects. We then infer that the same effects will occur in future. On what grounds do we base this inference? Hume's criticism gave two negative answers to the question:

1. The conclusion of the inductive inference cannot be inferred *a priori*, that is, it does not follow with logical necessity from the premises; or, in modern terminology, it is not tautologically implied by the premises. Hume based this result on the fact that we can at least *imagine* that the same causes will have another effect tomorrow than they had yesterday, though we do not believe it. What is logically impossible cannot be imagined — this psychological criterion was employed by Hume for the establishment of his first thesis.

2. The conclusion of the inductive inference cannot be inferred *a posteriori*, that is, by an argument from experience. Though it is true that the inductive inference has been successful in past experience, we cannot infer that it will be successful in future experience. The very inference would be an inductive inference, and the argument thus would be circular. Its validity presupposes the principle that it claims to prove.

Hume did not see a way out of this dilemma. He regarded the inductive inference as an unjustifiable procedure to which we are conditioned by habit and the apparent cogency of which must be explained as an outcome of habit. The

From *Theory of Probability*, University of California Press, Berkeley, 1949, pp. 470–482. Reprinted by permission of the University of California Press, Berkeley.

[1] *An Enquiry Concerning Human Understanding* (1748).

power of habit is so strong that even the clearest insight into the unfounded use of the inductive inference cannot destroy its compelling character. Though this explanation is psychologically true, we cannot admit that it has any bearing on the logical problem. Perhaps the inductive inference is a habit — the logician wants to know whether it is a good habit. The question would call for an answer even if it could be shown that we can never overcome the habit. The logical problem of justification must be carefully distinguished from the question of psychological laws.

Up to our day the problem has subsisted in the skeptical version derived from Hume, in spite of many attempts at its solution. Kant's attempt to solve the problem by regarding the principle of causality as a synthetic judgment *a priori* failed because the concept of the synthetic judgment *a priori* was shown to be untenable. I may add that Kant never attempted to make use of his theory for a detailed analysis of the inductive inference. In the empiricism of our time the problem has come to the fore, overshadowing all other problems of the theory of knowledge. It has held this place persistently without changing the skeptical form that Hume gave it.

A few philosophers tried to escape Hume's skepticism by denying that a problem of the justification of induction exists. Various reasons were given for such a conception. It was said that the rule of induction does not belong to the content of science; that Hume's criticism concerns only a linguistic problem; that the problem of justification is a pseudoproblem; and so on. It is hardly comprehensible that such arguments could ever have been seriously maintained. They misuse an important modern discovery — the distinction between levels of language — for the purpose of contesting the legitimacy of an old problem, upon which, however, this distinction has no bearing.

It is true that the rule of induction belongs, not in the object language of science, but in the metalanguage. It is a *directive* for the construction of sentences, since it tells how to proceed from verified sentences to predictive sentences. I have therefore called it a rule of derivation (§ 87),* the only one that inductive logic requires in addition to the rules of derivation of deductive logic. Such rules, however, are admissible within a scientific language only when they can be justified, that is, when they can be shown to be adequate means for the purpose of derivation. Such a justification is easily given for the rules of derivation of deductive logic: it can be shown that the rules always lead to true sentences if the premises are true. In a systematic exposition of deductive logic this justification of the rules of derivation must be formally given. [2] For the rule of induction such a proof is not possible; that is why the problem of its justification is so involved that it requires a comprehensive analysis.

The frequency theory of probability, with its interpretation of probability statements as posits, makes it possible to give a justification of the rule of induction. The problem will be discussed with respect to the wider form of statistical

* [Ed. note: not included here.]

[2] See § 5 above, and *Elements of Symbolic Logic*, New York, 1947, §§ 12, 14. [Ed. note: § 5 is not reprinted in this volume.]

induction; the results will then include the special case of classical induction. The generalization expressed in the use of statistical induction is relevant because it weakens the inference. Whereas classical induction wishes to establish a rigorous inference that holds for every individual case, statistical induction renounces every assertion about the individual case and makes a prediction only about the whole sequence.

There is another sense in which the statistical version involves a different interpretation of the problem. The classical conception entails the question whether the rule of induction leads to true conclusions, but the statistical version deals only with the question whether the rule of induction leads to a method of approximation, whether it leads to posits that, when repeated, approach the correct result step by step. The answer is that this is so if the sequences under consideration have a limit of the frequency. The inductive posit anticipates the final result (§ 87) and must eventually arrive at the correct value of the limit within an interval of exactness.

The method of anticipation may be illustrated by an example from another field. An airplane flies in the fog to a distant destination. From two ground stations the pilot receives radio messages about his position, ascertained by radio bearings. He then determines the flight direction by means of a map, adjusts the compass to the established course, and flies on, keeping continuously to the direction given by the compass. In the fog he has no other orientation than to follow the adopted course. After a while, however, he inquires again of the ground stations for another determination of his position. It turns out that the airplane was subject to a wind drift that has carried the ship off its course. The pilot, therefore, establishes a new course that he follows thereafter.

This method, repeatedly applied, is a method of approximation. The direction from the position ascertained to the destination is not the most favorable one because of wind currents; but the pilot does not know the changing currents and therefore at first *posits* this direction. He does not believe that he has found the final direction. He knows that only when he is very close to his destination will the straight line be the most favorable flying direction — but he acts as though the coincidence of the most favorable flying direction and a straight-line connection were reached. He thus anticipates the final result. He may do so because he uses this anticipation only in the sense of a posit. By correcting the posit repeatedly, always following the same rule, he must finally come to the correct posit and thus reach his destination.

The analogy with the anticipative method of the rule of induction is obvious. In the analysis of Hume's problem we thus arrive at a preliminary result: if a limit of the frequency exists, positing the persistence of the frequency is justified because this method, applied repeatedly, must finally lead to true statements. We do not maintain the truth of every individual inductive conclusion, but we do not need an assumption of this kind because the application of the rule presupposes only its qualification as a method of approximation.

This consideration bases the justification of induction on the assumption of the existence of a limit of the frequency. It is obvious, however, that for such an assumption no proof can be constructed. When we wish to overcome Hume's skepticism we must eliminate this last assumption from our justification of induction.

The traditional discussion of induction was dominated by the opinion that it is impossible to justify induction without an assumption of this kind, that is, without an assumption stating a general property of the physical world. The supposedly indispensable assumption was formulated as a postluate of the uniformity of nature, expressed, for instance, in the form that similar event patterns repeat themselves. The principle used above, that sequences of events converge toward a limit of the frequency, may be regarded as another and perhaps more precise version of the uniformity postulate. So long as logicians maintained that without a postulate of this kind the inductive inference could not be accounted for, and so long as there was no hope of proving such a postulate true or probable, the theory of induction was condemned to remain an unsolvable puzzle.

The way out of the difficulty is indicated by the following considerations. The insistence on a uniformity postulate derives from an unfortunate attempt to construct the theory of inductive inference by analogy with that of deductive inference — the attempt to supply a premise for the inductive inference that would make the latter deductive. It was known that the inductive conclusion cannot be asserted as true; but it was hoped to give a demonstrative proof, by the addition of such a premise, for the statement that the conclusion is probable to a certain degree. Such a proof is dispensable because we can assert a statement in the sense of a posit even if we do not know a probability, or weight, for it. If the inductive conclusion is recognized as being asserted, not as a statement maintained as true or probable, but as an anticipative posit, it can be shown that a uniformity postulate is not necessary for the derivation of the inductive conclusion.

We used the assumption of the existence of a limit of the frequency in order to prove that, if no probabilities are known, the anticipative posit is the best posit because it leads to success in a finite number of steps. With respect to the individual act of positing, however, the limit assumption does not supply any sort of information. The posit may be wrong, and we can only say that if it turns out to be wrong we are willing to correct it and to try again. But if the limit assumption is dispensable for every individual posit, it can be omitted for the method of positing as a whole. The omission is required because we have no proof for the assumption. But the absence of proof does not mean that *we know that there is no limit*; it means only that *we do not know whether there is a limit*. In that case we have as much reason to try a posit as in the case that the existence of a limit is known; for, if a limit of the frequency exists, we shall find it by the inductive method if only the acts of positing are continued sufficiently. Inductive positing in the sense of a trial-and-error method is justified so long as it is not known that the attempt is hopeless, that there is no limit of the frequency. Should we have no success, the positing was useless; but why not take our chance?

The phrase "take our chance" is not meant here to state that there is a certain probability of success; it means only that there is a possibility of success in the sense that there is no proof that success is excluded. Furthermore, the suggestion to try predictions by means of the inductive method is not an advice of a trial at random, of trying one's luck, so to speak; it is the proposal of a systematic method of trial so devised that if success is attainable the method will find it.

To make the consideration more precise, some auxiliary concepts may be introduced. The distinction between necessary and sufficient conditions is well known in logic. A statement c is a *necessary* condition of a statement a if $a \supset c$ holds, that is, if a cannot be true without c being true. The statement c will be a *sufficient* condition of a if $c \supset a$ holds. For instance, if a physician says that an operation is a necessary condition to save the patient, he does not say that the operation will save the man; he only says that without the operation the patient will die. The operation would be a sufficient condition to save the man if it is certain that it will lead to success; but a statement of this kind would leave open whether there are other means that would also save him.

These concepts can be applied in the discussion of the anticipative posit. If there is a limit of the frequency, the use of the rule of induction will be a sufficient condition to find the limit to a desired degree of approximation. There may be other methods, but this one, at least, is sufficient. Consequently, when we do not know whether there is a limit, we can say, if there is any way to find a limit, the rule of induction will be such a way. It is, therefore, a necessary condition for the existence of a limit, and thus for the existence of a method to find it, that the aim be attainable by means of the rule of induction.

To clarify these logical relations, we shall formulate them in the logical symbolism. We abbreviate by a the statement, "There exists a limit of the frequency"; by b the statement, "I use the rule of induction in a repeated procedure"; by c the statement, "I shall find the limit of the frequency". We then have the relation [3]

$$a \supset (b \supset c) \tag{1}$$

This means, $b \supset c$ is the *necessary* condition of a, or, in other words, the attainability of the aim by the use of the rule of induction is a necessary condition of the existence of a limit. Furthermore, if a is true, b is a *sufficient* condition of c. This means, if there is a limit of the frequency, the use of the rule of induction is a sufficient instrument to find it.

It is in this relation that I find the justification of the rule of induction. Scientific method pursues the aim of predicting the future; in order to construct a precise formulation for this aim we interpret it as meaning that scientific method is intended to find limits of the frequency. Classical induction and predictions of individual events are included in the general formulation as the special case that the relative frequency is $= 1$. It has been shown that if the aim of scientific method is attainable it will be reached by the inductive method.

[3] The implications occurring here must be regarded as nomological operations: the first as a tautological implication, the second as a relative nomological implication. See *Elements of Symbolic Logic*, § 63.

This result eliminates the last assumption we had to use for the justification of induction. The assumption that there is a limit of the frequency must be true if the inductive procedure is to be successful. But we need not know whether it is true when we merely ask whether the inductive procedure is justified. It is justified as an attempt at finding the limit. Since we do not know a sufficient condition to be used for finding a limit, we shall at least make use of a necessary condition. In positing according to the rule of induction, always correcting the posit when additional observation shows different results, we prepare everything so that if there is a limit of the frequency we shall find it. If there is none, we shall certainly not find one — but then all other methods will break down also.

The answer to Hume's question is thus found. Hume was right in asserting that the conclusion of the inductive inference cannot be proved to be true; and we may add that it cannot even be proved to be probable. But Hume was wrong in stating that the inductive procedure is unjustifiable. It can be justified as an instrument that realizes the necessary conditions of prediction, to which we resort because sufficient conditions of prediction are beyond our reach. The justification of induction can be summarized as follows:

Thesis θ. The rule of induction is justified as an instrument of positing because it is a method of which we know that if it is possible to make statements about the future we shall find them by means of this method.

This thesis is not meant to say that the inductive rule represents the only method of the kind described. In (1, § 87) were formulated other forms of posits that also must lead to the limit if there is one. Let us investigate whether the rule of induction constitutes the *best* method of finding the limit.

In order to answer the question we must divide the possible methods in two classes. In the first class we put all rules of the form (1, § 87), rules that differ from the rule of induction only inasmuch as they include a function c_n that is formulated explicitly so as to converge to 0 with increasing n. In the second class we put all other methods that will lead to the limit of the frequency. These methods will also converge asymptotically with the rule of induction; but they differ from the form (1, § 87) because they do not state the convergence explicitly.

As to the first class, it was explained in §§ 87–88 that we cannot prove the rule of induction to be superior to other methods included in the class. There may be, and in general will be, forms of the function c_n that are more advantageous than the function $c_n = 0$. If we knew one of these forms we should prefer it to the rule of induction. The method of correction (§§ 89–90)* may be regarded as an instrument for finding such forms. When, on the contrary, we know nothing, we can choose what we like. The rule of induction has the advantage of being easier to handle, owing to its descriptive simplicity. Since we are considering a choice among methods all of which will lead to the aim, we may let considerations of a technical nature determine our choice.

* [Ed. note: not included here.]

In regard to the second class the situation is different. If a method is presented with the assertion that it is a method of this class, the difficulty arises of how to prove the assertion. Of course, there may be such a method. Every oracle or soothsayer maintains that he has found one. Such a method is usually presented in the form of a prediction of individual events. This is included in our theory as the case in which the probability, or the frequency limit, is $= 1$. We may, therefore, generalize the problem so as to concern the prediction of any value of the limit of the frequency. Assume that a clairvoyant asserts that he is able to predict only the probability of an event — to predict the limit of the frequency in a sequence. We shall not be willing to believe him until we have checked his abilities. He might well be following a method that will never lead to the limit of the frequency. Such methods are certainly possible. For instance, if we were to posit that the limit is *outside* the interval $f^n \pm \delta$, we should certainly never reach the limit by continued application of this rule. The inadequacy of the methods of oracles and soothsayers is not so clearly apparent. But how can such methods be tested?

Obviously, there is only one way — to test these methods by means of the rule of induction. We would ask the soothsayer to predict as much as he could, and see whether his predictions finally converged sufficiently with the frequency observed in the continuation of the sequence. Then we would count his success rate. If the latter were sufficiently high, we would infer by the rule of induction that it would remain so, and thus conclude that the man was an able prophet. If the success rate were low, we would refuse to consult him further. It is true that in the latter case the soothsayer may refer us to the future, declaring that on continuation of the sequence his prediction of a limit may still come true. Although clairvoyants favor such an attitude, finally even the most ardent believer no longer places any faith in them. In the end the believer submits his judgment to the rule of induction. He must do so because the rule of induction is a method *of which he knows that it will lead to the aim* if the aim is attainable, whereas *he does not know anything* about the oracle and the clairvoyant.

We see, by the way, that with this subordination to induction the oracle in all its forms loses its mystical glamor. Like other methods of prediction, it is subject to a scientific test. It was explained above that science itself is at work to find methods of better convergence by the construction of a network of inductions in the form of the method of correction. There is no need, therefore, to ask the help of oracles or clairvoyants in order to improve our methods of approximation.

We thus come to the result that the rule of induction can by no means be maintained to be the best method of approximation. But with its help it is possible to find better methods of approximation. Scientific method makes use of this fact to a great extent. The concatenation of empirical results in a scientific system is the way to improve the method of approximation. The rule of induction, or one of its equivalents, is the only method that can be used in the test of other methods of approximation, because it is the only method *of which we know* that it represents a method of approximation.

In discussing the method of correction we have presented methods that offer ways to a better approximation. However, a proof that the approximation will, in fact, be better cannot be given; only the possibility of a better approximation can be proved. We have no means of excluding the equality sign in the inequalities (1 and 2, § 90) so long as we abstain from the use of inductive inferences. When we regard the use of posits of higher levels as a better method of convergence, the result must be strictly formulated as follows: in employing posits of higher levels we carry through the necessary conditions for obtaining a better convergence. The justification of the method of correction is therefore given in the same way as that of the inductive inference in general.

A remark about the limit condition must be added. It was stated earlier that success by the inductive method is possible only if the sequences under consideration have a limit of the frequency. This statement requires qualification. For the inductive method to have success, it is not necessary that all the sequences considered have a limit. It is possible that some have no limit of the frequency and that we shall discover this fact by using other sequences that do have limits. Assume, for instance, that in continuing a sequence we find its frequency to oscillate between the values 1/4 and 3/4. We then regard a frequency value close to 1/4 as an event B_1, and a frequency value close to 3/4 as an event B_2. When we now consider the sequence of events B_1 and B_2, we may find that it has a limit of the frequency for each of these events. Using the rule of induction in the latter sequence, we thus find that the former sequence has no limit of the frequency.

Since it is mathematically possible to construct sequences that have no limit of the frequency, it seems reasonable to assume that there are sequences of natural events having this property. It is clear, in any case, that we have no right to assume that all sequences of natural events have a limit of the frequency. The question has been asked whether we cannot prove, at least, that there must exist some sequences of natural events having a limit of the frequency. A theorem of this kind is presumably demonstrable; that is, it seems plausible that, given any system of sequences without a limit, we shall always be able to construct from them another sequence that has a limit. For the inductive problem, however, the question is irrelevant. In making inductive posits it does not help to know that there are sequences with a limit of the frequency; what we must know is whether the sequence under consideration has one. Since the question cannot be answered *a priori*, the justification of induction must be given independently of a limit assumption, as it is achieved in thesis θ.

Returning to a consideration of this thesis, we shall analyze the kind of justification it affords for induction. To clarify the analysis, we shall refer to the distinction between formulations I and II of the inductive rule (see p. 450). Formulation II postulates the existence of a probability relation between an observed frequency and future events, whereas formulation I does not. This formulation, we said, expresses the conception that between an observed frequency and the statement of probability merely the ground-for-assertion relation holds.

We are now able to give the final explanation why this relation can be maintained and thus why the rule of induction can be justified. The title to employ the inductive rule is based on a logical relationship between the aim of knowledge and a method the applicability of which constitutes a necessary condition of success. This relation, which can be formulated only in the metalanguage and is expressed in (1), may be abbreviated as the *condition relation.* The justification, therefore, is made possible only because we use formulation I, which differs from formulation II in that it does not identify the ground-for-assertion relation with a probability relation. For anticipative posits, the ground-for-assertion relation is derived from the condition relation.

Attempts at identifying the ground-for-assertion relation with a probability relation, and thus at basing the justification of induction on a probability relation, are doomed to failure because they lead to a conception in which the rule of induction asserts an object-language relation between an observed frequency and future events as soon as the object interpretation of probability is used (§ 87). The rule would then constitute a synthetic statement of the object language, depending for its support on arguments that are derived from a rational belief, from an *a priori* insight into the structure of the physical world — claims that cannot be taken seriously by anyone who is accustomed to apply the gauge of scientific truth to logical analysis. It was explained above (p. 372) that there is no such thing as synthetic self-evidence; self-evidence can be admitted as a criterion of truth only for analytic statements. That adherence to this fundamental principle of empiricism does not exclude a justification of induction is shown through thesis θ; by means of the condition relation we can construct a justification of induction that is free from all forms of synthetic self-evidence.

The condition relation (1), which is formulated in the implication that constitutes the second part of thesis θ, is a tautology; this relation follows from the definition of a limit. Therefore, an empirical assumption is not used for the justification; this avoids the fallacy analyzed in Hume's second result (p. 470).* But Hume's first result is not contradicted: it is not maintained that the inductive conclusion is tautologically implied by its premise. A synthetic inference is justified by means of a tautology. Such a procedure involves no contradiction: whereas the relation between the premise and the conclusion of the inductive inference is synthetic, the relation between the inductive procedure and the aim of knowledge, that is, the condition relation, is analytic. The recognition that a tautological justification of a synthetic inference can be given makes the solution of the problem of induction possible.

This solution presupposes a moderation of the requirements to be satisfied by a justification: it involves the renunciation of a proof that the inductive conclusion is true or probable. To be sure, it would be a superior justification if we could prove that predictions must come true, or that there is some probability of their coming true. But if such a proof is impossible we shall be glad

* [Ed. note: This is the first page of the selection included here.]

to have, at least, a method that we know will lead to success if success is possible. This logical relation may be illustrated by the example used in the Preface. When Magellan planned to find a passage through or around the Americas to the Pacific, he did not know whether there was one, and he did not even have a probability for the assumption of its existence. But he knew that if there was one he would find it by sailing along the coast — so his enterprise was justified.

Such illustrations suffer from the fact that they belong, not in primitive, but in advanced, knowledge. Thus the implication, "If there is a passage he will find it by sailing along the coast", is synthetic and therefore established by means of inductive inferences. In other examples the attainability of the aim can be judged in terms of probabilities; if the probability of reaching the aim turns out to be very low, the realization of the necessary conditions may seem scarcely advisable. Such a situation corresponds practically to a case where it is known that the aim is not attainable, at least not until further conditions are satisfied. Thus if a man wants to be a millionaire he must have a bank account; but taking out a bank account is usually not associated with the hope of ever being able to write out six-figure checks.[4] In all such instances, inductive inferences are applied and the legitimacy of induction is taken for granted. Only in the ultimate justification of induction itself must we renounce the use of inductive methods; the justification must be given within primitive knowledge, and therefore we have no other means at hand than considerations concerning necessary conditions, not supported by an estimate of the attainability of the aim.

Some critics have called my justification of induction a weak justification. Such judgments originate from a rationalistic conception of scientific method. In spite of the empiricist trend of modern science, the quest for certainty, a product of the theological orientation of philosophy, still survives in the assertion that some general truths about the future must be known if scientific predictions are to be acceptable. It is hard to see what would be gained by the knowledge of such general truths. As was pointed out earlier, if we knew for certain that sequences of natural events have limits of the frequency, our situation in the face of any individual prediction would not be better than it is without such knowledge, since we would never know whether the observed initial section of the sequence were long enough to supply a satisfactory approximation of the frequency. It is no better with other forms of the uniformity postulate. How does it help to know that similar event patterns repeat themselves, if we do not know whether the pattern under consideration is one of them? In view of our ignorance concerning the individual event expected, all general truths must appear as illusory supports.

The aim of knowing the future is unattainable; there is no demonstrative truth informing us about future happenings. Let us therefore renounce the aim and renounce, too, the critique that measures the attainable in terms of

[4] Similar considerations apply to a problem known as Pascal's wager, which has sometimes been wrongly compared to my justification of induction; see my answer, "On the Justification of Induction" in *Jour. of Philos.*, Vol. 37 (1940), pp. 101–102.

that aim. It is not a weak argument that has been constructed. We can devise a method that will lead to correct predictions if correct predictions can be made — that is ground enough for the application of the method, even if we never know, before the occurrence of the event, whether the prediction is true.

If predictive methods cannot supply a knowledge of the future, they are, nevertheless, sufficient to justify action. In order to analyze the applicability of the inductive method as a basis for action, we must inquire into the presuppositions on which an action depends.

Every action depends on two presuppositions. The first is of a volitional nature: we wish to attain a certain aim. This aim can, at best, be reduced to more general volitional aims, but it cannot be given other than volitional grounds. A man who likes to exercise may justify his volitional aim by stating that he wants to retain a healthy body — but thereby the special volitional aim is only reduced to a more general one. The second presupposition is of a cognitive nature: we must know what will happen under certain conditions in order to be able to judge whether they are adequate for the attainment of the aim. If, for instance, I set up the general volitional aim of a healthy body, I can derive from this aim the usefulness of athletics only when I know that exercise makes the body healthy. Thus for every individual action I must know a statement about the future if the action is intended to contribute to the achievement of a general volitional aim. Only the combination of the two presuppositions, the volitional aim and knowledge about the future, makes purposive action possible. When the physician induces the patient to take an anodyne, he must know, first, whether the patient wants to get rid of his pain, and second, whether the drug will relieve it. When a politican advocates a new aw, he wants to reach some goal and assumes that the law will attain it. The two presuppositions for action are of this kind.

The first presupposition, the volitional decision, need not be discussed here. Within the boundaries of a logical analysis we investigate the second presupposition for action, that is, the cognitive presupposition. Now it is clear that, though the inductive rule does not supply knowledge of a future event, it supplies a sufficient reason for action: we are justified in dealing with the anticipative posit as true, not because we can expect success in the individual case, but because if we can ever act successfully we can do so by following the directive of induction.

The justification of induction constructed may, therefore, be called a *pragmatic* justification: it demonstrates the usefulness of the inductive procedure for the purpose of acting. It shows that our actions need not depend on a proof that the sequences under consideration have the limit property. Actions can be made in the sense of trials, and it is sufficient to have a method that will lead to successful trials if success is attainable at all. It is true that this method has no guaranty of success. But who would dare to ask for such a guaranty in the face of the uncertainty of all human planning? The physician who operates on a patient because he knows that the operation will be the only chance to save the patient will be regarded as justified, though he cannot guarantee success. If we cannot base our actions on demonstrative truth, we shall welcome it that we can at least take our chance.

That is a rational argument. But who refers to it when he applies the inductive method in everyday life? If asked why he accepts the inductive rule, he answers that he believes in it, that he is firmly convinced of its validity and simply cannot give up inductive belief. Is there a justification for this belief?

The answer is a definite "No". The belief cannot be justified. As long as such a "No" was averred by a philosophy of skepticism, it constituted a negative judgment on all human planning and acting, which it seemed to prove utterly useless. It is different for the philosophy of logical analysis, which distinguishes between justification of the belief and justification of the action. Actions directed by the rule of induction are legitimate attempts at success; no form of belief is required for the proof. He who wants to act need not believe in success; it is a sufficient reason for action to know how to prepare for success, how to be ready for the case that success is attainable. Belief in success is a personal addition; whoever has it need not give it up. For his actions it is logically irrelevant: whether or not he believes in success, the same actions will follow.

I say "*logically* irrelevant", for I know very well that, psychologically speaking, belief may not be irrelevant. Many a person is not able to act according to his posits unless he believes in their success, since few have the inner strength to take a possible failure into account and yet pursue their aim. Nature seems to have endowed us with the inductive belief as a measure of protection, as it were, facilitating our actions, though without it we would be equally justified, or obliged, to act. It is difficult, indeed, to free oneself from such a belief; and Hume was right when he called the belief in induction an unjustified but ineradicable habit. But since Hume could not show that even without this belief action is justified when it follows the rule of induction, there remained for him only skeptical resignation.

The logician need not share this negative attitude. He can show that we must act according to the rule of induction even if we cannot believe in it. This result may be the reason why it is easier for him to renounce the belief; with the loss of the belief he does not at the same time lose his orientation in the sphere of action. We do not know whether tomorrow the order of the world will not come to an end; tomorrow all known physical laws may be invalidated, the sun may no longer shine, and food no longer nourish us — or at least our own world may come to an end, because we may close our eyes forever. Tomorrow is unknown to us, but this fact need not make any difference in considerations determining our actions. We adjust our actions to the case of a predictable world — if the world is not predictable, very well, then we have acted in vain.

A blind man who has lost his way in the mountains feels a trail with his stick. He does not know where the path will lead him, or whether it may take him so close to the edge of a precipice that he will be plunged into the abyss. Yet he follows the path, groping his way step by step; for if there is any possibility of getting out of the wilderness, it is by feeling his way along the path. As blind men we face the future; but we feel a path. And we know: if we can find a way through the future it is by feeling our way along this path.

34 *Reichenbach's Defense of Induction*

JOHN W. LENZ

The purpose of this paper is to examine critically Reichenbach's pragmatic justification of induction.[1] I shall, first, explain his formulation of the rule of induction; second, explain his pragmatic justification of this rule; and, third, assess the significance of his defense. Nowhere in this paper shall I discuss the much larger question whether induction needs some kind of justification, though, in my opinion, the answer is yes. And though I shall be highly critical of Reichenbach's pragmatic vindication, I shall leave aside the residual question of how induction should be justified.

1. *Reichenbach's rule of induction.* The rule of induction has been formulated in many ways, some of which are none too precise: "When predicting, assume that the future will be like the past," "make one's predictions on the assumption that nature is uniform," etc. To understand Reichenbach's justification we must first see what specific formulation of the inductive rule he is defending.

Reichenbach's rule of induction can be illustrated by the following simple application of it. Suppose that we have tossed a coin 200 times, and that it has turned up heads 98 times. Suppose, that is, that in an initial segment of a series of coin tosses the relative frequency with which heads has turned up is 98/200. Reichenbach's rule of induction tells us to predict that, if the coin is tossed long enough, the relative frequency with which heads occurs remains approximately 98/200. More exactly and more generally, his rule is: If in an initial segment of a series of events the relative frequency with which *A*'s have been *B*'s is m/n (where n is the number of *A*'s and m is the number of *A*'s that are *B*'s), predict that in the long run, that is, as the number of *A*'s gets larger and larger, the relative frequency will after some point continue to be approximately m/n. Those who are familiar with Reichenbach's frequency interpretation of probability will see that his rule of induction tells us to predict that the limit of the relative frequency in an infinite series of events is identical with, or close to, the relative frequency in the initial segment of the series.[2]

Reprinted by permission of the author.

[1] The present paper is a slightly revised version of my "The Pragmatic Justification of Induction," contained in *The Structure of Scientific Thought*, ed. E. H. Madden, Boston, 1960, 299–303. For Reichenbach's formulation of his justification of induction, see his *Theory of Probability*, Berkeley, 1949, 429–482 and *Experience and Prediction*, Chicago, 1938, 339–363.

[2] Here as elsewhere in this paper I am trying to avoid technicalities. Reichenbach's exact formulation is: "If an initial section of n elements of a sequence x_i is given, resulting in the frequency f^n, and if, furthermore, nothing is known about the probability of the second level for the occurrence of a certain limit p, we posit that the frequency f^i $(i > n)$ will approach a limit p within $f^n \pm \delta$ when the sequence is continued." *Theory of Probability*, 446.

It is necessary to always keep in mind that it is *this* rule of induction alone which Reichenbach tries to justify. Certainly there are many other formulations of the rule of induction to which his pragmatic justification is irrelevant. We must note too that while in one sense Reichenbach's formulation of the rule of induction is fairly broad, in another sense it is extremely narrow. It is broad in the sense that the usual inductive rule: "When all observed *A*'s have been *B*'s, predict that all *A*'s will continue to be *B*'s" is simply a particular case of Reichenbach's more general rule. It is a particular case in that here the observed relative frequency with which *A*'s have been *B*'s is 1. Reichenbach's rule has the virtue of allowing us to make not only universal generalizations but statistical generalizations as well.

On the other hand, Reichenbach's rule of induction is narrow in at least two ways. It is narrow, first of all, in that it is only one among many inductive rules that are actually employed in science and everyday life. For example, it is also a rule of science and of common sense that we should not make predictions on the basis of small samples. Reichenbach's reply here, however, would be that all other such rules can be established by using his inductive rule.[3] The conclusion that we should "avoid predicting on the basis of small samples" is itself inductively inferred from our having observed that in the past such predictions have been very unreliable. Whether Reichenbach's general claim here is valid is a complex question into which I cannot enter in this paper.

In any case, Reichenbach's rule of induction is narrow in a more crucial sense. It is narrow in that the predictions it advises concern only what will happen in the long run (for example, that, as the coin is tossed more and more, the relative frequency with which heads occurs will after some point remain approximately 98/200). His rule of induction does not enable us to predict what will happen in the short run (for example, to predict that in the next 100 tosses of the coin, the frequency with which heads occurs is 98/200). This means that even if Reichenbach succeeds in justifying his rule of induction, it does not follow that he will have succeeded in justifying a rule of induction enabling us to predict what happens in the short run.

2. *Reichenbach's justification of induction.* The traditional problem of induction is easily formulated. In any inductive inference employing Reichenbach's rule, the conclusion asserts more than the evidence upon which it is based. The problem of induction is simply to justify such inferences in which "the conclusion goes beyond the premises," or more exactly, to justify the rule which such inferences employ.

Reichenbach points out that obviously the conclusion of an inductive inference does not logically follow from a statement of the evidence; it is not contradictory to affirm the evidence and deny the conclusion. Hence, he concludes that it is not possible to justify induction "logically" in the sense of demonstrating that all, or even some, inductive conclusions are correct. He insists, moreover, that one cannot inductively justify the rule of induction, that is,

[3] *Theory of Probability*, 442-444.

infer that because it has been successful it will continue to be successful. Such a justification, Reichenbach insists, would be circular. In denying that one can give such *a priori* or *a posteriori* justifications of induction Reichenbach follows Hume completely.

Nonetheless Reichenbach assures us that we need not despair, for another kind of justification is possible. It can best be explained in terms of the simple example we used in explaining his rule of induction. Suppose, again, that we have tossed a coin 200 times, and that it has turned up heads 98 times. Reichenbach's rule, we will remember, tells us to predict that in the long run the relative frequency with which heads occurs will remain 98/200. Reichenbach admits that no guarantee can be given that this particular prediction is correct. It might be that as the coin is tossed more and more the frequency with which heads occurs remains 1/4. Reichenbach admits, furthermore, that we cannot guarantee that even the repeated use of his rule of induction will ever lead to a successful prediction. Suppose, that is, that as we toss the coin more and more we use the "latest" observed relative frequency with which heads occurs in making our predictions of the relative frequency in the long run. Reichenbach admits that no guarantee can be given that a single one of these predictions is correct. It might be the case that as the coin is tossed more and more the relative frequency with which heads occurs continues to oscillate considerably.

Reichenbach's justification of induction rests upon a different claim. Reichenbach shows that if it is the case that, as the coin is tossed more and more, there is some point after which the relative frequency with which heads occurs remains more or less constant, then the *repeated* use of the rule of induction will discover that relative frequency. One can easily generalize his claim here: If, as the number of *A*'s gets larger and larger, there is some point after which the relative frequency with which *A*'s are *B*'s remains fairly constant, then the repeated use of his rule of induction will lead to correct predictions of that relative frequency. This, Reichenbach shows, is demonstrably true.

Several points are important here. First, Reichenbach's claim is hypothetical in form. It says that *if success is possible* (where success is interpreted narrowly to mean correctly predicting long-run relative frequencies) then the repeated use of the inductive method will bring success. Second, Reichenbach does not defend any particular use of the rule of induction but only its *repeated* use. The rule of induction is self-corrective in the precise sense that its repeated use will eventually lead to success, if success is possible. Thirdly, Reichenbach admits that one cannot know *at what point* the repeated use of the inductive method will bring success, if success is possible. Fourthly, Reichenbach shows that we can *know*, prior to any inductive evidence, that the rule of induction is self-corrective in the above sense.

So far Reichenbach's defense consists simply in stating certain properties which his rule of induction has. We must now turn to Reichenbach's further claim that, in comparison with other methods of predicting, the rule of induction is the *best* means we have of attaining our end of successful prediction.

At times Reichenbach makes the very misleading statement that the method of induction is a necessary condition of successful prediction. This is surely misleading in that it suggests that only the inductive method will lead to successful prediction. This cannot be Reichenbach's claim, for he agrees that other methods, for example, that of the clairvoyant, could be successful. Reichenbach agrees, even, that other methods, for example, that of the soothsayer, might be successful more quickly than the inductive method. Reichenbach's claim is, first, that if any other method of prediction is successful then the repeated use of the inductive method will eventually lead to success. In other words, the eventual success of the repeated use of the inductive method is a necessary condition of any successful prediction. His claim is, second, that only the inductive method can be known in advance, and without any prior inductive inference, to lead to success if success is possible. This is enough, Reichenbach claims, to justify our use of the inductive method.

3. *Criticism.* To deny that Reichenbach has justified induction would be, I think, to enter into a somewhat fruitless quarrel concerning the word "justify."[4] However, a clear understanding of Reichenbach's pragmtaic justification of induction will show how very weak it is. In this section I shall simply underline the insignificance of Reichenbach's defense.

First, it must never be forgotten that since his rule of induction speaks only about relative frequencies in the long run, his justification leaves entirely aside the problem of justifying predictions of short-run relative frequencies. And surely in science and everyday life we are most concerned with the latter. An insurance company does not care to know the long-run relative frequency with which American males of age 32 die before reaching 60. The company is, very likely, concerned only with the next 50 years or so. Of course, if one could assume that the short-run relative frequencies will approximate those of the long run, Reichenbach's justification would be helpful. But of the truth of this assumption Reichenbach gives us no assurance. As we shall see, this problem is further complicated by the last difficulty I shall mention.

Second, it must always be remembered that Reichenbach in his pragmatic justification of induction gives us no assurance that any of the predictions one actually makes using his rule of induction are correct or even probably correct. He does show, it is true, that the repeated use of the inductive rule will lead to success (in his narrow sense of success) if success is possible. However, as he readily admits, there is no reason to believe that success will come.

Third, even if success does come, it may do so too late. It hardly helps to be assured that the repeated use of the inductive method will eventually lead to success, when that eventuality may come too late not only for one man but also for every member of the human race. This is all the more disconcerting in view of Reichenbach's admission that methods other than induction could well lead to success earlier.

It is true that Reichenbach tries to mitigate the force of this objection by

[4] One could, perhaps, charge Reichenbach with using words like "justify," "success," "self-corrective," etc. in an unusual and, therefore, potentially misleading way. Cf. Max Black, *Problems of Analysis*, Ithaca, N.Y. 1954, 187.

putting at times his justification of induction in terms of a practical limit, that is, a limit of a series whose convergence is rapid enough to be discovered in practice. But Reichenbach gives us no more assurance that such a limit exists than he does that there is a limit of any kind.

Fourth, even if success is achieved by using his rule of induction, one will never *know* it on the strength of Reichenbach's justification. As Reichenbach admits, we do not know how many tries with the inductive method we must make before we shall correctly predict the limit of a relative frequency. We can safely say, therefore, that the epistemic significance of Reichenbach's justification of induction is slight.

My last point is one that cannot be easily explained, but since it is an extremely crucial one, I shall outline it here. Actually, one can show that there are other inductive methods which are known to be self-corrective in Reichenbach's sense. Reichenbach not only "justifies" his rule of induction but also a whole class of inductive rules. It is true that the predictions made on the basis of any of these rules converge towards the limit of the relative frequency in an infinite series of events, if there is such a limit. That is, as the evidence gets larger and larger the predictions these rules lead to vary less and less. But before this happens, the predictions we make will vary tremendously depending upon which rule is used. Since we have, on Reichenbach's own terms, no decisive reason for choosing between these rules, our predictions will accordingly be almost entirely arbitrary. We simply shall not know what predictions to make.

One of these rules may lead to the best predictions, as a simple illustration will show. Suppose that the long-run relative frequency with which *A*'s are *B*'s is 3/5. Suppose further that the observed relative frequency with which *A*'s have been *B*'s is 40/60. There exists an inductive rule, justified in Reichenbach's sense, which would predict, on the basis of this evidence, that the long-run relative frequency is 3/5. This rule, if used in this case, would, therefore, actually be superior to Reichenbach's own rule of induction, which would predict that the long-run relative frequency was 2/3. It would be superior to Reichenbach's rule of induction in that by using it, we would achieve success earlier. The trouble is, of course, that we do not know in advance what the actual long-run relative frequency is, and accordingly we do not know which rule to use, which predictions to make.

This difficulty is relevant to the first problem I mentioned, that of justifying predictions of short-run relative frequencies. Presumably, any attempt on Reichenbach's part to solve this latter problem would have taken the form of showing that we can "work back" from long-run to short-run relative frequencies. The fact that there are an infinity of inductive rules, all equally justified in Reichenbach's sense, would, however, make it impossible to "work back" in any but an arbitrary way. That is, there would be an infinity of ways of working back, each giving different values to the short-run relative frequency, among which we would have no reason to choose.

4. *Conclusion.* In conclusion I want to make just two points. First, nowhere in this paper have I denied that Reichenbach has done valuable service in clari-

fying the logical properties of his rule of induction. Pragmatic considerations aside, it is worthwhile having shown that his rule of induction is "self-corrective" in at least one precise sense. Second, I want to suggest why any such "justification" as Reichenbach's must remain pragmatically insignificant. When one understands Reichenbach's principle of induction one sees that all it asserts is that there is a limit to a given relative frequency in an infinite series of events. Reichenbach's justification of this principle is that it is true, if there is such a limit. Thus his justification of the principle of induction reduces to the bare tautology that if there is a limit, there is a limit. In his formulation of the problem of induction, Hume pointed out that no tautology can by itself lead to "useful" conclusions, and the one upon which Reichenbach bases his justification of inductive inference is no exception.

35 *The 'Justification' of Induction*

PETER F. STRAWSON

(1) We have seen something of the nature of inductive reasoning; of how one statement or set of statements may support another statement, *S*, which they do not entail, with varying degrees of strength, ranging from being conclusive evidence for *S* to being only slender evidence for it; from making *S* as certain as the supporting statements, to giving it some slight probability. We have seen too, how the question of degree of support is complicated by consideration of relative frequencies and numerical chances.

There is, however, a residual philosophical question which enters so largely into discussion of the subject that it must be discussed. It can be raised, roughly, in the following forms. What reason have we to place reliance on inductive procedures? Why should we suppose that the accumulation of instances of *A*'s which are *B*'s, however various the conditions in which they are observed, gives any good reason for expecting the next *A* we encounter to be a *B*? It is our habit to form expectations in this way; but can the habit be rationally justified? When this doubt has entered our minds it may be difficult to free ourselves from it. For the doubt has its source in a confusion; and some attempts to resolve the doubt preserve the confusion; and other attempts to show that the doubt is senseless seem altogether too facile. The root-confusion is easily described; but simply to describe it seems an inadequate remedy against it. So the doubt must be examined again and again, in the light of different attempts to remove it.

From *Introduction to Logical Theory*, copyright 1952 by Methuen & Co., Ltd., London. Reprinted by John Wiley & Sons, Inc., 1953, pp. 248–263. Reprinted by permission of the publishers and the author.

If someone asked what grounds there were for supposing that deductive reasoning was valid, we might answer that there were in fact no grounds for supposing that deductive reasoning was always valid; sometimes people made valid inferences, and sometimes they were guilty of logical fallacies. If he said that we had misunderstood his question, and that what he wanted to know was what grounds there were for regarding deduction in general as a valid method of argument, we should have to answer that his question was without sense, for to say that an argument, or a form or method of argument, was valid or invalid would *imply* that it was deductive; the concepts of validity and invalidity had application only to individual deductive arguments or forms of deductive argument. Similarly, if a man asked what grounds there were for thinking it reasonable to hold beliefs arrived at inductively, one might at first answer that there were good and bad inductive arguments, that sometimes it was reasonable to hold a belief arrived at inductively and sometimes it was not. If he, too, said that his question had been misunderstood, that he wanted to know whether induction in general was a reasonable method of inference, then we might well think his question senseless in the same way as the question whether deduction is in general valid; for to call a particular belief reasonable or unreasonable is to apply inductive standards, just as to call a particular argument valid or invalid is to apply deductive standards. The parallel is not wholly convincing; for words like 'reasonable' and 'rational' have not so precise and technical a sense as the word 'valid.' Yet it is sufficiently powerful to make us wonder how the second question could be raised at all, to wonder why, in contrast with the corresponding question about deduction, it should have seemed to constitute a genuine problem.

Suppose that a man is brought up to regard formal logic as the study of the science and art of reasoning. He observes that all inductive processes are, by deductive standards, invalid; the premises never entail the conclusions. Now inductive processes are notoriously important in the formation of beliefs and expectations about everything which lies beyond the observation of available witnesses. But an *invalid* argument is an *unsound* argument; an *unsound* argument is one in which *no good reason* is produced for accepting the conclusion. So if inductive processes are invalid, if all the arguments we should produce, if challenged, in support of our beliefs about what lies beyond the observation of available witnesses are unsound, then we have no good reason for any of these beliefs. This conclusion is repugnant. So there arises the demand for a justification, not of this or that particular belief which goes beyond what is entailed by our evidence, but a justification of induction in general. And when the demand arises in this way it is, in effect, the demand that induction shall be shown to be really a kind of deduction; for nothing less will satisfy the doubter when this is the route to his doubts.

Tracing this, the most common route to the general doubt about the reasonableness of induction, shows how the doubt seems to escape the absurdity of a demand that induction in general shall be justified by inductive standards. The demand is that induction should be shown to be a rational process; and this turns out to be the demand that one kind of reasoning should be shown to be another and different kind. Put thus crudely, the demand seems to escape one absurdity only to fall into another. Of course, inductive arguments are not deductively valid; if they were, they would be deductive arguments. Inductive reasoning must be assessed, for soundness, by inductive standards. Nevertheless, fantastic as the wish for induction to be deduction may seem, it is only in terms of it that we can understand some of the attempts that have been made to justify induction.

(2) The first kind of attempt I shall consider might be called the search for the supreme premise of inductions. In its primitive form it is quite a crude attempt; and I shall make it cruder by caricature. We have already seen that for a particular inductive step, such as 'The kettle has been on the fire for ten minutes, so it will be boiling by now,' we can substitute a deductive argument by introducing a generalization (e.g., 'A kettle always boils within ten minutes of being put on the fire') as an additional premise. This maneuver shifted the emphasis of the problem of inductive support on to the question of how we established such generalizations as these, which rested on grounds by which they were not entailed. But suppose the maneuver could be repeated. Suppose we could find one supremely general proposition, which taken in conjunction with the evidence for any accepted generalization of science or daily life (or at least of science) would entail that generalization. Then, so long as the status of the supreme generalization could be satisfactorily explained, we could regard all sound inductions to unqualified general conclusions as, at bottom, valid deductions. The justification would be found, for at least these cases. The most obvious difficulty in this suggestion is that of formulating the supreme general proposition in such a way that it shall be precise enough to yield the desired entailments, and yet not obviously false or arbitrary. Consider, for example, the formula: 'For all *f*, *g*, wherever *n* cases of *f* and *g*, and no cases of *f* and not *g*, are observed, then all cases of *f* are cases of *g*.' To turn it into a sentence, we have only to replace '*n*' by some number. But what number? If we take the value of '*n*' to be 1 or 20 or 500, the resulting statement is obviously false. Moreover, the choice of any number would seem quite arbitrary; there is no privileged number of favourable instances which we take as decisive in establishing a generalization. If, on the other hand, we phrase the proposition vaguely enough to escape these objections — if, for example, we phrase it as 'Nature is uniform' — then it becomes too vague to provide the desired entailments. It should be noticed that the impossibility of framing a general proposition of the kind required is really a special case of the impossibility of framing precise rules for the assessment of evidence. If we could frame a rule which would tell us precisely when we had *conclusive* evidence for a generalization, then it would yield just the proposition required as the supreme premise.

Even if these difficulties could be met, the question of the status of the supreme premise would remain. How, if a non-necessary proposition, could it be established? The appeal to experience, to inductive support, is clearly barred on pain of circularity. If, on the other hand, it were a necessary truth and possessed, in conjunction with the evidence for a generalization, the required logical power to entail the generalization (e.g., if the latter were the conclusion of a hypothetical syllogism, of which the hypothetical premise was the necessary truth in question), then the evidence would entail the generalization independently, and the problem would not arise: a conclusion unbearably paradoxical. In practice, the extreme vagueness with which candidates for the role of supreme premise are expressed prevents their acquiring such logical power, and at the same time renders it very difficult to classify them as analytic or synthetic: under pressure they may tend to tautology; and, when the pressure is removed, assume an expansively synthetic air.

In theories of the kind which I have here caricatured the ideal of deduction is not usually so blatantly manifest as I have made it. One finds the 'Law of the Uniformity of Nature' presented less as the suppressed premise of crypto-deductive inferences than as, say, the 'presupposition of the validity of inductive reasoning.' I shall have more to say about this in my last section.

(3) I shall next consider a more sophisticated kind of attempt to justify induction: more sophisticated both in its interpretation of this aim and in the method adopted to achieve it. The aim envisaged is that of proving that the probability of a generalization, whether universal or proportional, increases with the number of instances for which it is found to hold. This clearly is a realistic aim: for the proposition to be proved does state, as we have already seen, a fundamental feature of our criteria for assessing the strength of evidence. The method of proof proposed is mathematical. Use is to be made of the arithmetical calculation of chances. This, however, seems less realistic: for we have already seen that the prospect of analysing the notion of support in these terms seems poor.

I state the argument as simply as possible; but, even so, it will be necessary to introduce and explain some new terms. Suppose we had a collection of objects of different kinds, some with some characteristics and some with others. Suppose, for example, we had a bag containing 100 balls, of which 70 were white and 30 black. Let us call such a collection of objects a *population;* and let us call the way it is made up (e.g., in the case imagined, of 70 white and 30 black balls) the *constitution* of the population. From such a population it would be possible to take *samples* of various sizes. For example, we might take from our bag a sample of 30 balls. Suppose each ball in the bag had an individual number. Then the collection of balls numbered 10 to 39 inclusive would be one sample of a given size; the collection of balls numbered 11 to 40 inclusive would be another and different sample of the same size: the collection of balls numbered 2, 4, 6, 8 . . . 58, 60 would be another such sample; and so on. Each possible collection of 30 balls is a different sample of the same size. Some different samples of the same size will have the same constitutions as one another; others will have different constitutions. Thus there will be only one sample made up of 30 black balls. There will be many different samples which share the constitution: 20 white and 10 black. It would be a simple matter of mathematics to work out the number of possible samples of the given size which had any one possible constitution. Let us say that a sample *matches* the population if, allowing for the difference between them in size, the constitution of the sample corresponds, within certain limits, to that of the population. For example, we might say that any possible sample consisting of, say, 21 white and 9 black balls matched the constitution (70 white and 30 black) of the population, whereas a sample consisting of 20 white and 10 black balls did not. Now it is a proposition of pure mathematics that, given any population, the proportion of possible samples, all of the same size, which match the population, increases with the size of the sample.

We have seen that conclusions about the ratio of a subset of equally possible chances to the whole set of those chances may be expressed by the use of the word 'probability.' Thus of the 52 possible samples of one card from a population constituted like an orthodox pack, 16 are court-cards or aces. This fact we allow ourselves to express (under the conditions, inductively established, of equipossibility of draws) by saying that the probability of drawing a court-card or an ace was 413/. If we express the proposition referred to at the end of the last paragraph by means of this use of 'probability' we shall obtain the result: The probability of a sample matching a given population increases with the size of the sample. It is tempting to try to derive from this result a general justification of the inductive procedure: which will not, indeed, show that any given inductive conclusion is entailed by the evidence for it, taken in conjunction with some universal premise, but will show that the multiplication of favourable instances of a generalization entails a proportionate increase in its probability. For, since *matching* is a symmetrical relation, it might seem a simple deductive step to move from

I. The probability of a sample matching a given population increases with the size of the sample

to

II. The probability of a population matching a given sample increases with the size of the sample.

II might seem to provide a guarantee that the greater the number of cases for which a generalization is observed to hold, the greater is its probability; since in increasing the number of cases we increase the size of the sample from whatever population forms the subject of our generalization. Thus pure mathematics might seem to provide the sought-for proof that the evidence for a generalization really does get stronger, the more favourable instances of it we find.

The argument is ingenious enough to be worthy of respect; but it fails of its purpose, and misrepresents the inductive situation. Our situation is not in the least like that of a man drawing a sample from a given, i.e. fixed and limited, population from which the drawing of any mathematically possible sample is equiprobable with that of any other. Our only datum is the sample. No limit is fixed beforehand to the diversity, and the possibilities of change, of the 'population' from which it is drawn: or, better, to the multiplicity and variousness of different populations, each with different constitutions, any one of which might replace the present one before we make the next draw. Nor is there any *a priori* guarantee that different mathematically possible samples are equally likely to be drawn. If we have or can obtain any assurance on these points, then it is assurance derived inductively from our data, and cannot therefore be assumed at the outset of an argument designed to justify induction. So II, regarded as a justification of induction founded on purely mathematical considerations, is a fraud. The important shift of 'given' from qualifying 'population' in I to qualifying 'sample' in II is illegitimate. Moreover, 'probability,' which means one thing in II (interpreted as giving the required guarantee) means something quite different in I (interpreted as a proposition of pure mathematics). In I probability is simply the measure of the ratio of one set of mathematically possible chances to another; in II it is the measure of the inductive acceptability of a generalization. As a mathematical proposition, I is certainly independent of the soundness of inductive procedures; and as a statement of one of the criteria we use in assessing the strength of evidence of a generalization, II is as certainly independent of mathematics.

It has not escaped the notice of those who have advocated a mathematical justification of induction, that certain assumptions are required to make the argument even seem to fulfil its purpose. Inductive reasoning would be of little use if it did not sometimes enable us to assign at least fairly high probabilities to certain conclusions. Now suppose, in conformity with the mathematical model, we represented the fact that the evidence for a proposition was conclusive by assigning to it the probability figure of 1; and the fact that the evidence for and against a proposition was evenly balanced by assigning to it the probability figure 1/2; and so on. It is a familiar mathematical truth that, between any two fractions, say 1/6 and 1/5, there is an infinite number of intermediate quantities; that 1/6 can be indefinitely increased without reaching equality to 1/5. Even if we could regard II as mathematically established, therefore, it fails to give us what we require; for it fails to provide a guarantee that the probability of an inductive conclusion ever attains a degree at which it begins to be of use. It was accordingly necessary to buttress the purely mathematical argument by large, vague assumptions, comparable with the principles designed for the role of supreme premise in the first type of attempt. These assumptions, like those principles, could never actually be used to give a deductive turn to inductive arguments; for they could not be formulated with precision. They were the shadows of precise unknown truths, which, if one did know them, would suffice, along with the data for our accepted generalizations, to enable the probability of the latter to be assigned, after calculation, a precise numerical fraction of a tolerable size. So this theory represents our inductions as the vauge sublunary shadows of deductive calculations which we cannot make.

(4) Let us turn from attempts to justify induction to attempts to show that the demand for a justification is mistaken. We have seen already that what lies behind such a demand is often the absurd wish that induction should be shown to be some kind of deduction — and this wish is clearly traceable in the attempts at justification which we have examined. What other sense could we give to the demand? Sometimes it is expressed in the form of a request for proof that induc-

tion is a *reasonable* or *rational* procedure, that we have *good grounds* for placing reliance upon it. Consider the uses of the phrases 'good grounds,' 'justification,' 'reasonable,' etc. Often we say such things as 'He has *every justification* for believing that *p*'; 'I have *very good* reasons for believing it'; 'There are *good grounds* for the view that *q*'; 'There is *good evidence* that *r*.' We often talk, in such ways as these, of justification, good grounds or reasons or evidence for certain beliefs. Suppose such a belief were one expressible in the form 'Every case of *f* is a case of *g*.' And suppose someone were asked what he meant by saying that he had good grounds or reasons for holding it. I think it would be felt to be a satisfactory answer if he replied: 'Well, in all my wide and varied experience I've come across innumerable cases of *f* and never a case of *f* which wasn't a case of *g*.' In saying this, he is clearly claiming to have *inductive* support, *inductive* evidence, of a certain kind, for his belief; and he is also giving a perfectly proper answer to the question, what he meant by saying that he had ample justification, good grounds, good reasons for his belief. It is an analytic proposition that it is reasonable to have a degree of belief in a statement which is proportional to the strength of the evidence in its favour; and it is an analytic proposition, though not a proposition of mathematics, that, other things being equal, the evidence for a generalization is strong in proportion as the number of favourable instances, and the variety of circumstances in which they have been found, is great. So to ask whether it is reasonable to place reliance on inductive procedures is like asking whether it is reasonable to proportion the degree of one's convictions to the strength of the evidence. Doing this is what 'being reasonable' *means* in such a context.

As for the other form in which the doubt may be expressed, viz., 'Is induction a justified, or justifiable, procedure?', it emerges in a still less favourable light. No sense has been given to it, though it is easy to see why it seems to have a sense. For it is generally proper to inquire *of a particular belief*, whether its adoption is justified; and, in asking this, we are asking whether there is good, bad, or any, evidence for it. In applying or withholding the epithets 'justified,' 'well founded,' etc., in the case of specific beliefs, we are appealing to, and applying, inductive standards. But to what standards are we appealing when we ask whether the application of inductive standards is justified or well grounded? If we cannot answer, then no sense has been given to the question. Compare it with the question: Is the law legal? It makes perfectly good sense to inquire of a particular action, of an administrative regulation, or even, in the case of some states, of a particular enactment of the legislature, whether or not it is legal. The question is answered by an appeal to a legal system, by the application of a set of legal (or constitutional) rules or standards. But it makes no sense to inquire in general whether the law of the land, the legal system as a whole, is or is not legal. For to what legal standards are we appealing?

The only way in which a sense might be given to the question, whether induction is in general a justified or justifiable procedure, is a trivial one which we have already noticed. We might interpret it to mean 'Are all conclusions, arrived at inductively, justified?', i.e. 'Do people always have adequate evidence for the conclusions they draw?' The answer to this question is easy but uninteresting: it is that sometimes people have adequate evidence, and sometimes they do not.

(5) It seems, however, that this way of showing the request for a general justification of induction to be absurd is sometimes insufficient to allay the worry that produces it. And to point out that 'forming rational opinions about the unobserved on the evidence available' and 'assessing the evidence by inductive standards' are phrases which describe the same thing, is more apt to produce irritation than relief. The point is felt to be 'merely a verbal' one; and though the point of this protest is itself hard to see, it is clear that something more is required. So the question must be pursued further. First, I want to point out that there is something a little odd about talking of 'the inductive method,' or even 'the inductive policy,' as if it were just one possible method among others of arguing from the observed to the unobserved, from the available evidence to the facts in question. If one asked a meteorologist what method or methods he used to forecast the weather, one would be surprised if he answered: 'Oh, just the inductive method.' If one asked a doctor by what means he diagnosed a certain disease, the answer 'By induction' would be felt as an impatient evasion, a joke, or a rebuke. The answer one hopes for is an account of the tests made, the signs taken account of, the rules and recipes and general laws applied. When such a specific method of prediction or diagnosis is in question, one can ask whether the method is justified in practice; and here again one is asking whether its employment is inductively justified, whether it commonly gives correct results. This question would normally seem an admissible one. One might be tempted to conclude that, while there are many different specific methods of prediction, diagnosis, etc., appropriate to different subjects of inquiry, all such methods could properly be called 'inductive' in the sense that their employment rested on inductive support; and that, hence, the phrase 'non-inductive method of finding out about what lies deductively beyond the evidence' was a description without meaning, a phrase to which no sense had been given; so that there could be no question of justifying our selection of one method, called 'the inductive,' of doing this.

However, someone might object: 'Surely it is possible, though it might be foolish, to use methods utterly different from accredited scientific ones. Suppose a man, whenever he wanted to form an opinion about what lay beyond his observation or the observation of available witnesses, simply shut his eyes, asked himself the appropriate question, and accepted the first answer that came into his head. Wouldn't this be a non-inductive method?' Well, let us suppose this. The man is asked: 'Do you usually get the right answer by your method?' He might answer: 'You've mentioned one of its drawbacks; I never do get the right answer; but it's an extremely easy method.' One might then be inclined to think that it was not a method of finding things out at all. But suppose he answered: Yes, it's usually (always) the right answer. Then we might be willing to call it a method of finding out, though a strange one. But, then, by the very fact of its success, it would be an inductively supported method. For each application of the method would be an application of the general rule, 'The first answer that comes into my head is generally (always) the right one'; and for the truth of this generalization there would be the inductive evidence of a long run of favourable instances with no unfavourable ones (if it were 'always'), or of a sustained high proportion of successes to trials (if it were 'generally').

So every successful method or recipe for finding out about the unobserved must be one which has inductive support; for to say that a recipe is successful is to say that it has been repeatedly applied with success; and repeated successful application of a recipe constitutes just what we mean by inductive evidence in its favour. Pointing out this fact must not be confused with saying that 'the inductive method' is justified by its success, justified because it works. This is a mistake, and an important one. I am not seeking to 'justify the inductive method,' for no meaning has been given to this phrase. *A fortiori*, I am not saying that induction is justified by its success in finding out about the unobserved. I am saying, rather, that any successful method of finding out about the unobserved is necessarily justified by induction. This is an analytic proposition. The phrase 'successful method of finding things out which has no inductive support' is self-contradictory. Having, or acquiring, inductive support is a necessary condition of the success of a method.

Why point this out at all? First, it may have a certain therapeutic force, a power to reassure. Second, it may counteract the tendency to think of 'the inductive method' as something on a par with specific methods of diagnosis or prediction and therefore, like them, standing in need of (inductive) justification.

(6) There is one further confusion, perhaps the most powerful of all in producing the doubts, questions, and spurious solutions discussed in this Part. We may approach it by considering the claim that induction is justified by its success in practice. The phrase 'success of induction' is by no means clear and perhaps embodies the confusion of induction with some specific method of prediction, etc., appropriate to some particular line of inquiry. But, whatever the phrase may mean, the claim has an obviously circular look. Presumably the suggestion is that we should argue from the past 'successes of induction' to the continuance of those successes in the future; from the fact that it has worked hitherto to the conclusion that it will continue to work. Since an argument of this kind is plainly inductive, it will not serve as a justification of induction. One cannot establish a principle of argument by an argument which uses that principle. But let us go a little deeper. The argument rests the justification of induction on a matter of fact (its 'past successes'). This is characteristic of nearly all attempts to find a justification. The desired premise of Section 2 was to be some fact about the constitution of the universe which, even if it could not be used as a suppressed premise to give inductive arguments a deductive turn, was at any rate a 'presupposition of the validity of induction.' Even the mathematical argument of Section 3 required buttressing with some large assumption about the make-up of the world. I think the source of this general desire to find out some fact about the constitution of the universe which will 'justify induction' or 'show it to be a

rational policy' is the confusion, the running together, of two fundamentally different questions: to one of which the answer is a matter of non-linguistic fact, while to the others it is a matter of meanings.

There is nothing self-contradictory in supposing that all the uniformities in the course of things that we have hitherto observed and come to count on should cease to operate to-morrow; that all our familiar recipes should let us down, and that we should be unable to frame new ones because such regularities as there were were too complex for us to make out. (We may assume that even the expectation that all of us, in such circumstances, would perish, were falsified by someone surviving to observe the new chaos in which, roughly speaking, nothing foreseeable happens.) Of course, we do not believe that this will happen. We believe, on the contrary, that our inductively supported expectation-rules, though some of them will have, no doubt, to be dropped or modified, will continue, on the whole, to serve us fairly well; and that we shall generally be able to replace the rules we abandon with others similarly arrived at. We might give a sense to the phrase 'success of induction' by calling this vague belief the belief that induction will continue to be successful. It is certainly a factual belief, not a necessary truth; a belief, one may say, about the constitution of the universe. We might express it as follows, choosing a phraseology which will serve the better to expose the confusion I wish to expose:

I. (The universe is such that) induction will continue to be successful.

I is very vague: it amounts to saying that there are, and will continue to be, natural uniformities and regularities which exhibit a humanly manageable degree of simplicity. But, though it is vague, certain definite things can be said about it. (1) It is not a necessary, but a contingent, statement; for chaos is not a self-contradictory concept. (2) We have good inductive reasons for believing it, good inductive evidence for it. We believe that some of our recipes will continue to hold good because they have held good for so long. We believe that we shall be able to frame new and useful ones, because we have been able to do so repeatedly in the past. Of course, it would be absurd to try to use I to 'justify induction,' to show that it is a reasonable policy; because I is a conclusion inductively supported.

Consider now the fundamentally different statement:

II. Induction is rational (reasonable). We have already seen that the rationality of induction, unlike its 'successfulness,' is not a fact about the constitution of the world. It is a matter of what we mean by the word 'rational' in its application to any procedure for forming opinions about what lies outside our observations or that of available witnesses. For to have good reasons for any such opinion is to have good inductive support for it. The chaotic universe just envisaged, therefore, is not one in which induction would cease to be rational; it is simply one in which it would be impossible to form rational expectations to the effect that specific things would happen. It might be said that in such a universe it would at least be rational to refrain from forming specific expectations, to expect nothing but irregularities. Just so. But this is itself a higher-order induction: where irregularity is the rule, expect further irregularities. Learning not to count on things is as much learning an inductive lesson as learning what things to count on.

So it is a contingent, factual matter that it is sometimes possible to form rational opinions concerning what specifically happened or will happen in given circumstances (I); it is a non-contingent, *a priori* matter that the only ways of doing this must be inductive ways (II). What people have done is to run together, to conflate, the question to which I is answer and the quite different question to which II is an answer; producing the muddled and senseless questions: 'Is the universe such that inductive procedures are rational?' or 'What must the universe be like in order for inductive procedures to be rational?' It is the attempt to answer these confused questions which leads to statements like 'The uniformity of nature is a presupposition of the validity of induction.' The statement that nature is uniform might be taken to be a vague way of expressing what we expressed by I; and certainly this fact is a condition of, for it is identical with, the likewise contingent fact that we are, and shall continue to be, able to form rational opinions, of the kind we are most anxious to form, about the unobserved. But neither this fact about the world, nor any other, is a condition of the necessary truth that, if it is possible to form rational opinions of this kind, these will be inductively supported opinions. The discordance of the conflated questions manifests itself in an uncertainty about the status to be accorded to the alleged presupposition of the 'validity' of induction. For it was dimly, and correctly, felt that the reasonableness of inductive procedure was not merely a contingent, but a necessary, matter; so any necessary condition of their reasonableness had likewise to be a necessary matter. On the other hand, it was uncomfortably clear that chaos is not a self-contradictory concept; that the fact that some phenomena do exhibit a tolerable degree of simplicity and repetitiveness is not guaranteed by logic, but is a contingent affair. So the presupposition of induction had to be both contingent and necessary: which is absurd. And the absurdity is only lightly veiled by the use of the phrase 'synthetic *a priori*' instead of 'contingent necessary.'

36 *Inductive Inference: A New Approach*

ISRAEL SCHEFFLER

On what grounds do we choose the theories by which we anticipate the future? How do we decide what to predict about cases never before observed? These

From *Science*, Vol. 127, No. 3291, January 24, 1958, pp. 177–181. Reprinted by permission of the editors of *Science* and the author.

questions concerning what is traditionally called "induction" are among the most fundamental and most difficult which can be asked about the logic of science. Much reflection has been devoted to these questions in recent years, but no contribution has proved more incisive and challenging than that of Nelson Goodman of the University of Pennsylvania, whose papers on induction and allied problems have activated lively philosophic controversy over the past twelve years.

In 1955, Goodman published *Fact, Fiction, and Forecast*,[1] in which he presented the outlines of a new approach to the understanding of induction. This recent work has also aroused considerable comment by philosophers, both in print and out, and it is safe to say that the discussion is still in its early stages. The scientific public is, however, largely unaware of this new development, just as it was largely unacquainted with the controversies that preceded it. If there is no real boundary between science and the philosophy of science, the consideration of fundamental research in the logic of science ought not to be confined, even at the early stages, to circles of philosophers. The aim of this article is thus to acquaint the scientific reader with the background and the direction of Goodman's investigations, as they bear on the interpretation of induction.

Hume's Challenge and the Generalization Formula

The starting point for all modern thinking about induction is David Hume's denial of necessary connections of matters of fact: between observed cases recorded in the evidence and predicted cases based on the evidence there is a fundamental logical gap, which cannot be bridged by deductive inference. If, then, the truth of our predictions is not guaranteed by logical deduction from available evidence, what can be their rational justification? This challenge, arising out of Hume's analysis, has evoked a variety of replies. Leaving aside the reply of the skeptics, who are willing to admit that all induction is indeed without rational foundation, and that of the deductivists, who strive vainly to show Hume wrong, we find two replies which have gained wide popularity, the first primarily among philosophers, the second among scientists as well.

The first reply criticizes the assumption that rational justification can be only a matter of deduction from the evidence, pointing out that the normal use of expressions such as "rational," "reasonable," "based on good reasons," and so forth sanctions their application to statements referring to unexamined cases, and hence not deducible from accumulated evidence. This reply, although true, is, however, woefully inadequate. For not every statement which outstrips available evidence is reasonable, though some are. Outstripping the evidence is, to be sure, no bar to rationality, but neither does it guarantee rationality. If we are to meet the challenge posed, we must go on to formulate the specific criteria by which some inductions are justified as reasonable while others are rejected as unreasonable, though both groups outstrip the available evidence. Now it is

[1] N. Goodman. *Fact, Fiction and Forecast* (Harvard Univ. Press, Cambridge, Mass., 1955).

likely that at least part of the reason why this further task has been slighted is that the adequacy of the second reply has largely been taken for granted.

This second reply, stated in one form by Hume himself, is that reasonable inductions are those which conform to past regularities. In modern dress, it appears as the popular assertion that predictions are made in accordance with general theories which have worked in the past. What leads us to make one particular prediction rather than its opposite is not its deducibility from evidence but rather its congruence with a generalization thoroughly in accord with all such evidence, and the correlative disconfirmation of the contrary generalization by the same evidence. (I shall refer to this hereafter as the "generalization formula.") Of course, if no relevant evidence is available to decide between a given generalization and its contrary, or if the available evidence is mixed, neither generalization will support a particular inductive conclusion. But it is only to be expected that every limited body of evidence will fail to decide between *some* generalization and its contrary, and hence that we will generally not be able to choose between *every* particular prediction and its opposite. It is sufficient, therefore, for a formulation of the criteria of induction to show how certain bodies of evidence enable us to decide between certain conflicting inductions. This the generalization formula seems to accomplish. For if there is evidence which consistently supports a given generalization, then the contrary generalization is *ipso facto* disconfirmed, and our particular inductive conclusions seem automatically selected for us. There are, of course, details to be taken care of, relating to such matters as the calculation of degrees of support* which generalizations derive from past evidence, but, in principle, we have our answer to the challenge of induction.

Goodman's Refutation of the Generalization Formula

It is this sanguine estimate which has been thoroughly upset by Goodman's researches. Published in 1946 and 1947, his early papers in the philosophical journals dealt with a variety of interrelated questions: the nature of scientific law, of dispositional properties, of potentiality, of relevant conditions, of counterfactual judgments, of confirmation or induction.[2] They immediately aroused a storm of controversy. What made the papers so disturbing to the philosophic community was the fact that, while all these questions were shown to be intimately connected, Goodman's logically rigorous attempts to answer them without going around in circles ended in a big question mark. Appearing at a time when logicians had been making considerable progress in analyzing other aspects of scientific method, these results came as a shock. Goodman's investigations, it seemed, had sufficed to undermine all the usual formulas concerning the most basic concepts of the logic of science, but his repeated and ingenious efforts to supply a positive alternative had all turned out fruitless. In the philo-

* [Ed. note: See Section II of this volume for a discussion of this topic.]

[2] N. Goodman. "A Query on Confirmation," *J. Philosophy 43,* 383 (1946); "The Problem of Counterfactual Conditionals," *J. Philosophy 44,* 113 (1947).

sophic discussions that followed, every attempt was made to skirt Goodman's disheartening results. They were declared unimportant for the practicing scientist. The initial questions were asserted to be insoluble, hence worthless. Many papers, on the other hand, proposed what seemed perfectly obvious solutions that turned out to be question-begging. Only a very few authors fully recognized the seriousness of the situation for the philosophy of science and tried to cope with it directly.[3]

In 1953, with the whole matter still very much unsettled, Goodman delivered a series of three lectures at the University of London, in which he again addressed himself to the problem. These lectures, together with his major 1946 paper, were then published together in his book *Fact, Fiction and Forecast*, which appeared in 1955.[1] Here Goodman essayed a new and positive approach to some of the major questions he had faced earlier. He did not offer his book as a final solution to all the original problems. He did, however, present a fresh approach, worked out with sufficient rigor to put discussion of it on a fruitful basis. But we are getting ahead of our story and must now return to see how Goodman's early work affected the theory of induction.

How did Goodman's early papers upset complacency with respect to the generalization formula (according to which we make those predictions congruent with generalizations thoroughly in accord with past evidence)? We may profitably approach this matter in the light of a passage from J. S. Mill's *Logic*. Although it does seem true that, for every particular induction we make, there is some generalization related to it in the manner described, Mill argues that generalizations which are equally well supported by available evidence vary in the sanction they provide for their respective particular inductions: "Again, there are cases in which we reckon with the most unfailing confidence upon uniformity, and other cases in which we do not count upon it at all. In some we feel complete assurance that the future will resemble the past, the unknown be precisely similar to the known. In others, however invariable may be the result obtained from the instances which have been observed, we draw from them no more than a very feeble presumption that the like result will hold in all other cases. . . . When a chemist announces the existence and properties of a newly discovered substance, if we confide in his accuracy, we feel assured that the conclusions he has arrived at will hold universally, though the induction be founded but on a single instance. . . . Now mark another case, and contrast it with this. Not all the instances which have been observed since the beginning of the world in support of the general proposition that all crows are black would be deemed a sufficient presumption of the truth of the proposition, to outweigh the testimony of one unexceptionable witness who should affirm that in some region of the earth not fully explored he had caught and examined a crow, and had found it to be grey. Why is a single instance, in some cases, sufficient for a

[3] See in particular R. Carnap. "On the Application of Inductive Logic," *Philosophy and Phenomenological Research 8*, 133 (1947); N. Goodman. "On Infirmities of Confirmation Theory," *Philosophy and Phenomenological Research 8*, 149 (1947); R. Carnap. "Reply to Nelson Goodman," *Philosophy and Phenomenological Research 8*, 461 (1947).

complete induction, while in others myriads of concurring instances, without a single exception known or presumed, go such a very little way towards establishing an universal proposition?"[4]

And Goodman gives an analogous example when he writes: "That a given piece of copper conducts electricity increases the credibility of statements asserting that other pieces of copper conduct electricity, and thus confirms the hypothesis that all copper conducts electricity. But the fact that a given man now in this room is a third son does not increase the credibility of statements asserting that other men now in this room are third sons, and so does not confirm the hypothesis that all men now in this room are third sons. Yet in both cases our hypothesis is a generalization of the evidence statement. The difference is that in the former case the hypothesis is a *lawlike* statement; while in the latter case, the hypothesis is a merely contingent or accidental generality. Only a statement that is *lawlike* — regardless of its truth or falsity or its scientific importance — is capable of receiving confirmation from an instance of it; accidental statements are not." (*1*, p. 73)

But it is Goodman's further formulation of the problem that is crucial. For what has so far been shown is that, in addition to all credible particular inductions, generalization from the evidence also would select certain incredible ones. Now Goodman shows that among these incredible ones lie the very negations of our credible predictions concerning new cases. To apply his previous example, it is not merely that by generalization we selectively establish, in addition to the credible prediction that the next specimen of copper will conduct electricity, also the incredible one that the next present occupant of this room to be examined is a third son. Rather, we do not even establish that the next specimen of copper conducts electricity, for we can produce a generalization equally supported by the evidence and yielding the prediction that it does not. Or, putting this point in the form of a specific example, while the available evidence clearly supports:

(S_1) All specimens of copper conduct electricity.

and clearly disconfirms its contrary:

(S_2) All specimens of copper do not conduct electricity.

this is not sufficient to yield the particular induction concerning a new copper specimen c, to be examined:

(S_3) c conducts electricity.

since the same evidence also and equally supports:

(S_4) All specimens of copper are either such that they have been examined prior to t and conduct electricity or have not been examined prior to t and do not conduct electricity.

while clearly disconfirming *its* contrary:

(S_5) All specimens of copper are either such that they have been examined

[4] J. S. Mill, *A System of Logic* (Longmans, London, 1843: new impression, 1947), book III, chap. III, sect. 3, p. 205.

prior to t and do not conduct electricity or have not been examined prior to t and do conduct electricity.

thus giving rise to the negate of S_3:

(S_6) c does not conduct electricity.

if it is assumed true that:

(S_7) c has not been examined prior to t.

For cases assumed new, then, the generalization formula selects no particular inductions at all. Merely to be told to choose our inductions by reference to theories which work relative to past evidence is hence to be given worthless advice. Nor does this situation improve with the accumulation of relevant data over time. For even if we later find S_6 false and add S_3 to our evidence, leading to a rejection of S_4, we do not thereby eliminate other hypotheses which are exactly like S_4 but which specify times later than t. Accordingly, no matter how much empirical data we have accumulated and no matter how many hypotheses like S_4 we have disconfirmed up to a given point in time, we still have (by the generalization formula) contradictory predictions for every case not yet included in our data. No matter how fast and how long we run, we find we are standing still at the starting line.

This predicament holds, of course, only for cases assumed to be new. Using our previous example, if neither S_7 nor its negate is assumed, then S_4 yields neither S_3 nor S_6, while if S_7 is assumed false, then S_4 coincides with S_1, implying S_3 rather than S_6. This is not surprising, however, since, if S_7 is false, c is identical with one of our original evidence cases, all of which are described by the evidence itself as conducting electricity; S_3 is thus implied deductively by the evidence at hand, given the general understanding that no cases have been omitted.

As soon as we leave the safe territory of examined cases, however, and try to deal with a new one, generalization yields contradictory inductions, deciding for neither. And, further, since the adoption of a generalization constitutes wholesale endorsement of appropriate particular inductions yet to be made, then even if we do not know about some specific case that it is a new one, our unrestricted adoption of generalizations gets us into trouble if we can make the assumption of novelty for at least one case within the appropriate range. Since, moreover, we patently do choose between contradictory inductions covering new cases, as well as between competing generalizations, the generalization formula must be wrong as a definition of our inductive choices. In our previous example, we obviously in practice would *not* hold S_4 equally supported by uniformly positive evidence supporting S_1, nor would we under such conditions have any hesitation in rejecting S_6 in favor of S_3. This clearly indicates that the generalization formula is not adequate to characterize our inductive behavior. We apparently employ additional, nonsyntactic criteria governing the extension of characteristics of our evidence-cases to other cases in induction.

These criteria of what Goodman calls "projectibility" select just those generalizations *capable* of receiving support from their positive instances and in turn sanctioning particular inductions. Projectible hypotheses may, in individual cases, fail to sanction any particular inductions (for example, in cases where we have two such hypotheses which conflict), but no non-projectible hypothesis sanctions any induction, no matter how much positive support it has in the sense of the generalization formula. Goodman's problem is then to define projectibility, which is, in turn, needed to define induction. Since counterfactual judgments (for example, "If this salt, which has not in fact been put in water, had been put in water, it would have dissolved.") are, moreover, construable as resting upon just such generalizations as are projectible, that is, legitimately used for induction (in this case, "Every sample of salt, when put into water, dissolves."), and, furthermore, are themselves used to explain dispositional predicates, such as "is soluble," the definition of projectibility would throw light on these additional issues as well.

Attempts to Repair the Generalization Formula

It may be thought that the characterization of projectibility can be accomplished rather easily, simply by ruling out generalizations making reference to time. Recall that, in our above example, the trouble arose because the available evidence equally supported S_1 and S_4. But whereas the predicate "conducts electricity" makes no reference to time, the predicate "has been examined prior to t and conducts electricity or has not been examined prior to t and does not conduct electricity" makes reference to time of examination, and moreover can be explained, given such reference, in terms of the former predicate. It may further be pointed out that, without assumption S_7 (making reference to time of examination), no contradiction arises. It is only when we add S_7 to S_4 that S_6, which contradicts S_3, is derived. Why not use this, then, as a rule for eliminating S_4 — namely, its requiring an additional assumption about time of examination to produce one of our contradictory inductions?

The answer is that the situation is easily reversed. Symbolize the predicate "conducts electricity" by C and the other, more complicated one, of S_4, by K; symbolize "has been examined before t" by E. It is true that, as the present argument maintains, K is then definable as

$$(E \text{ and } C) \text{ or } (\text{not-}E \text{ and not-}C)$$

("has been examined before t and conducts electricity or has not been examined before t and does not conduct electricity"). However, it is also true that, taking K as our primitive idea, C is definable as

$$(E \text{ and } K) \text{ or } (\text{not-}E \text{ and not-}K)$$

Furthermore, in the latter mode of description, S_1 would become:

(S_1') All specimens of copper are either such that they have been examined prior to t and have the property K or have not been examined before t and do not have the property K.

while S_4 would become:

(S_4') All specimens of copper have the property K.

To derive a parallel to S_3, we need to show that a new case c does not have the property K. This we can do if we now supplement S_1' with S_7 getting:

(S_3') c does not have the property K.

And we derive our contradictory particular induction, parallel to S_6, from S_4' without using S_7:

(S_6') c has the property K.

Thus, neither the employment by a hypothesis of a predicate referring to time nor its need of supplementation by S_7 in order to produce contradiction is a reliable clue with which to try to repair the generalization formula. Neither is, strictly speaking, any clue at all.

But perhaps the generalization formula is being applied too narrowly. We have, after all, been considering isolated statements in abstraction from other, relevant and well-established, hypotheses. In the above illustration we have, for instance, so far ignored the fact that available evidence also supports (by the generalization formula) a number of hypotheses of the following kind:

(S_8) All specimens of iron conduct electricity.

(S_9) All specimens of wood fail to conduct electricity.

and that these in turn lend credence to the following larger generalization:

(S_{10}) All classes of specimens of the same material are uniform with respect to electrical conductivity.

This larger generalization, having independent warrant and conflicting with S_4, serves thereby to discredit it, thus eliminating the troublesome induction S_6. In this way, it may be argued, the generalization formula can be rendered viable simply by taking account of a wider context of relevant hypotheses.

It takes but a moment of reflection, however, to see the weakness of such an argument. For, by reasoning analogous to that initially employed in introducing S_4, it will be seen that the very same evidence which supports S_8, S_9, and S_{10} also and equally (by the generalization formula itself) supports:

(S_8') All specimens of iron have the property K.

(S_9') All specimens of wood fail to have the property K.

(S_{10}') All classes of specimens of the same material are uniform with respect to possession of the property K.

This latter large generalization, it will be noted, produces just the opposite effect from that of S_{10}. It conflicts with S_1, thereby, by analogous argument, discrediting it and eliminating the induction S_3 rather than S_6. Which of these conflicting large generalizations shall we now choose to take account of, S_{10} or S_{10}'? It is evident that we are again face to face with the very problem with which we started and that the proposal to repair the generalization formula by referring to other relevant hypotheses selected by it serves merely to postpone our perplexity. For these other hypotheses, in conflict themselves, are of no help unless we have some way of deciding which of them are projectible. In the face of difficulties such as these, *it becomes impossible to explain our choice of predictions by reference to whether or not they accord with generalizations which work*, no matter how widely the scope of this principle is construed.

Goodman's New Approach

Goodman's new idea is to utilize pragmatic or historical information that may fairly be assumed available at the time of induction, and to define projectibility in terms of such extra-syntactic information. The generalization formula, it will be recalled, rests on the notion of an *accordance* between a predictive generalization and the evidence by which it is supported, an accordance which can be determined solely by an examination of the generalization and its evidence-statements. In this sense, the relation of accordance is formal or syntactic (as the relation of deduction is), making use of no material or historical information. Goodman now suggests that, in order to specify the predictive generalizations we choose on the basis of given evidence, we need not restrict ourselves merely to the syntactic features of the statements before us. Rather, he makes the radical proposal that we use also the historical record of past predictions, and in partcular, the *biographies* of the specific terms or predicates employed in previous inductions. Our theories, he suggests, are chosen not merely by virtue of the way they encompass the evidence, but also by virtue of the way the language in which they are couched accords with past linguistic practice.

His basic concept is "entrenchment," applicable to terms or predicates in the degree to which they (or their extensional equivalents, that is, words picking out the same class of elements, like "triangle" and "trilateral") have actually been previously employed in projection: in formulating inductions on the basis of positive, though incomplete evidence. To illustrate with our previous example, the predicate "has been examined prior to *t* and conducts electricity or has not been examined prior to *t* and does not conduct electricity" is less well entrenched than the predicate "conducts electricity," *because the class it singles out has been less often mentioned in formulating inductions.* The factor of actual historical employment of constituent predicates or their equivalents can thus be used to distinguish between hypotheses such as S_1 and S_4, which are equal in point of available positive instances. Goodman appeals, then, to "recurrences in the explicit use of terms as well as to recurrent features of what is observed," suggesting that the features which we fasten on in induction are those "for which we have adopted predicates that we have habitually projected" (*1*, pp. 96, 97). With this idea as a guide, Goodman first defines presumptively projectible hypotheses. Next, he defines an initial projectibility index for these hypotheses. Finally, he defines degree of projectibility by means of the initial projectibility index as modified by indirect information embodied in what he calls "overhypotheses," *which must themselves qualify as presumptively projectible.* The latter use made of indirect evidence is worked out with great care and detail and is of independent theoretical interest.

Roughly, degree of projectibility is to represent what Goodman earlier called "lawlikeness" (that is, that property which, together with truth, defines scientific laws) and constitutes therefore not only an explanation but also a refinement of the latter. With the explanation of lawlikeness, Goodman suggests that the general problem of dispositions is solved. For this general problem is to define the *relationship* between "manifest" or observable predicates (for example, "dissolves") and their dispositional counterparts (for example, "is soluble") and manifest predicates may now be construed as related by true lawlike or projectible hypotheses to their dispositional mates. Other problems, such as the nature of "empirical possibility" are also illuminated by this approach, and some light is thrown on the difficult question of counterfactual judgments which, however, still resists full interpretation.

The most natural objection to Goodman's new approach is that it provides no explanation of entrenchment itself. In using this notion to explain induction, however, Goodman does not at all rule out a further explanation of why certain predicates as a matter of fact become entrenched while others do not. His purpose is to formulate clear criteria, in terms of available information, that will single out those generalizations in accordance with which we make predictions. The strong point of his treatment is that his criteria do indeed seem effective in dealing with the numerous cases he considers.

A possible misconception concerning the use of "entrenchment" as a basic idea is that it may lead to the ruling out of unfamiliar predicates, thus stultifying the growth of scientific language. Unfamiliar predicates may, however, be well entrenched if some of their extensionally equivalent mates have been often projected, and they may acquire entrenchment indirectly through "inheritance" from "parent predicates" — that is, other predicates related to them in a special way outlined in detail in Goodman's discussion (*7*, p. 105). Furthermore, Goodman's criteria provide methods for evaluating *hypotheses*, not predicates, so that wholesale elimination of new scientific terms is never sanctioned in his treatment.

As remarked previously, the critical discussion of Goodman's new approach is still in its early stages.[5] His formulations will undoubtedly undergo further refinement and revision with continuing study, but even in their present form they will have contributed much toward putting important questions in the philosophy of science on a scientific basis.

[5] See, in this connection, the long study of *Fact, Fiction and Forecast* by J. C. Cooley [*J. Philosophy 54*, 293 (1957)] and Goodman's reply [*J. Philosophy 54*, 531 (1957)].

Selected Bibliography

The following bibliography is not intended to cover all important works on induction. We have, however, selected works we consider to be pertinent to the readings in this volume. For a more extensive bibliography the reader may consult John M. Keynes, *A Treatise on Probability*, Rudolf Carnap, *Logical Foundations of Probability*, Georg Henrik von Wright, *The Logical Problem of Induction*.

Probability and Confirmation

Braithwaite, R. B. *Scientific Explanation*. Cambridge: Cambridge University Press, 1953. Chaps. 5–8.

Broad, C. D. "On the Relation Between Induction and Probability." *Mind*. XXVII, (1918); XXIX, (1920).

———. "The Principles of Problematic Induction." *Proceedings of the Aristotelian Society*. XXVIII, (1927–28).

Carnap, Rudolf. *Logical Foundations of Probability*. Chicago: The University of Chicago Press, 1950.

———. *Probability and Induction*. Chicago: University of Chicago Press, 1950.

———. "Probability as a Guide in Life." *The Journal of Philosophy*. XLIV, (1947).

———. "Reply to Nelson Goodman." *Philosophy and Phenomenological Research*. VIII, (1947–48).

———. *The Continuum of Inductive Methods*. Chicago: The University of Chicago Press, 1952.

———. *The Nature and Application of Inductive Logic*. Chicago: The University of Chicago Press, 1951.

———. "The Two Concepts of Probability." *Philosophy and Phenomenological Research*. V, (1945).

Churchman, C. West. "Probability Theory." *Philosophy of Science*. XII, (1945).

Copeland, Arthur H. "Predictions and Probabilities." *Erkenntnis*. VI, (1936–37).

Day, J. P. *Inductive Probability*. New York: The Humanities Press, 1961.

Dotterer, Ray H. "Ignorance and Equal Probability." *Philosophy of Science*. VIII, (1941).

Dubs, Homer H. "The Principle of Insufficient Reason." *Philosophy of Science*. IX, (1942).

Ducasse, C. J. "Some Observations Concerning the Nature of Probability." *The Journal of Philosophy*. XXXVIII, (1941).

Feibleman, James. "Pragmatism and Inverse Probability." *Philosophy and Phenomenological Research.* V, (1945).
Fisher, Ronald Aylmer. "Inverse Probability." *Proceedings of the Cambridge Philosophical Society.* XVI, (1930).
———. "Inverse Probability and the Use of Likelihood." *Proceedings of the Cambridge Philosophical Society.* XVIII, (1932).
Freudenthal, Hans. "Is There a Specific Problem of Application for Probability?" *Mind.* L, (1941).
Freund, John E. "On the Confirmation of Scientific Theories." *Philosophy of Science.* XVII, (1950).
Goodman, Nelson. "A Query on Confirmation." *The Journal of Philosophy.* XLIII, (1946).
———. "On Infirmities of Confirmation-Theory." *Philosophy and Phenomenological Research.* VIII, (1947–48).
Goodstein, R. L. "On von Mises's Theory of Probability." *Mind.* XLIX, (1940).
Hailperin, Theodore. "Foundations of Probability in Mathematical Logic." *Philosophy of Science.* IV, (1937).
Hawkins, David. "Existential and Epistemic Probability." *Philosophy of Science.* X, (1943).
Hay, W. H. "Carnap's *Continuum of Inductive Methods.*" *Philosophical Review.* LXII, (1953).
———. "Professor Carnap and Probability." *Philosophy of Science.* XIX, (1952).
Helmer, Olaf, and Paul Oppenheim. "A Syntactical Definition of Probability and of Degree of Confirmation." *The Journal of Symbolic Logic.* X, (1945).
Hempel, Carl G. "A Purely Syntactical Definition of Confirmation." *The Journal of Symbolic Logic.* VIII, (1943).
Hosiasson-Lindenbaum, Janina. "On Confirmation." *The Journal of Symbolic Logic.* V, (1940).
———. "Why Do We Prefer Probabilities Relative to Many Data?" *Mind.* XL, (1931).
Jeffreys, Harold. *Theory of Probability.* Oxford: The Clarendon Press, 1939.
———. "The Present Position in Probability Theory." *The British Journal for the Philosophy of Science.* V, (1955).
Kaufmann, Felix. "Scientific Procedure and Probability." *Philosophy and Phenomenological Research.* VI, (1945–46).
Kemble, Edwin C. "Is the Frequency Theory of Probability Adequate For All Scientific Purposes?" *The American Journal of Physics.* X, (1942).
———. "The Probability Concept." *Philosophy of Science.* VIII, (1941).
Keynes, J. M. *A Treatise On Probability.* London: The Macmillan Co., 1921.
Kyburg, H. E., Jr. *Probability and the Logic of Rational Belief.* Middletown, Conn.: Wesleyan University Press, 1961.
LaPlace, Pierre Simon de. *A Philosophical Essay On Probabilities.* Translated by F. W. Truscott and F. L. Emory. New York: Dover Publishing Co., 1951.

LeBlanc, Hugues. "A New Interpretation of c(h,e)." *Philosophy and Phenomenological Research.* XXI, (1960–61).

———. "On So-Called Degrees of Confirmation." *The British Journal for the Philosophy of Science.* X, (1960).

———. *Statistical and Inductive Probabilities.* Englewood Cliffs, N.J.: Prentice Hall, 1962.

———. "That Positive Instances Are No Help." *The Journal of Philosophy.* LX, (1963).

———. "The Problem of the Confirmation of Laws." *Philosophical Studies.* XII, (1961).

———. "Two Probability Concepts." *The Journal of Philosophy.* LIII, (1956).

Lehman, R. S. "On Confirmation and Rational Betting." *The Journal of Symbolic Logic.* XX, (1955).

Lewis, C. I. *An Analysis of Knowledge and Valuation.* LaSalle, Ill.: The Open Court Publishing Co., 1946. Chaps. 10, 11.

Madden, E. H. (ed.) *The Structure of Scientific Thought.* Boston: Houghton Mifflin Co., 1960. Part 5.

Margenau, Henry. "On the Frequency Theory of Probability." *Philosophy and Phenomenological Research.* VI, (1945–46).

———. "Probability and Physics." *The Journal of Unified Science.* VIII, (1940).

———. "Probability, Many-Valued Logics, and Physics." *Philosophy of Science.* VI, (1939).

Mehlberg, Josephine J. "Is a Unitary Approach to Foundations of Probability Possible?" *Current Issues in the Philosophy of Science.* (eds.) H. Feigl and G. Maxwell. New York: Holt, Rinehart & Winston, 1961.

Mises, Richard von. *Probability, Statistics and Truth.* New York: The Macmillan Co., 1939.

Molina, Edward C. "Bayes' Theorem; An Expository Presentation." *Annals of Mathematical Statistics.* II, (1931).

Nagel, Ernest. "A Frequency Theory of Probability." *The Journal of Philosophy.* XXX, (1933).

———. "Is The Laplacean Theory of Probability Tenable?" *Philosophy and Phenomenological Research.* VI, (1946).

———. *Principles of the Theory of Probability. International Encyclopedia of Unified Science.* I, 6. Chicago: The University of Chicago Press, 1939.

———. "Probability and Non-Demonstrative Inference." *Philosophy and Phenomenological Research.* V, (1944).

———. "Probability and the Theory of Knowledge." *Philosophy of Science.* VI, (1939).

———. "The Meaning of Probability." *Journal of the American Statistical Association* XXXI, (1936).

Northrop, F. S. C. "The Philosophical Significance of the Concept of Probability in Quantum Mechanics." *Philosophy of Science.* III, (1936).

Pap, Arthur. *An Introduction to the Philosophy of Science.* New York: The Free Press of Glencoe, 1962. Chaps. 9–13.

Popper, Karl. *The Logic of Scientific Discovery.* New York: Basic Books, 1959. Chap. 9.

———. "The Propensity Interpretation of Probability." *The British Journal for the Philosophy of Science.* X, (1959).

Putnam, Hilary. "A Definition of Degree of Confirmation for Very Rich Languages." *Philosophy of Science.* XXIII, (1956).

Reichenbach, H. *Experience and Prediction.* Chicago: The University of Chicago Press, 1938. Chap. 5.

———. "Reply to Donald C. Williams' Criticism of the Frequency Theory of Probability." *Philosophy and Phenomenological Research.* V, (1945).

———. *The Theory of Probability.* Berkeley: The University of California Press, 1949.

Rynin, David. "Probability and Meaning." *The Journal of Philosophy.* XLIV, (1947).

White, Morton. "Probability and Confirmation." *The Journal of Philosophy.* XXXVI, (1939).

Williams, D. C. "On the Derivation of Probabilities From Frequencies." *Philosophy and Phenomenological Research.* V, (1945).

———. "The Challenging Situation in the Philosophy of Probability." *Philosophy and Phenomenological Research.* VI, (1945–46).

———. *The Ground of Induction.* Cambridge, Mass.: Harvard University Press, 1947. Chaps. 2–4.

———. "The Problem of Probability." *Philosophy and Phenomenological Research.* VI, (1945–46).

Wisdom, J. O. *Foundations of Inference in Natural Science.* London: Methuen and Co., 1952. Part 3.

Wright, G. H. von. *A Treatise on Induction and Probability.* London: Routledge and Kegan Paul, 1951. Chaps. 7–10.

———. "Carnap's Theory of Probability." *Philosophical Review.* LX, (1951).

———. "On Probability." *Mind.* XLIX, (1940).

———. *The Logical Problem of Induction.* New York: The Macmillan Co., 1957. Chaps. 5–7.

Simplicity

Ackermann, Robert. *Simplicity and the Acceptability of Scientific Theories.* Doctoral Dissertation. Michigan State University, 1960.

———. "Some Remarks on Kyburg's Modest Proposal." *Philosophical Review.* LXXI, (1962).

Barker, S. F. *Induction and Hypothesis.* Ithaca: Cornell University Press, 1957. Chaps. 5, 9.

———. "The Role of Simplicity in Explanation." *Current Issues in the Philosophy of Science.* (eds.) H. Feigl and G. Maxwell. New York: Holt, Rinehart & Winston, 1961.

Beck, L. W. "The Principle of Parsimony in Empirical Scien ce." *The Journal of Philosophy*. XL, (1943).

Berenda, C. W. "On Verifiability, Simplicity, and Equivalence." *Philosophy of Science*. XIX, (1952).

Bunge, Mario. *The Myth of Simplicity; Problems of Scientific Philosophy*. Englewood Cliffs, N. J.: Prentice-Hall, 1963.

Cooley, W. F. "The Lure of Metaphysical Simplicity." *Studies in the History of Ideas*. New York: Columbia University Press, 1925. II.

Feuer, Lewis S. "Rejoinder on the Principle of Simplicity." *Philosophy of Science*. XXVI, (1959).

———. "The Principle of Simplicity." *Philosophy of Science*. XXIV, (1957).

Goodman, Nelson. "An Improvement in the Theory of Simplicity." *The Journal of Symbolic Logic*. XIV, (1949).

———. "Axiomatic Measurement of Simplicity." *The Journal of Philosophy*. LII, (1955).

———. "New Notes on Simplicity." *The Journal of Symbolic Logic*. XVII, (1952).

———. "On the Simplicity of Ideas." *The Journal of Symbolic Logic*. VIII, (1943).

———. "Recent Developments in the Theory of Simplicity." *Philosophy and Phenomenological Research*. XIX, (1959).

———. "Safety, Strength, Simplicity." *Philosophy of Science*. XXVIII, (1961).

———. "The Logical Simplicity of Predicates." *The Journal of Symbolic Locic*. XIV, (1949).

Jeffreys, Harold. *Scientific Inference*. Cambridge: Cambridge University Press, 1957.

Jeffreys, Harold, and Dorothy Wrinch. "On Certain Fundamental Principles of Scientific Inquiry." *Philosophical Magazine*. XLII, (1921).

Kemeny, John G. "A Logical Measure Function." *The Journal of Symbolic Logic*. XVIII, (1953).

———. "Two Measures of Simplicity." *The Journal of Philosophy*. LII, (1955).

Kyburg, Henry E., Jr. "A Modest Proposal Concerning Simplicity." *Philosophical Review*. LXX, (1961).

Laird, John. "The Law of Parsimony." *The Monist*. XXIX, (1912).

Lindsay, R. B. "Simplicity in Physics." *Philosophy of Science*. IV, (1937).

Mach, E. "The Economical Nature of Physics." *Popular Scientific Lectures*. Chicago: The Open Court Publishing Co., 1919.

Nelson, E. J. "A Note on Parsimony." *Philosophy of Science*. III, (1936).

Nogge, J. W. "Regarding the Law of Parsimony." *The Journal of General Psychology*. XLI, (1932).

Popper, Karl. *The Logic of Scientific Discovery*. New York: Basic Books, 1959. Chap. 5.

Rudner, Richard S. "An Introduction to Simplicity." *Philosophy of Science*. XXVIII, (1961).

Schlesinger, G. "Dynamic Simplicity." *Philosophical Review*. LXX, (1961).

———. "The Principle of Simplicity and Verifiability." *Philosophy of Science*. XXVI, (1959).

Suppes, Patrick. "Nelson Goodman on the Concept of Logical Simplicity." *Philosophy of Science*. XXIII, (1956).
Svenonius, Lars. "Definability and Simplicity." *The Journal of Symbolic Logic*. XX, (1955).
Thorburn, W. M. "The Myth of Occam's Razor." *Mind*. XXV, (1918).

The Justification of Induction

Achinstein, Peter. "Circularity and Induction." *Analysis*. XXIII, (1963).
———. "The Circularity of Self-Supporting Inductive Arguments." *Analysis*. XXII, (1962).
Alexander, Peter. "Convention, Falsification and Induction." *Aristotelian Society*. Supplementary. XXXIV, (1960).
Ambrose, Alice. "The Problem of Justifying Inductive Inference." *The Journal of Philosophy*. XLIV, (1947).
Barker, S., and Peter Achinstein. "On the New Riddle of Induction." *Philosophical Review*. LXIX, (1960).
Barrett, W. "The Present State of the Problem of Induction." *Theoria*. VI, (1940).
Black, Max. "Self-Support and Circularity: A Reply to Mr. Achinstein." *Analysis*. XXIII, (1962).
Buchdahl, G. "Convention, Falsification and Induction." *Aristotelian Society*. Supplementary. XXXIV, (1960).
Campbell, K. "One Form of Scepticism About Induction." *Analysis*. XXIII, (1963).
Chapman, H. W. "Induction Again." *Analysis*. VII, (1940).
Creed, Isabel P. "The Justification of the Habit of Induction." *The Journal of Philosophy*. XXXVII, (1940).
Cunningham, M. A. "The Justification of Induction." *Analysis*. VII, (1939).
Edwards, Paul. "Russell's Doubts About Induction." *Mind*. LVIII, (1949).
Feigl, Herbert. "De Principiis non est Disputandum . . . ? On the Meaning and the Limits of Justification." *Philosophical Analysis*. (ed.) M. Black. Ithaca: Cornell University Press, 1950.
———. "Scientific Method Without Metaphysical Presuppositions." *Philosophical Studies*. V, (1954).
Fen, S. "Has James Answered Hume?" *The Journal of Philosophy*. XLIX, (1952).
Goodman, Nelson. *Fact, Fiction and Forecast*. Cambridge, Mass.: Harvard University Press, 1955. Chaps. 3, 4.
———. "Positionality and Pictures." *Philosophical Review*. LXIX, (1960).
Gross, M. W. "Whitehead's Answer to Hume." *The Journal of Philosophy*. XXXVIII, (1941).
Harrod, Roy. *Foundations of Inductive Logic*. New York: Harcourt, Brace and Co., 1956.
———. "New Argument For Induction: Reply to Professor Popper." *The British Journal for the Philosophy of Science*. X, (1959–60).

Hartshorne, Charles. "Causal Necessities: An Alternative to Hume." *Philosophical Review.* LXIII, (1954).

Hobart, R. E. "Hume Without Scepticism." *Mind.* XXXIX, (1930).

Kading, Daniel. "Concerning Mr. Feigl's 'Vindication' of Induction." *Philosophy of Science.* XXVII, (1960).

Katz, J. *The Problem of Induction and Its Solution.* Chicago: The University of Chicago Press, 1962.

Kyburg, Henry E. Jr. "R. B. Braithwaite on Probability and Induction." *The British Journal for the Philosophy of Science.* IX, (1958–59).

———. "The Justification of Induction." *The Journal of Philosophy.* LIII, (1956).

Lewy, Casimir. "On the 'Justification' of Induction." *Analysis.* VI, (1939).

Madden, E. H. (ed.) *The Structure of Scientific Thought.* Boston: Houghton Mifflin Co., 1960. Part 6.

McLendon, H. J. "Has Russell Answered Hume?" *The Journal of Philosophy.* XLIX, (1952).

Oliver, V. D. "A Re-Examination of the Problem of Induction." *The Journal of Philosophy.* XLIX, (1952).

Popper, Karl. "On Mr. Roy Harrod's New Argument for Induction." *The British Journal for the Philosophy of Science.* IX, (1958–59).

———. *The Logic of Scientific Discovery.* New York: Basic Books, 1959. Chaps. 1, 10.

Rankin, K. W. "Linguistic Analysis and the Justification of Induction." *The Philosophical Quarterly.* V, (1955).

Reichenbach, H. "A Conversation Between Bertrand Russell and David Hume." *The Journal of Philosophy.* XLV, (1948).

———. "On the Justification of Induction." *The Journal of Philosophy.* XXXVII, (1940).

Russell, B. *Human Knowledge; Its Scope and Limits.* New York: Simon and Schuster, 1948. Part 5.

Salmon, Wesley. "Should We Attempt to Justify Induction?" *Philosophical Studies.* VIII, (1957).

———. "Vindication of Induction." *Current Issues in the Philosophy of Science.* (eds.) H. Feigl and G. Maxwell. New York: Holt, Rinehart & Winston, 1961.

Sass, L. D. "The Justification of Induction." *Analysis.* VII, (1940).

Small, Kenneth. "Professor Goodman's Puzzle." *Philosophical Review.* LXX, (1961).

Smart, H. R. "The Problem of Induction." *The Journal of Philosophy,* XXV, (1928).

Ullian, J. S. "More on 'Grue' and Grue." *Philosophical Review.* LXX, (1961).

Wang, Hao. "Notes on the Justification of Induction." *The Journal of Philosophy.* XLIV, (1947).

———. "On Scepticism about Induction." *Philosophy of Science.* XVII, (1950).

Whiteley, C. H. "On the Justification of Induction." *Analysis.* VII, (1940).

Will, Fredrick. "Donald Williams' Theory of Induction." *Philosophical Review.* LVII, (1948).
———. "Is There a Problem of Induction?" *The Journal of Philosophy.* XXXIX, (1942).
———. "Justification and Induction." *Philosophical Review.* LXVIII, (1959).
———. "Will the Future Be Like the Past?" *Mind.* LVI, (1947).
Williams, D. C. "Induction and the Future." *Mind.* LVII, (1948).
———. *The Ground of Induction.* Cambridge, Mass.: Harvard University Press, 1947.
Wright, G. H. von. *The Logical Problem of Induction.* New York: The Macmillan Co., 1957. Chaps. 2–4.

Index